Journal of
Biblical Ethics
in Medicine

Volumes 5 - 8: 1991 - 1994

with Subject and Scripture Index

Hilton P. Terrell, M.D., Ph.D. and

Franklin E. Payne, M.D., Editors

Covenant Books
P. O. Box 14488, Augusta, GA 30919-0488

Journal of Biblical Ethics in Medicine, Volumes 5-8, 1991-1994
ISSN 1050-3404

Library Cataloging Data: Ethics in the Bible; medical ethics; medicine -- religious aspects --
Christianity; religion and medicine; health -- Biblical teaching; medicine -- Biblical teaching;
philosophy -- theology; evangelicalism; public health; health behavior.

For purchase information, contact the publisher:

Covenant Books
P. O. Box 14488
Augusta, GA 30919-0488

1 (800) 766-7042

Printed and bound in the United States of America

Table of Contents

Volume 5 - 1991

Page

Volume 6 - 1992

Volume 7 - 1993

Volume 8 - 1994

Note:

The Fall issue of Volume 8 (1994) was never published. Currently, the *Journal of Biblical Ethics in Medicine* has been discontinued. A third bound edition may be published in the future to complement the two present bound editions. Contact Covenant Books for current information.

Animal Rights and The Image of God

Part I

T. Stuart Walker, PhD

Dr. Walker is Associate Professor of Medical Education in the Indiana University School of Medicine at Ball State University in Muncie, Indiana.

"Thou saw the fields lay bare and
waste,
An' weary winter comin fast,
An' cozie here, beneath the blast
Thou thought to dwell
Till crash! The cruel coulter past
Out thro' thy cell."

"But mousie, thou art no thy lane,
In proving foresight may be vain.
The best laid schemes o' mice an' men
Gang aft a'gley,
An' lea'e us naught but grief an' pain
For promis'd joy."

"Still thou art blest, compar'd wi' me!
The present only toucheth thee:
But, Och! I backward cast my e'e
On prospects drear!
An' forward, tho' I canna see,
I guess an' fear!"

"To a Mouse, On Turning Her Up in
Her Nest with the Plough,
November, 1785".
Robert Burns

Part I: the case for animal rights

It was 7:00 A.M., July 4, 1989, and the Texas Tech Health Sciences Center was quiet and empty. Since near dawn, six animal rights activists associated with the Animal Liberation Front (ALF) had been watching the comings and goings of the few security officers on campus. The signal was given, and four activists slipped into the building, heading for the laboratory of Dr. John Orem, a physiology professor in the School of Medicine. Because this was an inside job, as many such attacks are, the animal rights terrorists knew exactly where to look for records and what to destroy. Laboratory notebooks and some video records were quickly found and taken, and then the four began their jihad against Dr. Orem's equipment. Within a few frenzied moments, $70,000 of research equipment was reduced to scrap metal, and the intruders now turned their attention to the resident animals. Five cats were taken - cats which had been the subjects of Dr. Orem's work on sleep apnea and sudden infant death syndrome (SIDS). They were stuffed into burlap bags, and the four activists slipped away with their feline burdens like so many inverse Santa Clauses. As a parting shot, one of the activists, a high school history teacher calling himself "Dave", spray-painted a message on the wall, a play on words taken from a standard Texas road sign: "Don't mess with Texas animals."

The attack suffered by John Orem was only one of approximately 70 such attacks which have occurred in the United States during the past 6 years. Of these, 48 have involved burglary and destruction of equipment. Their impact has spread far beyond those investigators who have been victimized; they affect all of us who do research. Fear of attacks and the relentless onslaught of animal rights advocates have bred a bunker mentality within the research community. In some cases, universities have pressured investigators to stop doing research, even return grant funds, to avoid the embarrassment of defending research using animals as an integral mission of the university. It has been estimated that 15 - 20% of all funds earmarked for research are spent on meeting newly developed federal security and animal care regulations. Imagine the furor if the Office of Management and Budget cut federal research funds by this amount! Yet, this is, in effect, what has happened.

These trends have been reflected in an erosion in public support of research and in growing public misconceptions about how scientists treat their animals. Dr. Fred Goodwin, Administrator of the Alcohol, Drug Abuse and Mental Health Administration of the National Institutes of Health reported in March at a symposium in Lubbock, Texas, entitled "Conflict of the 90's: the Siege by Animal Rights Activists" that since the 1960's, federal support for research in the United States has dropped from 2.8% to 1.7% of the gross national product (GNP). Yet, the percentage of the GNP that Japan and Germany spend on research has risen to 2.8% during that same period. During 1989 the American Medical Association (AMA) surveyed public attitudes about animal use in research. Although the news was generally good - 77% recognized the necessity of animal use in medical research and 64% supported the use of animals in research - there were some disturbing trends. Between the ages of 16 and 29, the percentage of those who supported and opposed research animal use was split 50/50. Three quarters of those surveyed said they believed there was "some to a lot" of animal torture by scientists. Half of those surveyed believed there are no animal use regulations, and half of those aware of such regulations did not believe that scientists comply with them. Meanwhile, public support for animal rights groups has been growing. During 1989, *Town and Country* magazine listed the top ten animal rights groups. While the principal organization opposing the animal rights movement, the Foundation for Biomedical Research (FBR) has a staff of 5 and a modest budget, animal rights groups claim approximately 10 million supporters with PETA, the largest of these groups, having a national staff of 60. With total budgets of about 50 million dollars, these organizations have begun to wield considerable political and public relations clout.

Who are the animal rights advocates? Why has this movement, which seemed to have all but died out during the early part of this century, now reappeared with exceptional vigor? The roots of the animal rights movement lie in the antivivisection movement of the 19th century. This movement, which gained popularity during the latter half of the 19th century and continued into the early 20th century, achieved its greatest popularity in Great Britain. After lying dormant since World War I, the animal rights movement has once again burst on the scene, this time with a new philosophical base but brandishing the same secondary arguments they have used for over one hundred years.

Many have been confused with the goals and philosophy of the

movement because they have failed to recognize that there are two distinct movements concerned with human use of animals, each with its own agenda and philosophy. Adding to this confusion is that animal rights groups have used the arguments of groups concerned with animal welfare to further their own agenda. These movements can be differentiated by their philosophies and their goals.

Adherents of the animal *welfare* movement believe that we are to be responsible stewards of the animals which come under our influence, and that responsible stewardship involves humane care. As such, animal welfare advocates are generally supportive of research animal use, but seek to ensure that the animals are comfortable in their surroundings. They work with animal shelters to pick up stray companion animals, and promote pet adoption and neutering programs. They work with zoos and pet owners to educate them on the needs of animals and the responsibilities of animal ownership. A number of such organizations exist; the best known of these is the Society for the Prevention of Cruelty to Animals (SPCA).

The animal *rights* movement stands in stark contrast to the animal welfare societies. Animal rightists believe that animals and humans are morally equivalent, and, as such, have equivalent moral, ethical and legal rights. Because animals and humans are morally/ethically equivalent, many "rightists" believe that all human use of animals without their consent is immoral. Because animals cannot give consent, humans must not use them in any way for their own benefit. Thus, many animal rights advocates oppose *all* human uses of animals, including food, clothing, sport, biomedical research, zoos, entertainment, and pet ownership (which has been likened by some to slavery). Some, who call

themselves "vegans", oppose the use of animal products such as eggs and milk. Some representative animal rights organizations include PETA, the Animal Liberation Front (ALF), and the Physicians' Committee for Responsible Medicine (PCRM).

What is the underlying philosophy of the animal rights movement? Some, frustrated by emotion-laden confrontations with animal rights activists have wrongly concluded that the movement is populated with and driven by "crazies." For example, Larry Horton[1] writing in the journal *In Vitro* stated:

" ... *some observers would trace the bloodlines of the current activism back to Luddites, creationists, and others upset with science.*"

Thus, a line is quickly drawn between the rational (scientists) and the irrational reactionaries (Luddites, creationists and animal rights activists). Animal rights proponents have buttressed this image by their outspoken value statements ("a rat is a pig is a boy is a dog"),[2] and by their popular secondary arguments which claim that experiments performed on animals cannot be extrapolated to humans. I believe that most people are revolted by statements which devalue human life, concluding that only someone who has lost touch with reality could equate the life of a boy with that of a rat. Taken to its logical conclusion (*reductio ad infinitum, reductio ad absurdum*) such a stance would require either that humans be charged with murder when they willfully kill mice with traps, or would devalue human life as being equally incidental as that of a mouse. Either option is unacceptable. Additionally, scientists are repulsed by claims that studies which use animal models cannot be extrapolated to humans. The reality is that most significant medical advances that we enjoy today have been heavily based upon studies which could not have been performed without the use of animals. For example, it was only as we began to understand the mouse immune system that we had the necessary keys to unlock the secrets of human immune function. As the patterns of human immune structure and responsiveness began to unfold, we found that our immune system is amazingly like that of a mouse, with most of the differences being in the expression of particular cell surface antigens. Thus, the mouse model of immune responsiveness has allowed us to know much about our own immune system, and application of the principles learned in these animal studies have saved many human lives. Many of the foundational studies of immune function could not have been performed in humans because of the danger they would have posed to human life. It is odd that animal rights proponents use this particular argument to oppose animal use in research because it contradicts one of the key presuppositions of the ethical/philosophical base of the movement; that is, that humans and animals are phylogenetically interrelated. It is not my purpose to review here the medical and scientific advances which have depended upon the availability of research animals. Rather, I merely wish to point out that when animal rights proponents argue that animal studies cannot be extrapolated to humans they are dealing with an issue that is secondary to the real issues of animal rights. Furthermore, use of such secondary arguments damages the credibility of the animal rights movement in the eyes of medical scientists because it makes those who use these arguments appear to be ignorant or deceitful.

The arguments for animal rights are many, but the major non-Christian arguments can be reduced to a single unifying claim that humans and non-human animals are ontologically identical, and that all differences in creaturely categories are dif-ferences in degree rather than differences in essence. There is significant diversity within the movement as to how this claim of ontological unity is supported, and some proponents hold only one or two of the three most common arguments for unity. These arguments can be summarized as follows:

First, humans are, after all, animals and are phylogenetically interrelated with all other animals. For example, Michael Fox has stated:

"There is indeed kinship in the present diversity and evolutionary continuity of all life ... It is more important today than ever before for human beings to be aware of their kinship with all life. It is essential for our survival that we have a strong reverence for all forms of life as our kin and see all as part of creation (or of evolution as a godlike creative process if you wish)."[3]

Fox is unusual in his application of this philosophy, in that he encourages humans to use their evolutionarily derived role of overseer of the earth to act preemptively in managing the affairs of animals.[4] Others disdain this approach, and would prefer a "hands off" relationship with animals. If we are phylogenetically interrelated, they say, we cannot claim priority for our interests. Thus, it is imperative that we live in such a way as to minimally alter the evolutionarily determined life patterns and relationships of animals. Michael Fox has posited this argument:

"Fulfillment of any living creature would be its union with the environment for which it is best adapted and to which its whole being is receptively attuned. To deprive it of such natural fulfillment would be as inhumane as if its instincts and potentials were never fully actualized but instead were frustrated, blocked, or denied. This is the core philosophy of humanistic psychology, which is concerned with provision of an optimal environment for the ultimate fulfill-ment (self-actualization) of an individual's potentials ... Since there is no qualitative difference between the fulfilling unity of man and his world and that of any other animal and its world, certain human and ethical questions must be raised."[5]

It is easy to see in this a natural kinship between the animal rights movement and many in the environmental movement. Indeed, there have been increasing instances of cooperation between animal rights and environmental activists on behalf of animals.[6]

Second, some assert that there is spiritual continuity among all life forms, or at least among all sentient creatures. This view is espoused by Michael Fox in his article "What future for man and earth? Toward a biospiritual ethic."[7] This argument takes several modes, ranging from the mysticism of classic Buddhism at one extreme to a network of essential interrelatedness analogous to the much-celebrated "Gaia" cosmology [8] at the other. According to the proponents of "Gaia," the earth functions like a living organism, with each creature in the biosphere vitally interrelated by its function within the cosmic framework. Each creature is like a living cell within an organism called Gaia (the earth), and each of us is vitally dependent upon the survival and proper functioning of each of the cells and organelles of the Gaia organism. Fox's position seems to be more closely aligned to those who are Gaia proponents, but the language he uses is such that any in this spectrum could feel at ease with his terminology. A brief review of some of his statements reveals a view that is heavily influenced by Buddhism but is more Gaia in its application:

"I give my pledge as a world citizen to respect all life as I respect my own kind, to cherish nature's creations and riches which I shall neither use thought-

lessly nor abuse willfully, since man and nature are of one earth and one spirit."[9] (emphasis added)

"Man upsets the cosmic equilibrium of ecology, society, and spirit when he thinks and acts without feeling and empathy for others, including plants and animals, oceans and forests."[10]

"We must therefore transcend our illusory egocentric species-boundaries, a 'la Hartshorn, to discover our natural mind-potential in oneness with nature, a oneness for which we are genetically predisposed and predestined: one earth, one mind."[11]

"The Nirvana state or principle represents this center (a center of pure essence or spirit found in every relationship and experience) as the eternal void of infinite potential beyond death and yet within the life-awareness of pure being. It is the essence of life fulfilled in and through consciousness and expressed in thought, feeling, and action. This Nirvana principle therefore penetrates the time-space continuum of mortal transcience in all sentient beings, linking individuated species and patterned fields of relatedness with the aesthetic or cosmic potential of undifferentiated potential."[12]

Regardless of whether it is argued that this unity is an actual spiritual interconnection and communication, or if it is an expression of functional interrelatedness and interdependence among all creatures, the proponents of this stance all are asserting ontological unity.

Finally, Tom Regan and others have claimed ontological unity among all sentient creatures on the basis of an existential unity. Regan's critical point of unity is that we all are the experiencing subject of a life, and it matters to us what happens to us during that life. In Regan's words:

"And the really crucial, the basic similarity is simply this: we are each of us the experiencing subject of a life, a conscious creature having an individual welfare that has importance to us whatever our usefulness to others."[13]

This evidence of unity among all sentient creatures is evidence of the existence of a creaturely attribute associated with the presence of experiencing life, the attribute of "inherent value." Regan does not start by arguing that animals have rights. Rather, he argues that intuition tells us that all humans, regardless of their creaturely capabilities have inherent value. Speaking of the panoply of human life, Regan states:

" … all have inherent value, all possess it equally, and all have an equal right to be treated with respect, to be treated in ways that do not reduce them to the status of things, as if they existed as resources for others."[14]

Because animals, too, are the experiencing subjects of a life, they also have inherent value:

" … they too must be viewed as the experiencing subjects of a life, with inherent value of their own."[15]

Because the inherent value of a person is unrelated to the quality of his life, then we cannot say that animals possess less inherent value simply because their degree of sentience is less than is ours.

"What could be the basis of our having more inherent value than animals? Their lack of reason, or autonomy, or intellect? Only if we are willing to make the same judgement in the case of humans who are similarly deficient. But it is not true that such humans - the retarded child, for example, or the mentally deranged - have less inherent value than you or I. Neither, then, can we rationally sustain the view that animals like them·in being the experiencing subjects of a life have less inherent value. All who have inherent value have it equally, whether they be human animals or not. Inherent value, then, belongs equally to those who are the experiencing subjects of a life."[16]

In turning to the postulated existence of inherent value as the arbiter of human response and interaction with other creatures, Regan strongly opposes contractarianism and utilitarianism. The utilitarian sees each of us as a cup; our value is dependent upon what is in the cup. Regan abhors this, affirming that the value resides in the cup itself, and that all cups are of equal value.

If all creatures, or at least all sentient creatures are ontologically indistinguishable because all are animals, all share in the same spiritual essence, and all possess a nonquantitative attribute called inherent value which is related to the fact that we all are the experiencing subjects of a life, how should this mold my behavior toward other creatures? Michael Fox insists that these unities should propel us into a deontic application of ethics:

" … things identical in kind are equal in value, and this so-called formal 'deontic' logic leads to a natural ethical obligation toward all forms of creation."[17]

How this is actually played out varies considerably among the proponents of animal rights. We have already seen that Fox argues for a deontic ethic while also demanding that man should assert his rightful place in the cosmos to manage the affairs of the world, guided by a biospiritual ethic. Fox and Peter Singer, whose overriding concern is the relative presence of sentience, would allow humans to use animals for certain purposes if the ethical balance for all parties involved leans toward animal use as bringing about the greatest good. In those cases, every possible step should be taken to insure that the victim of the situation does not suffer. Contrast this with the abolitionist stance of Regan:

"That movement (the animal rights movement), as I conceive it, is commit-

ted to a number of goals, including:

> *the total abolition of the use of animals in science
>
> *the total dissolution of commercial animal agriculture
>
> *the total elimination of commercial and sport hunting and trapping."[18]

Thus, Regan opposes all animal use by humans, because it is animal use; that is, it involves using animals as resources, failing to respect their inherent value. Richard Ryder has melded these approaches:

"Whereas I agree with Singer on the importance of suffering as the bedrock of morality, I tend to agree with Regan that it is wrong to aggregate across individual sentients. This is because I believe that in such matters the individual consciousness is everything. It is therefore wrong for me to inflict suffering unless it brings greater advantages to the same individual."[19]

Using this ethic, in the absence of an ethical hierarchy, "lifeboat" decisions become impossible. That is, when creatures face situations where their interests are in direct conflict and each would face the same consequence if any of the choices available are made, there is no basis for determining which option is correct. The end result could be the loss of all the lives in the "lifeboat."

Thus, the animal rights movement insists on at least only minimal use of animals, with many demanding a total abolition of human use of animals coupled with a recognition that animals and humans have equal rights of existence and self-determination. Regan expresses this view when he reflects on the statement of Leonardo DaVinci that "the time will come when men such as I will look upon the murder of animals as they now look upon the murder of men." To this, Regan says, "One can only hope that time is soon."[20]

Does the Scripture agree with this assessment? Are we and the world of animals essentially equivalent with equal moral claims?

[Next issue: Part II. A Biblical Response to Animal Rights]

REFERENCES

1. Horton's editorial was published twice: first as *J. Natl. Cancer Inst.*, 81, 736 - 743 (1989) and again as *In Vitro Cell. Dev. Biol.* 25:486 - 493 (1989).

2. Attributed first to Ingrid Newkirk of P.E.T.A. by Katie McCabe in "Who Will Live and Who Will Die?" in *The Washingtonian* (August, 1986, p. 114). Novelist Isaac Bashevis Singer has taken this position a step farther by asserting "In relation to animals, all people are Nazis." and " ... for the animals it is an eternal Treblinka." (cited by Tom Regan in **The Struggle for Animal Rights,** International Society for Animal Rights, Inc., Clarks Summit, PA, 1987, p. 77). It has been popularly reported that Ingrid Newkirk and others have also made this connection, comparing the raising of broiler chickens with Nazi atrocities committed against Jews at Dachau.

3. Fox, Michael A. in "Man and Nature: Biological Perspectives," in: **On the Fifth Day,** Morris, Richard K. and Fox, Michael (eds.), Acropolis Books, Washington, D.C., p. 121.

4. For example, in an article entitled "What Future for Man and Earth? Toward a Biospiritual Ethic," *ibid.*, Fox states: "Animal rights will depend on man's assuming fully his role as steward of the planet earth, and he must judge, regulate, and even destroy in order to maintain order, health, life, and harmony in the biosphere. Animal rights must be addressed not from a zoocentric standpoint, nor from an anthropocentric one, but on a biospiritual basis. There is no room or future for the romantic preservationist who would leave nature to itself, since nature is man, and we must monitor and regulate both with understanding and compassion." He further states, " ... we must impose restraints in natural behaviors in certain contexts in our domesticated animals just as people must abide by certain rules and social restraints." (Both p. 229)

5. Fox, Michael W., *ibid*, p. 117-118.

6. For example, during 1989, environmental activists Jeremy Rifkin filed suit in Federal district court to halt all federally funded research on the basis that all such studies violated federal environmental regulations. In California, environmental and animal rights groups have cooperated in trying to halt the construction of university research facilities.

7. Fox, Michael W., *ibid*, p. 219 - 230.

8. The Gaia hypothesis is largely the child of James Lovelock who published his hypothesis that the earth is a single huge organism in his book **Gaia: A New Look at Life on Earth**, Oxford University Press, Oxford, 1979. During 1988 Lovelock modified his views somewhat, retreating under pressure by fellow scientists from the concept that the earth is actually a living organism. At a conference during that year sponsored by the American Geophysical Union, Lovelock conceded that his teleologic argument was too strong and proposed, instead, a nonteleologic model of the earth in which "the nonliving and the living represent a self-regulating system that keeps itself in a constant state." For a review of the evolution of the Gaia concept see *Science*, 240: 393-395 (1988).

9. Fox, Michael, W., *op. cit.*, p. 220.

10. *Ibid*, p. 223.
11. *Ibid*, p. 225.
12. *Ibid*, p. 227.
13. Regan, Tom, **The Case for Animal Rights**, International Society for Animal Rights, Inc., Clarks Summit, PA, 1987, 0.59.
14. *Ibid*, p. 58.
15. *Ibid*, p. 59.
16. *Ibid*, p. 60.
17. Fox, Michael, *op. cit.*, p. 227.
18. Regan, Tom, *op. cit.*, pp. 46-47.
19. Ryder, Richard D., **Animal Revolution,** Basil Blackwell, Ltd., Cambridge, MA, 1989, pp. 325-326.
20. Regan, Tom, *op. cit.*, p.81.

Editor's Note

For some time I have thought it possible to construct modern America's functional theology from a study of bumper stickers. How different the theology is from Biblical doctrine! The east coast's main north-south traffic artery, I-95, runs close by here. Who knows how many tons of illicit drugs travel up it daily to become an instrument of destruction in the lives of people? However destructive may be the concealed marijuana, cocaine and other chemicals, bumper stickers openly advertise ideas which may be much more destructive. Ideas have consequences.

A sticker sometimes seen on the back of expensive Florida-bound motor homes driven by gray-haired couples states: "We're spending our children's inheritance." (Cf.II cor. 12:14) In the individual cases, one suspects that the couples are being facetious. Nonetheless, the almost universal participation of Christians in an unbiblical debt-based monetary system appears now to be coming to fruition with the impending loss of the children's material (and spiritual) inheritance. Medical expenses incurred through government-mandated entitlement programs have played a considerable part in the monetary crisis facing the nation.

Another sticker demonstrates our fascination with material possessions: "I love my ...." "Love" is indicated by a large red heart, and almost any *thing* may follow, from a breed of animals to a beer. Only a small percentage indicate a proper object of love, such as, "I [heart] my wife."

As bumper stickers have served outdoors for years, T-shirts now catechize modern American religious indoors. Reflecting our mercantile genius is a predominance of advertising. Millions of young people offer themselves to merchants as living billboards, not only free, but paying for the privilege of doing so. As a special case of advertising, sexual innuendo has a large following. If I were to judge from her T-shirt, the woman of Proverbs 6 and 7 was in our office recently. Emblazoned shamelessly on her T-shirt were crude invitations. Her life apparently is following her T-shirt script. Not yet married at 24, she has three children, none of whom has the same father. As is described in Phil. 3:19, we glory in what should be our shame, and our belly has become our god. How pitiful is a medical care pitted against such beliefs, if that care is limited to physical ministrations only. We dare not use carnal weapons to cast down the arguments flaunted against God from our patients' mouths, their bumper stickers, and their T-shirts.

Neither may we use weapons which partake of another Spirit than God's. A young woman, much of her youth junked in the drug subculture, wore on the Psychiatric ward a T-shirt which proclaimed: "God made me, and God don't make no junk." Doubtless, it was an expression of an attempt to reconstruct her self-esteem, but sadly at variance with Scripture and a faulty stone to lay at the foundation of a new, drug-free beginning. (Cf., for example, Rom. 9.) If Paul had worn his theology on his shirt, it might have said, "Chief of sinners." If Solomon had put a message on the back of his conveyance, it might have said, "A good man leaves an inheritance to his children's children, But the wealth of the sinner, is stored up for the righteous." (Prov. 13:22)

Providence in the End of Life Ethics vs. The Pharisaic Fallacy

Rev. David W. Hall

*Mr. Hall is pastor of Covenant Presbyterian Church in Oak Ridge, TN. He is a graduate of Covenant Theological Seminary, a contributor to various theological journals and editor of **The Presbyter's Review**.*

Many late twentieth century Christian ethicists are confounded by end-of-life ethical issues raised by medical technology. One of the contributing factors is that the increased technology of the last generation has generated moral dilemmas heretofore unknown. As one recent report observed:

"A distressing irony of the on-going progress in science and related technology is that in many cases welcomed advances in these areas also create profound moral dilemmas ... However, this increasing ability on the part of the medical community to preserve life also raises the perplexing moral question of whether or not available technology ought always to be used."[1]

THE PHARISAIC FALLACY

Another of the contributions to this confusion, often unnoticed, is the operation of the Pharisaic Fallacy. This theological error is not a pejorative term, certainly not the same as scornfully calling someone a "Pharisee." It is merely the description of a logical mistake. The Pharisaic Fallacy is not referred to in any logic textbook, but it is a fallacy which is sometimes present in theological ethics. It should be understood that to speak of such is to speak of a logical problem, not to make an accusation against someone's character or behavior. The Pharisaic Fallacy does not imply that the one who commits it even vaguely resembles a Pharisee. Let me attempt first to illustrate and then to define it.

One instance of the Pharisaic Fallacy is what has been called the "seamless garment" approach to the sanctity of life. The seamless garment approach links disparate ethical issues under a single "pro-life" ethical heading. According to the seamless garment proponents, if we hold to a pro-life ethic we must also be anti-nuclear warfare and anti-capital punishment. For all of those, according to this instance of the Pharisaic Fallacy, are ethical correlates of a pro-life view. The Pharisaic Fallacy here is the yoking of a number of different ethical issues under the same absolute while disregarding the dissimilarities of those issues.

Another instance of the Pharisaic Fallacy is seen in the issue of divorce and remarriage. Many evangelicals, out of respect for Scripture and desire for absolutes, have lamented the exponential growth of divorce in our century. In order to speak against such a rising tide we, in agreement with Scripture, have sought to condemn divorce apart from adultery or desertion (by the unbeliever). There are some who extend that one variable (i.e., the impossibility of easy divorce) to the conclusion that remarriage is impossible in all cases. A charting of such ethic might look like the following, with divorce on one end and remarriage on the other end of a straight line, covered by the absolute, "No."

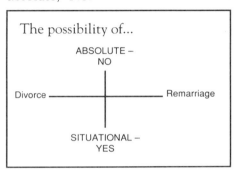

The possibility of...

ABSOLUTE –
NO

Divorce —————— Remarriage

SITUATIONAL –
YES

Another illustration of the Pharisaic Fallacy regards the role of women. Often in our zeal to properly protect women from the Eldership, evangelicals have been known to prohibit women from any responsible ministry in a church. That is another instance of taking one biblical teaching and absolutizing it to apply to other phenomena. If the Scriptures do not speak of that second or third phenomenon then as we *presume to link non-revealed categories under the same absolute*, we lapse into the Pharisaic Fallacy. No matter how well-intentioned we are, nonetheless, we are not permitted to over-absolutize. Good intentions do not excuse extending absolutes beyond their biblical applications.

A last example of the Pharisaic Fallacy is the recent environmental ethic, represented by some "Christian Greens." These Christians believe that God is the Creator of all of life on the cosmic scale. They further believe that all of life which is presently in the eco-sphere is to be regarded as equally "sacred," including whales, trees, and snail darters. To extinguish any of these, or any species, is tantamount to murder - even if the species is not created in the image of God. These enviro-ethicists link all species under one absolute without observing *biblical* distinctions. One consequence is that they believe in *equal* protection and *equal* treatment of all species. Such instance of the Pharisaic Fallacy results in the denigration of man, the only species created in God's own image. The culprit in this faddish ethical formulation is an ethic which blurs all distinctions, unites all species and prescribes the same ethical criteria for all.

A working definition of the Pharisaic Fallacy could be the following: The unwarranted (inappropriate) extension or application of one absolute truth to cover another ethical question which may be significantly different. Recall that it was the Pharisees who took God's law and extended it too far. Their error was not in being lawful, but in making what appeared to be logical extensions of the law to other cases without express authorization. For example, keeping the Sabbath was not wrong, but by the time of Jesus, the Pharisees had so truncated it as to render even the Co-Lawgiver in violation of it (cf. Mk. 2:27). In many other cases, the Pharisees were guilty *not* of keeping the Law but of *extending* it too far, to cover other cases without warrant. It was not the *first* instance of application which was improper, but the extension to a number of other insufficiently related cases which was improper. Such is what I have named the Pharisaic Fallacy.

In human life issues the Pharisaic Fallacy may have had more sway than we realize. The Christian who is sensitive to the whole counsel of God must be careful to heed the bib-

lical teaching on both beginning-of-life issues as well as end-of-life issues. The Pharisaic Fallacy, however, may be detected if we too closely link both of those *loci* despite their substantial differences. There is a Pharisaic Fallacy abroad in the church which sees the sanctity of life as equally constructed at both ends of the spectrum of life, a fallacy which this essay seeks to expose. Once this deficiency is recognized by relocating the absolute we can better decide the end of life ethics. The result is a preserved absolutism, but also one more sensitive to the range of biblical teaching, especially as it concerns the providence of God. To do away with the Pharisaic Fallacy is *not* to lapse into relativism.[2] One may, and should still hold ever so firmly to the same absolute, i.e., the providence (or sovereignty) of God in the beginning of life as well as at the end of life.

For a beginning definition of providence we could borrow Louis Berkhof's working definition as: "that continued exercise of the divine energy whereby the Creator preserves all His creatures, is operative in all that comes to pass in the world, and directs all things to their appointed end."[3] Of course, one could hardly improve on Calvin's definition of providence as "not that by which God idly views from heaven what is going on in the world, but that by which as if grasping the tiller He controls all events."[4]

SANCTITY OF LIFE LINKAGE

Let me attempt further illustration by way reviewing the teachings of some evangelicals who dealt with this issue after *Roe vs. Wade* in 1973. Francis Schaeffer was a leading voice, instrumental in awakening the consciences of many an evangelical to pro-life issues. Toward the late 1970's Schaeffer's books became increasingly attentive to pro-life ethical issues. As a pivotal thinker, he is

an example of this unconscious linkage. The following quotes note that growing emphasis, anecdotally bearing witness to the fact that both Schaeffer and other evangelicals began to see the link between abortion and euthanasia more and more inseparably related. Unintentionally, we may have shackled both of those issues with the same absolute, inappropriate to the end of life ethical issues.

In *How Should We Then Live* Schaeffer stated the principle which would guide him. "And (taking abortion as an example) if this arbitrary absolute by law is accepted by most modern people, bred with the concept of no absolutes but rather relativity, why wouldn't arbitrary absolutes in regard to such matters as authoritarian limitations on freedom be equally accepted as long as they were thought to be sociologically helpful? We are left with sociological law without any certainty of limitation."[5] Thus, Schaeffer cast the ethical principle. Later he would apply this principle in practice, as he predicted:

"The door is open. In regard to the fetus, the courts have separated 'aliveness' from 'personhood,' and if this is so, why not do the same with the aged? So the steps move along, and euthanasia may become increasingly acceptable." [6]

He further remarks, "As the Christian consensus dies, there are not many sociological alternatives," and resultingly, "...on this basis, if the majority vote supported it, it would become 'right' to kill the old, the incurably ill, the insane and other groups could be declared non-persons."[7] Thus is evidenced Schaeffer's early equivalency of abortion and euthanasia. His stern warning against Situationalism in 1976 was voiced as:

"... If there are no absolutes by which to judge society, then society is

absolute. *Society is left with one man or an elite filling the vacuum left by the loss of the Christian consensus which originally gave us form and freedom in Northern Europe and in the West ... Absolutes can be this today and that tomorrow...Arbitrary absolutes can be handed down and there is not absolute by which to judge them."*[8]

By the end of this book Schaeffer was observing, "Our own generation can thus disregard human life. On the *one end* we kill the embryo through abortion and on the *other end* we will introduce euthanasia for the old. The one is already here and the door is opened for the other."[9] Moreover, in the middle, Schaeffer also decried the use of genetic engineering as another possible relativistic measure to disregard the sanctity of human life.

Thus, one can see Francis Schaeffer defending moral absolutes and warning against incipient Situationalism. So determined was his defense of absolutes that he also yoked end-of-life ethics with beginning-of-life ethics, in the attempt to protect both from a relativism.

A few years later, Schaeffer went on to develop these thoughts with C. Everett Koop in *The Christian Manifesto*. His final published work, *The Great Evangelical Disaster* continued to demonstrate his conviction that abortion and euthanasia were ethical siblings. Hear Schaeffer toward the end of his life, as he says (after arguing that evangelicals must contend in this battle over ideas):

"This lowering of the view of human life may begin with talking about extreme cases in regard to abortion, but it flows on to infanticide and on to all of human life being open to arbitrary, pragmatic judgements of what human life is worthy to be lived - including your human life when you become a burden to society ... But the same principle applies equally in the crucial issues of

human life. A lowered view of life and a lowered view of scripture go hand-in-hand. The watershed issue is obedience to the Bible just as much as it is belief in the doctrine of inerrancy. Since the Bible teaches that life in the womb is human life, one cannot accept abortion without denying the authority and truth of scripture in practice. In drawing a line or not drawing a line ..."[10]

From this it seems clear that Schaeffer drew the line, both for abortion and euthanasia, along the same ethical coordinates. Still further in 1984, Schaeffer warned evangelicals:

"And if one thinks of human life as basically no different from animal life, why not treat people the same way? It would only be religious nostalgia to do otherwise. And so it first becomes easy to kill children in the womb, and then if one does not like the way they turn out, to kill the children after they are born. And then it goes on to the euthanasia of anyone who becomes a burden or inconvenience. After all, according to the secular world view, human life is not intrinsically different from animal life - so why should it be treated differently."[11]

Finally, let Schaeffer's testimony be heard, as he said:

"If human life can be taken before birth, there is no logical reason why it cannot be taken after birth. Thus the quality of life, arbitrarily judged by fallible and sinful people, becomes the standard for killing or not killing human life - whether unborn, newly born, the rich, or the aged. But what then does this say about the handicapped now alive? Isn't their life wrongly and tragically devalued? There are people who will read this book who would be allowed to die under these criteria if they were born today. The question of human life truly is a watershed issue."[12]

While being greatly appreciative for the entire ministry of Francis Schaeffer, and particularly grateful for his prescience in these and other

matters concerning human life, one must also observe his ethical linkage of the beginning-of and end-of-life ethics under the same rubric. One might want to biblically question the precision of this, while simultaneously appreciating the other aspects of pleading for the sanctity of life on end-of-life issues, in similar terms, and with the similar intensity as beginning-of-life ethical issues. Intentional or no, this caught on in the evangelical community, somewhat uncritically.

To see Schaeffer's influence, one could note, for example, these assertions in a 1983 work:

"Protecting from one end of the age spectrum to the other, we see euthanasia for the elderly as the counterpart to abortion for the very young. There is no moral distinction between the two. Quality-of-life proponent Joseph Fletcher agrees: 'To speak of living and dying, therefore ... encompasses the abortion issue along with the euthanasia issue. They are ethically inseparable.' Those who take comfort in the fact that euthanasia is not practiced at present in America are leaning on a slim reed. Infanticide is euthanasia for newborn children..."[13]

Thus did many other evangelicals join the chorus heralding that beginning-of-life and end-of-life ethical maxims were the same. Are the two really so identical and inseparable as these and other claims maintain? Is this a case of the Pharisaic Fallacy?

By the early 1980's Francis Schaeffer had been used of God to awaken a number of other evangelicals such as Jerry Falwell, James Kennedy and others to mount public platforms opposing abortion. Not only did they oppose abortion, they also yoked abortion with euthanasia as equally ultimate. They were certainly correct to see these as equally ultimate, but to lump them both under the same ethical formula might have been mistaken. As generic issues of life, both of which came under the umbrella of the same ethic, most evangelicals adopted this view of the equal ultimacy of the two, perceiving a mirror image between euthanasia and abortion. As Schaeffer and others warned, if we tread on the slippery slope of one we slide down the slope of the other. Francis Schaeffer and other biblical ethicists of the late twentieth century were effective in sensitizing a generation to avoid a situationalist ethic, particularly in regard to beginning-of-life as well as end-of-life ethical issues. The demon to be avoided was Situationalism.

THE LINKAGE QUESTIONED

By the mid 1980's a few Bible-believing ethicists began to move against the evangelical tide by raising questions about the supposed inseparability of these two ethical foci at the extremes of the life spectrum. One of the first pieces I saw of this sort was by Franklin E. Payne, M.D., of Augusta, Georgia, who in 1985 questioned whether or not we had an *absolute commitment* to extend human life as long as we could. His article, cautious and tempered by biblical moderation, raised the question in a strong, evangelical and pro-life publication. Though he raised the bare suggestion that we were not fully obligated to extend life to the farthest extent possible near the end of life in the very same manner as at the beginning, his essay was much criticized. He later noted, "To withhold or to withdraw medical treatment, as is being discussed here, does not constitute euthanasia and should not be placed in the same category with it." [14] Earlier, he wrote, "As Christians, however, we are also called to a wholistic approach. As God and His Word are a unity, so must we strive for unity in our ethics." [15] Similarly, he queried:

"Families [as opposed to govern-ments or companies] make choices every day according to the limits of their income. We choose the price and quality of clothes that we buy. With every purchase the family decides what it is willing to spend. Why should medical care be any different? Does not the family know what is best for its own? Is not only the family able to make this decision? Most importantly, does not the Bible clearly give this responsibility to the family, as we have seen? [16]

THE PROVIDENCE LINKAGE

Thus, what the Lord gives us by His Sovereign decree, our lot in life, His Providence, has an important role in these ethical decisions, which is substantively different from beginning-of-life issues. Soon a few other doctors began to raise similar questions. Then in 1988 one evangelical church even raised the question to what extent were heroic measures necessary. During this time many pastors and medical professionals dealing with death in hospital or hospice environments came to realize that this question might have substantially different ethical considerations from beginning-of-life issues. Yet none wanted to be seen as disloyal to pro-life premises. All this while, the Pharisaic Fallacy may have been the culprit.

One problem was the perception that there were two and only two options in beginning-of-life and ending-of-life ethics. These two mutually exclusive options were: (1) Liberal/situational or, (2) Conservative/absolute. The liberal Christian community was noted for its Situationalism. Following Joseph Fletcher's situational ethics, evangelicals wanted to distance themselves from that relativism. As a result, they held to the very same absolute in both cases, in hopes of insuring against relativism. The effect was that evangelicals held to an extreme limit both at the end-of-life and at the beginning-of-life. This view maintained that the

human life begins at the very point of conception. Correspondingly, they yoked that position with an end-of-life issue, holding that the human life should be seen as having the same sanctity *in extremis* as well. What happened was that the sanctity of human life became the anthropocentric absolute which yoked the whole spectrum of issues, instead of a theocentric absolute, the Providence of God. The extremes were covered, to be sure, but Providence, which had more bearing on one end of the spectrum, was nearly overlooked in the process.

Most evangelicals, in contrast to liberals, were absolutists. They wanted to be consistent absolutists on both ends of the spectrum. One can very easily erect an absolutist ethic in which life should be absolutely protected at its beginning without regard for situational factors. That life at the other end of its span should be protected or prolonged absolutely and apart from any situational factors whatsoever, is a Pharisaic Fallacy. - an illegitimate linkage of issues which have pertinent differences.

It was liberating, although somewhat terrifying, to question the tradition I had been taught. My initial reflection on Dr. Payne's articles was that they were mildly heretical. Yet, I found that, viewed in the light of God's Sovereignty and Providence, it was indeed valid that there were some situational factors in end-of-life matters. After all, it was decreed by God that at a certain time we die. Also, it should be recognized that there is a classic theological category which helps to elucidate these and to safeguard against unbridled Situationalism. That concept is the Providence of God.

Briefly, the end-of-life ethical absolute must be relocated from a man-centered sanctity of human life to the God-centered Providence of God Himself. The absolute we must maintain is the absolute of God's Providence. Providence, simply defined, is what God provides for our life, stemming from His eternal Decree both in the beginning-of-life and in the end-of-life. If our view is rooted in the Providence of God we are protected from a mindless relativism, since God's Providence is absolutely bound by His Word. His Word is no adversary of His actual Providence for us. The Providence of God is ontologically and ethically sufficient in and of itself to provide for the origin and preservation of human life from its conception to its end. The Providence of God is more ultimate than the sanctity of human life. The Providence of God itself gives life; it is not so much that life is "sanctious" in and of itself.

In end-of-life euthanasia cases, we ought to see the determining biblical variable as the Providence of God. Specifically, that means we shall ask, "What has God provided?" It is not the case that we are bound to extend life as far as humanly possible - due to its inherent sanctity. On the contrary, we are to attempt to extend life as far as possible *under* the Providence of God. This does not lead to euthanasia, even in difficult cases. It is hard to sustain the absolute compulsion to prolong life as long as it is now technologically possible to do. There is, after all, "a time to die" (Eccl. 3:2), that is part of God's Providence which we do not want to resist. This ethic is admittedly a more complex and difficult approach. For example, it is not uni-dimensional. No one ever promised that biblical absolutes would be easy, just absolute. In each case we must ask, "What has God provided?"

As we operate under the Providence of God we may find ourselves inquiring about end-of-life decisions with questions similar to the kind we ask about any other ethical dilemma. We'll explore not just one criteria or factor in a uni-dimensional frame,

but we'll pursue many factors. Of necessity, we'll ask about economic viability to the family. For example, could non-insured costs lead to violation of the 9th commandment by demanding either excessive borrowing or outright theft? We'll ask about healing, leaving room in our ethical formulation for God to work miraculously. We'll ask about the state of the faith of the ill person. (The believer may be ready to be with the Lord.) We'll ask closely about the likely *outcome* of the medical possibilities, not just about what medicine *offers*. We'll ask about God's provision of "three-score and ten years" (Ps. 90:10).

Adoption of this view yields many practical benefits. Besides being more theologically defensible than other views, it is of great utility to clarify for God's people from God's perspective, just what is going on, in a time of crisis. It holds promise to spare our people as much false guilt as possible should they choose *not* to opt for maximum technology. The saint of God can be comforted and encouraged to rest in the end-of-life providence of God, while avoiding the unconscious humanistic propulsion to extend the mortality beyond that which God decrees. These and other benefits can flow from such view, and should be taught as Scriptural counsel from God's Word.

We'll seek God's will in His Providence. It will be a complex question, yes, but not a situational one in the sense of Joseph Fletcher's relative Situationalism. We will be bound by an absolute - the Providence of God. We find ourselves frail mortals in search for that Providence. If the search is difficult we must face up to that and follow God's Word through difficult terrain - even through biblical casuistry - rather than to create a superstructure in which we arbitrarily choose one variable to become our absolute in order to apply it in a comprehensive manner to situations not wearing the same biblical yoke.

It is dangerous to select one focal point and attribute to it the recognition of absolute divinity. Making human life and its physical preservation the absolute errs in divinizing man.

Is this approach the harbinger of casuistry? It may be. Christians for centuries have known that casuistry in and of itself is not bad, although it is frequently spoken of pejoratively. *Biblical* casuistry, however, is another thing altogether. Biblical casuistry is the process when the ethicist finds himself bound by biblical absolutes, norms, and principles. Such casuistry, far from being a situational relativism, is the application of biblical teaching on a case by case basis. Development of it along with the prescription of biblical counsel by pastors and Christian physicians will help. It is theologically more defensible, avoiding, for example, the ungodly urge to achieve immortality in this physical body. It is time to recognize the Pharisaic Fallacy and realize the benefits of discarding it in favor of finding absolute value in the glory of God as He provides for us.

REFERENCES

1. Report of the Heroic Measures Committee (PCA), *Journal of Biblical Ethics in Medicine*, Vol. 2, No. 3, July, 1988, pp. 41 - 46.
2. For example, to see one medical ethicist's formulation of the differentiation between these two cases, listen to what Dr. Franklin E. Payne has recently said to strongly emphasize that one need not necessarily fall into relativism, if he unleashes a few of these ethical questions. "Many ethicists who are not pro-life see no difference between letting die and giving the patient an injection to end the process. We must separate these actions by an unbridgeable chasm. On the one hand, I will give up my tenure, my medical license, and my own

life before I will do an abortion or inject a patient to kill him. On the other hand, I have and will voluntarily 'let patients die' under certain conditions where no more can realistically be done." (cited from *Biblical Reflections*, Nov. 1990, p. 7) That's hardly slippery-sloping!

3. **Systematic Theology**, Eerdman's, 1949, p. 166.

4. cited in **Reformed Dogmatics**, Heinrich Heppe, ed., Baker, 1978, p. 252. One can further see the bearing of this on our subject, if a few of Calvin's phrases from **The Institutes** are reproduced. Calvin sees providence as "God's governance extended to all his works" which is "not the empty idle sort ... but a watchful, effective active sort, engaged in ceaseless activity" (I, xvi,3). He denies that "God idly observes from heaven" only, and sees providence as "that by which, as keeper of the keys, He governs all events. Therefore we must prove God so attends to the regulation of individual events, and they all so proceed from his set plan, that nothing takes place by chance" (I xvi,4). Later, Calvin asserts that "nothing happens except from His command or permission" (I, xvi,8), and even applies providence to an example of the death of a merchant, as he explains, "His death was not only foreseen by God's eye, but also determined by His decree. For it is not said that he foresaw how long the life of each man would extend, but that he determined and fixed the bounds that men cannot pass [Job 14:5]" (I,xvi,9). Thus the Christian is to view "a death of this sort" ... as it is .. [as] God's providence exercised authority over fortune in directing its end" (I,xvi,9). For Calvin, providence "is the determinative principle of all things" (I,xvii,1) and "Indeed, the principal purpose of Biblical history

is to teach that the Lord watches over the ways of the saints with such great diligence that they do not even stumble over a stone" (I,xvii,6). In sum, for Calvin, providence is essential, as well as practical, such that "ignorance of providence is the ultimate of all miseries; the highest blessedness lies in the knowledge of it" (I,xvii,11).

Of course, in addition to these definitions, one could quickly refer to the **Westminster Confession of Faith**, which in its fifth chapter reads, "God the great Creator of all things doth uphold, direct, dispose, and govern all creatures, actions, and things, from the greatest to the least, by His most wise and holy providence."

5. Schaeffer, Francis, **How Should We Then Live**, Crossway, 1976, p. 222.

6. Schaeffer, *Ibid*, p. 223, emphasis added.

7. Schaeffer, *Ibid*, p. 223-224.

8. Schaeffer, *Ibid*, p. 224.

9. Schaeffer, *Ibid*, p. 230.

10. Schaeffer, Francis, **The Great Evangelical Disaster**, Crossway, 1984, pp. 102 - 103.

11. Schaeffer, *Ibid*, pp. 104 - 105, emphasis added.

12. Schaeffer, *Ibid*, p. 108.

13. Young, Curt, **The Least of These,** Moody Press, 1983, p. 123, emphasis added.

14. Payne, *op. cit.*, p. 44.

15. Payne, Franklin E., Jr., The Economics of Medicine: A Wholistic Approach, *Journal of Biblical Ethics in Medicine*, Vol. 2, No. 2, April, 1988, p. 27.

16. Payne, *Ibid*, p. 30.

Defining the Christian Doctor

Robert Maddox, MD

Dr. Maddox is a graduate of the University of Missouri - Columbia School of Medicine. He practices in Monroe, Louisiana.

A pediatrician acquaintance retired last month, elated about getting out of medicine. He joins the ranks of many Christian doctors, who raise the question of what it means to be a Christian in medicine. They say that the "good old days" of medicine are over and practicing is no fun anymore — just competitive business. These doctors warn aspiring medical students that it is the worst possible time for a Christian to enter the field of medicine.

Another group is emerging, doctors who are not content to be doctors first, and then Christians. Focus on the Family publishes a magazine for this group, with articles on how to balance priorities, manage stress, and handle the system. They pray with patients, write prescriptions for Scripture reading, and witness to patients under certain circumstances. Some even enroll patients in discipleship programs. They have a prayer or study time for employees at the start of the day. They recognize that the body is only part of man and talk about the spirit and soul. Several have even planned or started associations of doctors, psychiatrists and ministers to treat the whole person.

There is a subset of this group that pick one issue to fight, and thus are distinguished as Christian doctors. They often are pro-life, repenting of our profession's involvement in the sin of abortion by fighting it. Others run adoptions services or lead semi- nars against teenage promiscuity or smoking.

Yet another group thinks that Christian doctors should be in ministry and not business. They donate their services to the poor, or become medical missionaries. They have started inner-city and rural clinics. They have mobilized efforts to feed and clothe the poor, and provide teaching about nutrition, cleanliness, and child care.

Other doctors work in Emergency Medicine, or Radiology, Anesthesiology, Pathology, or even in large group practices, with the goal of having time and money to spend in other Christian service. Some of these still recognize that their medical work can be Christian service — witnessing to patients or employees perhaps. Some medical groups form with the goal of sending one of their doctors overseas on a rotating basis.

In contrast to all these groups, there are many Christian doctors who think it is improper even to talk about Christian medicine as if it were separate. They believe that a Christian practicing good medicine would (and should) practice no differently than anyone else. Being the most competent is the most important to them. They think it is improper to mix faith and practice.

There are others that would say that it is not activities that distin- guish a doctor as a Christian, but rather ethics. Most who say this have in mind issues such as abortion or euthanasia, or attitudes such as the Hippocratic ideal or concern for the patient rather than money. [1] On closer examination, few of these doctors can articulate any ethical principle that secular medical ethicists could not agree with in the broad construction - principles such as autonomy of the patient, beneficence, and justice. Except on a few specifics, their ethics do not differ from the non-Christians. This is not to say that ethics should not define a Christian doctor, only that many who try to use ethics in this way fail.

Why even define a Christian doctor? What would it change to know what a Christian doctor is or does? For the medical student it is most important, since it defines success in medical training. Success in medical school is not getting good grades. As the joke says, both the student graduating with the lowest averages and the one with the highest are called doctor. Success is not even graduating with one's faith intact. As important as that is, it is not success. It is only survival. Success in any aspect of the Christian life is becoming what God requires of us. If God requires that we be Christian doctors, then we must know what that is.

Defining a Christian doctor is also necessary in order to choose the proper teachers. In Luke 6:37-45,

Christ teaches that a tree is known by its fruit, and a man's words and works reflect the condition of his heart. In this context, he tells a parable teaching that a fully trained student will be like his teacher. Christ is our ultimate teacher, and we must be like him when we are fully taught. Our human teachers must be chosen carefully, lest we be led by the blind. Recognizing a Christian doctor is essential for choosing a proper teacher.

It is also important to avoid improper teachers. You must not become like non-Christian doctors. It is difficult in a professional school to completely avoid improper teachers and influences. Stress and limited time force the student to accept loads of material without proper evaluation. You are even influenced by the massive influx of vocabulary that must be learned. Words are learned without context - words that should carry moral weight. Medical concepts are isolated from ethics simply by learning vocabulary. Medical training often doubles a student's vocabulary. Words are not neutral; they carry connotations and they represent concepts.

Becoming a Christian doctor is important. It necessitates defining a Christian doctor. As mentioned, activity or ethics are often the sole terms in this definition. There is no doubt that our ethics should be Scriptural, and should be distinct from any other consistent system of ethics. Christian activity is commendable as well. Christian medicine is caring medicine. It should be concerned with the poor, the orphan and the widow. These activities alone do not distinguish us from the pagans, however. In fact, pagans often outdo Christians at many of these activities. Christian medicine does treat the whole person but it was only *after* others began to promote "holistic medicine" that Christians began to adopt, modify

and claim the same depth of focus. The recent emphasis on medicine for the whole person scarcely can claim a thoroughgoing biblical genesis.

Activities and ethics should be important distinguishing factors. There is something deeper, however. Commitment, perhaps, though the pagans are often just as committed to their gods. No, there is a difference at the very root of medicine, the basis, the purpose. A Christian doctor practices medicine to glorify God. Everything we do should be to God's glory, whether we eat or drink or whatever we do.

That a Christian doctor practices to glorify God would not be disputed by any of the groups mentioned at the beginning. Yet, in all these groups there is an implicit understanding that there is a basic set of principles or tenets of medicine, to which may be *added* Christian attachments; which attachments are important is the only debatable question. It is agreed by all these groups that medicine itself is neutral, to be used for good or for evil, just like a nuclear reaction. After all, it is argued, to practice medicine everyone must learn anatomy, physiology, microbiology, and such. Even the veterinary students take these courses. There is not a distinctively Christian anatomy (unless some change occurs in, say, the pineal gland when one accepts Christ). Histology is no different for a Christian, since the same tissues are examined through the same microscope. So it is concluded that diseases are diseases, and the diagnosis, pathology, and treatment are morally neutral.

Of course, most Christians would admit that some diseases are the result of immoral behavior. Some would even admit that morality should be brought into the treatment decisions for some illnesses, perhaps sexually transmitted diseases or

AIDS, or those involving abortion. Everyone would agree that ethics are a part of every treatment decision, but most would deny personal morals from entering at all. This is an example of misused vocabulary begging the question. Some diseases, they would assert, can be viewed differently by a Christian, but for colds and congestive heart failure, for headaches and Huntington's chorea, for tuberculosis and thyrotoxicosis, there cannot be a distinctively Christian understanding. Some would still admit a Christian approach to the patient with these diseases, but the principles of disease remain the same. A Christian should respect the patient as made in the image of God, for example, or that our relationships should reflect Christ. But, these are seen as attachments to an otherwise neutral science. It is asserted that medicine itself cannot be Christian, only our use of it.

At the most basic level of the purpose of medicine, it is clear that medicine must glorify God. This is the only reason for any human activity, especially for a whole profession[2] It must be a service to God, and in serving him, a service to our fellowman. In itself, this contravenes the neutrality of medicine, since it takes away a mere existence from medicine, glorifies God as Creator, and places medicine under his Sovereign control, to be practiced by human agents responsible to Him.

In order to glorify and serve God, we must have specifics. Those specifics must include definitions. What is a doctor? What is medicine? What is disease? What is health? What is a person? Who decides the answers to these questions? Very few doctors can satisfactorily answer these questions. That's what philosophers are for, or theologians. A few doctors will try to answer and find themselves talking in circles, which is also what philosophers and theologians are for. If we allow someone other than the Supreme Authority to answer, we have biased the discussion. When man is allowed to answer, disaster and sin result. As God answered Job, "Who is this who darkens counsel by words without knowledge?" [3] Man has tried to answer the question, "What is a person?" and abortion has skyrocketed. Man has tried to define the role of a doctor, and he has gone from a slave to a god and back again. If man has the final authority to answer the questions, then he can change the answers.

Descartes changed the answers when he introduced his Cartesian dualism. To that point, man, body and soul inseparable, was sacred, to be handled with utmost respect, distinct from and set over all other creatures. Descartes' mechanistic view of the body desecrated it, described it in terms of machinery, allowed it to be invaded with impunity, by knives and drugs and all manner of instrumentation. [4] Now animals are used as models for man, corpses are dissected and men are treated as things, disposable things.

When man defines disease, alcoholism becomes a disease. Then all manner of sin is labeled as disease, to be cured with chemical, electrical and mechanical treatments. Any sinful habit, from gluttony to fornication, from stealing to bestiality, can become a disease. Now even normal and good functions, such as conception and pregnancy, are seen as diseases. [5] Fulfilling one's calling before God as a wife and homemaker has even been viewed as a disease.

It does matter who defines and who answers. As Christians, we recognize that God's Word is our authority, our answer, our source of definition. In the words of Isaiah, To the Law and to the Testimony. God asked Job where he was when the world was created. God did not ask our advice when he created the world. He did not need our advice.

He decreed the boundaries of the sea. He decreed how the wind would blow and precipitation would circulate. He decreed how animals would eat and how plants would grow. Both Job (10:10 - 12) and David (Ps. 139:15) tell us that God is the author and architect of our frames, our bodies. He is the one that oversees the process called embryology. He is the only one that knows the answers to our questions.

Definitions are not neutral, so the fact that medicine requires definitions also contravenes the neutrality of medicine. When Christians assume that medicine is neutral, man will define the terms and answer the questions. Unless we allow God to define and answer, man will define and answer wrongly. The results are the fruit of a bad tree, and evident all around us. Abortion, addictionology, and the American Medical Association (AMA) are just the beginning of man's achievements. The structure of medicine is being shaken, and the foundations are crumbling. High insurance rates point to a misplaced emphasis on health. Health care accounts for 11.5 - 12% of our nation's gross national product (GNP). For lower income families, insurance may require 20% of their annual income. There have been cries for more. In his recent inaugural address, the President of the AMA expressed the opinion that the majority of Americans would rather pay more, and have the latest technology and get it right away. [6] The fact is, however, that most Americans would be shocked to find out what they pay for health care. They would pay far less for it if they paid for it themselves. Doctors will order less expensive tests, according to the patient's payment source, as studies are now demonstrating. Tests and procedures would cost far less if payment came directly from the patient's pocket, since normal market forces would be allowed to operate. Third-party payment, allowing someone

else to make the decision and pay the bill, encourages and feeds upon individual irresponsibility. Scripture demands that the individual is held accountable for his stewardship of his body. When man is allowed to change the answers, irresponsibility and high costs are the bad fruit.

The high cost of health care reflected as a percent of the GNP is not the only aspect of this misplaced emphasis on health. Americans crave the latest technology, despite the fact that medicine has not been shown to be of much benefit in the health of a population. It has been estimated that less than 4% of the decline in mortality between 1900 and 1970 was due to medical measures. There has been a decline in deaths from infectious disease, but that decline is clearly not due to medical treatment. "The cure rates for the major life-threatening cancers remain unchanged since the war on cancer was started by Nixon." [7] Cancer death rates have actually risen slightly.

More Americans surviving birth are living a full life span. This does not mean that longevity has increased. Does it mean that a person has a better chance of living to age 80? Maybe, depending on whether you define a person as God defines him, or as modern statisticians do. By God's definition of a person as including all conceived, American life expectancy has actually dropped back below the 1900 level, due to abortion. Another measure of relative rates of moratlity, the years of potential life lost, makes it clear that abortion is the single leading cause of loss of life in America, with cancer and heart disease insignificant in comparison. [8]

Mortality figures may not be the best measure of efficacy. In fact, without defining death and health, it may be a fallacy. Scripture asserts that all will die, and that death entered the world as a result of sin. So health may be entirely, or partially, unrelated to death. Until health is defined from Scripture, we have no means of measuring it, and no basis for asserting advances. By its own definitions, medicine has been unable to deliver what it has promised. Even if it were able to deliver on its promises, the emphasis currently placed on health is unscriptural. God did indeed promise health as a blessing of the covenant, but he tells us to seek him first, not the physicians only, when we are sick. Rather than looking first to medical studies, we should look to the Scriptures. Most medical axioms have a short half-life, and textbooks are often outdated before they are distributed. The new view can no more be taken as truth than the one it replaced, since both are the result of the same flawed methodology. Scripture, on the other hand, is truth. It has always been true, and will never pass away, or change, or become outdated.

What remains, then, is to glean our definitions and principles from Scripture. This task is not easy, though there are a few principles of health which are quickly found. These principles are unequivocally true. Health is a blessing of obedience to God. Our spiritual attitude affects our physical health and vice versa. Improper use of the sacraments (especially the Lord's supper) can result in sickness and death. Sometimes the wicked are more healthy than the righteous, but their end is clear. Since physical health is not much advantage in hell, this teaches us the lesser importance of physical health.

Scripture also teaches our duty to the sick. In Mt. 25:31-46, Christ teaches that at the Final Judgment, he will judge us by whether we clothed the naked, fed the hungry and thirsty, sheltered the stranger, and visited or comforted the sick. We will not be judged on how many

were cured or how long we prolonged life, but whether we comforted the sick. Even if medical care were worthwhile, it is not a priority. Obedience is a priority. Food and water are priorities, but not medical care, especially not super high-tech medical care. Comfort, yes. Caring, yes. Not medicine. When cure rather than comfort becomes the focus, failure must result. Medical training forces the focus on cure. Morbidity and mortality conferences are only part of a system designed to reinforce that death or lack of cure means failure.

Even more basic, and necessary to the development of Scripture's view of medicine is a proper understanding of the way the world works. God created the world and actively sustains it. That is a tenet of Christian belief. The implications are often ignored, however. God tells us that he upholds, directs, disposes, and governs all creatures, actions and things. Psalm 104:10 makes it clear that God causes the winters to flow into the valley. God may use gravity, a force decreed by him, but he says that he causes it. Gravity is not automatic, nor is it a law of nature independent of God. Gravity is merely our description of his decree. It is even possible that gravity is mediated by angels carrying the molecules to a new location. Whatever means God uses, it is clear that he actively decrees and directs.

Psalm 104:15 declares that grass grows and seeds sprout not because of certain temperature and moisture conditions, but rather because God causes the grass to grow, and ordinarily under certain conditions. Nothing happens automatically. Everything happens as a result of God's active hand. God's Sovereignty is not reactive, merely the power to fix what happens. Rather, God planned everything in his good pleasure, decrees it, then works it all out in history. This is the teaching of Scrip-

ture and the historic confession of the church. It has important implications for medicine.

We are taught to pray for our daily bread by our Savior. He himself rejected Satan's offer of bread after he had fasted forty days. He reminds us in Mt. 4:4 that man does not live by bread alone but rather is sustained by the Word of God. In referring to Dt. 8:3, he makes clear his meaning. It is by his power alone that our life and strength are sustained. The manna that God fed the Israelites was unknown to them. They asked what it was. God used something other than bread to sustain them that they might learn that it is not bread that sustains them. God ordinarlly uses bread, but this is not proof of its power, only of its ordinary agency. God wanted to teach them that when they were prospering in the new land, it was not a natural result, or the result of their labors. Their prosperity, even life, is his gift. [9] The Krebs cycle does not work automatically. It is a description of the ordinary agency of God Almighty; he could accomplish its ends entirely otherwise.

God is active in disease and health. Cotton Mather, the great colonial American theologian and the first American advocate of the germ theory, said of germs, "What unknown Armies has the Holy One, wherewith to ... even destroy the Rebellious Children of Men? Millions of Billions of Trillions of Invisible Velites [soldiers]! Of sinful Men they say, Our Father, shall we smite them? On His order, they do it immediately; they do it effectually." He sought to find a spiritual lesson in every human ailment. A toothache, for instance, should remind us that it was with their mouths that our first parents sinned, and with our mouths we continue to sin, cursing both God and man. We may not always clearly see God's purpose, nor are we to be obsessed to find it, but we can be sure that he has a purpose and is working out all things according to his good pleasure.

Disease, then, is not just disease. The fact of an illness cannot stand in isolation. It is always seen in terms of more basic principles. A headache is different for a Christian. To view a headache apart from the Creator, apart from the biblical view of man, apart from God's view of illness, is not simply an incomplete view. It is a view based on entirely wrong principles, a view based on another system. Since God's system is reality, a headache not seen from a Scriptural perspective is necessarily viewed outside of reality, or in an inconsistent system. This accounts for the failure of modern American medicine to accomplish what it has promised, much less what God requires of it. In a sense, modern American medicine lives in a dream bubble and does not deal with reality.

What is needed is a rethinking of the entire foundation of medicine. Medical training has taught us to think as the world thinks. We must instead train ourselves to think as God thinks. There is no systematic development of medicine to which you can refer. At present, only piecemeal work on specific aspects of health and illness exist. Much work has been done by the church through the ages that is simply ignored, usually because it was written in the pre-scientific age. This fact makes it all the more useful. The ultimate basis for specific answers to the questions and dilemmas of modern medicine is in Scripture, not in chemistry or immunology or electronics.

What does it mean to be a Christian doctor? It means first to be a Christian, striving to please God in every area of life. It means to exercise that in our calling, our vocation. We must serve God in serving our fellowman. We must serve our fellowman by listening to his complaints and ailments. We must serve by comforting him, teaching him about his illness, diagnosis and prognosis, and treatments; but most importantly, we serve by reminding him that there is no comfort outside of Christ. We advise, and counsel, and rebuke on occasion. We sometimes use drugs or other remedies, if they may benefit; but we use nothing without thankfulness to God, asking for his blessing in its use. We seek daily to see God's hand in his world. We recognize that to ignore God's hand is to deny him. We treat the patient as fallen, a sinner in need of redemption far more than he needs our medicine. We remember that the patient has responsibility for himself before God, that we cannot force others to pay for his care, nor can he. We remember that resources are limited, and that medicine is not the highest priority.

The groups of doctors described at the beginning are not wrong for their approach or activities. They are not wrong for their ethics. The underlying view of medicine, however, needs to be rethought and based on Scripture instead of on the foundation of sand. Then medical practice can be truly exciting, fulfilling and Christian. This is a most exciting time to enter medicine, because the foundations of sand are being exposed and Christians can once again build on the foundation of Scripture, with Jesus Christ as the Cornerstone.

REFERENCES

1. For a critique of this position, see Adams, Jay E., What is/Are Christian Ethics, *Journal of Biblical Ethics in Medicine*, Vol. 1, No. 2, April, 1987, pp. 20,21.
2. The **Larger Catechism** of the Westminster Standards answers the question, "What is the chief and highest end of man?" Ans. "Man's chief and highest end is to glorify God, and fully to enjoy him forever."
3. Job 38:2
4. Kriel, J.R., Removing Medicine's Cartesian Mask: The Problem of Humanizing Medical Education, *Journal of Biblical Ethics in Medicine*, Vol. 3, No. 2, Winter 1989, pp. 34 - 35.
5. Terrell, Hilton, Ethics and the Medical Model of Disease, *Journal of Biblical Ethics in Medicine*, Vol. 3, No. 4, Fall 1989, pp, 68 - 74.
6. Tupper, C. John, Dreams, Dollars, and Deeds: The Sacred Fire and Health Access in America, *JAMA*, Vol. 264, No. 9, 5 Sept. 1990, p. 1151.
7. Townsend, Donald, Physical and Spiritual Care of the Terminally Ill, *Journal of Biblical Ethics in Medicine*, Vol. 2, No. 1, January 1988, p. 3.
8. Terrell, Hilton, P., Average Life Expectancy, or, "What is Truth?" *Journal of Biblical Ethics in Medicine*, Vol. 2, No. 3, July 1988, pp. 47-49.
9. In **Institutes of the Christian Religion**, III, 20:44, John Calvin says "...not even an abundance of bread would benefit us in the slightest unless it were turned into nourishment" [by God]. We are trying by an abundance of medical care to obtain healing, without God, trusting instead in impersonal automatic principles.

Inhabiting a Biblical Framework in Medicine

Spiros A. Lazarou, M.D.

Dr. Lazarou received his B.A. from Johns Hopkins University and his M.D. from the University of Maryland. He is currently in residency at the Eastern Virginia Graduate School of Medicine in Norfolk, engaged in Plastic and Reconstructive Surgery.

A previously healthy 20 year old woman has been experiencing abdominal discomfort over the past months. Due to a recent worsening of her pain she decided to see a doctor.

The doctor took a history and did a physical exam. He then ordered some tests. Having assured himself of a diagnosis of irritable bowel syndrome he prescribed a stool bulk agent. Knowing that in many such cases the problem is stress, he added a minor tranquilizer to his treatment. Indeed, if he were to perceive the stress to be severe he may even recommend a psychiatrist. He then tells his grateful patient to return soon for follow-up.

On the surface it would seem to most that the physician has adequately fulfilled his obligations to the patient and all is well. Indeed, this is today's acceptable "standard of care." But, "the first to present his case seems right, till another comes forward and questions him." (Prov. 18:17)

The problem with this case, indeed, begins with the "standard of care." By what and whose standard was this patient treated? There is, of course, no neutral ground. I believe a biblical standard would have resulted in an entirely different approach. The physician's approach to the patient was rooted in Humanism, as I will soon show.

A standard is a point of reference against which we evaluate and interpret reality. We all have an ultimate standard that serves as a grid through which we interpret life. It is a product of our worldview. Our worldview is the belief-ordering conceptual framework that we inhabit. It profoundly influences our daily actions. We are not infinite nor do we exist in a vacuum. We have a large number of assumptions or presuppositions about life (that most of us may not even articulate) and these together form our worldview. Our worldview provides answers to questions concerning, for example, our origins, significance and destiny. It establishes values, right and wrong, good and bad. It provides a means for us to integrate or discard ideas and phenomena that don't fit our expectations. It helps us to make "sense" out of life and equips us to investigate the world. Beginning with these presuppositions, we make observations of the world around us which are both directed and limited by our overall framework.

Ultimately, there are two reference points: God and man. For the unbeliever the reference point is man and leads to Humanism; for the regenerate man it is God as he is revealed in the Holy Scriptures. As unbelievers our concepts of what love is, or health, or justice or the roles or medicine and government, etc., are derived from man. That we have these notions at all evidences that we are made in the image of God and that we do have his "law" imprinted in our minds, though we have corrupted both the image and his law. When we become Christians our point of reference has become Christ and his Word. Our worldview changes. As babes in Christ, however, we invariably drag into the church many of our unbiblical presuppositions. Additionally, we have not expunged from our thinking many of the implications even of those unbiblical assumptions that we have rejected. These assumptions take a long time to change, for we first have to establish regular habits of Bible study, prayer and application of that which we do learn. In this way our mind is transformed and God restores what the locusts have taken away. Since God has commanded us to work out our salvation, it is our duty to bring the Scriptures to bear on all that we do.

My purpose, by way of the example at the beginning, is to expose some of the unbiblical assumptions involved in the way this commonplace case was handled, proposing some biblical corrections. We will consider the role of medicine and the physician as well as the basis for such thinking in the light of the Holy Scriptures.

First, a diagnosis of irritable bowel syndrome can be made with great accuracy by history and physical. No ancillary test can significantly improve on it. What purpose do hundreds of dollars worth of tests serve? In part they serve to spread the wealth among physicians. Partly they serve medicolegal purposes. (Actually, these two reasons feed on each other.) Partly, they serve to make the patient feel the doctor is doing something. Partly, the technological gadgetry combined with unintelligible medical language serve to keep the patient awed and marveling by maintaining an aura of mystery.

Second, the patient is stripped of her responsibility for her illness. By implication, her illness is a product of biochemical reactions and/or life circumstances. By implication, she is not in control of or responsible for her circumstances or, at the very least, her response to those circumstances. But, in fact, stress is ultimately a spiritual issue that implies not trusting the Lord in some or all areas of life. Or, it is the end result of deeply ingrained and yet unquestioned unbiblical habits. True medicine would bring this to the attention of the patient while not necessarily denying medicinal treatment for the physical manifestations of the problem.

Third, because of this unbiblical approach the patient is stripped of the hope of a true cure which would involve repentance and obedience to God's law as part of the process of healing.

Fourth, she is made dependant upon the doctor for her health. In such a role the doctor is playing God.

James 5:14-16 is pertinent. First, it is important to point out that sickness entered the world when sin entered the world. But, as the cases of Job and the blind man (Jn. 9:3) point out, an individual's sickness may in no way be related to his own sin. James says "if". However, God does bring judgement to the unbeliever and discipline to his own

through sickness and death. (Ex 16:26, 1 Kings 3:14, I Cor. 11:30-32)

Part of the function of the elders has been superseded by the physician. With reference to administering the oil, James does not use the word *chrio*, which means anoint. Instead he uses *aleipho* which means "to rub," implying not a ceremonial anointing but a medicinal treatment. However, the remaining obligations of the elders still stand. Indeed, in our present circumstances these obligations necessitate a cooperation between the elders and physician. The function of the elders is vital and commanded. The medicine was to be administered in Christ's name. The elders consecrate the medicine, trusting not in the medicine alone, but in medicine they ask God to bless. By their prayer they show God is active in healing. Humanism trusts in medicine. The elders were to counsel the patient regarding the possiblity of sin and what to do about it. Note that the ultimate cure is provided by God and acknowledged. Also, the church represented by the elders is in authority over the physician. The sick sister is part of the elders' flock and under their authority. Her well-being is their responsibility.

The situation today has changed through the rise of medicine and the physician. But the principles still stand. The physician is called upon by a sick patient. The physician's responsibility is to direct the patient to the Great Physician, Jesus Christ, who is the author of health and disease. (Deut. 32:39) Jesus healed in the context of directing people to the kingdom of God. He needs to direct the patient along the guidelines God has established. If the patient is an unbeliever and has no interest in these matters then, after having fulfilled his obligation before God to direct the patient (God's law applies to all), the physician must individualize his response. Jesus certainly

helped many who did not trust in him. We are still to provide for our enemies though our response has to be in the context of biblical wisdom, always thinking in terms of how to best direct the patient to repentance and salvation.

True healing is a wholistic concern. Jesus exemplified this and so does the language of the Scriptures. The Greek word translated "salvation" and that translated "healing" in many of Jesus' miracles is the same word. The truly saved man was saved inside and out. Of the ten lepers that were healed only the one that came back and gave thanks to God is said to be saved or healed. He was made whole. This is James concern in James 1:4.

As Jesus makes clear when he healed the paralytic brought down through the roof, true health is much more than the absence of disease. It begins internally with forgiveness of sins and a restored fellowship with God. It has to begin that way because disease and death entered the world when sin destroyed that fellowship. Although, certainly Jesus distinguished between the spiritual and the physical, he did not separate the two in the context of healing. He heals people and forgives their sins, then says, "Your faith has saved you," which is often translated, "Your faith has healed you." Thus, just as the kingdom of God is not here in its fullness so health is not here in its fullness. Just as the kingdom of God grows with obedience, so health improves. Compare the health of those nations where the gospel has gone, even if presently they live in rebellion, to those where it has never gone.

Jesus' concern was not merely the salvation of men's souls but the establishment of God's kingdom which includes men's souls but is much more comprehensive. His concern includes the totality of existence — man and his entire habitat or culture.

This fact should not surprise us. After the Fall of Adam, God renewed his covenant in the context of the curse and reiterated it to Noah, commanding him to multiply, fill, occupy and subdue. The original mandate was to be fulfilled even in the context of man's sin. Salvation would occur in the context of God's mandate.

In considering the covenant of creation that God established with Adam we must consider its general aspects (multiply, fill occupy and subdue) as well as its focal aspect (the specific prohibition against eating of the tree of the knowledge of good and evil). It is essential to consider the organic unity between this commandment and the total responsibility of man as created. If we do not observe the unity Christianity is conceived of narrowly in terms of salvation of the soul. We thus fail to consider adequately the effect of redemption on the total life-style of man in the context of an all-embracing covenant. That view results in a bypassing of redeemed man's responsibility to carry forward the implications of his salvation into the world of medicine as well as economics, politics, business and culture at large.

The ultimate goal of redemption will not be realized merely in a return to the pristine beginnings of the garden. A new imagery of paradise arises in Scripture — the imagery of a city, of a hustling, bustling center of activity for the redeemed echoing the charge to bring the whole earth into subjection to the glory of God. Indeed, what does it mean to glorify God? Paul says that we must do all to the glory of God. In the Hebrew glory means weight. We can't add weight to God since all that exists is his. Rather, it means to bring to bear on all things the full weight of God's relationship to those things. Therefore, if I am to practice medicine to the glory of God I must do more than say that this is the case, for, Christianity is not magic. Something doesn't glorify God because I said it does, regardless of my motivations. Rather, when I practice medicine in such a way that I apply biblical principles, that is, his Word, to fully bear on it, then I glorify God. God is not satisfied when we bring into the church pagan concepts and institutions. We must erect an edifice founded entirely on biblical presuppositions.

Animal Rights and The Image of God

Part II *(Part I appeared in Vol. 5, No. 1, Winter 1991)*

T. Stuart Walker, PhD

Dr. Walker is Associate Professor of Medical Education in the Indiana University School of Medicine at Ball State University in Muncie, Indiana.

In Part I of this article, we examined the philosophical bases of the animal rights movement. Animal rightists stake their claim for animal rights using an ontological argument, claiming that humans and animals are identical in essence and cannot be ethically distinguished. This argument for ontologic unity among all sentient creatures is based upon their insistence that humans and animals are essentially interrelated in at least one of three categories: (1) we are interrelated by a mutual phylogeny (phylogenetic unity), (2) we share in the same spiritual essence and our lives are interwoven with theirs (spiritual unity), and/or (3) we are all the experiencing subjects of a life, a life that has intrinsic value (existential unity). Having established ontologic equality among all sentient creatures, animal rightists then insist that all creatures of equal essence must be treated identically and must possess equal rights of life and self determination. This deontic ethic forbids all human use of animals unless that use specifically benefits the animal being used and the animal in use is a willing participant (analogous to human "informed consent").

Does the Scripture agree with this assessment? Are we and the world of animals essentially equivalent with equal moral claims? The Bible does point to certain similarities, but none of these are related to

the similarities which underlie animal rights arguments. In fact, Scripture tends to repudiate all three principal presuppositions which undergird the claim for animal rights.

First, Genesis 1:26-30 and 2:7, 21-25 clearly states that man was a special creation with no phylogenetic relationship to any other creature. Thus, there is a phylogenetic discontinuity between man and animals - we are not physically interrelated. Moses emphasized the uniqueness of man's creation in the text when he uses here the Hebrew verb "*bara*" (create) only twice - in Gen. 1:1 to refer to the beginning of creation, and in verse 27 when he describes the creation of man. This likely emphasizes both the uniqueness of man as a special creation and that the creation of man was the culmination of creation; creation was begun with the purpose of creating man. Man was made for the earth and the earth for man.

Second, we are not spiritually related. This argument of spiritual relatedness is drawn from Eastern mysticism and has more analogy with Greek dualism than it does Biblical revelation. Man was formed as a distinct unit with individual identity. Unlike the animals, man was animated with the breath of God (Gen. 2:7); this may indicate an essential difference between the life of man

and that of animals. Keil and Delitzsch[21] insist that when God breathed life into man, He made man a uniquely "living soul." This argument may be weakened somewhat by the Mosaic references to animals as "living souls" (Heb. "*nephesh chayim*"; Gen. 1:21,24; 2:7; 9:12ff) and by Moses speaking of animals in Genesis 7:15 & 22 as having "the breath (*ruwach*) of life." Nevertheless, God formed the whole man - body and spirit - as a unit with individual relationship with and responsibility to Him. This persistent individuality of identity permeates Scripture ("The soul who sins is the one who will die... The righteousness of the righteous man will be credited to him, and the wickedness of the wicked will be charged to him." Ezekiel 18:20, NIV); the concept of shared essence among individuals with loss of personal identity is completely foreign to the Bible. Rather, Scripture shows us as creatures created to be corporeal - not as spirits temporarily confined in bodies - with an ultimate destiny to live forever in glorified bodies on the new earth (Job 19:25-27; Phil. 3:21; Rev. 21:1 and others).

Finally, although the Scripture reminds us of several creaturely characteristics which are shared by men and animals and which are significant, experiencing is not one of these. Rather, the significant points of creaturely continuity seem to be that all of us as creatures share in the breath of life (Hebrew: "*ruwach*") and that we are all living souls (Hebrew: "*nephesh chayim*"; Gen. 1:21, 24; 2:7; 9:12ff) with the life principle centered in the blood (Gen. 9:4&5). Thus, we share in the life principle, but it is not the life principle itself that is precious. Rather, Genesis 9 in a single stroke demonstrates a sharp discontinuity between human and animal life by simultaneously prohibiting manslaughter (9:5-6) and establishing God's approval of humans killing animals for food (9:3-4). This discontinuity was first evident in Gen. 2:18-20 where Adam searched through the entire animal world to find a creature which corresponded to him (Hebrew: " *'ezer k negdo*"). Adam named each animal brought before him, signifying its function in doing so; not one animal satisfactorily corresponded to him - not one removed him from his personal isolation (Gen. 2:18). Thus, ontological continuity between human and animal life cannot be established upon the experiences of life, the intrinsic value of life itself, or physical parallels between animals and humans; rather, we are separated from the animal world by an impassable gulf - a chasm of essential difference in who we are.

If the putative parallels either do not exist or are insignificant before God, what then is the critical essence of man that distinguishes him from all of creation, and what are the ramifications of this distinction? The key is found in Genesis 1:26-28, 2:18-25, and 9:5-7; it is that only man is created in the image of God.

What does it mean to be created in God's image? Theologians have long wrestled with this concept and have proposed a variety of models which Anthony Hoekema[22] and P.E.

Hughes[23] have thoroughly discussed; a brief overview is presented here for perspective. These overviews are largely based on the descriptions given by Hoekema and Hughes.

Irenaeus (c. 130 - c. 200) argued that the image of God is "man's nature as a rational and free being, a nature which was not lost at the Fall."[24] Irenaeus considered "image" and "likeness" to refer to separate aspects of man's essence, with "likeness" being the possession of a spirit; he believed that the natural man lacked a spirit, and that regeneration resulted in the return of the spirit (and, thus, God's likeness) to man.

Thomas Aquinas (1225 - 1274), who was heavily influenced by Plato and Aristotle, proposed that man imaged God in possessing intellect or reason.[25] He rejected Irenaeus' division of image and likeness, but believed that man exhibited God's image in three stages:

"The first stage is man's natural aptitude for understanding and loving God, an aptitude which consists in the very nature of the mind, which is common to all men. The next stage is where a man is actually or dispositively (or habitually; Lat. *actu vel habitu*) knowing and loving God, but still imperfectly; and here we have the image by conformity of grace. The third stage is where a man is actually knowing and loving God perfectly; and this is the image by likeness of glory ... The first stage of the image is found in all men, the second only in the just, and the third only in the blessed."[26]

John Calvin (1509 - 1564) saw God's image not in man's mind, but in his soul. Like Aquinas, he reject-

ed the dichotomy of likeness and image, but he saw image as only a distorted relic in the unregenerate man. Calvin saw God's image in the "true knowledge, righteousness, and holiness" in which Adam was created, a state lost due to the Fall, and restored by sanctification after the new birth. As such, the concept of "dominion" held little importance to Calvin in his assessment of the meaning of "the image of God." The significance of this "weak" position on the role of "dominion" will be discussed later.

Karl Barth (1886-1968) looked in a completely new direction for his definition of image. Barth focused on the phrase in Gen. 1:27 that "male and female created he them." From this, Barth derived his theological anthropology of confrontation:

"Could anything be more obvious than to conclude from this clear indication that the image and likeness of the being created by God signifies existence in confrontation, i.e., in this confrontation, in the juxtaposition and conjunction of man and man, which is that of male and female ...?"[27]

Thus, to Barth, being in the image of God involves not an analogy of being, but an analogy of relation. It involves a capacity for relationship between man and God, and man to man as pictured in the man/woman relationship - a capacity for confrontation and encounter.

Emil Brunner (1889 - 1966) took the next step away from the early views of what constituted image. Brunner believed image to be man's relation to God, his responsibility to God, and the possibility of fellowship with God. Like Irenaeus, Brunner saw a dichotomy in image, but he described them as the "formal" and "material" aspects of image. The formal aspect he presented as being typical of the Old Testament, and involving freedom, reason, conscience and language. He believed the New Testament taught a "material" aspect which centered on love of God and neighbor.

Finally, G.C. Berkouwer (b. 1903), in his classic work *Man: the Image of God* [28] described the image as man's inescapable relatedness to God in the totality of his (man's) existence. To Berkouwer, image was a verb rather than a noun (we are to image God), and is an analogy of love rather than an analogy of being or relation.

Each of these views has its deficiencies, and both Hoekema and Hughes have described these deficiencies in detail. Hoekema quotes Herman Bavinck in his assertion that all these historic positions miss the mark in recognizing that man's unique position as image bearer is essential to being human:

"Man does not simply *bear* or *have* the image of God; he is the image of God.

"From the doctrine that man has been created in the image of God flows the clear implication that the image extends to man in his entirety. Nothing in man is excluded from the image of God. All creatures reveal traces of God, but only man is the image of God. And he is that image totally, in soul and body, in all conditions and relationships. Man is the image of God because and insofar as he is true man, and he is man, true and real man, because and insofar as he is the image of God."[29]

To both Hoekema and Hughes, it is not what we can do, what capacities we possess or what relationships we have that make us image; rather, image is what we are, and understanding the implications of being created in God's image is central to making sense of why man exists. For example, Hughes stated:

"Only of man is it said that God created him in his image. It is in this charter of his constitution that man's uniqueness is specifically affirmed as a creature radically distinguished from all other creatures. In this respect a line is defined which links man directly and responsibly to God in a way that is unknown to any other creature. Nothing is more basic than the recognition that being constituted in the image of God is of the very essence of and absolutely central to the humanness of man. It is the key that unlocks the meaning of his authentic humanity. Apart from this reality he cannot exist truly as man, since for man to deny God and the divine image stamped upon his being and to assert his own independent self-sufficiency is to deny his own constitution and thus to dehumanize himself."[30]

What, then, is it to be created in God's image? The clues to this must certainly lie in the passages which directly describe man as being in God's image. First, the totality of man is created in His image. When God formed man, He formed the entire man in response to His proposal in Gen. 1:26 to make man in His image. Second, fallen man must still bear the image of God, since Gen. 9 forbids the killing of any man on the basis that man is created in His image; if image were lost due to the Fall of man, only the killing of regenerate men could be forbidden under this proviso. This does not preclude the possibility that fallen men may not image God accurately in all aspects. Third, the image-related tasks to subdue the earth and have dominion over the created order must be central to a proper understanding of what it means to be created in God's image, since dominion of man over the earth is directly linked to God's creative purpose statement in Gen. 1:26, and this linkage is repeated in verse 28 to Adam as God gives him his image-related mandate. Fourth, those who are in God's image must bear some special identification with God that causes the wanton taking of human life to be tantamount to attacking God, as only human life is protected by God under penalty of death (Gen. 9:5-6). Finally, it is Jesus Christ that we image, because only He is the true image of God (Col. 1:15, Heb. 1:3).

Using these guidelines, I believe that when God made us in His image, He made us like Himself in characteristics and character so that we could be his vice-regents over the earth. Thus, unlike Calvin who believed that dominion was a side-issue, I believe, with Hughes[31] that dominion is the central issue. The Scriptures tell us that Jesus Christ is the Creator (John 1:3, 10; Heb. 1:2), that when He was on this earth the cosmos was subject to Him as he calmed the sea, fed the multitudes, healed the sick, and raised the dead, and that one day He will be revealed as the sovereign King of kings (Phil. 2:8-11; Eph. 1:20-23; I Pet. 3:22; Rev. 19 - 22). In being created in His image, we are to be sovereign over the earth as He is over all that exists; of course, our sovereignty is derivative from and subject to His preeminent sovereignty. In order to carry out this task of vice-regency, He has given us God-like characteristics to enable us to subdue the earth and have dominion. Hughes has listed[32] six principle God-like characteristics given us by God:

1. Personality: God is in eternal I-Thou relationship within the Godhead. We too are relational beings. As beings with personality, we are never alone, as we exist in perpetual I-Thou relationship with God. Compare this with the animal; although they may congregate, mate, and cooperate, there is no meeting of the minds for them, no interpersonal communion, no response to God. This difference is highlighted in the way in which God dealt differently with Noah and his family as compared with the animals; God saved *specific persons* and *representatives of the kinds* of non-persons.

2. Spirituality: Man is a religious being. In fact, the meaning of a man's life is wrapped up in knowing and glorifying God and being obedient to His will. In contrast, animals have no awareness of God, of His goodness, holiness or majesty, and cannot worship Him. Solomon reminded us of this gulf when he mused "Who knows the spirit of a man, which rises upward, or the spirit of the animal, which goes down into the earth." (Ecclesiastes 3:21; NIV, alt. trans.)

3. Rationality: Man is a thinking being. Aquinas believed this to be the key of "image" because he was influenced by the Greeks who taught that the divine spark was in the intellect. Rather, God is infinitely rational, and He has made us rational so as to be able to properly function within and have dominion over a rationally systematic cosmos.

4. Morality: Man is a moral being. God is holy, and He created us and demands from us holiness in all we do (Lev. 11:44; 19:2; 20:7; I Peter

1:15). He can demand this from us because He gave us an awareness of right and wrong, and a will by which we could choose either. Animals are not moral agents and are incapable of sin because they are unable to discern between right and wrong actions or motives. We are reminded of this distinction in the use of animals in the Old Testament sacrificial system; animals are analogous to us in having life ("*nephesh*") in the blood, allowing them to act as man's temporary substitute, they are appropriate as a substitute because they cannot sin and thus have no sins of their own to pay for, but they are ineffective as a propitiatory substitute because they are *essentially* different from man; only the sinless God-Man who is the true image of God and took upon Himself human form, becoming a man, could be our effective propitiatory substitute (Hebrews 11). Because every man is in God's image, every man is culpable before God.

5. Authority: Man is an authoritative being. God has given us the capability and a mandate to wield authority over the created order (Gen. 1:26-28; Ps. 8:6). This authority, which is derivative of and subject to the authority of God, has resulted in the domestication of animals, the development of agriculture and science, and the very existence of civilization.

6. Creativity: Man is an aesthetic being. God recognized man's aesthetic nature in Gen. 2:9 when He accounted for man's aesthetic needs in the creation, and in Gen. 2:15 when He gave man a cultural mandate to "dress" (or serve) the garden; this mandate was given before the Fall, and was a command for Adam to interpret that which was in the perfect Garden, transforming it to reveal the imprint of man's creativeness.

These characteristics were like God, and they equipped Adam and his descendants for the cultural tasks which lay before them. Governing these tasks was another aspect of God's image — His character. As Adam carried out his task of dominion, all his activities were to mirror the character of Him in whose image he was created. Thus, dominion would be exerted in perfect righteousness, holiness, justice, mercy, love, etc. When Adam rebelled against God, he did not lose the image of God (although Romans 1:21ff demonstrates that there was significant distortion of the image) in function, but he lost the perfect image of His character. To be sure men could still be kind, and love one another in a limited sense under common grace, but it was necessary for the second Adam, Jesus Christ, to restore man's ability to image His character through regeneration and sanctification.

If man acts as God's vice-regent, what are his tasks? Genesis 1:28 describes these as to fill the earth, subdue the earth, and have dominion over the created order.

The command to fill the earth (Gen. 1:28) is often ignored, but it is not without significance. Adam's cultural task was enormous — to have dominion over the entire created order and to subdue the earth according to the needs and dreams of man. Soon, the Fall would further complicate these tasks immeasurably. Thus, dominion and subduing the earth were tasks which could not be carried out by Adam alone; he must have task-oriented progeny to assist him in carrying out these tasks. Converesely, if man were to fill the earth, the cultural tasks given him must be taken seriously in the post-Fall world to bring the world into conformity with man's needs. To fail could mean the demise of man.

Adam was commanded to subdue the earth. The Hebrew word translated "subdue" (*kabash*) is variously described by Strong[33] as "to tread down," "to bring under subjection" and other similar phrases. This word is used in two other Pentateuchal or near-Pentateuchal references: Numbers 32:22,29 and Joshua 18:1. In each case, "kabash" is used to denote the pacifying of Canaan, subduing all the enemies of Israel so that Israel no longer would experience strife or opposition from those outside, so that they could fully enjoy the promises of God within a peaceful land. Thus, to "kabash" is to face that which opposes us and is inimicable in its present state to our goals and well-being, and bring it into conformity with our needs — completely pacifying it.

Adam was also commanded to exert dominion. In fact, David reminds us in Psalm 8:6 that God has brought the entire created order under man's dominion. The Hebrew word translated "dominion" is "radah". There is some overlap between "radah" and "kabash," but Strong describes "radah" as "to crumble," "to have dominion," and "to tread down." "Radah" is also used in Numbers 24:19 to speak of the absolute sovereignty of the Messiah, and in Judges 5:13 to emphasize the preemptive authority Deborah wielded over the Jewish nobility of her day. Thus, it can be inferred that when God gave Adam dominion over the created order, He was describing a preemptive authority which man would wield over the creation as he interpreted the cosmos and manipulated its functions to man's benefit, to reflect the man's presence and activity, and to glorify God.

What are the implications of

these activities? First, as we subdue the earth, we face a world which, because of the Fall, is hostile to us. Our task is to conform the earth to the legitimate self-interests of man. When we squander resources, waste, and pollute, we not only fail to image God's character, but we violate the command to pacify the earth. Adam was told to "dress' (Hebrew: "'abad" — to serve, to work, to compel[34]) the garden and to "keep" it (Hebrew: "shamar" — to hedge about, to guard, to protect[35]). "Abad" is used in one other Mosaic passage (Deut. 28:39) where it is used to describe the cultivation of a vineyard. Thus, Adam was told to manipulate and cultivate the earth for his benefit (like a vineyard) while protecting it and guarding it from any who would destroy or damage it.

God's second command was to have dominion over the created order. Our model for dominion must be the dominion that God wields. We stand in covenant relationship with God, and although we have legitimate self-interests, these are subject to and secondary to those of God, so are the self-interests and prerogatives of the creatures of this world to us. The animals are not inanimate *machina*, they are not without significance, but their signification and meaning occur when they stand in proper relation to us as God's vice-regents, and we are given the task to interpret their significance and meaning.

The performance of these tasks, then, are subject to two constraints:

1. Accountability. We are representing God. Scripture repeatedly points out that we are accountable to God for the ways in which we represent Him. This message of accountability for opportunities, motives and actions permeates the message of the

Bible (some examples: I Cor. 3:10-15; 4:1-5; II Cor. 5:10; Jas. 4:17). It cannot be possible that God would assign us with so great a task and not hold us accountable for the way in which we carry it out.

2. Character. It is God's plan that we be like Jesus Christ in His character (Romans 8:29; II Cor. 3:18 and many others). This means that all our attitudes, thoughts, motives, desires, plans, actions, and relationships image Jesus Christ — we are to image Him in the totality of our being. Our standard is always Jesus Christ, who *is* the True Image (Colossians). Fallen man destroys as he carries out his cultural mandate because he so incompletely images God in his character. Thus, Jesus, the True Image, became the second Adam (I Cor. 15) to make it possible for us to be like Him.

Let's now return to the central issue; how are we to interact with the animals with whom we share this world? We know that we are to have dominion over them and we are to subdue the cosmos. Are there certain interactions with animals that have God's specific imprimatur? All actions which reflect the character of God and involve man's legitimate self-interest and are central to man carrying out his cultural mandate are legitimate. For example, Gen. 9:2-3 demonstrates to us that animals can be legitimately used for food by humans. This point was reiterated when God sent the Israelites quail in the wilderness, when he commanded Peter to kill and eat the "unclean" animals in his vision[36], when He established eating the lamb as part of the Passover, and when Paul taught that eating meat itself was not sinful unless doing so tempted a believer with a weak conscience to violate his conscience (Romans 14, I Cor. 8,10). In fact, Paul warned against those who inject dietary laws, such as forbidding to eat meat, into their Christian walk (Col. 2:16; I Tim. 4:3). Other Scriptural examples of animal use are the provision of skins by God to clothe Adam and Eve (Gen. 3:21), and the demand of an animal sacrifice to picture His redemptive work and atone for the sins of the repentant. God allows animals to work for us but cautions us to reward their work appropriately (Deut. 24:4).

We can also look to the sinless life of the Lord Jesus to example for us appropriate treatment of animals. Jesus rode into Jerusalem on a colt. As a Jew, He partook of the Passover. He fed the multitudes with fish, and caused fish to jump into the disciples' nets. He caught a fish to provide Himself with a coin to pay His taxes. In Gen. 18, we find the preincarnate Christ in the tent of Abraham eating meat. All of these were sinless and blameless acts for Him; can they be any less to us? The key is that these acts are to be done unto the Lord (Romans 14:6-8).

But what about animal use in experimentation? Experimentation as we know it is a fairly late methodological addition to our cultural activity. It is largely responsible (along with our increased communication and information storage capacities) for the incredible explosion of knowledge during the twentieth century. Research is part of our cultural mandate to subdue the earth. R.J. Rushdoony has pointed out[37] that science has replaced mythology as man's means to control the cosmos; it is the new "magic." This does not seem to be illegitimate in the Scriptural framework, for the concept of subduing the earth certainly involves understanding the created order in order to control it appropriately so as to make the earth more

habitable for us. Noah performed an early series of experiments in Gen. 8 when he sent out first a raven and then a series of doves from the ark. This involved significant risk to the life and well-being of the birds released, and was performed to establish the current state of the earth and to determine a time appropriate for disembarking so as to maximize the survival of all on board the ark. As we seek to understand disease, the body or the cosmos, we are given the prerogative to use animals when necessary to this process. But, in our dealing with them, we are called to image His character. This means we must be committed to the humane care of the animals entrusted to us.

When considering the effects of men on animals, one must consider our environmental impact on species survival. We eschew the pantheistic philosophy that seems to permeate the environmental movement, but we must also recall our mandate to keep and dress the earth. This involves preserving the earth in our stewardship to God. God was concerned to preserve the genetic diversity of the earth through the flood (Gen. 6 - 8); I believe that we should support measures to conserve the species unless to do so would render the earth hostile to human survival. A hostile earth has not been properly subdued; it remains outside the dominion of our cultural mandate.

Finally, what about animal rights? Do animals have rights? We have seen that animal rightists have typically argued that animals are at least parallel with human infants and the mentally retarded in their capacities and awareness, and that animals and humans are of one essence, so that if any humans have rights, so should animals. Ryder[38] has proposed a system of graded rights based on each creature's phylogenetic position. But

we have also seen that the Scripture denies any sort of essential interrelatedness between man and animals, so no comparisons based on ontology can be drawn to establish rights for animals. In fact, it should be stated that *no* created creature has inherent rights, that all rights belong to and emanate from God, and that any rights possessed by man are wholly derivative. The focus of Scripture is not upon the "rights" of man but on the supreme worth of God (Rev. 4:11). Because we are created in His image, we have dignity and worth conferred upon us because of our association with God. Thus, to strike a fatal blow upon a man is to attack God through His representative and incur God's demand that the murderer pay with his own life. Animals represent an entirely different category, and being non-image they lack the privilege and position given man as God's vice-regents. Because we (humans) are all "sons of Adam and daughters of Eve," as put by C.S. Lewis, we are all created in God's image no matter what our individual capabilities; the anthropological and sociological implications of this position are immense. Rather than possessing rights, animals fall under our dominion (Ps. 8:6) where they are to be participants in man's task to subdue the earth; it falls to man to interpret the appropriate role of each animal in this enterprise. When they become part of the world of man, whether as food, clothing, scientific subject or fond companion, they should be cared for in a manner consistent with the character of God, who we image.

ENDNOTES

21. Keil, C.F. and Delitzsch, F., **Commentary on the Old Testament**, Vol. I, William B. Eerdmans Publishing Company, Grand Rapids, MI, 1983, pp. 79 - 80. Delitzsch states, "The beasts arose at the creative word of God, and no communication of the spirit is mentioned even in ch. ii. 19; the origin of their soul was coincident with that of their corporeality, and their life was merely the individualization of the universal life, with which all matter was filled in the beginning by the Spirit of God. On the other hand, the human spirit is not a mere individualization of the divine breath which breathed upon the material of the world, or of the universal spirit of nature; nor is his body merely a production of the earth when stimulated by the creative word of God. The earth does not bring forth his body, but God Himself puts His hand to the work and forms him; nor does the life already imparted to the world by the Spirit of God individualize itself in him, but God breathes directly into the nostrils of the one man, in the whole fulness of His personality, the breath of life, that in a manner corresponding to the personality of God he may become a living soul."

22. Hoekema, Anthony A., **Created in God's Image**, William B. Eerdmans Publishing Company, Grand Rapids, MI, 1986.

23. Hughes, Philip Edgecumbe, **The True Image**, William B. Eerdmans Publishing Company, Grand Rapids, MI, 1989.

24. Brunner, Emil, **Man in Revolt**, translated by Olive Wyon, Charles B. Scribner Co., New York, NY, 1939, p. 93.

25. Aquinas, Thomas, **Summa Theologica**, I. 93.4.

26. Aquinas, *op. cit.*

27. Barth, Karl, **Church Dogmatics**, III/2, T & T Clark, Edinburgh, 1960, p. 195.

28. Berkouwer, G.C., **Man: The Image of God**, translated by Dirk W. Jellema, William B. Eerdmans Publishing Co., Grand Rapids, MI, 1962.

29. Bavinck, Herman, **Dogmatiek**, 2:595 - 596, cited in Hoekema, op. cit., p. 65.

30. Hughes, P.E., *op. cit.*, pp. 3 - 4.

31. Hughes, P.E.; *ibid*, Chapters 1 and 5.

32. Hughes, P.E., *ibid.*, pp. 51 - 64.

33. Strong, James, **The Exhaustive Concordance of the Bible**, Riverside Book and Bible House, Iowa Falls, IA.

34. Strong, James, *ibid.*

35. Strong, James, *ibid.*

36. Although the primary purpose of this passage was to prepare Peter to present the Gospel to the gentile Cornelius, the secondary implications of the abolition of the dominion of the Old Testament dietary laws over the Christian and the permission to eat meats of all sorts should not be passed over.

37. Rushdoony, Rousas John, **The Mythology of Science**, The Craig Press, Nutley, NJ, 1979, pp. 1 - 2.

38. Ryder, *ibid*, p. 332.

The Goals of Medicine

Franklin E. Payne, Jr., MD

*Dr. Payne is Associate Professor in the Department of Family Medicine at the Medical College of Georgia. He is the author of **Biblical/Medical Ethics** and **Making Biblical Decisions**.*

"I don't think a medical student is ever told what his mission in life is. Certainly no one told me when I was a medical student what was expected of me as a lifetime goal in assuming the role of a physician."

C. Everett Koop, M.D., 1976 [1]

Dr. Koop recognized a glaring and serious omission in modern medical education: the goals of medical care for physicians. That is, what are physicians to set as their standards so that they will know what they are to accomplish with their patients?

In an earlier issue of this *Journal*,[2] I told of my own surprise when I began to see patients and found that my medical training had little prepared me for the majority of the patients that I would encounter. Perhaps, a better understanding of my goals with patients would have eased that transition.

Other than one's own philosophical premises, is any subject more important for a physician than his goals with patients? Unfortunately, physicians who are Christians have paid as little attention to this subject as non-believing physicians.

My own conclusions are not final.

My first intention when I started to write this article was to develop a Biblical argument. On further reflection, however, the goals of medicine cannot rest directly upon Scripture because there are no explicit instructions for either physicians or patients relative to medical care.[3] Thus, the goals of medicine are a derivative ethic.

Such goals could be supported with Scripture, e.g., to relieve suffering is clearly identifiable as a responsibility for all Christians. However, such support would be somewhat artificial when general instructions for all Christians are narrowed to the field of medicine. The more important application, however, is that the means used to achieve these "ends" (goals) must be consistent with and not violate any Biblical principles that relate to these issues. (See discussion below)

It seems that a physician's goals are a two-step process: to diagnose and then, according to that diagnosis, to manage the patient according to this diagnosis. (I am purposefully avoiding "treat" for reasons to be explained below.) Obviously, management will be a more complex task because of the variety of options and possibilities that may or may not be available.

FIRST, TO DIAGNOSE

To say that *a physician must first diagnose* what is wrong with the patient that comes to him is to say the obvious. We must assume this goal as an axiom. No one can solve another's problem, whether medical or not, without first having some understanding of the cause of the problem. A common example in medicine is the patient with pneumonia caused by a bacteria called *Pneumococcus pneumoniae*. When the patient presents with chest pain, I may diagnose simply that he is in severe pain. Thus, I can give him a narcotic that will totally relieve the pain, but he may die from the infection. If, however, I proceed to diagnose the *Pneumococcus* as the cause, then penicillin will quickly assist him to full recovery.

Before passing on, *to diagnose* is not so simple. If a person with a form of arthritis goes to an acupuncturist, he will be treated to correct some imbalance of *yin* and *yang*. If he goes to a chiropractor (of the "old school"), then his spine will be adjusted. If he goes to a medical doctor, he will be treated with an anti-inflammatory medication.

Thus, one's fundamental understanding of what is normal and abnormal or health and disease determine one's diagnosis. A discussion of this subject would take us too far afield. It, too, has been discussed on these pages, although the subject is far from exhausted.[4]

Let us assume then, that the first goal of the physician is to diagnose.

SECOND, TO MANAGE

The second goal of the physician is *to manage (assist) the patient*. I have avoided "treat" because, as we will see, the role of the physicians is more comprehensive relative to patients.

First, and perhaps most obviously, the physician is to heal. The patient presents with a problem and the physician does whatever is necessary to heal him. *The difficulty is that physicians are rarely able to heal.* I have written a chapter on the "Empirical Uncertainties of Modern Medicine"[5] where I discuss this subject in some detail. Thus, I will not go into it here. In the large majority of instances, we do something else. These, "something elses" are the primary goal of my discourse here.

If a physician does not cure, then he may: 1) relieve suffering, 2) prognosticate (including reassure), 3) rehabilitate, 4) prevent illness, injury or further deterioration, and 5) do research.

Perhaps, *the most common role of the physician is to relieve suffering.* This goal may be carried out in a variety of ways. First, it overlaps with the goal to cure. Surely, the best way to relieve suffering is to cure the patient of his illness or injury. Second, a physician may relieve suffering simply by making the diagnosis. Most people accept and learn to live with a condition if they know what is causing their suffering. Third, a physician may alleviate pain directly

or indirectly. He may give an analgesic (a medication that is primarily given to lessen or alleviate pain) and one that acts indirectly, but does not cure. For example, aspirin decreases and may entirely alleviate the pain of arthritis both by its analgesic and its anti-inflammatory effect.

Fourth, a physician may relieve suffering by other modalities. The blockage of an intestine by cancer may be removed, while the cancer continues its malignant course. Cancer that has invaded the bone may be relieved by radiation that shrinks the tumor, but does not kill it entirely. Special wheelchairs, beds, and other appliances may be designed to make life more comfortable for patients. Modern technology has surely helped in this regard.

Fifth, the physician relieves suffering by his very presence. I remember when I had infectious mononucleosis. I had run high fevers and been in bed for several days. (I fully expected that I would die before I could get better!) Just seeing the doctor and knowing the diagnosis made me quite hopeful for recovery. Of course, he could not "cure" my illness, but *I had seen the doctor.* In my mind, that of itself was almost as good as a "cure."

The role of the physician is to prognosticate. Medical education, including specialty training, teaches a physician something of the usual course of specific disease processes. His experience thereafter usually becomes an even better teacher. Obviously, however, this role is quite imprecise. Many people know a patient who had only a few months to live, yet lived for many years beyond that prognostication.

Prognostication, however, does have value. In general, diseases and injuries do follow some, albeit variable, pattern. Again, knowing something about the unknown (the future course of the affliction) lessens anxiety and enables the patient and his family to prepare. The prognosis that death is imminent seems especially useful. Wills and living trusts can be set up, life support measures that are or are not wanted can be discussed, and special efforts at reconciliation should be made with those whom the patient has unresolved conflicts (especially between husbands and wives).[6]

The role of the physician is to rehabilitate. Perhaps, modern medicine has made more progress here than anywhere else. Intensive physical therapy, progressive re-education, and "space age" appliances go far beyond anything possible in the past. People who would have had to spend their lives in wheelchairs and/or confined indoors now function at a much higher level and with little need for constant care.

The role of the physician is to do research. If physicians did not build upon their predecessors, then medicine would not advance. Research, however, is more than that performed in the laboratory or in clinical settings. Research includes the physician in his everyday practice. He notes patterns of diseases and responses to medications and manipulative procedures. He also notes *iatrogenic disease and injury*, as many modalities of management cause their own unintended effects, some quite severe and even deadly.

Perhaps, the greatest distinction between "orthodox medicine" (that generally practiced by physicians licensed by the state) and "alternative therapies" is the unwillingness of the latter to do research. Yes, orthodox medicine has its problems of iatrogenic diseases, ineffective and expensive treatments, unscrupulous practitioners, all of which have not been avoided by extensive research.

Nevertheless, without some systematic, scientific approach to disease and injury, we actually know nothing. The courses of disease, the people who have them are too variable to make any conclusions, otherwise. While I am not totally opposed to alternative therapies,[7] their great weakness is their unwillingness to design and carry out any kind of formal study and publish its results for others to scrutinize. Under the goals that I am presenting here, then, these alternatives approaches would not fulfill the goals for medical practice and, on this basis, be relatively disqualified as a valid means of medical treatment.

TO SUBSCRIBE TO AN OBJECTIVE ETHICAL VALUE

Non-Christians likely would not differ with the above goals, although Christians and non-Christians might differ on the emphasis given to each or allocation of resources for each. It is the means to these goals that divides the Christian from the non-Christian. Thus, the final goal for physicians in their care of patients should be *to commit to a stated standard of objective value.*

Why is this goal necessary? First, the above goals are quite general and the means to their end can be quite varied. For example, a physician may interpret an abortion as "relieving and suffering" of a woman with an inconvenient pregnancy. For the Biblical Christian, however, "Thou shalt not kill" (Exodus 20:13) proscribes that means. The same would be true of euthanasia to "relieve the suffering" of a severely ill patient. While the goal is acceptable, the means is not. God says, "Thou shalt not commit adultery" (Exodus

20:14). Thus, the counsel and practices of Christians are not to encourage or assist fornication[8] in any way. "Honor thy father and thy mother" (Exodus 20:12) means that minor children must not be treated without their parents' permission (except in an emergency).

Why should this goal be objective? Again, choices or means (especially by fallen men and women) are too diverse to be left to individual (subjective) choice. While an objective standard cannot prevent wrong (unbiblical) practices, it will serve to restrict choices. For example, the Hippocratic Oath is an objective standard. If physicians subscribed to it, we would not have abortions today, as it states, "I will not give to a woman a pessary to cause abortion." The problem, then, is to call physicians to an objective standard and the Christian to the Biblical standard.

What must be realized is that we may agree with non-Christians on most of our goals, but we are strictly limited on means to those goals. In fact, the failure of modern medicine to subscribe to an objective standard is causing an increasing difficulty for the Christian to practice medicine without offending his peers or even violating the laws of the state. It also allows the pursuit by virtually any means to achieve these goals.

PRESERVATION OF LIFE AS A GOAL

The goal of medical care is not to preserve life. Perhaps, more confusion exists today among Christians and non-Christians on what is not a goal of medicine than the above goals that I have already stated. "Heroic measures" are commonplace in virtually every hospital and nursing home where severely ill patients are simple

"kept alive" with no reasonable hope of improvement in their condition.

That preservation of life cannot be a goal for medicine is simply proved by the fact that *all patients eventually die.* To strive toward a goal that is ultimately doomed to failure hardly seems consistent with any rational or reasonable argument. Yet, that goal seems to be assumed by physicians. Early in their training, medical students experience the breast-beating that goes on when a patient dies. "If only I (we) had done this, the patient would still be alive." This thinking is rarely carried to its logical extreme, that medically correct decisions can prevent all deaths. Stated thusly, the futility of that argument is apparent.

The Bible does not support the simple preservation of life as a goal either. Men and armies are called into battle to defend righteouis causes (e.g., Judges 1:1-9; I Samuel 17). Paul goes on missionary journeys that severely imperiled his life (II Cor. 11:22-33). Modern missionaries answer the same call, often to situations that endanger their health and their lives (as well as their families).

Further, the Commandment "not to kill" (the positive side of which is the value of human life) cannot be carried out *if an action violates another Commandment.* For example, I may not steal from others to provide for myself or my starving family. A woman may not commit adultery to preserve either her life or that of her husband or children.

The sanctity of human life is a high value, but there are other values equally as high, such as honesty and sexual fidelity. *There are even higher values, such as the worship of God and the righteous works to which He calls and directs us,* such as missions.

THE RELIEF OF SUFFERING AS THE COMPREHENSIVE GOAL

Perhaps, all of the five other goals can be included under the relief of suffering. To diagnose is to relieve the anxiety associated with an unknown illness or injury. To prognosticate is to relieve the anxiety and uncertainty of the course and outcome of the illness or injury. To rehabilitate is to lessen pain, improve function, and give objective hope to patients. To do research is to improve the means to all other goals.

I have said nothing new here. Summary statements, however, focus our attention for agreement, debate, and further refinement. Dr. Koop was correct. Goals for physicians are virtually ignored except as they are implied by medical training and medical behavior. It is past time for Christian physicians to clarify their goals and within that structure to delineate Biblical means to those goals.

1. Koop, C.Everett, **The Right to Live, the Right to Die**, Wheaton, Illinois: Tyndale House Publishers, Inc., 1976.

2. Payne, Franklin E., Jr., "Spiritual Challenges in a Physical (Medical) Practice, *Journal of Biblical Ethics in Medicine,* Vol. 3, 1989, pp. 1-5.

3. Kriel, J.R., "Removing Medicine's Cartesian Mask: Part I and II, *Journal of Biblical Ethics in Medicine,* Vol. 3, 1989, pp. 33-36; Terrell, Hilton, P., "Ethics and the Medical Model of Disease," *Journal of Biblical Ethics in Medicine,* Vol. 3, 1989, pp. 68-74.

5. Payne, Franklin E., Jr., **Biblical/ Medical Ethics**, pp. 33-50.

6. Adams, Jay E., **Shepherding God's Flock**, Phillipsburg, New Jersey: Presbyterian and Reformed Publishing Company, 1974, pp. 128-256.

7. Payne, **Biblical/Medical...**, p. 111.

8. "Fornication refers to sexual sin of any and all sort ... (not just) sexual sin by unmarried persons (as it is used in American law) ... Scripture writers used the word fornication (*porneia*) to describe *sexual sin in general,* and in the Bible it referred to cases of incest (I Cor. 5:1), homosexuality (Jude 7), and even adultery (Jeremiah 3:1,2,6,8 ff) as fornication." **Jay E. Adams, Marriage, Divorce and Remarriage** in the Bible, Phillipsburg, New Jersey, 1980, pp. 53-55.

Editor's Note

Marlene Cimons of the Los Angeles Times recently reported the story of a Texas Baptist pastor and his wife who obtained a fetal liver tissue transplant for their unborn child. The tissue was obtained from the aborted fetus of a tubal pregnancy and injected into the recipient while he was still in the womb. The unborn infant was found through prenatal genetic testing to be affected by Mucopolysaccharidosis, which is inherited and inevitably fatal in childhood. The parents are quoted as stating that they are opposed to abortion. It is hoped that the experimental procedure may alter their child's dismal prognosis, but is not yet known that it will.

Christians who have been content to comprehend their position as merely "pro-life" are likely to be presented with more and more hard cases challenging the attractive simplicity of that view. These parents were obviously acting in favor of the life of their unborn child in obtaining the transplant, though one wonders why they consented to prenatal testing prior to knowledge of a possible treatment, as the reporter relates what happened. View in a broader perspective, however, was this transplant decision truly "pro-life?"

Given that the embryo in the tubal pregnancy could not survive, this particular decision has similarities to any other organ or tissue transplant decision. However, the use of organs or tissue from a baby in a tubal pregnancy, whose presence is a clear threat to the mother's life, can only encourage the use of the more abundant "resource" of abortions for convenience. As techniques are developed which succeed (from the recipient's viewpoint), a constituency will develop to exert pressure for more "resources". The act of abortion for convenience could then be recast as an act which is not merely for the convenience of the mother, but also "pro-life." Advertising brochures for aborturaries, underneath the inevitable butterflies, might urge the unhappily pregnant to "Share the gift of life."

Letters to the Editor

Dear JBEM:

I enjoy the *Journal* very much. The article, "Medical Services - Our Stewardship by W. Crenshaw, M.D. [Vol. 4, No. 4] was something I am pondering at this time.

My son has an aneurysm of the pulmonary artery as a result of corrective surgery for Tetralogy of Fallot as well as a leaking pulmonary valve. Last April our cardiologist seemed in a big hurry to speed in with surgery. Then, in August, I brought my son in with fatigue and another cardiologist saw him. This one stated that the child "would not drop dead" and that surgery is not "to save his life" but to give a "better quality" of life. The surgery has not yet been booked and I am having second thoughts about it all. The child (11 years old) is terrified of surgery, especially due to past traumas, but he says he is not so afraid of dying. I am wondering why the M.D.'s seemed of such opposite opinions and if there are things I am not being told.

There is sort of a little panic here that seeps into the papers now and then of parents fearful surgery will be delayed too long for their children.

Some of the M.D.'s and the secretaries on the phone are downright snarly. Some nurses make hints that parents should petition government for more funds (socialized medicine here). [The writer lives in Canada. - *ed.*]

I do not want my child used as a pawn to get more money out of government. I want God's will done and I want to know it. I don't want the doctors to think they are the "savior" because I'm sure some parents are pleading with them. Of course, I don't want my son to die. I don't want him to go through a horrible experience and I don't want a problem with surgery ruining his life. ... Deciding to step back and pray some more, I have postponed our next appointment to better prepare us for the next one. God holds us in His hands....

Sincerely,

Name withheld by request

Editor's Note: Since this letter the child has had the surgery and is doing well.

The Nature of Man and Mental Illness

Andrew A. White, MD, M.A.T.S.

Dr. White is a 1978 graduate of the University of Michigan Medical School now in the private practice of family medicine in the North Shore of Boston. He also holds a Master of Arts in Sacred Theology from Gordon-Conwell Seminary.

Engraved over the entrance of the Harvard school of philosophy are the following words, "What is man that thou are mindful of him?" Rather ironic to find such words over a building peopled by professors who for the most part distain the Author of the Book in which those words are found. But those words still capture in a lovely way one of the most important philsophical and theological questions of all times, "What is man?" And that question is not only relevant to philosophers and theologians, It is critically important for anyone trying to understand mental health and mental illness.

While the question "What is man?" can be approached in many different ways, this paper will address the question from the perspective of the ongoing theological debate regarding trichotomy, dichotomy and the whole person. For how this debate is finally resolved has enormous implications for treating mental illness.[1]

First we must briefly dispense with two clearly non-Christian anthropologies prevalent in the medical community. Many believe that man is purely a physical being. This *material* view of the nature of man is popular among premedical students, medical students and physicians. This view sees man as little more than a complex interaction between atoms and molecules, a delicate balance of chemical reactions and electrical activity, an intricate interplay between various cells, tissues and organs. There are, of course, good reasons for the popularity of the material view of man. Premedical requirements emphasize biology, pathology and pharmacology. On clinical rotations the differential diagnosis and management of organic disease is by far the most prominent aspect of clinical training. Even in psychiatry, the disease model of illness is so prominent that we often mislabel temperamental differences as personality disorders or mistake attitudinal and behavioral problems for mental illness. In short, the material view of man is often due to premedical and medical school training bias and is not often the result of serious reflection by those who hold the view.

Another view of the nature of man that is commonly held by non-Christian psychiatrists and psychologists is one that we will call the *spiritless* view. According to this anthropology, man is thought of as a body and a mind without a spirit. This

> " . . . a tripartite view of the nature of man holds that man is made up of three distinct metaphysical entities, namely body, soul (or mind), and spirit. . . ."

view of man conceptualizes man as composed of both material and immaterial entities. But the spiritless view rejects a spiritual aspect to the immaterial entity. This view may or may not make a radical distinction between organic and nonorganic mental illness. If a radical distinction is made, and it often is, organic mental illness is viewed as treatable by exclusively physical modalities such as drugs and ECT, whereas nonorganic mental illnesses are seen as amenable to only counseling and psychotherapy. The spiritless view is not universally held by psychologists. On the one hand, a number of psychiatrists and psychologists are developing a more material view of man. This shift toward the physical parallels the rise of psychopharmacology. On the other hand, there are a number of religious psychiatrists and psychologists who would not deny the reality of the spiritual in man.

Among Christians, a *tripartite* view of the nature of man (often called trichotomy) was held as early as the second century A.D. by Irenaeus, the Bishop of Lyons.[2] This view holds that man is made up of three distinct metaphysical entities, namely body, soul (or mind), and spirit. However, the trichotomist view originated not in Christianity, but in Greek philosophy. As G.C. Berkouwer points out, trichotomy "finds its origin in the problem of mediating between the two worlds of Greek dualism ... It arises from the need for some intermediary between the two poles of visible and invisible things, for something which should bridge the gulf between the two worlds of body and spirit. This need was met with the 'soul,' which so to speak formed the bond, the juncture, between two things which could actually not be united."[3] This connection to Greek dualism made the trichotomist view unpopular in the early church. There was, however, a revival of this view by a number of biblical scholars and theologians in the nineteenth century[4] and it is held to this day by many Christians, including many Christian psychiatrists and psychologists.

A few who hold the tripartite view of man conceive of the three entities, body, mind, and spirit, as having little or no interrelationship. Thus neurologists and neurosurgeons alone should deal with diseases of the brain, psychiatrists and psychologists alone with diseases of the mind, and ministers and priests with the spirit. However, others who hold the tripartite view see man as a unified person composed of distinct but closely interrelated entities of body, mind, and spirit. Because of the close interrelationship between these entities a spiritual illness may affect the mind or body and vice versa. According to this *unified tripartite* view, a minister must not neglect the mind and body, nor a psychiatrist the body and spirit, nor a neurologist the mind and spirit. One might, of course, have relatively more or less expertise in the care of the body, mind, and spirit, but no

one really interested in the health of the person should be entirely ignorant of any part of man's nature or fail to use that knowledge when appropriate.

From a Christian perspective the unified tripartite view of the nature of man has much to commend it in comparison with the material or spiritless view. In the first place, it recognizes a material and an immaterial aspect of man. Secondly, it does not neglect the spiritual in man. Thirdly, the unified tripartite view recognizes the unity of the person. All three of these features of the tripartite view are consistent with the biblical view of man as depicted in the creation account. For in Genesis 2:7 we read that "the Lord God formed man from the dust of the ground and breathed into his nostrils the breath of life, and man became a living being." Here we see that man has a material aspect of his being which originates in the dust of the earth. Man like the animals is an earthly being (vs. 19). But man also has an immaterial aspect which originates more directly from the breath or Spirit of God. Man is not only an earthly being. He is also a spiritual being. Man is "formed from dust but endowed with the *nesama* (breath-spirit)," says Henri Blocher.[5]

The distinction between the material and immaterial aspects of man, between body and spirit, is found not only in biblical teaching on the original creation of man but also in biblical teaching on death. For example, our Lord made clear this distinction when he said, "Do not be afraid of those who kill the body but cannot kill the soul." (Matthew 10:28, see also James 2:26). But while recognizing this distinction, Scripture also clearly teaches that during life on earth man is a unity of body and spirit. Biblical authors simply do not

conceive of man in this life as a body without a spirit or vice versa. He is, in the Hebrew, a *nephesh* - a person (again see Genesis 2:7). He is not partly a body and partly a spirit as though the two existed side by side with little or no interrelationship. Rather he is a person - a thoroughly integrated body - spirit. Karl Barth put it well when he described the human person as both "bodily soul" and "besouled body."[6]

Despite its favorable features, even a unified tripartite view purified from contamination by Greek dualistic philosophy is problematic. It is true that various biblical terms are used to describe the different aspects of man's nature, including the words which in many English versions of the Bible are translated body, soul (or mind), and spirit. For the most part, however, soul and spirit are synonyms in Scripture. John Murray has shown, for example, that devotion to God, as well as joy and sorrow, are attributed to both the spirit and the soul in Scripture. With such insights and with adequate refutation of such *cruces interpretum* for the trichotomist's position as Hebrews 4:12 and 1 Thessalonians 5:23, Murray is justified in concluding his essay on trichotomy by saying, "The evidence does not support the tripartite construction." [7]

Now the fact that the Bible does not recognize a tripartite view does not immediately allow us to reject that view. There are, after all, many ideas which God did not deem significant enough to warrant special revelation in Scripture. In other words, it is possible that God chose to reveal to us that there are at least two entities in man, namely the body and the spirit, and further chose to allow us to discover a third entity, i.e., the mind, through general revelation. This argument, however, is not convincing since Scripture, from beginning to end, is concerned with the nature, as well as the destiny, of man. If Scripture did in fact describe and differentiate two entities and omitted such descriptions and differentiations of the third it would be a significant omission. But this is not the only reason I find the tripartite view problematic. If there is a distinction between the mind and the spirit, what is it? I have great difficulty conceptualizing the difference. For example, is memory of the mind or spirit? The mind most would say. But I have wonderful memories of things I have read about God and joyful experiences in his Spirit. So what, then, is memory, of the mind or spirit? Or, what about the will? By faith an act of the will enabled me (as a secondary cause of course) to become a recipient of God's saving grace. But my will also enables me to make rather mundane choices like whether or not I'll snooze for five more minutes after the alarm clock rings in the morning. So then what is my will a function of — the spirit or the mind? And when I die will my mind be ushered into the presence of God or just my spirit? If just my spirit, what is a spirit without a mind? I have trouble enough trying to conceive of a spirit without a body.

Before turning to the bipartite view, let us examine the monadic view which Henri Blocher says "was fashionable among theologians" earlier this century.[8] This "whole person" movement was so concerned with emphasizing the "psychosomatic unity" of man that it rejected every form of anthropological duality. Man, according to the *monadic* view, is a monad — an indivisible and impenetrable uniform substance. The Hebrew mind, they said, did not conceive of man as a duality but only as a unity. This view, however, was based on a hermeneutic that was fun-

damentally flawed. For it was based on a presumed understanding of the function of "the Hebrew mind" which has been shown by linguistic analysis to be pure speculation.[9] Further, Robert Gundry in his scholarly work *SOMA in Biblical Theology*, shows that the OT evidence raised to support the monadic view is open to a better interpretation, i.e., "because of their interpretation the soul is the animation of the body and the body is the incarnation of the soul .. a psychophysical unity - but a unity not a monad."[10] Gundry goes on to show that the somewhat equivocal evidence for anthropological duality (within unity) in the OT becomes unequivocal in the NT, as well as in NT Judaism. A small sample of some of the biblical citations Gundry draws on to support duality includes Genesis 2:7, Ecclesiastes 12:7, Isaiah 10:18, Matthew 10:28, II Corinthians 4:16, and James 2:26. He is especially convincing when he argues that "body" (*soma*) in Pauline theology has a strictly physical meaning. Since "spirit" (*pneuma*) has a clearly non-physical meaning, we must accept that Paul conceived of man as an anthropological duality, as well as a unity.

In summary, then, I reject the tripartite and monadic view of man's nature and hold to the *bipartite* view (often called dichotomy). According to this view, man is made up of two distinct metaphysical entities, *body* and *spirit*, the *material* and the *immaterial*. But I do not hold to a bipartite view of man which fails to fully recognize the close interrelationship and interpenetration between body and spirit. Rather, a *unity of duality* would best characterize my view. It should be noted, however, that the recognition of only two metaphysical entities does necessarily entail a rejection of a variety of different aspects of the immaterial in man. Indeed,

Scripture affirms the variety with such diverse terms as spirit, soul, mind, heart, bowels, and kidneys.

Having arrived at a *unified bipartite* view of man's nature, what then is mental illness? Mental illness, in my judgement, would include some illnesses which are *primarily bodily or material dysfunctions*, like many severe depressions, and some illnesses which are *primarily spiritual or immaterial dysfunctions*, like at least some anxiety disorders. That many severe depressions are primarily bodily dysfunctions is evident by their prompt response to appropriate psychopharmacologic and electrophysiological treatments, i.e., antidepressants and electroconvulsive therapy. Anyone who regularly treats severely depressed patients, as I do, cannot help but be impressed by the dramatic improvement that these physical modalities have on his patients. And a recent well-designed study has confirmed these anecdotal impressions.[11] While counseling may slowly help a severely depressed patient recover, antidepressants work much more quickly and save many depressed patients untold agony. Of course, counseling is necessary to aid the patient's recovery and to help prevent future episodes of depression. Many mild anxiety reactions, on the other hand, respond promptly to appropriate counseling alone.

I remember, for example, one time when I became acutely anxious after purchasing a camera which was beyond my means financially. Conditioned by the poverty I had witnessed in Africa as the son of a missionary, my conscience would simply give me no rest. Fortunately, I went to a wise counselor, my mother, who advised me to return the camera. For while everything is permissible, not everything is beneficial (I Corinthians 10:23). On returning the camera, my anxiety immediately disap-

peared. *You see the most effective way to treat a guilty conscience is to repent. In my case, the primary dysfunction was spiritual, i.e., sin. For had I listened to my wisely tutored conscience, I would have never purchased the camera.*

But there are many mental illnesses which do not fit into neat categories. For example, what about a mild to moderate depression in the context of a strained marriage. Is the dysfunction primarily of the body or the spirit? Or, how about an anxiety disorder in which the anxiety escallates to the point where the person is functionally incapacitated? A panic disorder, for example, which is characterized by episodes of the sudden onset of overwhelming anxiety, often responds promptly to small doses of antidepressants without the use of tranquilizers. While counseling is often helpful in uncovering and resolving underlying unnecessarily conflict, the panic episodes themselves respond much more quickly to psychopharmacologic maneuvers than to counseling. Before we go on I should try to clarify in an overly simplified way an important difference between antidepressants and tranquilizers. While tranquilizers make virtually all people feel more calm (even those who do not consider themselves to be anxious), antidepressants only make truly depressed people feel and function better. In other words, antidepressants seem to target a specific neurochemical imbalance, while tranquilizers have a more generalized and global effect. This is not to say that tranquilizers have no place in our psychopharmacologic armamentarium. However, to illustrate the physical aspects of some mental illnesses,

antidepressants are more useful than tranquilizers.

How, then, do we explain the *overlapping dysfunctions* of body and spirit? Man, as we have seen, is a unity of duality. Man is spirit united to body with an integration of both entities. Thus *a spiritual dysfunction may cause a bodily dysfunction, and vice versa.* Indeed, given the unity of man it would be highly unlikely to find any mental dysfunction in which both the material and the immaterial in man were not affected even if the dysfunction originated in one entity or the other. Take again the case of my "photosensitivity." While sin leading to a guilt-ridden conscience (spirit) was clearly the cause of my anxiety, the mediation of that anxiety was neurochemical (body). And what if my anxiety escallated to the point where I was incapable of even deciding whether my counselor's advice to return the camera was good advice. The neurochemical component of the dysfunction might have become the primary dysfunction, even though it was not the cause of the dysfunction. In that case a brief course of a mild tranquilizer might have calmed me down to the point where I could make a rational decision. You see *the entity (spirit or body) in which the primary manifestation of a mental dysfunction presents itself is not always the primary cause of the dysfunction.* Interestingly, there are biblical examples of disorders in one entity leading to dysfunction in the other. Job's body, for example, was afflicted from head to toe with painful sores (Job 2:7), and this physical illness almost certainly contributed to his depressed spirit which had "no peace,

> " man is made up of two distinct metaphysical entities:
> body and spirit, the material and the immaterial."

no quietness ... no rest, but only turmoil" (Job 3:26). And Elijah's depressed spirit (1 Kings 19:3 - 4) seemed to respond, at least partially, to sleep and, especially, food and drink (1 Kings 19:5 - 9).

But some mental illnesses are hard to understand even on the basis of a cause originating in one entity leading to an effect in the other. Could there be another way to understand at least some overlapping mental illnesses? It seems to me that the union of the material and the immaterial in a person could result in *some mental dysfunctions which are unique to man as a unity.* This is a difficult concept, so let me illustrate with an analogy. If water and oil are mixed together they separate one from the other and each retains its own characteristics with no new characteristics resulting from their mixture. However, if salt is mixed with water, the mixture still has some characteristics of both salt, namely a salty taste, and water, namely water's fluidity. But the mixture of the two also produces some unique features, like a lower freezing point. I would suggest, then, that in man as a unity there are some characteristics of his being which are clearly material, others immaterial and some which are unique to man's unity of body and spirit. Thus some mental illnesses are primarily spiritual in origin, others primarily bodily, and some are unique to man as a unity. Could schizophrenia be due to mental dysfunction unique to man as a unity? Schizophrenia does not seem to fit well into the earlier mentioned categories; and most psychiatrists believe that both organic and nonorganic factors contribute to the disorder. What about many existential crises? Solomon's existential concerns seem to have been partly due to the "burden" of God having "set eternity in the hearts of men" without giving them the ability to "fathom what God has done from beginning to end" (Ecclesiastes 3:10-11). And problems related to the eternal, immaterial spirit of a man being confined to a temporal, material body have troubled philosophers down through the ages.

In the light of this discussion two propositions of Jay Adams' early teaching on nouthetic counseling must be challenged. The first proposition is that all mental illness, apart from a few organic malfunctions, are really disguised spiritual illnesses resulting from the sinful behavior of the sufferer.[12] The overlapping nature of many mental illnesses (even Adams considers schizophrenia to be "a gray area") makes this assessment simplistic. But worse, this proposition illegitimately injures people who are already hurting. Adams even discourages the use of the term "mental illness" because it declares "a host of people 'sick' who are not."[13] My experience, however, has taught me that many are truly mentally ill. To mislabel their illness as a self-inflicted "spiritual" problem adds to the already great suffering of many. I am not talking about straight-forward cases of sin leading to mental dysfunction as in the case of the camera which we discussed earlier. Rather, I am talking about more complicated cases where the nouthetic counselor seeks a devil behind every bush because he believes that the vast majority of mental illnesses are really spiritual illnesses in disguise and are the direct result of the counselee's sinful behavior. Only as a last resort will he send his counselee for professional help, and then only to a physician who is to look for those rare organic malfunctions. As case from my practice may illustrate the point.

I was sent a patient by a conscientious elder of a fine evangelical church who had been trained as a nouthetic counselor. After months of unsuccessful counseling the woman was sent to me. Within fifteen minutes I knew that the patient was suffering from an agitated depression with an associated panic disorder. This nouthetic counselor had rightly searched for and found some attitudes and behaviors in the patient's past and present which needed changing and set about trying to help her change them. He became convinced, however, that most of the patient's problems began as defensive responses to being sexually molested by her natural father as a young girl. Since according to the presuppositions of nouthetic counseling, most mental illnesses are really spiritual illnesses in disguise and are the direct result of the counselee's sinful behavior, it naturally followed that the patient needed to repent of her sinful defensive responses. But what, may I ask, is morally culpable behavior requiring confession of sin in a young child who is sexually violated by her own father? What is considered the right response to being sexually molested at a tender age by someone who is supposed to love and care for you — someone who is supposed to show you by example something of what God is like, i.e., Father? The father needed to repent of his sinful incestuous behavior, not the patient! Through the only defensive responses she had available to her at her vulnerable age, she was trying to preserve her sense of self and the world from intolerable confusion and utter chaos. To suggest that this patient confess her sinful defensive responses reveals an unbalanced hamartiology - a hamartiology that overemphasizes sinful agency and minimizes victimization by sin. If, in fact, mental illness is really spiritual illness whose root cause is the sufferer's sin, then this counselor's approach is commendable. But I believe (and hope to demonstrate in a future paper) that mental illness often results from being a victim of sin - sin resulting indirectly from the general effects of the Fall and more directly from the particular sinful behavior of others.

Fortunately, with a course of antidepressants this patient promptly improved and has not relapsed.

A second proposition of Adams that must be challenged is his rejection of psychiatry as a valid profession.[14] While I sympathize with his distrust of Freudian psychology, he has thrown the baby out with the bath water. Mental illnesses are incredibly complex. Classifying mental dysfunctions as primarily spiritual or bodily or as overlapping is not an easy task. Investigating mental dysfunctions which are unique to man as a unity are particularly challenging. So is determining cause and effect especially when the primary manifestation is not found in the causal entity (spirit or body). And discovering appropriate therapy for many of these illnesses, whether the therapy be found in Galatians or in a textbook on psychopharmacology, requires an expertise that many laypersons who think they are competent to counsel simply do not have. Christian psychiatrists, on the other hand, can (and should) as a part of their vocational calling devote much more time to both serious study of medicine, psychology and Scripture, particularly Scripture as it bears on their profession. As a result, they would advance our understanding of many mental illnesses and would be of invaluable assistance to those of us who are trying to help people suffering from mental illness, whether we be a nouthetic counselor or a family physician with a Bible.

There is, however, no neutral "mind" which psychiatrists and psychologists can safely address while ignoring God's Word. The two aspects of man's being recognized by Scripture are spirit (the immaterial) and body (the material). The "mind" is simply an improper conceptualization. The fact that people consciously ignore God's Word does not, however, prevent them from contributing to our understanding of mental illness. For through common grace, they may contribute (indeed have contributed) valuable insights. And while we might expect more fruit from their labors when they study the body, there is no a priori reason why they should not contribute to our understanding of the spirit and the interrelationship and interaction of the body and spirit. As Christians, however, we will need to be even more cautious of pagan "scientific" findings regarding the immaterial than we already are of the material. For if Scripture has much to reveal to us about the visible world (and it has), it has even more to reveal of the invisible.

Our understanding of the nature of man has, as we have seen, many implications for our understanding of mental illness. We have argued from a biblical perspective for a unified bipartite view of man's nature. Though we have only scratched the surface, we have seen how the unified bipartite view leads us to accept some ways of conceptualizing and treating mental illness while rejecting others. Hopefully these insights will help us better understand and care for the mentally ill.

ENDNOTES

1. Adams, Jay, **A Theology of Christian Counseling - More ThanRedemption**, 1979, p. 110. Adams has recognized the importance of this debate for counseling

2. Hoekema, Anthony, **Created in God's Image**, 1986, p. 205.

3. Berkouwer, G.C. Man: **The Image of God**, 1962 (reprinted 1981), pp. 208 - 209

4. Hoekema, Anthony, op. cit., p. 205.

5. Blocher, Henri, **In the Beginning**, 1984, pp. 186 - 187.

6. Barth, Karl, **Church Dogmatics**, 1960, III, 2, p. 350. The present author, however, does not accept the technical meaning that Barth gives to these phrases. For Barth clearly holds to a monadic view of man's nature.

7. Murray, John, "Trichotomy," **Collected Writings of John Murray**, published post mortem in 1977, 2, p. 32. Hebrews 4:12 speaks of "the word of God" as "sharper than a double-edged sword" which "penetrates even to dividing soul and spirit, joint and marrow." Murray exegetically demonstrates that the idea behind the word "divide" (*merismos* in Greek) never means "distinguishing or separating two things" in the NT. Rather the thought is "cleaving within." Murray says, "joints and marrow represent the most occult parts of our physical frame, soul and spirit our inmost spiritual being." The "The Word penetrates to the inmost parts of our being and like a sharp sword can rend them asunder." (pp. 31 - 31). 1 Thessalonians 5:23 speaks of the "whole spirit, soul and body" being kept blameless. Murray points out that in Scripture an accumulation of terms (like heart, soul, mind and strength in Mark 12:30) expresses completeness and "is not intended to provide us with a definition of the components of human nature." (p. 31)

8. Blocher, Henri, *op cit.*, p. 88.

9. Barr, James, **The Semantics of Biblical Language**, 1961, (reprinted 1983), see especially chapters 2 and 3.

10. Gundry, Robert, **SOMA in Biblical Theology**, 1976, (reprinted in 1987), p. 121.

11. Kaplan, Harold, et al., **Comprehensive Textbook of Psychiatry**, 1989, Vol. 1, pp. 943 - 944. In a recent NIMH multisite collaborative study, 250 outpatients with major depression were placed in one of four treatment groups: one control group on a pill-placebo, one group on a standard antidepressant drug (imipramine) and two groups on psychotherapeutic regimens. After those with the severest symptoms were treated three and a half weeks, 10% of the control group had recovered, 35 - 45 % of the two psychotherapy groups had recovered and 75% of the antidepressant drug group had recovered.

12. Adams, Jay, **Competent to Counsel**, 1970. While Adams does have a short section in his book entitled "Not all Sickness Related to Particular Sins" (pp. 108 - 109), one cannot read this book without being convinced that Adams believes that the vast majority of mental illnesses are the direct result of sinful behavior. I cannot recall one contemporary example in **Competent to Counsel** where a person's mental illness (excluding medical problems like "brain damage" and "toxic problems") was not demonstrated to be the direct result of sinful behavior.

13. Ibid, pp. xiv and 12.

14. Ibid., I base my assessment that Adams has rejected psychiatry as a valid profession on the following: (1) his conviction that "qualified Christian counselors" are "more competent [to counsel] than psychiatrist" (p. 18), (2) his calling psychiatry a "cult" (p. 110), (3) his discouraging Christian counselors from referring to psychiatrists of even "difficult cases and special problems" (pp. 268 - 269), and (4) the recurring derogatory remarks he makes regarding psychiatry in reference to psychotherapy (e.g., p. 139), institutional care (e.g., 183), psychotherapeutic agents (e.g., p. 142) and electroconvulsive therapy (e.g., p. 122).

On the Nature of Arguments For Mental Illness:
A Reply to Dr. Andrew White

Hilton P. Terrell, MD, Ph.D.

Dr. Terrell is Assistant Professor of Family Medicine at the McLeod Redgional Medical Center in Florence, S.C.

"The brain you stole from my laboratory was a *criminal* brain." [from *Frankenstein* (the movie)]

In this issue Dr. Andy White discusses mental illness, taking a positive view that the term is valid, covering a spectrum from those which primarily originate in the physical body to those which arise primarily in the human spirit. Whereas his article begins with a creditable review of the tripartite vs. bipartite issue, the remainder of it calls for considerable correction. An underlying issue is that of human responsibility. Dr. White takes nouthetic counseling to task for relating virtually every counseling issue to sinful behavior. Such treatment, he indicates, practically omits the possibility that the counselee could, in fact, be *victimized* by someone else's sin or by bodily illness. Jay Adams and other nouthetic counselors are charged with an overemphasis on the "sinful agency" of counselees and with minimizing the fact that humans are also the victims of the sinful agency of others.

I would like to begin by highlighting one distinction implied by Dr. White followed by critique of his argument, an alternative to it and, finally, a prediction of the results of following his reasoning.

First, a distinction must be recognized between that which a person experiences, including his *subjective* experiences, and that for which a person is responsible. We are *not* responsible for all of our experiences. The literature of nouthetic counseling teaches that we are accountable for our thoughts and actions. Our actions often determine our experiences, but not always. A person may be held accountable by a counselor or physician for his behavior, but not for the feelings he experiences.

It may seem that a counselor is holding a person accountable for his feelings when he connects a counselee's feeling state with certain behaviors, but it is the behavior which must be the issue on which the change is focused. Some nouthetic counselors may not make the distinction plainly enough; none should require a counselee to repent of acts committed *against* him, nor to repent of *feelings*. Dr. White presents no evidence against that school of counseling that these errors have been taught by it or widely practiced in it.

A person's subjective experience of anger may be his response to something someone else did, or it may be the result of a mess he has created for himself. In either case the person may "be angry and sin not." Or, a person may be angry and behave sinfully in that anger. Someone may feel blue or dispirited because of things that have happened *to* him, including bodily disease, known or unknown. Or, the feelings may arise *because* of something he has done wilfully, or because he knows he has responded sinfully to wrongs against him. That person may be depressed and not sin in how he acts during his depressed state. Or, the person may behave sinfully in the midst of his depression. A person may feel panicky, and respond sinfully or righteously.

The *origin* of the anger, depression or panic is a separable issue from the way the person manages them. Such inner feelings as these may arise from behaviors for which the person experiencing them is culpable, or they might not. If the person is culpable in the origin of the situation which provoked the anger, then the logical remedy is counsel for the situation, not chemicals for the body. If the person is innocent of the origin of the unhappy situation, he is still ac-

> " The origin of the anger, depression or panic is a separable issue from the way the person manages them. "

countable for the way he *manages* his behavior while experiencing the feelings.

Sometimes my patients request tranquilizers to reduce feelings of anxiety when that anxiety is, in their opinion and mine, engendered by a situation of chronically disturbed interpersonal relationships. My approach is to point out that it is inconsistent to use chemicals to change a body which is merely responding normally. It is the situation which is abnormal and which needs to be normalized. The body is not the problem. The solution is to be found in straightening out the problematic relationship. It is recognized that the person may, through no fault of his own, be unable to normalize the relationship. However, insofar as it lies with him, he should do so (Cf. Romans 12:18).

FAULTY EPISTEMOLOGY

Secondly, Dr. White must be corrected in his epistemology. What is the method, or methods, by which physicians and counselors may know anything about the non-material aspects of those who seek their help? Second Timothy 3:15 - 17, reads in part, "All Scripture is given by inspiration of God, and is profitable for doctrine, for reproof, for correction, for instruction in righteousness, that the man of God may be complete, thoroughly equipped for every good work." Righteousness is a spiritual issue. Reproof is for the spirit. If a matter is in the spirit, then the method for knowing how to tackle it can only come from God's revelation in Scripture.

Sciences based on empirical observations of the natural world are by definition excluded from having any say whatsoever about the things of the spirit (the non-material). Our

bodies are part of the physical world. To the extent that psychology, as an empirical science, does not deal with the physical body, its epistemology is no longer empirical but theological. To the extent that psychiatry attempts to deal with the non-material aspects of a person, it, too, is theology. On what ground do these professions stand to help us understand *anything* about the nature of the human spirit? If they have systematic observations and conclusions about human physiology as it relates to special functions of the nervous system, they can offer something of value. In so doing, however, they are not truly *psy*chology or *psy*chiatry but a section of physiology. In matters of the mind they cannot use the methodology of the natural sciences. If they want to speak to the metaphysical issues of human nature they are engaged in philosophy or in doctrines of *theology*. Honest psychologists should turn their collars around backwards to indicate to the world what their calling is. They should also turn their epistemology around so that it leaves any pretense at a base in natural science and focuses on the Bible's revelation to us of the nature of our spirit.

Introspection is the examination of one's own thoughts, which does not include revelation of them. The counsellee's verbalization of his thought as a means of knowing about the spirit cannot be validated. Even if it could be validated, our experiences are not normative for right behavior. Our method of knowing about the culpability of ourselves and the persons we deal with, therefore, is by comparing behavior to Scripture. Rather than being normative, our own experiences are brought to Scripture for examination and judgment. That includes the experiences we have as physicians with our patients as well as the collective reports of experiences gathered and sifted by psychology and psychiatry.

One simply cannot judge the issue of the existence or non-existence of an illness of the mind, which is a spiritual entity, by citing, as Dr. White does, "My experience ... has taught me..." It is a metaphysical issue. Right knowledge of the issue must stand on normative *revelational* information, not something decided on the basis of one's experience. To allow anyone's experience into the argument as a basis for a decision on the existence of mental illness circumvents a root issue. Our own introspections and our inferences from the behavior of others are full of error. As a means of "general revelation" they are not a judge of Scripture.

A "general revelation" which supersedes special revelation in Scripture is not a general revelation, but a general misconception. If the "general revelation" of our experience tells us that we are not responsible for our moral behavior, then we are under a general misconception, for Scripture indicates that we are accountable. It follows that what we would be calling "general revelation" is not a revelation at all. If our experience tells us that a feeling we experience is not under our direct control, then we may be correct. We remain accountable, however, for how we behave in our feeling state. A general misconception rampant in the nation, fostered heavily by the medical profession, is that the empirical methodology of the medical sciences may apply to the non-material aspect of human beings. We are trying to make metaphysics obey physics!

We sometimes speak of our feelings as if they were irresistible juggernauts, pushing aside our will and *causing* us to behave in this or that fashion. "She made me so angry that I just *had* to tell her off." "This whole affair has gotten me down so much that I couldn't follow through with it, even though I had said I would." Such is careless talk, not biblical talk. It is granted that feelings can be very powerful, but to denigrate the position of the will to the role of victim is to treat persons in a way the Scripture does not allow. Physicians or counselors may legitimately discuss feelings and how they may be controlled, may infer, discuss, and admonish regarding underlying attitudes, but may only make decisions on overt behaviors, including speech. God alone is lord in the privacy of one's conscience.

RE-DISSECTING A CASE HISTORY

Dr. White cites an illustrative case from his practice, showing how, in his opinion, a nouthetic counselor missed the diagnosis of agitated depression with panic disorder and unsuccessfully treated a counselee for "sinful defensive responses" instead. He asks the rhetorical question, "What is considered the right response to being sexually molested at a tender age by someone who is supposed to love and care for you - someone who is supposed to show you by example something of what God is like, i.e., Father?" [1]

The operative phrase here is "sinful defensive responses." We are not told what the woman was actually *doing*. For Dr. White's critique to be valid, it must be that he does not actually believe that the woman was engaged in anything sinful. For, if she *was* engaged in sin, he has proposed that: (1) she had nothing to repent of, only the father had and, (2) he fixed it instead with antidepressant medication, which of course is no remedy for sin. If she was *not* engaged in "sinful defensive responses", then there is a valid critique if a counselor was selling sin as an inter-

pretation of her behavior where there was no sin. Without describing the behavior the counselor was addressing, we can make no fair judgment of the aptness of his example. Biblical counseling, while recognizing the awful situations people may be caught in even as victims, examines the situation and the behavior of the woman in the light of Scripture - what does God require of her - to determine whether or not there is sin.

What is *not* determinative of whether or not she is engaged in sin is the *consequence* of her counseling. That she "improved promptly and has not relapsed" is no proof that the counselor was wrong and Dr. White correct. Both, or neither, may have been correct. The woman may have been engaged in sinful behaviors and have had a bodily illness causing feelings she did not like. The former may respond to biblical counsel and the latter may change with the administration of chemicals. He seems to admit that the counselor had a point, then he retreats from that admission to point out that the counsel did not relieve her. Further, Dr. White did not certainly indicate that the lady actually followed the biblical counsel she received.

Again, it is key that we are not told exactly what "it" was for which she received relief through chemicals. He has used medical terminology to name whatever "it" was - "mental *illness*," "agitated depression," "panic disorder," "patient." That usage begs the question of illness vs. sin. The counselor presumably used words relating to sin and responsibility. Does the outcome determine whose terminology was correct? To determine that it does is to submit the definition of sin to empirical observation. That is, if one applies the "treatment" for sin and there is no desirable response, it must be con-

cluded that there was no sin. Don't tell Isaiah! Contrarily, if one applies chemicals and the person is relieved, it must be concluded that a chemical issue was primarily the problem, not sin. From the invention of heroin to methadone, we have tried that reasoning on opiate abusers with no success. From the data given, one could conclude, if one did not know Dr. White's character, that he was just a "Dr. Feelgood," who prescribes chemicals to produce good feelings without due regard for identifying and rectifying the actual problem. Instead, one must conclude that he has lapsed unwittingly into a pragmatic definition of sin — if medical therapy "works" it must be our guide to truth.

Did the woman have bad feelings only - something entirely subjective? It is not a sin to feel bad, even to feel very bad for a very long period of time. There is nothing in principle which would preclude the use of chemicals to relieve such. Physicians have done it for millennia, even when we do not know how the chemicals work, though with a due consideration for the known risks and benefits. Did the woman exhibit bad behavior? Alteration of that with chemicals a dehumanizing manipulation of persons.

AN ALTERNATIVE

Dr. White has an excellent point in his assertion that the "neurochemical component of the dysfunction might have become the primary dysfunction, even though it was not the cause of the dysfunction." Though the use of the word "dysfunction" indicates that we are in the realm of speculation,[2] it is definite that the central nervous system is the one system of the human body that is designed to be plastic. It is designed to be changed by our experiences. It may be molded by willful experiences we create for ourselves, both good and bad, and it may be molded by experiences created for us by others, good and bad. It seems likely that the "molding" would be in the form of chemical changes. Once the chemicals are changed, there is the option of chemical intervention. That the chemical change might have been wrought by sin would not mean that the option of chemical treatment is voided. Physicians routinely and properly treat persons chemically whose bodies bear changes wrought by sin. We treat cirrhosis of the liver wrought by alcohol, seizure disorders from head injuries earned by fractious behavior, and emphysema brought on by smoking.

It is reasonable to further suppose that the changes in the central nervous system may constitute a "pull" from our body toward something evil or toward something good through the medium of what we call "habit." For example, a central nervous system engram established by habitual lying might constitute an internal enticement to repeat the behavior. The person with such an (in this case self-created) experience might describe the powerful feelings which are now being labeled "addiction." It is biblically essential, however, to comprehend the effect of the central nervous system as an enticement, not a *cause* of behavior. To suppose that any part of the body becomes a cause of behavior[3] is to remove that behavior from the province of reproof and correction. It is to make "the word of God of no effect." [Mark 7:13]

In a section detailing some objections to the Pelagian view of sin, Louis Berkhof states, "It is an undeniable fact that, as a man increases in sin, his ability to do good decreases. He becomes in an ever greater mea-

sure the slave of sin. According to the theory [of Pelagianism] under consideration this would also involve a lessening of his responsibility. But this is equivalent to saying that sin itself gradually redeems its victims by relieving them of their responsibility. The more sinful a man, the less responsible he is. Against this position conscience registers a loud protest. Paul does not say that the hardened sinners, which he describes in Romans 1:18 - 32 were virtually without responsibility, but regards them as worthy of death." [4] If you wish to get away with murder in the United States today, do not murder your intended victim only, but several others. You will be adjudged mentally ill. Along with his concern that we not illegitimately further damage a suffering person with counseling, Dr. White needs to show us how to stay clear of this hazard.

THE BODY AS MUSICAL INSTRUMENT

Jay Adams has likened the physical body to a musical instrument which is played by the spirit. Work on that image for a while. That is a decidedly different concept than Dr. White's image of the body *causing* a spiritual dysfunction. If morally significant behaviors are an issue, just what is in charge? The body or the spirit? Can the body "play" the spirit? Does a musical instrument play a musician, or vice versa?

There is no reason to suppose that we would all have exactly the same type or quality of instrument. Some are athletic. Some have poor eyesight. Some are subject to seizures. Some have excellent memories. In every case, the body would *limit* what music we can play. We are created finite beings and are, furthermore, fallen in Adam and under a curse. There is no reason to exempt the

central nervous system from the effects of the curse. Due to the effects of the fall some of us may be born with a genetic tendency to be more or less subject to certain elements of our environment — sexual lusts or alcohol or what have you. God does, nonetheless, hold us all accountable to obey Him in our wills.[5]

In addition to the siren call to sin which may be inborn through genetic defects, our bodily musical instrument may acquire damages through victimization by others or through our own misuse of it. While it would be foolish to deny the damage wrought by victimization, the will may be still held accountable to make the best "music" possible with the damaged instrument.

There is a valid issue here for medicine. It is our job to discover the hidden defects which account for disabilities. We must do our job carefully, however. It will not do to push aside biblical admonitions and encouragements used in counseling as inappropriate based merely upon speculations as to the presence of an illness. The empiricism of medicine is a clumsy tool to stir the hermeneutic pot. There is a great difficulty in understanding the contribution of the body and the spirit in our feeling state. Dr. White's attempt at explaining it via a "unity of duality" hopelessly fogs the issue of accountability. The contribution of the medical profession most needed is progress in producing *material pathology*, not in pharmacologic manipulation of feeling states. Biblical counselors, likewise, need to recollect that patients do have bodies, that bodies do get sick, that the sicknesses represent temptations to disobedience, and that by no means all sicknesses are known.[6]

The Journal of Pastoral Practice is a publication of the Christian

Counseling and Educational Foundation which accurately reflects the position of nouthetic counseling. For years, that journal has run a medical article in every issue in order to alert counselors to organic problems they must know about in order to refer to a medical doctor. That Dr. Adams does not deal extensively with bodily illness in many of his books is simply that it is not his subject matter. One finds more attention to organic illness in nouthetic literature than one finds attention to spiritual issues in psychiatric literature.

WHERE WE ARE GOING IF WE DON'T RESOLVE THE ISSUE

Christians who believe with Dr. White that the mind can be ill have a responsibility to show how we maintain accountability before God, if our behaviors can be attributed to the illness. Illness is a *result* of our sin nature, if not always of our particular sins. As a consequence, it is not ever itself sin. Since illness is not sin, it is under no condemnation and we are not accountable to God for it. If there is no sin, then we have no need of repentance, confession and restitution. To the extent that we can transform our outwardly sinful behaviors into victimizations by others, to that extent we have no need of a Savior.

As a nation we are far from a hamartiology which is unbalanced in the direction of *over*emphasizing sin. Instead, we are far down the path of removing our sense of sin and responsibility. The contrast that nouthetic counseling offers to our culture's position creates the sense of imbalance only for someone who has been shifted from a biblical sense of the pervasiveness of sin toward our culture's therapeutic society. For we are all now simply victims, right back to Adam, who, if he joined our mod-

ern chorus, might say that he merely suffered an attack of fruit-lust, or that he was afflicted with a bad case of oversusceptibility to his wife's suggestions.

While granting that it is a complex issue, the dangers of the route are so clear that we must have clear discriminators from those who would have us believe that morally significant behaviors can be caused by diseases. We are already overdue for guidelines. The plague of attributing everything to addictions is well-advanced in the nation, excusing as illness everything from lying to adultery and is inside the Church with excuses for sins only slightly less obviously sinful.

A recent article in *JAMA* illustrates the pathway down which otherwise intelligent individuals are taking us medically. Reflecting on the interaction of psychiatry with the recent federal Americans With Disabilities Act, Dr. David Orentlicher, of the Ethics and Health Policy Counsel of the American Medical Association, opined that the noncompliant patient has a much broader scope for his noncompliance. Nontheless, he continued, a noncompliant patient may retain his right to treatment on the grounds that his noncompliant behavior is part of his illness or is an illness in itself. After recounting some details of the persistent and flamboyant misbehavior of a couple of dialysis patients who disrupted their dialysis clinics, he states, "Dialysis patients are at substantially increased risk for depression, and they commit suicide at a rate more than 100 times that of healthy individuals. ... Psychiatric complications of dialysis are not surprising. Hemodialysis results in profound disruptions of the patient's life. The need for dialysis three times a week, 4 hours per session, can seri-

ously compromise patient independence. In particular, it is difficult for dialysis patients to maintain gainful employment or to travel. In one study, only about half of the patients undergoing hemodialysis were able to work full-time or part-time. The strict dietary restrictions imposed to prevent fluid overload and electrolyte abnormalities are also burdensome. Dialysis patients typically respond to the psychological stresses of their disease and its treatment with the coping mechanisms of denial. Too much denial by a patient of his or her condition may cause rejection of therapeutic recommendations..."[7]

Thus, a psychological defense mechanism called denial is raised to the status of a disease. By that elevation, a person is empowered by civil government to abuse the staff of a dialysis clinic routinely for years and commit other sinful acts, for it is not sin; it is a severe case of denial.

In the *JAMA* article we can see the implicit belief that a patient is a pawn of his/her condition, merely *reacting* mechanistically to environment through psychological mechanisms. The patient is unable to act by responsible choice. Further, there is the common circular reasoning employed in psychology. One knows that the patient has a psychological condition because of one's behavior. The behavior *defines* the condition. That task accomplished, the defined condition then is used to explain, or, in this case, *excuse* the behavior. The excuse of the irresponsible behavior is not by reference to an objective standard of proper vs. improper behavior, such as the Bible. It is an excuse by definition that such behavior should be excusable. [8]

"If a patient's noncompliance reflects psychiatric dysfunction, then a denial of treatment because of noncompliance would in effect be a denial of treatment based on a psychological disorder. Under the Disabilities Act, such a denial apparently would be prohibited."[9]

"Trying to provide care for a non-compliant patient can be exceedingly frustrating for physicians, and the patients need to be held accountable for their actions. At the same time, it would be problematic if physicians provided care only to patients who were easy to care for, especially since the most difficult patients may not be capable of exercising sufficient control over their behavior."[10] Here is the nub of the issue. It seems that those patients who exercise the least control over their behavior are exactly those who are decided, on that basis, not to be capable of controlling their behavior. If there is no physical pathology which can be reasonably implicated in explanation of their incapacity, then the presumption should be that the patient can indeed control his behavior. To do otherwise is to undercut the whole idea of responsibility.

A medical profession which departs from a line of evidential reasoning, has entered into the metaphysical, and has abandoned its particular expertise. It is part of the general office of believer for Christian physicians to do so, since to fail to do so is to treat people as mere mechanism. However, the physician must abandon the methodology of natural science and the trappings of authority which derive from that source in our society. He must utilize revelational data, and use it correctly.

SUMMARY

There are a number of other corrections Dr. White's article calls for, such as his misrepresentation of Jay Adams' handling of the issue of organic illness (see *Competent to Counsel*, pp. 36 - 40) and the implication that nouthetic counseling extensively utilizes demonic explanations.

> " A medical profession which departs from a line of evidential reasoning, has entered into the metaphysical, and has abandoned its particular expertise. "

While one appreciates the attempt to solve a knotty issue, his attempt to help by emphasizing the unity misfires. The Bible clearly identifies two parts in our being. That in medical or counseling practice it is not at all easy to separate the contributions of the two into the parts to be dealt with by two professions does not justify the creation of a functionally new part. Neither does it permit the retreat from responsibility.

Should the foregoing arguments fail to dislodge Dr. White from his position, however, there may be a simple way to move him. We just do it the way he has managed the subject — by definition. We need only define the practice of nouthetic counseling as *itself* a mental illness which renders the counselors so dysfunctional they cannot comprehend the obvious reality of mental illness. We know nouthetic counselors have the disorder because they do not accept mental illness as more than a metaphor, though nearly everyone else (the normative group) does. Therefore, we know they are sick. As mentally ill people we must see them as in need of medicine, not of condemnation or counsel. Applied thus to nouthetic counseling, Dr.

White's argument could appear to be an attempt to counsel nouthetic counselors out of their disease, the very thing he is cautioning us in general against, lest we heap more difficulties on the heads of those who are suffering mental illness.

ENDNOTES

1. One needs to escape the mode of rhetorical questioning in which this is cast. One could ask if Dr. White believes there is *no biblical answer* to his question. If a molested girl were to ask, "How am I supposed to act?" must the Christian remain mute? Is the incestuous rape of children too hard for our God? Has He nothing to say? Where Dr. White did not choose to tread, let me dare the following partial and idealized answer: For all victims of rape the answer must include removal from the offender. For very young girls, that and locating a home with proper models may be all the specific answer they can absorb until later. While it may be that the child would experience disturbing and powerful feelings regarding the incident, and that these feelings might beckon her toward misbehavior, the child should not be indulged in misbehavior under the excuse that "she can't help it, poor thing." At an appropriate age, the offended person may be taught the gospel, including the sinful nature of mankind and our accountability before God. An important and neglected feature of the management of such hard cases is the didactic function of discipline. The church needs to discipline members who so victimize others, and the victim needs to be aware of it. So also the civil government should punish evildoers, and the victim and

society at large needs to be aware of it. Psychiatrist Karl Menninger wrongly disparaged criminal punishment as a "morality play" in *Whatever Became of Sin?* Individually and corporately, we sorely need the teaching.

2. Use of the unqualified term "dysfunction" is a problem. Not functioning well *for what purpose?* Jay Adams' emphasis in depression is the sinful disregard of duties. There is a "dysfunction," for sure, but it is related to the functions God requires of the counselee in his/her situation. The functions he would see people fulfill are Biblically-defined. Medically, the same failure to do certain duties are transmogrified into "dysfunctions" with no specific normative reference function. If the failure to function is a failure in a legitimate duty, it is dangerous to excuse it on the basis of a bodily dysfunction with *no proven lesion.* It is doubly a problem to import medical terminology into the spirit and state that there is a "dysfunction" where moments before there was a sin. The same would apply to the multifarious uses of the term "disorder." One of the problems of psychiatry and psychology is that they each deal with "pathology" which is defined almost entirely by behaviors. There is no autopsy possible for the items in the DSM-IIIR. In a manner analogous to a Chinese restaurant menu, the diagnosis is established by two behaviors from list B and 3 from list A. The behavior is the only objective reality available to these professions. One result is that the taxonomy is churned more often than in other branches of medicine. A worse problem is that these professions first *define* their patholo-gy behaviorally, then use their pathology to *explain* the behavior. It is a circular endeavor. At best they can state that they have delineated clusters of behaviors which predict that other behaviors are likely to accompany. A layman of equal intelligence and experience with people can do as good a job of such predictions as the professionals. The escape route is available if they would accept the "autopsy" of the human spirit laid out in Scripture and the taxonomy of sin and righteousness.

3. There are bare "behaviors" which do not require a mental participation. They are all on the order of reflexes, such as the startle reflex, or of stereotypical and very simple sequences, such as in temporal lobe epilepsy. These things the body can indeed cause, without mental input. They are virtually never at issue in assessing a person's accountability.

4. Berkhof, Louis, **Systematic Theology**, William B. Eerdmans Co., Grand Rapids, MI, 1941, p. 234.

5. That the will is also fallen is beyond the scope of this article to address. It is enough to demonstrate that the will is *not* in the body, to make the point. As example, it is conceivable that a criminal's brain might contain certain limitations which constituted a temptation to him, but it would never *make* him into a sinner.

6. Terrell, Hilton P. "A Caution Against Overstating a Case", *Journal of Pastoral Practice*, Vol. IX, No. 4, 1989, pp. 39 - 43.

7. Orentlicher, David, M.D., Denying Treatment to the Noncompliant Patient, *JAMA*, March 27, 1991, Vol. 265, No. 12, pp. 1579 - 1582. p. 1580.

8. What such reasoning does for all the responsible patients undergoing hemodialysis is also interesting. By the same reasoning, their behavior is merely their reaction to the powerful situational factors, based upon their genetics and prior conditioning. They are no more responsible for their compliant behavior than the noncompliant are for theirs.

9. Orentlicher, *op. cit.*, pp. 1580 - 1581.

10. *Ibid*, p. 1582.

A Biblical Response to Baby-Making

Surrogacy, Artificial Insemination, *In Vitro* Fertilization and Embryo Transfer

Dawn McColley, J.D.

Miss McColley received her B.S. in Biology from Pacific Lutheran University and her law degree from the University of Puget Sound. She is currently the executive director of the Crisis Pregnancy Center of Pierce County in Tacoma, Washington.

"Baby-making," the science of the future, has become the science of the present. Surrogacy, artificial insemination, *in vitro* fertilization (IVF) and embryo transfer are four of the methods used today to enable childless couples to have children. A few years ago the solution to infertility was adoption, but the legalization of abortion and the change in societal attitudes toward single parenting has dramatically decreased the number of children available for adoption. Beyond that, it has become increasingly important to potential parents to have a baby who is genetically like one, if not both, of them. To provide a child for a childless couple — an awesome and worthy achievement. Does it justify the means we have used to accomplish it? If the end is a good one, how should we decide what means are proper to achieve that end?

RESPONSE TO INFERTILITY

In a day in which everyone is concerned about his or her "rights" it is common for couples, even Christian couples, to feel that they have a "right" to have a child. However, our lives are not made up of "rights." Rather, we have been given responsibilities and God has graciously bestowed many of these responsibilities on us in the form of gifts. Children are not objects to which we have a right; children are gifts from God. Some God has blessed with many such gifts, and from some God has chosen to withhold that blessing. Infertility is a state, whether permanent or temporary, in which God has placed some couples. As devastating as the problem of infertility can be, these couples can, by God's grace, acknowledge His will in all things and recognize that the promise of Romans 8:28 is true and meaningful. Peter says, "In this you greatly rejoice, though now for a little while you may have had to suffer grief in all kinds of trials. These have come so that your faith — of greater worth than gold, which perishes even though refined by fire — may be proved genuine and may result in praise, glory and honor when Jesus Christ is revealed."[1] If we see children as gifts rather than as a guarantee, then we can more readily accept God's will for our lives with a proper attitude.

God doesn't always give us what we want, no matter how desperately we want it. Paul asked the Lord three times for relief from his "thorn" but was refused.[2] Our response in disappointment must be Paul's: to be content and to acknowledge that the Lord's grace is sufficient and that He is wiser than we are.

This is not to say that cures for infertility may not be used. God has given men the ability to invent and discover new and marvelous things, not the least being medical techniques. If there is a cure for infertility, then we certainly may use it, provided it falls within Biblical parameters. The question discussed in this article is the morality of methods like surrogacy, artificial insemination, IVF, and embryo transfer, which are not cures to infertility but alternative forms of conception.

SCIENCE AND TECHNOLOGY

Human beings are made in God's image: amazingly intelligent, ingenious, and creative. Our creative genius must be used with care, however. Any bystanders at the scene of the Tower of Babel might have been in awe of the ability and genius of the men who created such a structure. But God knew the hearts and the worldly presumptions of those men and was displeased. They were building for their own glory and wanted nothing to do with the God who created them. God did not appreciate their architectural genius and so foiled their plans.[3]

The same danger exists for us today. The tendency of man is to want to control his fate, to be the master of his destiny, to glorify himself; and this tendency leads him to believe that anything he can do, he should do.

Our advancements in science

and technology must have Biblical bounds. Modern, humanistic man, like his forebears, has conveniently forgotten this boundary and eagerly seeks whatever ideas enter his head. When we attempt to master our own fate, not only do we fail to glorify God, we defy His deity. God, in His Word, has established the truth of His supremacy. This truth requires us to use our creative abilities for one purpose only — to glorify God. As Christians, we are not free to partake in all the developments that tempt us from every side. We must be careful to behave in a way that acknowledges God as Lord and Master of this universe and of our own bodies.

METHODS OF BABY-MAKING

The simplest form of IVF is that in which several ova are removed from the wife and fertilized with the husband's sperm in a petri dish. The fertilized ova are then placed in the wife's womb with the intent that a normal pregnancy occur. This method is one way a couple who cannot conceive naturally can have children who are genetically like themselves. IVF can also occur using the ova and/or sperm of donors, where, of course, the child would not be the genetic product of both husband and wife.

Artificial insemination is a common and simple procedure whereby the wife of an infertile man is artificially inseminated by the sperm of a donor. The child is genetically the wife's and in most states the husband is by law the father, eliminating the need for adoption. In situations in which the husband has viable sperm but conception hasn't occurred naturally, e.g., low sperm count, his sperm can be used in this procedure.

Embryo transfer is a method by which a donor woman is impregnated through artificial insemination with the husband's sperm. The embryo is washed out of the donor's uterus before it has a chance to implant and is then placed in the infertile wife's uterus so that she may carry it to term. The danger here is that the embryo might implant in the donor's womb. The "solution" to this problem is often abortion.

Surrogacy has received much media attention of late. This method is generally used when the wife is infertile. A contract is signed by the couple and the surrogate stating that the couple will pay all necessary expenses and will take custody of the baby when it is born. The surrogate is artificially inseminated with the sperm of the husband. The husband is the legal father of the child who must be relinquished by the surrogate and adopted by the wife. An alternate form of surrogacy is used when the wife is fertile but cannot carry a child to term. The wife's ovum is fertilized with the husband's sperm *in vitro*, then the embryo is implanted in the womb of the surrogate. The embryo is the genetic product of the husband and wife, however the legal ramifications are still being sorted out.

RESPONSE TO BABY-MAKING

What is a Biblical response to these amazing scientific breakthroughs in baby-making and how ought we to respond? There are three truths that must fence the Christian's acceptance of modern solutions to the problem of infertility:

1. The embryo is a human being from conception and must be treated with the respect that God requires of us in treating all of His image-bearers.

The Bible is clear about who man is and what is his relationship to God.[4] The Bible is also clear about God's relationship to the developing baby in the womb,[5] its nature and abilities,[6] and God's plan for its future.[7] *Therefore, the embryo ought never to be the subject of experimentation that is not intended for its own benefit.* Our God is not a utilitarian God. It does not matter what scientific "good" might come from such experimentation, nor how many other lives could be saved.

It is a common practice in many baby-making techiques to discard embryos who have not developed normally and to encourage the abortion of fetuses who have genetic or physical problems. These practices are contrary to God's law[8] and must be repudiated. If Christians are looking at options for themselves, they must be aware of these occurrences, seek to educate their physician regarding the evil of treating the embryo as a pre-human, and refuse to allow these practices to occur with their offspring.

2. God has ordained heterosexual monogamous marriage. Any attempts to have children must take place within this relationship.

Marriage was designed to provide companionship,[9] to provide sexual fulfillment,[10] and to produce children.[11] The Bible doesn't rank these purposes in any particular order and, therefore, none should be overemphasized or purposely deemphasized.

Marriage is an exclusive relationship. Man and wife are said to become one flesh.[12] Although several polygamous marriages are seen in the Scriptures, monogamous marriage is presented as the ideal, the only permissible type of marriage now. The Bible does not provide for the fulfillment of intimate companionship, sexual fulfillment or childbearing outside of that relationship.[13]

Thus, there is no justification for the use of any form of baby-making in any relationship other than marriage. Homosexual relationships, whether "married" or not, violate

God's law[14] and do not justify the use of medical technology in order to bear children.

We see in Scripture that the sexual act is reserved for the marriage bed only.[15] Since sex outside of marriage is wrong, babies ought not to be conceived outside of marriage. Thus the single woman who wants to use artificial insemination in order to bear a child of her own without being "tied down" to a man, or because she feels that she will never be married, is violating God's standards.

Not only is it permissible that only married couples attempt to have a baby, but because of the exclusivity of the relationship, it is important that only those two be involved. Some call the use of third party donor gametes (i.e., sperm and ova) adultery, even though there has been no physical unfaithfulness. Regardless of the name given to it, the use of donor gametes is an act that includes a third party in an event that was meant to remain strictly within the marriage covenant.

Because of the special union in marriage, problems such as infertility are shared by both spouses and should be borne by both. Our traditional marriage vows say, "for better for worse, ... in sickness and in health." By using the gametes of a donor, the fertile spouse refuses to share the burden.

This refusal to share burdens is not a Biblical response to God's will, nor is it the way Christian spouses ought to treat each other. Children are not the sole, sacred purpose of marriage. If God has chosen to withhold that blessing from one spouse, He necessarily chose to withhold it from the other.

3. The relationship between a parent and his or her offspring is a sacred one that must be protected and encouraged.

An 89 year-old friend of mine told the story of when her parents were expecting their third child. They were asked by some friends who were unable to conceive if they would be so kind as to give up their third baby. After all, they had a girl and a boy and hopes for more. When her parents refused, the couple was offended. Were her parents selfish and unfeeling toward this poor couple who longed for children? Should they have given up that baby? They already had children and were able to have more (and did — eight altogether). We would regard any such request as preposterous and would think any parents who gave up their child for this supposedly worthy cause irresponsible, cruel, and unfeeling. Of course, there are instances in which the best decision for the baby and for the parents is to relinquish that baby in adoption, but for loving parents it is an exquisitely painful thing and is not done simply because they should share. We do not consider children fungible goods to be bought, sold, or shared.

APPLYING THE PRINCIPLES TO BABY-MAKING

It is in light of these three principles that the four methods of baby-making will be discussed.

Surrogacy is perhaps the most blatant example of a wrongful use of modern technology. For two reasons Christians should not consider this method an option. First, it is clear that a third party is being drawn into the intimate marital relationship. Instead of relying solely on his wife for all aspects of marital pleasure, the husband has used another woman to achieve his heart's desire.

Second, when a woman becomes a surrogate mother she reduces herself to a mere incubator. She must convince herself that the baby, who is genetically hers, belongs to some-

one else. She must suppress any maternal feelings she has for her baby. If the alternate form of surrogate parenting is used and the baby is not genetically hers, the bonding that occurs during prenatal development is not necessarily diminished and her maternal feelings must still be suppressed.

It might be argued that in this case her denial is good and necessary. She is performing a selfless act by conceiving and bearing a baby for a childless couple. She should be commended. However, it is clear that surrogacy cheapens the maternal relationship and makes it something easily broken. It denies the natural feelings that God has created between mother and child. Christians must uphold and honor this maternal relationship.

Using our three principles we can see that there is no problem with artificial insemination if the husband's sperm are used to fertilize his wife's ovum. Using donor sperm, however, violates both the principles that surrogacy violates. The marriage covenant is broken by including a third party in the process and a man, although in a much less personal way than in surrogacy, is enabled to procreate without being responsible for his children's nurture.

God did not create us for procreation only and He did not give us the option of having children without having true responsibility for them. Under God's creation-order, fathers and mothers nurture and care for their children, they don't merely receive intellectual gratification from their children's existence.

Embryo transfer presents a Christian with the same concerns as does artificial insemination through a donor. Even though the wife carries the child to term, she and her husband have made use of the gamete of another woman and have broken the marital covenant. And, like artificial insemination, the donor woman is not able to take proper responsibility for her offspring.

IVF is a different question. Using the previous arguments it can be said that using the gametes of any but the spouses is unbiblical. This leads us to the question of whether IVF, using the gametes of the husband and wife, is an appropriate option for Christians? There is no danger of breaking the marriage covenant here. It is obvious that God has blessed us with medical technology that can circumvent many physical problems. Some Christians believe that there is a point at which they must accept God's will for their lives and that IVF is going too far. Others believe that their time and money are well spent in the pursuit of having a child in this way. These controversial choices must be left to the couple, with two limitations. The first is that only their gametes be used. If one spouse is unable to provide gametes, the couple is not qualified for this option. The second is that *all* fertilized ova or embryos must be implanted regardless of their condition.

Typically, improperly developing embryos are discarded and sometimes experiments are performed on extra embryos. These practices must not be allowed because they violate our first principle that embryos are human beings created in God's image.

Another problem with IVF is that it is often ineffective. Usually several ova are fertilized and placed in the uterus to increase the chances of successful implantation. In some cases, however, multiple pregnancies have resulted that are doomed to certain or almost certain failure. The solution that has been used in some of these cases is called fetal reduction, which is the killing of all but one or two of the unborn infants in order to increase the chance of their survival. This method has had signif-

icant success in ensuring that parents who use IVF (or fertility drugs) will have surviving children. Fetal reduction is said by some to be necessary because it's better to have one or two surviving infants than none at all.

Christians must recognize that despite the appearance of reasonableness, fetal reduction is not an option. Sovereignty over life and death belongs to God alone. Fortunately, the number of ova fertilized in IVF procedures can be controlled — therefore, the number of embryos put back into the uterus can be regulated. The physician must decide from a medical standpoint how many infants could survive gestation and only that number of ova should be fertilized. Thus there ought never to be the "need" for fetal reduction in IVF. Although this limitation reduces the chances of success, Christians should not put themselves in situations where their children could not possibly survive.

CONCLUSION

God's will for our lives is always for our good and for our further sanctification.[16] If infertility is His will, we must accept it with submission and humility and look only for solutions to the problem that are in accordance with Biblical principles.

If we believe that both marriage and parenthood are God-ordained relationships, then we can easily reject surrogacy, artificial insemination with donor sperm, and embryo transfer, since they violate those relationships. The morality of IVF is less clear and Christians who desire to use it must do so within the bounds set by Scripture. "Whatever you do, do it all for the glory of God."[17]

In order to glorify God we must protect and preserve human life at all stages of development. For God has known us in the womb — "your eyes saw my unformed body ..."[18] We

must protect the marriage covenant — couples must share one another's burdens and be one as God commands them to be. Finally, we must honor the relationship between parents and children. We must value and cultivate a society where attachments to our children are far from a matter of indifference and are held to be sacred.[19]

ENDNOTES

1. I Peter 1:6-7, NIV
2. II Corinthians 12:7-10.
3. Genesis 11:5-9.
4. Genesis 1:26.
5. Psalm 139:13-16.
6. Psalm 51:5; Luke 1:41-48.
7. Isaiah 48:5; Jeremiah 1:5.
8. Exodus 20:13
9. Genesis 2:18.
10. Genesis 2:24.
11. Genesis 1:28.
12. Genesis 2:24; Matthew 19:15; Ephesians 5:31.
13. Proverbs 5:18-19; Song of Solomon; I Timothy 3:2.
14. Romans 1:26, 27.
15. I Corinthians 6:13-20, 7:3-4.
16. Romans 8:28.
17. I Corinthians 10:31, NIV.
18. Psalm 139: 16.
19. See discussion in **Choosing Life or Death**, Wm. J. Winslade, J.W. Ross, The Free Press (1986), p. 138.

Acknowledgments

The author thanks the following for their advice and editing help: Robert S. Rayburn, M.Div., Ph.D; William D. McColley, M.Div; Eric Irwin; Laurie O'Ban; C. John Collins, Ph.D.; M. Reid Jackson, M.D.

Can Anyone Heal Me?

Randall W. Crenshaw, M.D.

Dr. Crenshaw lives near Birmingham, Alabama. He exercises his gifts of prophecy and teaching as part of a PCA church there. He also practices trauma surgery and emergency medicine. He has been married twenty-two years and has two teenage daughters. He loves baseball!

After twenty years of medical practice, I have concluded that many deeply committed Christians are using physicians as a substitute for Christ. Of course, this misuse is nothing new. The writer of II Chronicles brought a similar indictment against King Asa, the zealous reformer of Judah circa 900 B.C. "In the thirty-ninth year of his reign Asa was afflicted with a disease in his feet. Though his disease was severe, even in his illness he did not seek help from the Lord, but only from the physicians." (II Chr. 16:12)

The royal physicians possessed technology that was light years behind what we have at our disposal, but the chances are that the results of our treatments are little better than theirs. Dr. Paul Ellwood, a leading health services researcher and author of the term "health maintenance organization" (HMO), states flatly that "half of what the medical profession does is of unverified effectiveness."[1] Experience bears this out. Three villages in an undeveloped country were chosen as the site for an experiment to determine what changes had the greatest impact on the health of the inhabitants. One village got modern medical care, one got better nutrition, and the third got both. The results? Nutrition had a far greater impact in improving health than medical care had.[2]

Charles Stewart conducted research showing that education of the populace and clean drinking water had more to do with health than medical research and treatment.[2]

Why, then, has the incidence of "illness" and the use of personal medical services doubled in the last sixty years?[3] Two things come to mind.

Rick Carlson has claimed, and most general practitioners will testify, that "well over half of those who seek physicians' services do not have medical disorders. Rather, they are afflicted by disorders of the spirit bred by the suffering and anguish that accompany life." Further, "medicine has fostered a profoundly dependent public which searches for cures that do not exist."[4]

The rise of headache and other pain clinics provides further evidence of the despair which dogs modern man. Arguing against such a technical and mechanical approach, Ivan Illich stated that "pain is the sign for something not answered; it refers to something open, something that goes on the next moment to demand, what is wrong? How does this kind of evil exist, and why does it strike me?" Doctors are trained to "smother pain's intrinsic question mark." They "pride themselves on the knowledge of pain mechanics and

thus escape the patient's invitation to compassion."[5]

How sadly true!

The second factor contributing to the increased use of personal medical services is what I will call self-inflicted diseases. The majority of the true medical disorders — as opposed to problems of the *psyche* (Greek for soul) discussed above — fall into this category.

We eat and drink too much. We use tobacco. We have sex outside marriage. We drive too fast. We strive too hard to succeed. We stay wired-up on coffee. These eventually exact their toll from us in the form of heart disease, emphysema, herpes, ulcers, and high blood pressure — if we don't go through a windshield first. And, that's not all the bad news. The "cures" are often worse than the diseases.

Experts recently concluded that one-third of the operations to clear blockages out of the arteries in the neck (to prevent strokes) were clearly inappropriate for the patients who had them. They said another third were equivocal. This operation is no Sunday school picnic, either! One out of every ten patients in those two categories either died or had a stroke anyway within thirty days of the surgery.[6]

Tonsillectomy is the most commonly performed operation in Western civilization. Estimates of the number of unnecessary tonsillectomies range from fifty to ninety-five percent. No long term benefit is discerned, yet twenty to thirty percent of American children have their tonsils removed. Don't think this is a simple matter, either. One of every thousand dies! That totals about two hundred annually in the U.S. Serious complications occur fifteen times out of a thousand.[7]

Drug prescriptions offer no more encouragement than surgery. Often what a doctor knows about the drug he prescribed for you on your last visit he learned from the salesman of that product. The Senate Committee on Aging recently reported that in the last eight years the number of important new drugs brought to market by the twenty-five major pharmaceutical companies totalled twelve. Twelve, in eight years! The hundreds of other new drugs introduced during that period, 1980-87, offered no significant advantage over existing drugs, yet all were more expensive.[8]

It appears, then, that many, if not most, visits to American doctors involve self-inflicted diseases or problems in the soul. I would argue that the medical establishment has usurped the Church's role as guardian of the souls of its members by proclaiming that the cause of these problems is a chemical imbalance in the brain.

A common thread binds these two groups of patients. Whether we choose mental health professionals to dispense them, or whether we use the pain-killers available to us in nature, our goal as patients is the same — to numb our souls to the hurts and humiliations we constantly encounter in a fallen, hostile world. Psychotropic drugs, rich food, alcohol, tobacco, caffeine, and illicit sex have this in common: they anesthetize us, for a moment, to the distress of the accumulated disappointments of our lives. So we demand prescriptions for the relief of our fears and our shame or to alleviate the symptoms of our self-inflicted diseases. In this way, we substitute physicians for Christ.

In the Scriptures, healing is equated with salvation. The Holy Spirit, through Isaiah, the prophet, declares that we are healed by Christ's punishment for our sin. A commitment to the Lord Jesus Christ, based on repentance and faith, is the route to real health and happiness.

Now, please do not mistake me for a faith healer. If I suffer a serious illness or injury, I will seek the best surgeons and physicians I can afford. If they judge that the chances for cure are reasonable I will undergo the treatments they recommend. But we should not blindly accept their advice, without considering the costs, in time, money and energy, and the realistic chances for cure.

ENDNOTES

1. Faltermayer, Edmund, Medical Care's Next Revolution, *Fortune*, Oct. 10, 1988, p. 126.
2. Carlson, Rick J., **The End of Medicine**, New York: John Wiley & Sons, 1975, pp. 26-27.
3. Anderson, Odin W. & Morrison, Ellen, The Worth of Medical Care: A Critical Review, *Medical Care Review*, Vol. 46 (Summer 1989), pp. 126-127.
4. Carlson, *op. cit.*, p. 37.
5. Illich, Ivan, **Medical Nemesis: The Expropriation of Health**, New York: Parthenon Books, 1976, pp. 142-146.
6. Winslow, Constance, et al., The Appropriateness of Carotid Endarterectomy, *New England Journal of Medicine*, Vol. 318, pp. 721-727.
7. Carlson, *op cit.*, **The End of Medicine**, pp. 12-13.
8. Carveth, W. Bruce, ed., Prescription Drug Prices: Are We Getting Our Money's Worth?, *Medical Benefits*, Mar. 15, 1990, pp. 1-2.

Doctrine & Ethics

Alister E. McGrath

Alister McGrath is a lecturer in Christian doctrine and ethics at Oxford University in England.

Reprinted from the Journal of the Evangelical Theological Society, Vol. 34, No. 2, June 1991, pp. 145-156, by permission.

A story is told about Kenneth Kirk, sometime professor of moral theology at Oxford University. His wife was once asked what she felt about her husband's work. "Kenneth," she said, "spends a lot of time thinking up very complicated and sophisticated reasons for doing things we all know perfectly well to be wrong." This illustrates neatly the way in which moral theology is viewed by many people these days. I want to suggest that a recovery of Christian doctrine is fundamental to a recovery of Christian ethics. In other words, Christian doctrine is what sets Christian ethics apart from the ethics of the world around us. It defines what is distinctive, what is Christian, about Christian ethics. To lose sight of the importance of doctrine is to lose the backbone of the faith and to open the way to a spineless ethic. I hope that the following observations will explain why I believe this to be the case.[1]

Commitment is fundamental to any but the most superficial forms of human existence. In his famous essay "The Will to Believe," psychologist William James makes it clear that there are some choices in life

> A recovery of Christian doctrine is fundamental to a recovery of Christian ethics.

that cannot be avoided. To be human is to make decisions. We are all obliged to choose between options that are, in James' words, "living, forced and momentous." In matters of morality, politics and religion we must make conscious choices — and, as James stresses, our whole life hangs upon the choices made.

Every movement that has ever competed for the loyalty of human beings has done so on the basis of a set of beliefs. Whether the movement is religious or political, philosophical or artistic, the same pattern emerges: A group of ideas, of beliefs, is affirmed to be in the first place true and in the second important. It is impossible to live life to its fullness and avoid encountering claims for our loyalty of one kind or another. Marxism, socialism, atheism — all alike demand that we consider their claims. The same is true of liberalism, whether in its religious or political forms. As Alasdair MacIntyre demonstrates so persuasively, liberalism is committed to a definite set of beliefs and hence to certain values. It is one of the many virtues of MacIntyre's important work that it mounts a devastating critique of the idea that liberalism represents some kind of privileged

and neutral vantage point from which other doctrinal traditions (such as evangelicalism) may be evaluated. Rather, liberalism entails pre-commitment to liberal beliefs and values. Liberal beliefs (and thus values) affect liberal decisions - in ethics, religion and politics. The following quotation illustrates the general tenor of MacIntyre's work:

> *To the readership of the New York Times, or at least to that part of it which shares the presuppositions of those who write that parish magazine of affluent and self-congratulatory liberal enlightenment, the congregations of evangelical fundamentalism appear unfashionably unenlightened. But to the members of those congregations that readership appears to be just as much a community of prerational faith as they themselves are but one whose members, unlike themselves, fail to recognize themselves for what they are, and hence, are in no position to level charges of irrationality at them or anyone else.*[2]

Time and time again, life-changing decisions are demanded of us. How shall I vote at the next election? What do I think about the riddle of human destiny? What form of educational system do I consider the best? Is the use of deadly force justifiable to defend democracy? What rights to animals have? All these questions force us to think about our beliefs and to make choices. You cannot sit on the fence throughout life, as William James demonstrated with such remarkable clarity. To suspend judgment on every question that life raises is to be trapped in an insipid agnosticism, where all the great questions arising out of human experience receive the same shallow response: "I don't know — and I don't care."

Thinking people need to construct and inhabit mental worlds. They need to be able to discern some degree of ordering within their experience, to make sense of its riddles

> **It is a lie to say that dogma does not matter; it matters enormously. It is fatal to let people suppose that Christianity is only a mode of feeling.**

and enigmas. They need to be able to structure human existence in the world, to allow it to possess meaning and purpose, to allow decisions to be made concerning the future of that existence. In order for anyone — Christian, atheist, Marxist, Muslim — to make informed moral decisions, it is necessary to have a set of values concerning human life. Those values are determined by beliefs, and those beliefs are stated as doctrines. Christian doctrine thus provides a fundamental framework for Christian living.

A common complaint about doctrine runs along the following lines: "Doctrine is outdated and irrelevant. What really matters is our attitudes toward other people, and our morality. Doctrine does not matter." Dorothy L. Sayers reacted as follows to this suggestion:

The one thing I am here to say to you is this: that it is worse than useless for Christians to talk about the importance of Christian morality, unless they are prepared to take their stand upon the fundamentals of Christian theology. It is a lie to say that dogma does not matter; it matters enormously. It is fatal to let people suppose that Christianity is only a mode of feeling; it is virtually necessary to insist that it is first and foremost a rational explanation of the universe. It is hopeless to offer Christianity as a vaguely idealistic aspiration of a simple and consoling kind; it is, on the contrary, a hard, tough, exacting and complex doctrine, steeped in a drastic and uncompromising realism.[3]

Not so long ago there was a movement within liberal theology arguing that there existed a universal morality that Christianity reflected. It was not necessary to know anything about Christian theology to make ethical judgments. This universal morality, it was argued, was adequate in itself. The Christian, Buddhist, Hindu, Muslim, humanist and atheist were all, it was argued, committed to much the same set of moral principles (with unimportant local variations). In *The Abolition of Man*, C.S. Lewis described these as "the ultimate platitudes of Practical Reason." That view is now regarded as so seriously vulnerable as to be virtually defunct. Works such as Jeffrey Stout's *Ethics after Babel* destroyed the credibility of the idea of a "universal morality." Like every other form of morality, Christian morality is something special and distinct, not just a subspecies of some nonexistent

universal morality. With the passing of the myth of a universal morality, Christian writers have begun to write with much greater confidence on the theme "Christian morality" in the knowledge that there is a distinctly Christian outlook on many matters. And this outlook, it is increasingly being stressed, is based upon Christian doctrine.

To make this point we may consider two highly-acclaimed recent works on the theme of Christian ethics: Oliver O'Donovan's *Resurrection and Moral Order*, and John Mahoney's *The Making of Moral Theology*. Despite differences between the two authors, one theme emerges as of major importance: Ethics rests upon doctrine. To give but one example: For O'Donovan, Christian ethics rests upon a proper understanding of the objective order imposed upon creation by God. To act in a Christian manner rests upon thinking in a Christian manner.[4]

Let us explore this briefly by considering the ethical authority of Jesus Christ. To allow that Jesus is a religious teacher is to raise the question of his authority. Why should we take him seriously? Although we have been fortunate enough to have had the advice of countless moral and religious teachers in human history, what makes Jesus so different? What singles him out as commanding attention? It is untenable to suggest that Jesus' authority rests upon the excellence of his moral or religious teaching. To make this suggestion is to imply that Jesus has authority only when he happens to agree with us. We thus would have authority over Jesus.[5]

In fact, however, the teaching of Jesus has authority on account of who Jesus is — and the identity and significance of Jesus can only be spelled out in doctrinal terms. "We cannot go on treating and believing in Jesus Christ in a way in which it would be wrong to treat and believe in another man, without a theory of his person that explains that he is something more than man."[6] It is doctrine that explains why and how Jesus' words and deeds have divine rather than purely human authority. It is doctrine that singles out Jesus Christ, and none other, as being God incarnate. To pay attention to Christ reflects our fundamental conviction that God speaks through this man as through no other. Here is no prophet, speaking on God's behalf at second hand; here is God himself, speaking to us. "We have to do with God himself as we have to do with this man. God himself speaks when this man speaks in human speech" (Karl Barth). Quite contrary to the Broad Church liberals of the nineteenth century (who believed it was possible to uphold the religious and ethical aspects of Christianity while discarding its doctrines), the authority of Jesus' moral and religious teaching thus rests firmly upon a doctrinal foundation.

This point is made with care and persuasion by philosopher of religion Basil Mitchell, who stresses that ethics depends upon worldviews and that worldviews in turn depends upon doctrine:

> Any world-view which carries with it important implications for our understanding of man and his place inthe universe would yield its own distinctive insights into the scope, character and content of morality. To answer the further question, "What is the distinctive Christian ethic?", is inevitably to be involved to some extent in controversial questions of Christian doctrine.[7]

The liberal Christianity-without-doctrine school thus finds itself in something of a quandary. If Christianity is primarily about certain religious or moral attitudes, it seems that those attitudes rest upon doctrinal presuppositions. Doctrine determines attitudes. It is utterly pointless to argue that we all ought to imitate the religious and moral attitudes of Jesus. That is a demand for blind and unthinking obedience. The question of why we should regard these attitudes as being authoritative demands to be considered. And that means explaining what it is about Jesus Christ that demands singling him out as authoritative — in short, developing doctrines about Jesus.

This point was made clearly and prophetically by William Temple. Writing against the "religion without dogma" movement in 1942, he declared:

> You would hardly find any theologian now who supposes that Christian ethics can survive for half a century in detachment from Christian doctrine, and this is the very last moment when the church itself can come forward with outlines of Christian ethics in the absence of the theological foundation which alone makes them really tenable. Our people have grown up in a generally Christian atmosphere, and take it for granted that all people who are not actually perverted hold what are essentially Christian notions about human conduct. But this is not true.[8]

He then goes on to illustrate this

point tellingly with reference to the rise of Hitler and Stalin in the 1930's. Although many liberal and radical writers of the 1960's suggested that Christian ethics could be divorced from doctrine and maintain an independent existence, the wisdom of Temple's words is once more apparent. Distinctive ethics (whether Marxist, Christian or Buddhist) are dependent upon world-views, which are in turn shaped by doctrines, by understandings of human nature and destiny.

Beliefs are important because they claim to describe the way things are. They assert that they declare the truth about reality. But beliefs are not just ideas that are absorbed by our minds and that have no further effect upon us. They affect what we do and what we feel. They influence our hopes and fears. They determine the way we behave. A Japanese figher pilot of the second world war might believe that destroying the enemies of his emperor ensured his immediate entry into paradise — and, as many American navy personnel discovered to their cost, this belief expressed itself in quite definite actions. Such pilots had no hesitation in launching suicide attacks on American warships. Doctrines are ideas — but they are more than mere ideas. They are the foundation of our understanding of the world and our place within it.

What we might call the "common-sense-Christianity" school will probably continue to insist that faith is a "practical and down-to-earth matter," having nothing to do with "airy-fairy theories" (if I might use phrases I was fond of myself at one

> **If Christianity is primarily about certain religious or moral attitudes, it seems that those attitudes rest upon doctrinal presuppositions. Doctrine determines attitudes.**

time). Economist John Maynard Keynes came across similar attitudes among industrialists and politicians. "We are practical people," they declared, "who have no need for abstract theories about economics." Yet these people, Keynes scathingly remarked, were little more than the unwitting slaves of some defunct economist. Their allegedly practical outlook actually rested upon unacknowledged economic theories. They lacked the insight to see that what they regarded as obvious was actually based upon the theories of some long-dead economist. Without knowing it, "common-sense Christianity" rests upon quite definite doctrinal foundations. The man who declares in the name of common sense that Jesus was simply a good man may genuinely believe that he has avoided matters of doctrine, whereas he has actually echoed the doctrines of the enlightenment. The study of Christian doctrine is thus profoundly liberating, since it exposes these hidden doctrinal assumptions. Every version of Christianity that has ever existed rests upon doctrinal foundations, but not every version of Christianity has grasped this fact. The genuine question of importance is quite simple: Which of those doctrinal foundations are the most authentic and reliable?

This is to raise the question of truth in Christian doctrine and ethics. To some modern religious writers it may seem slightly quaint and old-fashioned to talk about "truth." "Relevance" and "meaningfulness" were words that captured the imagination of a recent generation. Unless something was relevant or meaningful there was no point in

bothering with it. Christian doctrine, many suggested, was outdated and irrelevant. The brave new world that was dawning could manage very well without such relics of the past.

The danger of all this is clear. Beneath all the rhetoric about relevance lies a profoundly disturbing possibility: that people may base their lives upon an illusion, upon a blatant lie. The attractiveness of a belief is all too often inversely proportional to its truth. In the sixteenth century, the radical writer and preacher Thomas Muntzer led a revolt of German peasants against their political masters. On the morning of the decisive encounter between the peasants and the armies of the German princes, Muntzer promised that those who followed him would be unscathed by the weapons of their enemies. Encouraged by this attractive and meaningful belief, the peasants stiffened their resolve.

> *Every version of Christianity that has ever existed rests upon doctrinal foundations, but not every version of Christianity has grasped this fact.*

The outcome was a catastrophe. Six thousand peasants were slaughtered in the ensuing battle, and six hundred were captured. Barely a handful escaped. Their belief in invulnerability was relevant. It was attractive. It was meaningful. It was also a crude and cruel lie, without any foundation in truth. The last hours of that pathetic group of trusting men rested on an utter illusion. It was only when the first salvos cut some of their number to ribbons that they realized they had been deceived.

To allow relevance to be given greater weight than truth is a mark of intellectual shallowness and moral irresponsibility. The first and most

fundamental of all questions must be this: Is it true? Is it worthy of belief and trust? Truth is certainly no guarantee of relevance, but no one can build his personal life around a lie. Christian doctrine is concerned to declare that Christian morality rests upon a secure foundation. An obedient response to truth is a mark of intellectual integrity. It marks a willingness to hear what purports to be the truth, to judge it, and — if it is found to be true — to accept it willingly. Truth demands to be accepted because it inherently deserves to be accepted and acted upon. Christianity recognizes a close link between faith and obedience — witness Paul's profound phrase "the obedience of faith" (Rom. 1:5) — making it imperative that the ideas underlying and giving rise to attitudes and actions should be judged and found to be right.

Christian doctrine aims to describe the way things are. It is concerned to tell the truth in order that we may enter into and act upon that truth. It is an expression of a responsible and caring faith, a faith prepared to give an account of itself and to give careful consideration to its implications for the way we live. To care about doctrines is to care about the reliability of the foundations of the Christian life. It is to be passionately concerned that our actions and attitudes, our hopes and our fears, are a response to God and not to something or someone making claims to deity, which collapse upon closer inspection.

Perhaps the German Church struggle of the 1930's highlights the importance of doctrine in the modern world. When Adolf Hitler came to power he demanded that he and the Nazi government of the Third Reich should have authority over the Church and its preaching. The

German Church polarized into two factions: (1) the "German Christians," who believed the Church should respond positively to National Socialist culture (following the general liberal tendency to put culture above doctrine), and (2) the "Confessing Church" — including such writers as Karl Barth and Dietrich Bonhoeffer — who believed that the Church was answerable to Jesus Christ, as we know him through Scripture, and to him alone. Representatives of the Confessing Church met at Barmen in 1934 where they issued the famous *Barmen Declaration*, perhaps one of the finest statements of the Lordship of Jesus Christ over his Church and its implications:

> "I am the way, and the truth, and the life. No one comes to the Father except through me" (John 14:6). "I tell you the truth, the man who does not enter the sheep pen by the gate, but climbs in some other way, is a thief and a robber ... I am the gate; whoever enters through me will be saved" (10:1,9).

> "Jesus Christ, as he is attested for us in Holy Scripture, is the one Word of God which we have to hear and which we have to trust and obey in life and in death. We reject false doctrine that the church could and would have to acknowledge as a source of its proclamation, apart from and besides this one Word of God, still other events and powers, figures and truths, as God's revelation.

In other words, the Church cannot and must not substitute anything (for example, the state government or German culture) or anyone (such as Adolf Hitler) for Jesus Christ. If the Church ever loses her faithful obedience to her Lord, she has lost her life and her soul.

Thus far I have spoken in general terms about doctrine and ethics. But how do specific doctrines affect Christian morality? To illustrate the importance of doctrine I wish to consider the way in which two major Christian doctrines have a direct impact upon the way we think ethically in a Christian manner.

1. *The doctrine of justification by faith.* What is the motivation for ethics? Why should we want to do good works of any sort? The doctrine of justification by faith makes two central points of relevance here. First, it stresses that there is no way that our moral actions can earn our salvation. They have no purchasing power in respect to salvation. Second, works are thankfulness to God. The gift of our justification lays upon us the obligation to live in accordance with our new status. We are made children of God through our justification as an act of free grace, and now we must act in accordance with this transformation. The slogan "Become what you are!" neatly summarizes this situation and encapsulates the essence of Pauline ethics with some brilliance. In justification we are made to be the light of the world (Matt. 5:15-16), and therefore we must shine out as lights in a dark world, as a city on a hill (Matt. 5:14, Phil. 2:15). We are the light of the world, and therefore we must become the light of the world. Our justification brings about a new obedience, an obedience that would not be conceivable before our justification and that ultimately rests upon the grace of God.

There is thus an automatic or natural connection between the justification of the sinner and his or her desire and ability to perform good works. The NT analogy of the tree and its fruit expresses the fundamental idea that the radical transformation of individuals (and it is worth remembering that the English word "radical" comes from the Latin *radix*, "root") is prior to their ability to produce good works. In the sermon on the mount, Jesus points out that a good tree bears good fruit and a bad tree bad fruit (Matt. 7:16-18). The nature of the fruit is biologically determined by the plant itself. Thus grapes do not grow on thornbushes, nor do figs grow on thistles. These are just the biological facts of life. If you want to get figs, you have to establish a fig tree and get it to fruit.

Underlying these remarkably simple analogies is profound theological insight. The transformation of humanity is a prerequisite for its reformation. Or, as Martin Luther put it: "It is not good works that makes an individual good, but a good individual who does good works." The NT, particularly the Pauline writings, emphasizes that this transformation is to be understood as God's transformation of us rather than our own attempt to transform us. Thus Paul speaks of the "fruit of the Spirit" (Gal. 5:22), drawing attention to the fact that this fruit is the result of God's action within us rather than of our action independent of God. Whereas secular ethical systems tend to discuss moral acts in terms of their goal (in other words, what they achieve or are intended to achieve), a theological ethical system based upon the doctrine of justification by faith will therefore discuss moral acts in terms of what they presuppose or are intended to express (in other words, the individual's radical transformation through his conversion). The starting point of an authentically Christian ethics is the recognition that the conversion of the individual leads to a new obedience, a new lifestyle and a new ethic.

2. *The doctrine of original sin.* A central insight of an authentically Christian morality is its realism concerning the limitations of human nature. Where some secular moral thinking degenerates into little more than a blind utopianism, Christian morality addresses the human situation with an informed realism about its strictly limited possibilities. Reinhold Niebuhr, perhaps one of the greatest Christian ethical thinkers of the twentieth century, poured scorn on the "perfectionist illusions" that so confused and misled many liberal Christian thinkers in the 1930's. The doctrine of original sin destroys naive views of human perfectability. There is, according to this doctrine, something inherently wrong with human nature, something that makes it self-centered, rebellious and disobedient. There is simply no point in informing sinful humanity that the world would be a better place if everyone stopped doing things that are wrong. What is required is a transformation of the human situation so that the motivation for doing wrong is eliminated or reduced. Underlying both the view that the human predicament arises from ignorance and the view that Jesus Christ is nothing more than a good teacher is a remarkably shallow understanding of the nature of humanity itself. As Niebuhr emphasized, all too many modern thinkers tend to work with a remarkably naive view of human nature, probably reflecting the fact that their middle-class intellectual backgrounds tend to inhibit them from encountering and experiencing the darker side of human nature.

The radical realism of the Christian view of sin, and its devastating consequences for our understanding of human beings as moral agents, is captured in the words of Robert Browning in *Gold Hair*: "Tis the faith that launched point-blank her dart/ At the head of a lie-taught Original Sin,/ The Corruption of Man's Heart." The bland assumption of the natural goodness of human nature, so characteristic of much western liberal thought, is called into question by this doctrine. The myth of human perfectibility and inevitable progress has been shown up for what it is by the savagery and cruelty of the twentieth century. If ever there was a period in human history when human evil was evident, it has been the twentieth century. How many outrages such as Auschwitz must we experience before the naive assumption that all human beings act out of the best of intentions is exposed for what it is — a cruel and seductive lie? Even those who are reluctant to call this inborn and inbuilt discord "sin" are prepared to recognize its reality. Witness the famous words of the atheist poet A.E. Housman: "The troubles of our proud and angry dust/ Are from eternity, and shall not fail."

The doctrine of original sin brings a breath of refreshing realism to Christian ethics. It allows us to understand that human beings are fallen, with an alarming degree of ability to do evil while knowing that it is evil. The implications of human self-centeredness for political institutions (for example, evident in the way in which they can be manipulated and exploited) and moral action will be obvious. Sin is not just something personal; it is something structural, affecting institutions and societies as well as individuals. Niebuhr's argument for democracy — an excellent example of the political application of a Christian doctrine — was quite simple: It was just about the only way of controlling human self-centeredness and forcing national leaders to respect the needs of others. Put very simply, the doctrine of original sin tells us that morality concerns weak, self-centered and exploitative human beings — in other words, real humans, not the perfectible angels of wishful liberal thinking. Power, capital, force — all can be and will be abused and exploited for personal ends unless the political and moral will exists to control them.

Let me also make a more controversial point. Roman Catholic moral theologian Charles Curran also pointed out some central ethical consequences of the Christian doctrine of original sin. Even human reason, the central resource upon which so much secular ethical theory rests, must be regarded as compromised by sin: "In the total Christian horizon the disrupting influence of sin colours all human reality ... Sin affects reason itself." Furthermore, sin is so deeply embedded in human nature and society that there are points at which it is impossible to adopt a course of action that avoids sin. The Christian is obliged to choose between two decisions, each of which is sinful. "In some circumstances the Christian is forced to do something sinful. The sinner reluctantly performs the deed and asks God for forgiveness and mercy." As Helmut Thielicke argued in his *Theological Ethics*, human society is so thoroughly saturated with sin that Christian ethical decision-making must learn to come to terms with compromise, adjusting to the sinful realities of the world rather than pretending that an ideal situation exists in which it is possible to draw a clear-cut decision between "right" and "wrong." To pretend that it is possible to make ethical decisions without coming to terms with the severe limitations placed upon human reason and will by sin is to live in a Walter Mitty world of unreality and dreams. This ethic of compromise is clearly controversial because it suggests that in certain situations one has to speak of "sinful" and "more sinful" choices. But in a fallen world it may well be that we cannot avoid getting our hands dirty.

Curran and Thielicke are excellent examples of Christian writers on ethics who are concerned to develop genuinely Christian approaches to ethical questions rather than just rehashing secular ideas and values. Time and time again these writers show the importance of doctrine to ethics. Christian ethics is simply too important to be left to those whose values are determined by the world rather than by the gospel.[9] To quote once more from the *Barmen Declaration*:

> *Jesus Christ, as he is attested for us in Holy Scripture, is the one Word of God which we have to hear and which we have to trust and obey in life and in death. We reject the false doctrine, that the church could and would have to acknowledge as a source of its proclamation, apart from and besides this one Word of God, still other events and powers, figures and truths, as God's revelation.*

The Church cannot and must not substitute anything (for example, modern American liberal middle-class culture and its values) or anyone (such as the latest liberal cult figure) for Jesus Christ. If the Church ever loses her faithful obedience to her Lord, she has lost her life and her soul.

Doctrine thus defines who we are to obey. It draws a firm line of demarcation between a false Church, which answers to the pressures of the age, and a true Church, which is obedient and responsible to God as he has revealed himself in Christ. "True knowledge of God is born out of obedience" (John Calvin). Inattention to doctrine robs the Church of her reason for existence and opens the way to enslavement and oppression by the world. The German Christians, through well-intentioned but muddled attitudes toward the world, allowed that world to conquer them. A Church that takes doctrine seriously is a Church that is obedient to and responsible for what God has entrusted to it. Doctrine gives substance and weight to what the Christian Church has to offer to the world. A Church that despises or neglects doctrine comes perilously close to losing its reason for existence and may simply lapse into a comfortable conformity with

> Inattention to doctrine robs the Church of her reason for existence and opens the way to enslavement and oppression by the world.

the world — or whatever part of the world it happens to feel most at home with. Its agenda is set by the world; its presuppositions are influenced by the world; its outlook mirrors that of the world. There are few more pathetic sights than a Church wandering aimlessly from one "meaningful" issue to another in a desperate search for relevance in the eyes of the world.

Why, then, are such considerations important? I would like to reflect on their importance to the modern American situation, using Robert Bellah's *Habits of the Heart* and Alasdair MacIntyre's *After Virtue* as dialogue partners. Bellah and his coauthors, surveying individualism and commitment in modern American life, concluded that morality was in a state of chaos. There is no longer any consensus. There is no common language of morality. There is no moral Esperanto, which can be abstracted from the moral traditions of humanity. Bellah quotes Livy's reflection on ancient Rome: "We have reached the point where we cannot tolerate either our vices or their cure." And MacIntyre, pursuing the analogy with ancient Rome a little further, declares that "the New Dark Ages are already upon us." I would like to add to this that the so-called new-age movement is simply a new dark age, a new age of distortion and darkness in which the light of faith came dangerously close to extinction.

The foundations of secular ethics are in serious disarray. The notion of some universal morality, valid at all places in space and time, has lost credibility. Secular ethics has been fascinated by the notion of moral obligations, based on the Kantian notion of a sense of moral obligation. But, as MacIntyre pointed out with great force, there are alarming parallels between the western appeal to a sense of moral obligation and the eighteenth-century Polynesian idea of taboo. Captain Cook and his sailors were puzzled by the Polynesian concept, which seemed quite incomprehensible to them. MacIntyre points out that the liberal notion of moral obligation is just as arbitrary as taboo. The difference is that liberals fail to realize it.

So there is a need to be able to develop a foundation for ethics. No longer need we pay excessive attention to the fictional idea of a universal framework of morality. Instead, we may concentrate upon what ways of thinking and what ways of acting are appropriate to the Christian community of faith. MacIntyre calls for "the construction of local forms of community through which civility and the intellectual and moral life can be sustained through the Dark Ages which are already upon us." I would like to suggest that this vision is helpful to us.

It encourages us to see ourselves as a "city upon a hill" (to use a Biblical image) or a "local form of community in the New Dark Ages" (to use MacIntyre's). Within that community a distinctive way of thinking and acting exists, nourished by the gospel, sustained by the grace of God, oriented toward the glory of God. It is a vision that Americans may share with their Puritan forebears who settled Massachusetts Bay with such hope and faith in the seventeenth century. Their vision can be ours. As MacIntyre stresses, it does not matter if those outside this community fail to understand or share this vision; the important thing is that the vision is presented to them, is kept alive. By joining this community of faith they may come to understand its hopes, beliefs and values.

But let me end with a Pauline image, lent new importance by trends in secular moral philosophy. It is the image of Christians as "citizens of heaven," developed with such force in Phil. 3:20-21. The model is that of a colony, an image familiar to the Philippians, Philippi then being a Roman colony. It was an outpost of Rome on foreign territory. Its people kept the laws of the homeland, they spoke its language, they longed for the day when they could return home to the *patria*, the motherland.

Let us think of ourselves, our seminaries, our churches and our families as colonies of heaven, as outposts of the real eternal city, who seek to keep its laws in the midst of alien territory. C.S. Lewis gave us many helpful ways of thinking about the Christian life, and one of the most helpful is that of the world as enemy territory, territory occupied by invading forces. In the midst of this territory, as resistance groups, are the communities of faith. We must never be afraid to be different from the world around us. It is very easy for Christians to be depressed by the fact that the world scorns our values and standards. But the image of the colony sets this in its proper context. At Philippi the civilizing laws of Rome contrasted with the anarchy of its hinterland. And so our moral vision — grounded in Scripture, sustained by faith, given intellectual spine by Christian doctrine — stands as a civilizing influence in the midst of a world that seems to have lost its moral way. If a new dark age does indeed lie ahead of us — indeed, if it is already upon us — then it is vital that the Christian moral vision, like the torch of liberty, is kept alight. Doctrine, I firmly and passionately believe, gives us the framework for doing precisely that. It can be done — and it must be done.

ENDNOTES

1. Some of the ideas developed very briefly in this paper are explored at greater length in my book **Understanding Doctrine** (Grand Rapids: Zondervan, 1991).

2. A. MacIntyre, **Whose Justice? Which Rationality?** (Notre Dame: University of Notre Dame 1988) p. 5.

3. D.L. Sayers, **Creed or Chaos?** (London: Methuen, 1947) p. 28.

4. O. O'Donovan, **Resurrection and Moral Order: An Outline for Evangelical Ethics** (Grand Rapids:Eerdmans, 1986).

5. I explore the manner in which Jesus Christ can be a moral example for us in the essay "In What Way Can Jesus Be a Moral Example for Christians?" (forthcoming in JETS 34/3 [September, 1991]).

6. C. Gore, **The Incarnation of the Son of God** (London: Murray, 1922) p. 23.

7. B. Mitchell, *How to Play Theological Ping-Pong* (London: Hodder and Stoughton, 1990), p. 56.

8. Letter cited in F.A. Iremonger, **William Temple, Archbishop of Canterbury: Life and Letters** (London: Oxford University, 1948) p. 490.

9. See further my article, "Sin and Salvation" in **New Dictionary of Christian Ethics and Pastoral Theology** (ed. D. Atkinson and D. Field; Leicester: Intervarsity, forthcoming).

Pastor's Column

The Reverend Byron Snapp

Rev. Snapp holds a B.A. from King College and an M.Div. from Reformed Theological Seminary. He is assistant pastor of Covenant Presbyterian Church and prinicipal of Covenant Christian School in Cedar Bluff, Virginia.

(1) "I am not sick. I do not need to see a doctor."

(2) "The doctor can take care of my illness and get me back on my feet again."

The above typify two responses those in the pew and, we must confess, those in the pulpit often make toward personal illness. They can be summed up in this way: (1) I am a good and thus indestructible, (2) The doctor is god. He can know immediately what is wrong with me and cure me.

Both statements must be looked at in light of Scripture. The pastor needs to remind himself and his congregation of the errors in either of these statements.

Since the Garden of Eden man has been tempted to "be as God." In our day of self-help and multitude of health fads and emphasis (Not all are bad - our bodies are God's temples. We are to take good care of them.) our humanistic culture would tell us that we can defeat death. Sickness is not a part of the life of the macho man nor the perfect "10." Why should it be a part of our life? Certainly we do not deserve it. After all, gods do not get sick, do they?

Once we are admittedly sick it is easy to set up the physician as god.

Surrounded by his pills, surgical instruments, or other medical technology surely he has the power to make us well. Admittedly it is tempting for the physician to assume the role of deity. This is a false assumption. Sadly, the doctor can easily be blamed if the patient does not get well.

Scripture provides clear answers to these presumptions.

Our bodies are dying as a result of original sin. The inspired Paul correctly wrote, "Though outwardly we are wasting away, yet inwardly we are being renewed day by day." (II Cor. 4:16) Interestingly, this was written by one whom God had used as an instrument to heal others. Today we have faith-healers who claim the sick are not healed due to a lack of faith. How unbiblical!

Our bodies will one day return to dust. No amount of oil of olay, hair dye, vitamins or exercise equipment will prevent this. Only the Lord's return will cause anyone to miss a physical death.

Sickness reminds us that we are sinners. Our sinful state results in a weak body and an imperfect immune system. Sin affected man's entire being - even his physical constitution.

In its failure to preach and teach on man's sinfulness the modern church has encouraged man in his natural thinking that sickness has no place in the Christian life. Sadly faith healers have led many Scripturally ungrounded people in the church to believe that sickness is foreign to one who is spiritual.

Illness reminds us that not we but God is sovereign. We must realize that some sickness is a direct result of sinful action. This can happen on a personal basis as a result of an intemperate use of food or alcohol. It can happen on a national basis as a result of national sin. (Deut. 28:21,22)

Illness is allowed by a sovereign God to test God's people. (Job, 1,2) Is their faith true? Do they serve God just because of blessings they receive? The world asks these questions. Watching a faithful Christian endure affliction the world sees enduring well-grounded faith.

Through illness God is glorified. Nowhere is this more clearly seen than in John 9:3. The blind man was healed not just for the purpose of giving him sight. More importantly the miracle taught an important lesson to a blind society. The Great Physician alone can make the spiritually blind to see. In fact, that is His chief work. The ill Christian is to be reminded that restored to health or not, "All things work together for good to them that love the Lord and are called according to His purpose." (Rom. 8:28) God sovereignly deals through sickness to build us up inwardly.

Finally, we must admit that all things are held together by Christ. (Col. 1:17) Without His sustaining hand our bodily structure would come loose.

God may well allow healing to come through the work of doctors and their use of medicine. Doctors remain instruments in God's hands. God must receive all the glory.

Man is not god. Modern man must face the fact that death is a part of life. This does not mean that we should not take care of our bodies or be proud of bodies built on junk food. It does mean that our ultimate trust must not be in our own physical fitness nor the knowledge of our doctor. Our ultimate trust must be in Jesus Christ who has defeated death on behalf of all who trust in Him. Only on death's other side will the Christian leave behind all suffering, pain and affliction and physical death.

Editor's Note

A couple of invitations arrived on my desk earlier this year, each offering a steak dinner at one of the better local restaurants along with a $100 "honorarium." Of course, the sponsors were pharmaceutical companies and attendees would be treated to speakers whose topics were drugs produced by the firms. Perhaps the "honorarium" could be explained away by having the attendees complete a questionnaire or some other simple task, lest the affair lack some pretense at propriety. Yet, no one is under any illusions about the real purpose of such enticements. They are bald attempts at bribery.

The reaction of physicians to such approaches is interesting. Reports of the attendance at the two I was invited to indicated most local physicians had better things to do. Those who attend, however, indicate that they aren't swayed at all by the blandishments of some drug companies. Just who is the fool here? Are the drug companies wasting their money? Or, perhaps, the physicians are naive as to our own reaction to the psychology of the sale.

If physicians were being induced to buy products for ourselves, there would seem to be no ethical issue. There might be a bargaining point, in that the physician-buyer could ask that the seller forego the steak dinner and reduce the product's price accordingly. But, physicians are not generally being induced to buy products for ourselves. Our relationship to patients is similar to that of a purchasing agent to his employer. The purchasing agent may be given the power of deciding which purveyor gets the business, but the money is not from his pocket. We decide what drug our patient will receive, but we don't ordinarily pay the price of the drug.

Is our relationship to drug companies one of the many ethical issues now troubling the house of medicine? Proverbs 15:27 says, "He who is greedy for gain troubles his own house, but he who hates bribes will live."

****

Dr. Richard Watson of Newington, Virginia, sent us excerpts from a recent issue of the *Linacre Quarterly,* the official journal of the National Federation of Catholic Physicians' Guilds (850 Elm Grove Road, Elm Grove, WI, 53122). Among the numerous interesting items scanned is one regarding a Dr. Richard Wetzel, from the Olive Crest Treatment Center for Abused Children in California. Dr. Wetzel "makes a strong and optimistic case for promoting chastity as the definitive answer to teenager promiscuity. "I am amazed that I can discuss chastity for seven hours with the high risk teens in my classes and have them ask me to come back to tell them more."'

****

Drs. John Custis and Darrell Lockwood of Cresham, Oregon (adjacent to Portland), are looking for a third Board-certified internist to join their practice. In practice there for 14 years, the practice is largely general internal medicine, though one of the partners has a subspecialty in endocrinology. Am important feature of the practice is the application of Biblical principles by which the doctors seek to distinguish between spiritual and physical problems in their patients. Influenced by the teaching of Dr. Jay Adams, they minister to patients with spiritual problems in a biblical manner. Internists interested in joining such a practice may write to them at College Square, 3030-F N.E. Hogan Dr., Gresham, OR, 97030-3134.

What a Secularist is Saying About Medical Limits

What Kind of Life: The Limits of Medical Progress by Daniel Callahan (Simon and Schuster, 1990), 318 pp. $19.95.

Reviewed by Rev. David W. Hall

This new book, following its earlier sibling, *Setting Limits*, by the Founder and Co-Director of the Hastings Institute is at long last a sane voice amidst the cacophony of medical flirtations with aspirations for infinity. Callahan persistently argues for limits to our faith and hope for the efficacy of medical science. He is one to know, and in this book he contends for the priority of "care" over "cure" in medical economics. Hand in hand with this, Callahan is consistent in rebutting the "*right* to cure" mentality, often parroted today.

Callahan pleads for us to accept "a more modest standard - sufficiency not perfection" (p. 120) and asserts that the best success for medical enhancement have come when groups, rather than individuals have been targeted. He calls for the use of principles of technological assessment, and research prioritization (Chapter 6). His thesis is that medical ethics (as well as medical economics) will be on better footing if we reverse the nascent priority by restoring the preference for communal medical needs over an individual and rights-oriented approach. Callahan's most direct statement of purpose deserves to be heard in his own words:

"*My goal in this book is to show that we have a more difficult problem on our hands, that the*

standard nostrums of neither right nor left will any longer suffice to cope with the problem before us. That problem can be directly stated: The very nature of medical progress is to pull to itself many more resources than should rationally be spent on it, often more than can be of genuine benefit to many individuals, and much, much more than can be socially justifiable for the common good. The power of medical progress feeds off of a potent dynamic. There is the force of technological advancement, ever ingenious in finding new ways to improve and extend life, many of them as attractive as they are expensive. The combined force of that dynamic has resulted in an explosion of health care costs." (p. 21).

The Christian will welcome this, although Callahan's entire book includes little reference to biblical, or even religious (only one reference to God, on p. 228) considerations. Yet, he reaches many of the same conclusions being discovered by biblical medical ethicists. It is nice to have such a clarion call by a noted and secular author. He does evidence that lack of biblical mooring in a few instances. For example, he does believe that the government should provide base-line care for all citizens, but restrict its tentacles so as to be

under no mandate to provide all procedures, even the top of the pyramid procedures for each individual. Still, we might be more comfortable with an even further diminished role of government than he advocates. Further, he does recommend a universal health insurance plan (p. 219) as well. He also has a good discussion on euthanasia, but at a few points, left the reader wondering. Notwithstanding these lapses, one feels quite at home with Callahan in terms of medical ethics.

A few quotes will reveal how close he comes to affirming some of the conclusions of this journal. At one point he says, "We might wonder whether our ultimate problems with healthcare are not moral rather than practical, more about our chosen ends than our managerial means" (p. 261). Also, (on p. 34) Callahan says, "We have lost our way because we have defined our unlimited hopes to transcend our mortality as our needs, and we have created a medical enterprise that engineers the transformation." Earlier he'd articulated, "The deepest thrust of this approach, however, is to pursue the idea that we cannot solve the allocation problem without doing that which is most resisted — deciding what is good for us as a society, not just as individuals" (p. 28).

Callahan states his contention as

follows:

"I argue that the ideal of meeting the individual need for cure and the faith in efficiency as a way of making that possible are mistaken. It is not simply that they are impractical as goals, which is one way they are wrong. More fundamentally, they are goals that fail to take account of inherent human limitations. They thereby run the risk of deluding us as individuals about the posibilities of our lives, and of severely distorting a balanced pursuit of societal well-being. Our present system of healthcare is faulty, but not just because it is chaotic and poorly designed. It is faulty because it seeks the wrong ends" (pp. 29-30).

Moreover, the reader must hear Callahan as he critiques medical salvationism.

"Let me try to articulate that reigning vision. It consists of three major ingredients: a broad, limitless definition of health; a highly subjective notion of individual need, one captivated by the diversity of personal goals and desires; and a strong view of human rights, in particular the right of individuals to have access to adequate healthcare. It is a vision that sees health as an unbounded good, that allows the one to make in principle as much demand on the help of fellow citizens — in the name of his or her rights and their obligations — as is required to meet those needs. It is a wonderful vision, but it is seriously flawed. It is collapsing under its own weight, and it will not longer suffice to provide the foundations for a healthcare system" (pp. 33-34).

The criticisms of this book which I'd offer are few. One of the slight irritations is the too-frequent repetition of major themes. Yet I would rather have the author err in this direction than in being too short. Also, the weak point of the book seems to arrive in Chapter 7 as the author seeks to "Devise a Political Strategy" to implement his recommendations. Not that his was entirely wrong, but I was unconvinced as to the likelihood of any possible implementation. Again, it is disconcerting to see so little divinity or theological reference in a matter so close to theology. Hopefully many will profit from this, especially medical and political leaders. One more fine feature of this book is the set of appendixes which would aid anyone making a public presentation on these topics.

Teaching Teenagers on Fornication

Tom Farmer, M.D.

Dr. Farmer practices emergency medicine in Brevard, N.C.

Many teenagers are suffering physically, emotionally, and spiritually because of the lack of proper teaching by their parents, teachers, doctors, counselors, and pastors concerning sexual intercourse. Teenagers are often improperly taught that fornication (premarital sexual intercourse) is an individual freedom to be exercised if they are "responsible." The word "responsible" is then defined as "using contraception." By this our children are taught that fornication is not wrong, only fornication without contraception is wrong. This ungodly teaching has led to an increase in fornication, an increase in pregnancies, an increase in sexually transmitted diseases, and increase in abortions, and an increase in spiritual poverty. When we abandon God's truths, we welcome misery.

Teenagers must be taught the Biblical truth that fornication is a sin with a great price. God tells us, "Know ye not that the unrighteous shall not inherit the kingdom of God? Be not deceived: neither fornicators, nor idolators, nor adulterers, nor effeminate, nor abusers of themselves with mankind, nor thieves, nor covetous, nor drunkards, nor revilers, nor extortioners, shall inherit the kingdom of God." (I Cor., 6:9-10)

However, God does not just pro-hibit, but mercifully provides a pathway to righteousness: "...to avoid fornication, let every man have his own wife, and let every woman have her own husband." (I Cor. 7:2) But what of the teen that does fall to the sin of fornication? God in His mercy allows for repentance: "...if a man entice a maid that is not betrothed and lie with her, he shall surely endow her to be his wife." (Ex. 22:16) Therefore, fornication should be contemplated with all the seriousness of marriage. Teens must realize that if they are not ready for marriage, they are not ready for sex. God's word confines sex to marriage. This is the truth our children should be taught, to train their minds so as to restrain their bodies.

Let me illustrate with a true story. A fellow Christian doctor told me about a teenage boy and girl at a Christian school in his town who fornicated. The girl became pregnant. He told me their parents arranged for the teens to marry. After they were married, the girl had a miscarriage and the child died. The doctor told me he thought it was unfortunate that they had not waited a little longer to marry, that is, until after she miscarried, because then the marriage would not have been necessary. I believe, however, that my friend is missing the point of God's teaching that fornication is a sin that requires repentance, whether or not a pregnancy or birth occurs. This teenage couple properly repented of their fornication by seeking God's forgiveness and by marriage (with their parents' consent, Ex. 22:16-17).

Biblical thinking and teaching has become foreign in today's world. Many teachers, parents, counselors, doctors, school board members, and pastors have abandoned God's word as authoritative. They have supplanted the Biblical truth that "fornication is sin" with the lie that "premarital sex without using contraception is irresponsible." Many teens have been taught this lie and have accepted its implication that fornication is wrong if you do not use contraception. So, many teens scurry off to "health" clinics or to doctors' offices for contraception. Sadly, many doctors will prescribe contraceptive medicines even without parental consent. Sadder still are the incidents in which parents bring their children in and demand contraception for them! How far we have wandered from God's truth: "Do no prostitute thy daughter, to cause her to be a whore; lest the land fall to whoredom, and the land become full of wickedness." (Lev. 19:29)

Another result of the lie that "premarital sex without using contraception is irresponsible" is that many conclude that fornication is premissible but pregnancy is not. Thus, society focuses on the problem of teenage pregnancy rather than teenage fornication. To my knowledge, nowhere in the Bible is pregnancy called sin, although certainly the way some in the Scripture became pregnant was sin. Still, in these materialistic times we narrowly focus on pregnancy as the problem. We worry about the girl finishing her education so she can materially support herself. We worry about how the welfare system can materially support the baby. We worry about the physical health consequences of the pregnancy on the mother. Now, certainly, there are some legitimate physical and monetary concerns to address, but not to the exclusion of the spiritual consequences of fornication. We cannot correct the problem of teenage pregnancy without addressing the problem of teenage fornication. Further, we cannot correct either problem by divorcing their physical dimensions from their spiritual dimensions.

God is grieved by sin, including fornication. Fornication is destroying our youth and destroying the sanctity of marriage. The Bible's teaching is clear; do not fornicate. If you do not abstain, seek the Lord's forgiveness and repent by marriage. If we love our children we will teach them the truth. Our children are bombarded with worldly teaching about sex through movies, music and television, as well as by many teachers, parents, doctors, and pastors. Instead, pastors must preach against fornication. Churches must discipline fornicators and lead them to proper repentence. Schools must teach the propriety of chastity. Doctors must counsel about chastity rather than prescribe contraceptives. Consumers must refuse to support movies, television programs, and magazines which glamorize fornication or pander to lust.

All Christians must pray to God to forgive our failure to teach our children His truths, and we must pray that He will henceforth strengthen our resolve to love and teach His ways. Our children desperately need proper teaching. They have suffered too long from the silence of Christians and the boisterousness of those who have abandoned God's truths and adopted lies.

"The wrath of God is being revealed from heaven against all godlessness and wickedness of men who suppress the truth by their wickedness. ... They exchanged the truth of God for a lie, and worshipped and served created things rather than the Creator — who is forever praised. Amen." (Rom. 1:18, 25)

What Is Truth?
A Biblical Perspective

William L. Isley, M.D.

Dr. Isley is associate professor of medicine and chief of the division of endocrinology and metabolism at the University of Missouri-Kansas City. He has served as elder and teacher in his church. A husband and father of three, he enjoys reading, running and gardening.

Unfortunately modern evangelicalism, like theologic liberalism, has all too often redefined terms (frequently with slogans), so that many a professing Christian's theology is no deeper than the latest evangelical cliche. Truth is one term that has suffered sorely. We are told that "All truth is God's truth" and that we must "integrate faith with learning." The notion that God has two bodies of "truth" (special revalation in His Son and His Word) and "natural revelation" that are equally authoritative and necessary for godly living is especially pernicious. I think few people have actually considered the biblical notion of truth.

The biblical concept of truth is far different than that conveyed by the popular "All truth is God's truth" mentality. The idea of truth is conveyed primarily in the Old Testament by two words. Scott in *Theological Wordbook of the Old Testament* says of *emet* (truth, faithfulness, verity).

This word carries underlying sense of certainty, dependability. We find it used in several categories of contexts, all of which relate to God directly or indirectly.

First, it is frequently applied to God as a characteristic of his nature. In Gen. 24:27, for example, it describes God who leads Abraham's servant to the right wife for Isaac. In Ex 34:6,

it is given as one of the verbal descriptions of God which constitute God's goodness...

It is a term fittingly applied to God's words (Ps 119:142, 151, 160; Dan. 10:21).

As a characteristic of God revealed to men, it therefore becomes the means by which men know and serve God as their savior (Josh 24:14; I Kgs 2:4; Ps 86:11; Ps 91:4; Isa 38:3), and then, as a characteristic to be found in those who have indeed come to God (Ex 18:21; Neh 7:2; Ps 15:2; Zech 8:16).

As we study its various contexts, it becomes manifestly clear that there is no truth in the biblical sense, i.e., valid truth, outside God. All truth comes from God and is truth because it is related to God.[1]

The other major Hebrew word for truth is *emuna*, translated as "firmness, faithfulness, fidelity." Scott says that this word expresses God's total dependability (Deut 32:4), or the faithfulness of believers (Prov 12:22).[2]

While truth as "conformity to fact" is sometimes considered (for example, Deut 13:14), it is usually in a moral sense and not in a sense of empiricism (the best hypothesis for the data). Therefore the Old Testament concept of truth is tied closely to the unchanging character of God, and no truth in the biblical sense can at all

be inconsistent with His Person (sovereignty, holiness, omniscience, etc.).

Truth in the New Testament is characterized by the Person of Christ (John1:14,17: John 14:6), the Holy Spirit (I John 5:7), and the Word of God (John 17:17, James 1:8). Since God and His Word last forever, but the creation is transient (I Peter 1:24, 25), the derivation of any empirically derived "truth" must also be of a transient nature.

Since man rejects "general revelation" of God (Rom 1) and may only know God by special revelation, it would seem likely that truth is similarly dispensed, by revelation, not empiricism. The advocate of empiricism must grapple with the problem that his body of "truth" is ever changing and contradictory (we in medicine see this almost daily), while truth in the biblical sense is settled forever. Even when man studies creation, he cannot learn truth (Rom 1), but suppresses it.

The empirical notion of "truth" as commonly applied to medicine is one based on statistical probabilities. How foolish it must seem to God that we revel in a "statistically significant p value" and think that we have arrived at truth. The medical literature contains thousands of articles which have now been corrected, disregarded, or even been shown to be flagrantly wrong despite the presence of a "statistically significant *p* value" for the results. Our practice of medicine is really one of "functional hypothesis" based on statistical probabilities, not a static, once-for-all empirically derived "truth."

Men are commanded to serve the Lord "in truth" (I Sam 12:24) and to "obtain truth (Prov 23:23). If this process is to include empiricism, then God obliges Himself to teach men an empirical approach to find truth. Obviously, the scientific method is not to be found in the pages of Scripture.

Truth is inseparably related to righteousness in the 15th and 26th Psalms. Truth is related to godliness (Titus 1:1). It is contrasted with wickedness in Prov 8:7, Jer 7:28, and Rom 2:8. The biblical concept of truth does not view truth as amoral "facts of nature."

The saint is preserved by God's truth (Psa 40:11). To equate contemporary science with this kind of truth would be to impugn God for not having earlier allowed men to discover cures of diseases, the neurochemical processes involved in cognition, etc. The saint can be steadfast without the help or explanations of modern science. The notion of God's gift to the believer of "everything pertaining to life and godliness" (II Peter 1:3,4) is undermined if we hold out for contemporary and yet to be discovered "truth" that will enable the Christian to live in a manner pleasing to God.

God's truth is to bring men to Him so they can worship Him (Psa 43:3,4). While some pre-Darwinian scientists studied creation and perceived God's glory in that study, more often than not in the modern context scientific exploration concludes in a doxology for man and not for God.

Truth is involved in atonement for sin (Prov 16:6) and must be believed for salvation (II Thess 2:12,13). The concepts of "truth" as generally conceived by science are incompatible with such concepts as sin and atonement. A purpose of truth is to make men free (John 8:32). Empirically derived "facts of nature" do not serve this function.

God desires all men to come to know the truth (I Tim 2:4). The worshipper at the altar of empiricism must answer how this can be God's will, and yet He left no instructions for a method to obtain this sort of "truth."

God's truth is absolutely reliable (I John 2:21). Man's best hypothesis to explain natural phenomena are changing and often unreliable. Walking in the truth (II John 4, III John 3,4) has to do with a way of life related to God, not science. The way to know the truth is to abide in God's Word (John 8:31,32), not by scientific investigation. Jesus promised that the Spirit of truth (the Holy Spirit) would guide His disciples into all the truth (John 16:13). To the best of my knowledge, no scientific explorations were carried out (or deemed necessary) by the post-Pentecost disciples.

Those who delight in the Lord study His works (Psa 111), but they are the ones related to His character and sovereign working in history. Truth only belongs to God's children (John 18:37). Unbelievers are deprived of truth (I Tim 6:5). Knowledge of the truth comes not by scientific exploration, but by God granting repentance (II Tim 2:25). The truth includes a corpus of doctrine (II Tim 2:18, 4:4; Hebrews 10:26). The church, not scientists, is the pillar and support of the truth (I Tim 3:15). Men's wisdom is foolishness by God's standard (I cor 1:18-25). Learning does not equal learning the truth (II Tim 3:7).

"Truth" ascertainable by physical evidence failed to transform lives in countless examples in Scripture (the miracles of Moses and the prophets and the miracles of Jesus). Supernatural revelation, not natural understanding, brings man into relationship with the Lord Jesus Christ (Matt 16:17; John 1:12,13).

In summary, truth relates to god Himself and is eternal. It is only perceived by man by special revelation. To view the study of nature (including man) as providing supplementary truth to that revealed in Scripture is contrary to God's revelation of Himself and His working in history. We are called, not to *integrate* two bodies of "truth," but to know **the truth**, love **the truth**, live **the truth**, and teach **the truth**.

Evangelicalism is in epistemologic crisis. "Natural revelation" has not supplemented the Bible, but supplanted it in many areas. As a whole, we seem destined to repeat the errors of those in the past who have compromised the faith on the altars of added "truth," be they higher criticism, Darwinian biology, or "new revelations." Christian physicians should readily admit that our functional hypotheses ("truths") are changing daily. While we should not discard empiricism in dealing with the temporary problems of physical health and disease (we only have temporary solutions), where the Bible has clearly spoken we should not try to "supplement" truth with changing transient functional hypotheses.

O Timothy, guard what has been entrusted to you, avoiding worldly and empty chatter and the opposing arguments of what is falsely called "knowledge" — which some have professed and thus gone astray fromthe faith. Grace be with you. I Timothy 6:20,21, New American Standard Bible.

ENDNOTES

1. Scott, J.B., in **Theological Wordbook of the Old Testament**. Harris, R.L., Archer, G.L., Jr., & Waltke, B.K., (ed). Chicago: Moody, 1980, pp. 52-53.

2. *Ibid*, p. 52.

The Medicalization of America

Franklin E. Payne, Jr., M.D.

*Dr. Payne is Associate Professor at the Medical College of Georgia. He is author of **Biblical/Medical Ethics, Making Biblical Decisions,** and **What Every Christian Should Know about the AIDS Epidemic.***

Everyone today seems to want maximal health care. Christians, humanists, conservatives, and liberals argue that every American should not only have access to health care, but *the best medical care.* Because of this sentiment, national health insurance would already exist if politicians could only figure out how to pay for it.

However, *medical care is one of the major means whereby Americans are being further enslaved to the state.* Further, *no matter what method or how much money the state spends, health care will not be achieved.*

A Brief Digression in Philosophy, Ethics and Law

Too many Christians in the United States believe that politics is an a-moral endeavor; that it is wrong to try to apply Biblical principles as laws for society. But, to maintain this position they must contend against this simple argument. Politics and legislation are inevitably based upon some principle of right and wrong, i.e., ethics. Is it right to limit highway speeds to 65 miles per hour or not? Is it right to allow physicians to abort unborn babies or not?

Having said that, whose ethics will be enacted into law? The Supreme Court has said that the Ten Commandments will not be taught in public schools, and by implication

and application, will not become law. So, what ethics are left — only some godless humanism that is applied at the whim of voters, politicians, and judges. *And Christians accept this situation!*

My question to them is, "How can right and wrong be determined apart from God's ways?" The answer is, "It can't." Until Christians *en masse* come to understand this simple relationship of societal law and religion (humanism is a religion), there will be no improvement in either the quality of life or the morality of the American people.

American Medicine: Solutions of Disease and Death

"The wages of sin is death."

"All them who hate me love death."

In light of these verses and other teachings of Scripture, what is the humanist solution for unwanted pregnancy? The *death* of the unborn baby. What is the solution for those with chronic and incurable illnesses? Lethal injection. What is the solution to the AIDS epidemic? "Safe sex." (That is, risky sex that leads to *more* infections of all sexually transmitted diseases.)

Beyond these "death solutions," why do people smoke cigarettes? Drink alcohol to excess? Engage in risky sexual behavior? Eat too much?

Use IV drugs? Medical experts and psychologists say that addictions cause people to behave in these ways.

America is being medicalized. More and more problems facing both individuals and society are being "medicalized." That is, they are being given either a medical or psychological "diagnosis." And — *far too many Christians are following this pattern.* "So what?" you ask. Just this.

First, the question must be asked, "Does God know more about behavior than man?" God says that drunkenness is a sin (I Corinthians 6:10; Ephesians 5:18), that sexual intimacy outside of marriage is sin (Exodus 20:14), that homosexuality is sin (I Corinthians 6:9), and many other behaviors are sins (I Corinthians 6:9-10; Galatians 5:19-21).

You see, if these problems are medical or "psychological," then the afflicted person needs a physician or psychologist, not the Great Physician. One of the great doctrines of orthodox theology is that the body (as physical matter and as God's creation) is "very good" (Genesis 1:31). To place these immoral (sinful) behaviors in the category of physical causation contradicts that teaching.

The worse effect is that the afflicted person will be deluded as to what his real need is: Jesus Christ and obedience to Him, not the escape of his or her conscience into physical causation with the remedy in humanistic counsel and/or in a pill.

The second major effect of the re-classification of sins into medical/psychological problems is the economic cost. Insurance is based upon pooled risk. For insurance programs to work, they must be actuarially sound. That is, the risk that is being insured against must be rare enough that a sufficient equity can be built into a fund to pay for a calamity when it comes *and* pay the administrative costs to run the program.

With behavioral problems being increasingly diagnosed as medical problems and states mandating that virtually any self-destructive behavior be insured by private agencies, then the risk being insured approaches 100 percent in any individual.

No wonder the cost of medical insurance is so high! Collection on a medical insurance policy is no longer a chance possibility, but a virtual certainty. It has become a return-on-investment program that carries the higher administrative costs of a greater number of claims on top of the claims themselves — a very expensive endeavor. And - everyone wants to be sure that they collect their "fair share."

In addition to this huge private cost is that of government programs, primarily Medicare and Medicaid. Soon, if it has not occurred already, more will be spent by the federal government on medical care than on national defense! In addition, *the largest taxation on the American people is now Social Security*, a very large share of which goes to pay for Medicare.

Thus, all medical care in the United States now consumes almost 13 percent of the Gross National Product — far more than a tithe towards the care of a dying entity, the human body.

The third major effect of medicalization is that every government program and legislation is backed by the full power and enforcement of the state and federal governments. After about 10 years of Medicare, the federal government saw that they could not afford to pay for the services being provided for the program's recipients. So, they have increasingly regulated what physicians can and cannot do.

When their laws are not followed, physicians can be fined and even imprisoned, often without a jury trial. That is, *physicians are presumed guilty and must prove their innocence.*

From the patient's side, physicians can "report" under child and spouse statutes *the possibility of such abuse and be free of any civil or criminal liability.* In this case, the patient and his family are guilty until proven innocent.

And — so it goes. Medicine is a primary means whereby spiritual problems (sins) need medicine as their savior. Since these problems originate in the depths of man's depravity, their cost exceeds all available resources. As the state increases the care of its citizens from cradle to grave (not womb to tomb, as the state does not protect the child in the womb), it increases its police state surveillance and enforcement.

The irony of modern medicine gone awry is that *it promises what it cannot deliver, i.e., health.* All in all, American medicine does more harm than good. While I cannot digress to prove that point here, one only needs to look at abortion, the management

of the AIDS epidemic, the specter of euthanasia to understand that American medicine is anything but "health-promoting."

From a Romans 1 perspective, this bad situation is understandable. What boggles my mind is the number of Christians who accept most, if not all, of this situation as what ought to be. Some even call the government's stranglehold on medicine "charity."

The realities are these. Sins can never be healed on a physical basis. Greater disease, disability, and death is all that humanism has to offer. There is not enough money in existence to pay for all the effects of self-abuse that are possible. Medicine is already socialized and a means by which the government is decreasing the freedom of individuals and families, as it increases its own police state.

Those Christians that think I exaggerate are blind to any Biblical understanding of the medical situation in the United States. Until some significant numbers of Christians and their leaders understand the above and the Biblical solutions that apply, American medicine will continue to be the agent whereby it accomplishes the very opposite of what it intends. The cost in souls, money, and freedom will be exceedingly great!

> *The worse effect of medicalization is that the afflected person will be deluded as to what his real need is: Jesus Christ and obedience to Him.*

Pastor's Column

The Reverend Byron Snapp

Rev. Snapp holds a B.A. from King College and an M.Div. from Reformed Theological Seminary. He is assistant pastor of Covenant Presbyterian Church and prinicipal of Covenant Christian School in Cedar Bluff, Virginia.

The information surfaced only briefly in the sea of media attention before it sank out of sight and out of thought. You may remember the reported research on the brain cells of heterosexual males and those of homosexual males. A California scientist claimed "the cluster of brain cells that may guide the sex drive of men is twice as large in heterosexual males as it is in homosexual males, suggesting to him that homosexuality could be a matter of biological destiny.

In microscopic examinations of the brains of 41 men and women, including 19 homosexual men, Simon LeVay of the Salk Institute for Biological studies, San Diego, California, said he found that a specific cluster of cells was always larger for heterosexual males than the other specimens." (Homosexuals Weigh Research News; Could Be Good, Bad", *World*, Sept. 7, 1991, p. 12)

No matter the results, the scientist used a very small test base of 41 people. However, let us suppose for a moment that his results are right. What is the response of the church to be?

First, the church must continue to set forth in its ministry the clear teaching of Scripture. The Bible repeatedly states that homosexuality is a sin. In Leviticus 22:18 we read, "Thou shalt not lie with mankind as with womankind: it is an abomination." Here God explains that homosexuality is one way the seventh commandment is broken. In Romans 1:26, 27, Paul points out that homosexuality is a result in a society that has "changed the truth of God into a lie." As we think of Sodom's destruction we know that God will not put up with such activity. In our day particularly the church must stand against societal trends towards downplaying the awfulness of sin. In so doing, we are testifying to the validity of Scripture and its relevance to every issue.

Secondly, we must remember that we do not all have the same weakness to the same sin. Peter is a good example. We never read that he got drunk or that he was a homosexual. Peter's problem was his tongue. He was impulsive in its use at times. He did not always think before he spoke. He who said he would die rather than deny Christ also told Christ "Thou shalt never wash my feet." (John 13:8a) Neither Paul nor Barnabas would give an inch in their controversy over whether or not John Mark ought to accompany them. The two leaders parted their ways, one taking Silas, the other taking John Mark. Thankfully, later Paul writes favorably of John Mark. Thus through God's grace the rift was apparently healed.

In the Old Testament we remember Jacob's proneness to deception. Samson loved the ladies, especially those from foreign countries.

Is a minute part of the brain shaped differently if one easily becomes uncontrollably angry? Within one's brain is there a difference between one who gets drunk and one who does not? I cannot say. Yet, one thing is true. Deception, unfaithfulness, unrighteous anger, drunkenness, etc., are sins. They are sins because God says so. The Bible nowhere treats them as illnesses although the practice of these and other sins can result in physical effects on the body.

Society's desire to deny God leads to a denial of sin. After all, if God does not exist He has no law that can be broken. Man then redefines these Biblical sins as illnesses. They have no other suitable term.

The Church must faithfully proclaim the truth of God's Word. We must not accept society's attempts to redefine that which God has clearly defined in His Word.

The Determination of Disability:
A Case Study with Brief Scriptural Commentary

Hilton P. Terrell, M.D., Ph.D.

Dr. Terrell is Assistant Professor of Family Medicine at McLeod Regional Medical Center in Florence, S.C.

Robert Galloway can remember something commonplace to childhood, but which only a very few people can remember. He remembers when he first walked. He was five years old when he took his first steps to his grandmother.

Now in his sixth decade, his posture and facial features continue to reveal moderately severe cerebral palsy, but one or both of us has improved over the decades, for I can now understand his speech with little difficulty. As a small child, answering the door to find him there selling Christmas cards, he was pleasant but incomprehensible to my ears. As his limbs tried to disobey his mind's intentions, he required concentration for movements that were effortless for me. In spite of the balky muscles, that fear of the unusual which often attaches itself to a disabled person was absent from my child's mind in regard to Mr. Galloway. I won't say that fascination was absent. It continues over thirty-five years later, though for different reasons.

Over the years since, as a family practitioner, I've had many opportunities to wonder what makes Mr. Galloway different from some other disabled people I've met. Medical school and residency taught me to approach physical disability as an issue of measuring and "documenting" deviations from "normal." I was wrong-

ly taught. Implicit in the teaching was the idea that the reduction of observations to writing makes what is written not only a fact, but a controlling fact.

"Documentation" has insinuated itself into our medical parlance as a substitute for "prove." I observe, measure, consult a book, and write down my findings on a piece of paper. It is a straightforward proceeding which places on a document that the patient before me appears disabled, how the disability occurred, for what duration it may persist, and in what degree it exists. So it is written. It is not *proven*. The forms that are provided to guide our writing frequently fail to ask the more pertinent questions.

Nevertheless, for some, the document is the climax of a troubled trail. A piece of paper is the proof they have been looking for. Agencies will accept the document, and money or other benefits will follow — relief from many responsibilities and a regular check in the mailbox are two of the common benefits.

Early in my medical career it began to occur to me that relief from responsibility and undeserved income are not always beneficial. Some of those checks must be made of powerful acid, for they can corrode character in recipient households. Perhaps they act more to expose a pre-existing

corrosion than to cause it. Embarrassingly late in my career has it dawned on me that disability is often as much a state of the spirit as it is a state of body.

The state of Mr. Galloway's spirit was to look for work — not that disability documentation would have been very lucrative in the 1950's, before government programs and widespread disability insurance. People were more often dependant upon their own devices and associations then. While in high school he had a weekend job in a neighborhood grocery store. Ownership of the store changed during his senior year and he lost his job. That same year his mother, Nellie C., died. He tried to find work in chain grocery stores, but his obvious disability froze him out of the work without even a trial on the job.

Several members of a fraternal organization, the Benevolent Protective Order of Elks, renovated a building on the grounds of the organization. Some wholesalers donated initial grocery stock, and he opened his own neighborhood grocery store. He found that he couldn't make a living there and went into the advertising specialty business, selling personalized pens, pencils, lawn signs for politicians and the like, working on commission. Later, he worked for a six month interval as an outside salesman for a local printing company, selling office supplies and printing. The company compared his sales to those of his predecessor, who had worked the territory for twenty years. Mr. Galloway's sales didn't measure up to that standard, and they let him go.

He then put up a building in his own backyard and stocked it with office supplies, paying another printing company, Sumter Printing Company, to do his printing for him. In 1963, Sumter Printing Company came up for sale. An uncle put up the money to buy the company. The two were in partnership for three years, then Mr. Galloway bought out his uncle, retaining the company's name.

The company has grown over the years and now employs ten people. Employees describe Mr. Galloway as a marvelous person to work for, and some have done so for a very long time. They are proud of the fifty-six hundred square foot facility they moved to a few years ago. They point out a new printing machine which only the day before printed a million labels. Sumter Printing is competitive.

Through mutual friends in the South Carolina Cerebral Palsy Association, Mr. Galloway met the lady who is now his wife and the mother of their 18 year old, college-bound son. She, too, has cerebral palsy. The son, of course, does not have this acquired disorder, perhaps to the surprise of a few town doomsayers.

By many measures of the success of a man — marriage, fatherhood, financial security, community respect — Mr. Galloway is a success despite his disability.

How may a physician discern disability? Could such success as Mr. Galloway's have been predicted? If he had been examined in 1950 at the time of high school graduation, would he have been "documented" as dis-

abled? If he had been, would the determination have been a boon or a bane?

A clue is affixed to the wall of Sumter Printing Company's customer consultation area. A bronze plaque there declares: "This business is dedicated to the glory of God and in loving memory of Nellie C. Galloway. 1967." Mr. Galloway is a Christian, and firmly convinced that God's hand of blessing has been on him all his life, despite some external appearances. He believes that he is not handicapped. To him, a handicapped person is one with a physical disability who has never accepted it. Since he was born with his, he has never known it any other way. You don't miss as much what you never had. Those who acquire their disability later in life have a tougher time with the acceptance, he believes.

Should a physician, or whomever is charged with "documenting" disability, concern himself with such intangible character features as faith, determination, and endurance? With Mr. Galloway, the words "disability determination" could more easily be construed as the determination *of* disability. Modern science teaches us that if we cannot objectively measure something, we cannot deal with it objectively. What is the scale for endurance under adversity? Modern medicine under bureaucratic fire is pressed to "document" everything. "If it isn't documented, it didn't happen."

How absurd! Why must the measurable *physical* reality of Mr. Galloway's muscle tone, range of motion, or the like be the only determinants of his disability? Why may not the *spiritual* reality of a life lived in practical faith and devotion to God be a large term in the equation of success?

> *Disability is often as much a state of the spirit as it is a state of the body.*

The spiritual realm is not less real than the physical. It is granted that, barring a miracle, the spirit works within the limits of the physical body. However, if we take into account only those physical limits we omit consideration of all the spiritual assets and liabilities. Is our obstinate "objectivity" a form of deliberate stupidity? Who is it in medicine that dictates we discard of due consideration of the spirit of a man?

We are, rather, sometimes *required* to make inferences about the spirit of another person, based upon outward evidences. II Thessalonians 3:7-12 says, "For you yourselves know how you ought to follow us, for we were not disorderly among you; nor did we eat anyone's bread free of charge, but worked with labor and toil night and day, that we might not be a burden to any of you, not because we do not have authority, but to make ourselves an example of how you should follow us. For even when we were here with you, we commanded you this: If anyone will not work, neither shall he eat. For we hear that there are some who walk among you in a disorderly manner, not working at all, but are busybodies. Now those who are such we command and exhort through our Lord Jesus Christ that they work in quietness and eat their own bread."

In this passage we see Paul commanding the Church to determine who *will* not work. Those who *cannot* work are to be distinguished from those who will not. The "will" here is an issue involving the spirit of a man. The will is manifested to us indirectly by means of the observable behavior of the person in question.

Physicians examining for disability are expected to offer testimony regarding the objective physical defects and the ordinary course of diseases affecting employment. During the encounter we may also get an impression of the "will" of the person. Is he exaggerating or holding back in efforts, or, is he extending himself to painful degrees as we examine range of motion, strength, and so forth? Are the findings consistent with known pathophysiological patterns? We may offer comment on these "subjective" impressions and we may refer selected patients for more sophisticated testing on machines which can uncover patterns of inconsistency. For some issues in disability, such as pain, the matter is more difficult.

Although in many cases the physician's testimony on disability determination may be key, the final determination should be in the control of the person(s) who are going to provide the assistance. Far more valuable than a physician's evaluation, even a very careful one, are the observations over time of those persons close to the one with the disability. Is he bedfast and delirious? Is he playing golf several times weekly? Is she driving long distances to visit relatives? The Thessalonican issue came up in the context of one of the results of wilfull unemployment — the disorderliness of idleness. Those being fed without working were becoming busybodies. To provide sustenance without oversight is poor stewardship. We need to know what is happening to the Lord's resources. It is not necessarily, or even usually, the case that a physician can provide that sort of information.

Practical assistance to the disabled runs into a number of barriers in the United States today, which are more formidable even than the architectural barriers recently addressed by federal law. Chief among them is the minimum wage. The federal legislature pretends to know the minimum

value of a person's labor. People who cannot produce $4.25 an hour, plus the costs of taxes on the employer, are worth nothing — except to politicians who recognize a personal interest in having the largest possible number of clients dependant upon a regular government check.

If federal proposals for employer-funded comprehensive medical "insurance"[1] come to fruition, yet another burden will fall on employers and further tend to make employees with disabilities less affordable.

So long as such barriers exist, creativity is needed in seeing to it that the disabled have an opportunity to "work in quietness and eat their own bread." Disabled persons whose families operate businesses may find suitable positions. Another disabled person may need to do volunteer work at no remuneration other than expenses, in order to "labor, working with his hands what is good, that he may have something to give him who has need" (Eph. 4:28b). By careful evaluation and training many disabled, the large majority if the definition is broad enough, can be worth more than the minimum wage plus expenses. Failing that, an employer may choose to take a loss on some employee(s). There is a "bottom line" below all financial bottom lines. I suspect that the members of the Benevolent Protective Order of Elks had God's bottom line more clearly in view in the 1950's. They saw value and capability in Mr. Galloway, and sought a way to encourage and develop it. Even though the grocery business didn't work out, they tried with him, and he kept trying.

Though none could have foreseen it in 1950, God has blessed Mr. Galloway in his determination *of* disability. The intangible spirit of determination, by the power of the indwelling Spirit of God, has produced the tangible fruit of Sumter Printing

Company. You hold a piece of the fruit in your hand just now. Since its inception five years ago, this journal has been printed by Sumter Printing Company.

ENDNOTES

1. Though the word "insurance" is being commonly used for plans to fund the medical demands of the public, it is actually a misnomer in the case of known, pre-existing conditions, where there is no risk. There is, rather, a known entity. By analogy, you may truly buy fire *insurance* for your house, until it actually catches fire. At that point, your pursuit of financial assistance for fire damage would properly come under another rubric, such as, perhaps, *charity*, or *welfare*.

A Time to Be Silent and a Time to Speak (Ec 3:7): The Dilemma of Confidentiality and the Christian Health Care Worker

Gregory W. Rutecki, M.D. and John D. Geib, M.A.

Dr. Rutecki is Clinical Associate Professor of Medicine at Noirtheastern Ohio University College of Medicine. Mr. Geib is Instructor of Religion in the Department of Theology at Malone College in Canton, Ohio.

A sweeping history of medical ethics has been preserved in the so-called "oaths" of medicine. These oaths embrace the dimensions of time (from circa 2000 B.C., Code of Hammurabi),[1] of race (Arabic, European,[2] and Chinese[3]), of world perspectives (Hindu, Jewish, Islamic)[4] and of Greek influences (Hippocrates). Consistently noted are seven principles:[5] 1) First of all, do no harm, 2) Respect for human life, 3) The alleviation of suffering, 4) The right to truth, 5) The right to informed consent, 6) The right to die with dignity and 7) Confidentiality of the physician-patient relationship. While the first six of these do not seem to conflict with Scripture, absolute confidentiality of the physician-patient relationship may present such a conflict. An analysis of this principle in light of Biblical revelation is the focus of this paper.

The principle of confidentiality is necessary to protect information essential for intimate relationships. However, carefully timed and chosen speech used to breach a confidence may protect a neighbor's life. Therefore the difficult choice of whether to remain "silent" in maintaining a confidence or to "speak" and in so doing justly decide the appropriate person, place and time of speech, demands the wisdom of Solomon. The inherent conflicts engendered by this si-

lence versus speech dilemma are particularly germane to modern medicine of which the following cases are exemplary. During the AIDS epidemic, who has a right to know positive HIV tests without patient consent?[6] Recently, a physician was sued for breaching his confidential relationship with a commercial airline pilot who admitted to cocaine abuse.[7] If a minor seeks a Christian health worker's advice concerning access to abortion, should her parents be notified without her consent? In an era of ubiquitous computerization of medical records, can a physician maintain the secrecy of these records during a time of increasing access (third party payers, quality assurance committees, utilization review, etc.) to sensitive medical information?

The prevalent secular humanist world view answers all these questions by making individual autonomy the primary concern. This practice has led to "right to privacy"[8] laws that demand absolute confidentiality from the professional. From a Biblical perspective, however, one can ask whether patients who reveal confidential matters to their physicians have a completely binding right to expect that such matters will not be revealed to "significant others"? Even the wording of the Hippocratic Oath[9] — "...if it be what should not be published abroad, I shall never divulge,

holding such things to be holy secrets..." — implies that there are some circumstances and events that of necessity should be "published abroad." Even though very few Christian health workers would challenge the general good of maintaining confidences, there do seem to be times when other responsibilities outweigh secrecy. This is the ethical dilemma of confidentiality: both the "silence" of confidentiality and the "speech" used to protect neighbors are goods to be desired at different times and in different situations.

It should become apparent that the "oaths" of medicine are inadequate for the Christian. Even though the wisdom of these codes is a reflection of God's natural revelation (Romans 2:1-16), they must be viewed as precursors to and supplemental of God's ultimately authoritative revelation, the Bible.

Therefore, this paper will review Biblical support for both the practice of and limitations on confidentiality. Then, we will present an approach to the Biblical limits on confidentiality when applied to the practice of medicine.

METHODS:

The authors hold that the Bible is inspired by God, and thus not subject to the limitations of human reason or verification techniques. However, in the Bible God provides the principle that matters of fact and legality, assertions that one is telling the truth must be verified by the congruent testimony of two or three witnesses (Deut. 19:15, Matt. 18:16, II Cor. 13:1, I Tim. 5:19). Jesus expanded the application of the "multiple witness" principle to include truth claims in the metaphysical realm. To support His claims that He had a unique relationship with God the Father (John 5:1-30, esp. 5:17-18), Jesus summoned multiple witnesses who agreed with His claims (John 5:31-47). John the Apostle followed Jesus' example and cited multiple witnesses to support his interpretive assertions that Jesus is the Christ who gives eternal life to those who believe in Him (I John 5:6-12).

Therefore, the authors will support each of their assertions regarding confidentiality with the multiple testimony principle, citing the three-fold division of the Old Testament ratified by Jesus (Law, Prophets and Psalms, Luke 24:44) and the New Testament writings as our witnesses.

Background of Medical Confidentiality: Justification

A working definition of and justification for confidentiality are summarized in "The Limits of Confidentiality."[10] This reference can serve as an outline on which to apply a Biblical scrutiny of confidentiality. The concept of confidentiality when applied to medicine entails four interrelated tenets:

1) Respect for individuals as capable of having secrets.

2) The ability for individuals to share secrets within a framework of intimacy of their own choosing. Thus, it is a natural extension of #1. Together they allow people to maintain identity, intimacy, privacy, fami-

ly, friendship and national relationships. Obviously, once a secret is shared with another any disregard for the intimate or private nature of that information can lead to "gossip." Gossip is defined as the spreading of "intimate" facts or rumors inappropriately.[11]

3) Thus, the person receiving a secret offers a pledge of silence. This pledge is where the boundaries surrounding secrets are drawn and this boundary is where the dilemma of silence vs. speech resides. It is actually a dual dilemma in that inappropriate speech on one hand (gossip) can irreparably damage intimacy and friendships; but on the other hand, the recipient of intimate information may feel compelled to reveal a secret if danger exists to another. This particular speech is not viewed as gossip. If one views confidentiality as absolute, one may not speak under any circumstances. If it is not, however, one may speak and breach the trust but must carefully identify the circumstances and the persons to whom to speak.

4) The final rationale relates specifically to "professional" secrecy. This secrecy is confidentiality beyond ordinary loyalty supported in numerous professional societies (medicine, law, social services, clergy). The secrecy of professions originated in the practice of medicine.[9,12] It exists philosophically because of its utility to society.[13] This means that the codes of privacy in professions allow people to reveal intimate details to professionals with binding secrecy for the good of the greatest number of society. Since professional secrecy, per se, is not discussed in the Bible, professional conduct will be justified

with the Biblical principles used for the first three concepts.

Biblical Justification for Confidences (Secrets)

God used the secret of Joseph's trials and identity to restore his brothers and reconcile their family. (Genesis 42-45)[14] If Joseph had revealed his identity at an inopportune time, this positive result of secret keeping may not have occurred. When Joseph did reveal his secret, he did so privately to avoid embarrassment to his family. Though Joseph had many tales he could have told, his conduct anticipates and illustrates the Mosaic injunction against "tale bearing" (slander, Lev 19:16).

The Wisdom literature highlights the importance of "secret" keeping for a trustworthy man (Prov. 11:13). Also, in the "Writings" (*KETHUVIM*), Esther at the behest of Mordecai keeps her Hebrew identity a secret (Es 2:20).

In the prophets, another Godly use of "secret" keeping is presented (Jeremiah 36, esp. 36:19 and 36:26). The justification for secret keeping in Jeremiah was the preservation of human life. The "secret" protected the safety of Jeremiah and Baruch and is accompanied by the divine imprimatur, i.e., "the Lord had hidden them." On numerous occasions in the New Testament, Jesus speaks to his disciples "privately" (e.g., Mark 9:28, Mark 13:3, Luke 10:23, and Matt 24:3). One particularly important "confidence" takes place in the Gospels (Matt 17:9). After Jesus' transfiguration, He warns the Apostles not to tell anyone what had occurred (Matt 17:9). The transfigura-

Secret keeping, the use of speech for edification, and the censure of gossip are supported in the Old and New Testaments.

tion and many of Jesus' private talks with the Apostles from this point on (vide supra) were to be kept secret until after the resurrection. Paul writes of appropriate secrets in his "weak" and "strong" passage: "Whatever you believe about these things, keep them between yourself and God" (Rom 14:22). Here it is implied that some things should be "secret" because of the potential injury to a brother.

Edifying Speech and the Negative Effects of Gossip

In the Biblical review on the importance of secret keeping, both the positive result of edifying speech and the negative effects of gossip can be seen. In the New Testament, Jesus himself says "for out of the abundance of the heart, the mouth speaks" (Matt 12:34-37). The "speech" of Jesus was always truthful (John 8:40-45), and He was subsequently described as "one who did no sin, neither was guile found in his mouth (I Peter 1:22). Thus, Jesus completely fulfilled the standard of a "perfect" or "complete" man according to James 3:2. Conversely, in the Wisdom Literature (Ps 55:21), David demonstrates that words from a friend can violate and in deception become "drawn swords." Proverbs 16:27-28 shows the negative power of speech to "scorch like a fire, and separate close friends." In Jeremiah 38, Jeremiah is placed in a cistern by King Zedekiah because of "gossip." Though the charge was false, Zedekiah's behavior was founded on his recognition of the inherent danger of speaking inappropriately about state affairs. The Pauline letters use these same caveats for speech in II Corinthians 12:20, Colossians 4:26 and Ephesians 4:24-29, as does the third chapter of James.

In summary, a rationale for confi-dentiality begins with a person's capacity to have secrets (#1), supplemented by the fact that a person chooses intimate relationships in which to share those secrets (#2). Others must guard these confidences by silence or limiting themselves to edifying speech only. Secret keeping, the use of speech for edification, and the censure of gossip are supported in the Old and New Testaments. Since these scriptural directives should be behavioral norms for the Christian health care worker, we will move on to the main point of contention which arises at issue (#3), i.e., a pledge of silence limiting speech. Attempting to demonstrate the Biblical limits on absolute confidentiality will involve the following:

A) OLD TESTAMENT: Protection of Neighbors,

B) THE LAW OF LOVE: Supported in the Gospels, Pauline letters and other Writings,

C) MOSES MAIMONIDES: Successful integration of Biblical Law and medical practice.

#3A) Protection of Neighbors: The authors believe that the Bible presents a deontological ethical system, not a relativistic ethical system. Thus, situations become the occasion for the application of Biblical norms. The correct interpretation of and application of Biblical norms to varied situations enables the Christian to avoid the ethical dilemmas posed by "situational" ethics. The Christian is never forced to "sin" when applying deontological Biblical norms to difficult situations (I Cor 10:13).

Thus, when a Christian professional considers breaching confidential information, this breach does not necessarily represent indiscriminate speech or "sin." Rather, contemplation of such a breach can be motivated by the desire to avoid potential in-jury of a "neighbor's" health by disease or abuse.

The concept of neighbor protection is present throughout the entire Bible, but is explicitly stated in Leviticus 19:16-18. In fact, the philosophy of neighbor protection is particularly apparent in dealing with communicable diseases. Leviticus 13 can serve as a paradigm concerning limits of confidentiality, since Old Testament communicable diseases such as leprosy are analogous to modern day "plagues" such as acquired immune deficiency syndrome.[15] In ancient Israel patients with diseases were removed from the general community for protection of neighbors. However, before a certain diagnosis of communicable disease was made, the patient's condition was known only to the priest and possibly to family members (significant others, Lev 13:1-44). Only after a definite diagnosis of a communicable disease was pronounced were patients with these diseases removed from the general community for the protection of themselves and others (Lev 13:45-46). Even though their separation would alert others in the community that something was wrong (i.e., a breaking of strict confidentiality), the ethical framework presented in Leviticus 13 suggests that this practice of limited confidentiality was justified by the higher good of protecting a neighbor's life. This principle of protection of neighbor is also taught in the Wisdom Literature (Prov 24:11-12).

B) **The Law of Love:** The consistency of neighbor protection-love is continued in the New Testament in the Gospels (Luke 11:27-28), Pauline letters (Rom 13:10), and other writings (II Pet 1:5-7, I John and James 2:8). Thus, the Bible seems to suspend the good of "silence" when a greater good of neighbor protection is present. The caveat, however, is that the professional must truly be guided by love and the protection of life in the dissemination of confidential information. By doing so, the professional completely fulfills the law of love without committing sin (Gal 5:13-14).

C) **Moses Maimonides:** Christians share a common conviction with Maimonides that the ethical assertions contained in the Law are to be obeyed while we differ on the motive power that drives our obedience (Matt 5:17-20, Rom 8:1-4, 13:8-10).

Thus, Maimonides' successful integration of medicine with an ethical system also embraced by Christians is a preliminary, analogical model of integration that can be expanded upon by the Christian health care worker.

This successful integration of Biblical Law and medical practice was achieved by Maimonides because he and the consensual opinion of Jewish Torah scholars articulated a hierarchical system of ethical and religious values contained in the Tanak (Old Testament). This system recognizes the superior obligation to save life as a precedent over other important ethical demands. In particular, Maimonides argued that: *"Like all other precepts, the Sabbath is set aside where human life is in danger."*[16] This specific dictum of Maimonides is part of a comprehensive obligation to preserve life as follows: "The duty of saving an endangered life (*PIKKUAH NEFESH*) suspends the operation of all the Commandments in the Torah, with the exception of three prohibitions: no man is to save his life at the price of murder, adultery, or idolatry ... from a Jewish point of view, it is sinful to observe laws which are in suspense on account of the danger to life and health."[17] When we apply these precepts to the issue of confidentiality, we can reach the conclu-sion that confidentiality is to be sedulously guarded except when human life is threatened. At that point, the commitment to confidentiality must give place to the superior ethical and medical commitment to preserve life. Moses Maimonides serves as an eminent example of one who successfully integrated Biblical law and medical practice. He thus provides the modern health care professional with a Biblically and ethically responsible exodus from the dilemma of absolute confidentiality.

The authors would like to apply the Biblical methods reviewed to four difficult but typical cases of the 1990's. A seven point discussion will follow in an attempt to clarify the conflict between silence and speech inherent in these medical cases (Ec 3:7).

CASES

1) As a primary care physician, you've cared for a family — husband, wife, two children ages 7 and 5 for approximately 11 years. The father of this family comes to your office very distraught. He admits to you that he is bisexual, a fact you had not known before and is extremely distressed because his illicit lover has AIDS. He is admitted to the hospital by a psychiatrist for depression. You aren't consulted but you review the chart and find that this gentleman is HIV positive and you confront him with the issue of his bisexuality and AIDS. His wife has not been told and he steadfastly refuses to tell her.

2) A 14 year-old who attends your church asks to talk to you about something important. She tells you in your office that her 16 year-old sister, the daughter of an Elder at your church, is pregnant. She tells you that she is very concerned because both her mom and dad are asking her sister to have an abortion to spare embarrassment. She tells you this and then insists that you not tell anyone because she feels she will upset her parents.

3)[18] Mrs. S. is a 55 year-old white female with Huntington's disease. She is mildly compromised neurologically at present, but will progress to irreversible mental and motor deterioration barring divine intervention. The inheritance of this diseases is autosomal dominant. Mrs. S. has three children, ages 38, 30 and 27 and has 11 grandchildren. She is embarrassed by her neurological dysfunction and refuses to tell her children, and wants her diagnosis absolutely confidential.

4) A 32 year-old woman who has seen you for approximately one year comes to your office for treatment of injuries sustained in physical abuse by her husband. You don't have significant concern for her life based on the degree of injury and she does not want her husband or anyone else told. She fears that if her husband discovers she told you, she may sustain further injury later.

Discussion

1) Confidentiality has a very important place in medicine and requires safeguards. The Bible precludes gossip and respects secrets. Because of this, Christian health care workers are responsible for education concerning secret safekeeping for themselves and others. They need to be current in appropriate protections for computer information.[19] Special care should be taken in the dissemination of information to third parties. Patient permission or notification prior to any discussion of sensitive data should be procured.

2) Protection of Life: These cases are listed in order of greatest to least risk to "neighbor's" life. Our Biblical discussion suggests that the

husband in case one and the family in case two be apprised of the Biblical wisdom and obligation to practice "limited" confidentiality. Since a risk to life exists (wife-AIDS, unborn child-abortion) select dissemination must occur. Case three will probably progress to a similar risk over time (in driving or workplace activities) and will eventually require the same response (i.e., notification of people endangered by her disease). Case four allows counseling time because the risk to life is not as emergent.

3) If the issue of confidentiality involves an interaction with a fellow Christian, one must follow Jesus' guidelines in Matthew 18 for determining the time for "silence" and "speech." There are two very important motivations involved in this interaction. First, in this sequence of discipline, Jesus allows for protection of information between the party, the "professional" and trusted witnesses. Secondly, the entire motivation for this practice (Matt 18:15) is protection, growth and possibly repentance-restoration of the "brother." Its use for these edifying ends can be seen in the New Testament (I Cor 5:5 and II Cor 2:5-11) and illustrates the positive result that comes from limited dissemination of seemingly confidential data. This is particulary germane for case 2.

4) The Christian health care worker does not have to offer value neutral counseling. Because of this, the typical "social contract" of absolute confidentiality in the doctor-patient relationship is not applicable. In fact, legal proceedings against physicians who have breached confidential information utilize an implied social contract

ethic of absolute confidentiality in medicine.[8] The Christian health care worker should volunteer his/her Biblical views regarding the protection of and love of neighbor prior to the verbalization of any confidential information. In fact, one can argue that Christian health care workers should publish a statement for both patients and colleagues that presents a philosophy of limited confidentiality according to Biblical revelation.

5) Since we are called on to be "salt and light," we can use John Stott's outline for appropriate times to persuasively argue the need for the above Biblical paradigms in dealing with confidentiality in the medical profession.[20]

6) Be aware of the laws concerning confidentiality in your state. If these laws seem to conflict with scriptural revelation, remember that there may be times when the professional must obey God's law if human law is in direct contradiction. As Peter (Acts 4) and Daniel (Dan 8) learned, this may actually lead to arrest or prosecution.

7) Information given to health care workers by minors is to be handled differently by Christians because of Biblical mandates related to the authority of parents, sanctity of marriage and importance of the family. Particularly when consent laws for abortion and birth control do not require parental notification this may serve as an example of man's law being an affront to God's law. Notification of parents in the situation of abortion is clear cut because of the danger to unborn life.

Confidentiality is a relative good to be sedulously guarded by the Christian. However, it is limited whenever

a confidence endangers another's life. Despite the trend in society towards autonomy and privacy as absolute goods, the Christian follows Biblical revelation as one who is in but not of the world. Therefore the Christian follows Biblical revelation that teaches only one absolute good (God), and from whom all other relative goods (i.e., confidentiality) find their source, definition, and hierarchical arrangement. To do otherwise is to commit idolatry (I John 5:20-22).

ENDNOTES

1. Pritchard, J., (ed.), **Ancient Near East Texts...**, 2nd Ed., Princeton, 1955, pp. 163-180.

2. Reich, W.T., (ed.), **Encyclopedia of Bioethics**, The Free Press, New York, 1978.
   - Arabic: Advice To a Physician, Advice of Haly Abbas, Tenth Century A.D., p. 1734.
   - European: Medical Ethics: Statements of Policy Definitions and Rules, British Medical Association, 1974. p. 1758.

3. Chinese: Lee, T., *Bulletin of the History of Medicine* 13, (1943), pp. 271-272.

4. Reich, W.T., *op cit.*
   - Hindu: Oath of Initiation (Caraka Samhira), 1st Century A.D. (?) p. 1733.
   - Jewish: Oath of Asaph (3rd to 7th Century A.D.?), p. 1733.
   - Islamic: A Physician's Ethical Duties from Kholasah Al Kekmah (1770), p. 1736.

5. Bird, L.P. (ed.) & Barlow, Th.M., (ed.), **Codes of Medical Ethics, Oaths and Prayers, an Anthology**, Christian Medical and Dental Society, Richardson, Texas, 1989, p. 5.

6. Hill, P.T., "Imposing Mandatory Testing, Is It a 'Just Cause?'" *Med-*

ical Ethics Vol. 3, pp. 1-10, 1988.

- Brodeur, D. (ed.), "Screening for AIDS: Confidentiality: Individual Liberty Must Be Balanced Against Protecting Safe Workplace", *Public Health Issues* 2:1-8, 1987.

7. Marvinney, C.A., Esq., "Legislation Proposed to Protect Physician 'Whistle Blowers'." *Colorado Medicine*, May, 1990, p. 144.

8. Horne v. Patton, 291 Ala. 701, 287 So. 2d 824 1973 and South Florida Blood Service, Ins. v. Rasmussen, 467 so. 2d 798 (Ct. app. Fla. 1985) and Ct. Simonsen v. Swenson, 104 Neb 224, 177 N.W. 831 (1920).

9. Jones, W.H.S., (ed.), **Hippocrates Vol. 1**, London, Heinemann, 1923: 301 Loeb Classical Library.

10. Bok, S., "The Limits of Confidentiality", *The Hastings Center Report*, Feb. 1983, pp. 24-31.

11. **The American Heritage Dictionary, 2nd ed.**, Houghton Mifflin Co., Boston, 1985.

12. Gracia, Diego, "Profesion O Sacerdocio", *JANO*, 1983, p. 42.

13. Frame, J.M., **Medical Ethics - Principles, Persons and Problems**, Presbyterian and Reformed Publishing Company, Phillipsburg, New Jersey, 1988, p. 45.

14. Swindoll, C.R., **Joseph from Pit to Pinnacle**, Insight for Living, Fullerton, California, 1990.

15. Schiedemeyer, D., "Letters from the 21st Century", *Christian Medical Society Journal*, Fall, 1987, pp. 4-16.

16. Maimonides, Sabbath 2:1-3, MISHNEH TORAH.

17. Birnbaum, Phillip, **Saving a Life. A Book of Jewish Concepts**, Hebrew Publishing Company, New York, 1975, p. 512.

18. "The Price of Silence", *Hastings Center Report*, May-June, 1990, pp. 31-35.

19. White, R. "Computer Secrecy. An Introduction for The Medical Practitioner", *Urologic Clinics of North America*, Vol. 13, pp. 119-128, 1986.

- Van Der Poel, K.G. & Smit, P.C., Protection of Computerized Medical Data - A Problem? Vol. 68, pp. 106-109, 1985.

- de Dombal, F.T., "Ethical Considerations Concerning Computers in Medicine in the 1980's", *Journal of Medical Ethics*, Vol. 13, pp. 179-184, 1987.

20. Stott, J., **Decisive Issues Facing Christians Today**, F.H. Revell Co., New Jersey, 1990, pp. 45-57.

Book Review

The Quick and the Dead: RU-486 and the New Chemical Warfare Against Your Family

by George Grant (Crossway, Wheaton, 1991), 156 pp. $8.95

Reviewed by David W. Hall

George Grant has scooped the liberal press again. With his latest expose of RU-486 Grant, one of the most informed evangelicals in these areas, provides information which will be of service to concerned parents, teachers, public officials, and medical personnel. What with the NEA's recent endorsement of this abortifacient, Christians will want to be armed with the facts. One of Grant's purposes is to provide those facts in a fair manner. This journalist-*cum*-theologian does just that.

Laced with several testimonies by women who've unsuspectingly been duped, one of this books strengths is the appeal from actual — albeit regretful — users of RU-486. Following a lengthy introduction to this ethical issue by way of the experience of one young lady, Grant gives a recapitulation of the history and development of Mifepristone, Mifegyne, and other related chemical components of RU-486. This second chapter is eminently factual and adaptable for use in public debate. As one of the intended uses of this work is to arm evangelicals in the public sector, this chapter will be essential reading. Although technical by nature, Grant does a yeoman's job in translating these medical inscrutabilities into intelligible text for the expert and non-expert alike.

Another outstanding aspect of this short work is Grant's review of our modern search for medical salvation. His fourth chapter is also a review of the Biblical basis for modern medicine, along with the assertion that such medical practice has departed from its Judaeo-Christian foil. In these Grant retains the knack for summing up weighty subjects in a few sentences for the layman.

Grant is helpful as he waxes philosophic. Comparing modern medicine to some modern art, he observes, "Goya knew that medicine, like art, when not in the service of heaven, is most likely in the service of Hell" (p. 94). A little later he states the "failure of modern medicine is much more a maltheory than a malpractice. In other words, the problem with health care is not so much bad technologies as bad philosophies" (p. 94). Citing S. Ladourvec, Grant opines, "With the subtle secularization and industrialization of medicine, has come a rootlessness, a lack of cohesiveness, and a latitudinarianism. There is no longer a philosophical definition of [the] profession. The tragic result is that young doctors have no real sense of calling, and they either have to find meaning and purpose in raw financial gain or in some ideological pursuit. What we are seeing then is the inevitable fragmentation of medicine into a thousand cults and sects" (p.

94). The author is also helpful in his expose of the World Health Organization. This work might be strengthened from criticism if it provided the comparative failure rates of other surgical or pharmaceutical procedures.

Also included in this brief monograph is a critique of the pro-death bias in the modern media who, according to Grant, exhibit "Milli Vanilli-like lip-synching of the pro-abortion party line provid[ing] stark evidence that it has tossed any semblance of impartiality or objectivity to the four winds" (p. 112). The final chapter is a setting of this problem in the larger historical context, and some concluding suggestions as to how to practically battle this plague. The book is enhanced by abundant endnotes for further reference, and a listing of bibliographic resources.

This book has the punch of Grant's earlier *Legacy of Planned Parenthood* and is written in that same admirable style. In fact, I wondered as I began, would this book be up to the previous classical style? I found it not only to be stylistically superior, but equally excellent in content as well. The opening Latin quotes and the juxtaposition of citations from Theodore Roosevelt and Charles Spurgeon sweeten the excellence. Grant's information is a real service to the Christian community, and his readable style will make this a resource for every Christian home and church concerned with teenagers. Christians will also want to distribute widely some of these to legislators, physicians, educators, and others in the public domain. Above all, the Christian community will welcome this as a theological evaluation of RU-486. The underlying philosophies are exposed as various "radicalism[s which], like most other ancient religions, [are] largely made up of false prophecies and unshackled perversities."

His thesis is well summarized by his reference from T. Roosevelt (p. 61): "There are those who believe that a new modernity demands a new morality. What they fail to consider is the harsh reality that there is no such thing as a new morality. There is only one morality. All else is immorality. There is only true christian ethics over against which stands the whole of paganism. If we are to fulfill our great destiny as a people, then we must return to the old morality, the sole morality." Grant may help us toward that end and has provided able leadership in this crucial area.

_____

Letter to the Editor

Dear Editor,

I read with interest Randall Crenshaw's article "Can Anyone Heal Me?" in Volume 5, No. 3. There is no doubt to the underlying truth of the basic tenet of Dr. Crenshaw's article that many of our ailments are caused by spiritual problems and that help is often sought from physicians who either don't know how to help or cover up the problem with medicine and surgery.

However, his paragraph regarding tonsillectomies is either uninformed or using very old data to try to prove a point. As a Christian Otolaryngologist I know that tonsillectomy is no longer the most common operation performed in the United States as this has been surpassed by the placement of ventilation tubes for serous otitis media refractory for medical treatment. I would tremble with fear if it was true that one out of every thousand tonsillectomy patient dies. It is true that there is one report in the literature with a death rate of 1/1000, but all the recent literature suggests a death rate of 1/10,000 - 1/15,000. Moreover, there are several studies reporting no deaths in more than 170,000 operations. Serious complications are nearly all due to bleeding and may require transfusion in 1 - 2%. Furthermore, there are approximately 800,000 tonsillectomies done per year in the United States which includes a significant percentage of adults who have persistent tonsil disease. Simple mathematics make it clear that nowhere near 20 - 30% of American children have their tonsils removed.

Finally, his assertion that 50 - 95% of tonsillectomies are unnecessary requires further qualification. A tonsillectomy is nearly always an elective procedure designed to improve the quality of life for that individual. It is, however, elective in almost all cases except severe obstruction. With more stringent criteria in use today nearly all patients having tonsillectomies obtain significant benefit.

For those who are interested in this subject there is a comprehensive review with extensive literature, references in the 1987 Otolaryngologic Clinics of North American (May 1987, Vol. 20.2). This should be available in nearly any hospital library, or ask your local Otolaryngologist.

As a Christian, we must strive for truth in all aspects of communication.

Sincerely,

Scott Voorman, M.D.
Simi Valley, CA

Stephan Jay Gould informs us in a new book entitled The Meaning of Life (Little, Brown Co.) that human evolution is "quirky, improbable, unrepeatable and utterly unpredictable." Yet, he maintains that "human evolution is not random." He is described as a paleontologist, essayist and humanist.

Perhaps. Logical, he is not.

* * * * * * *

Drs. Mary and Gary Jewell, co-authoring "How to Assess the Risk of HIV Exposure" in the American Family Physician (July 1989), tell us that "some physicians have personal prejudices, fears or discomfort in discussing sexuality" with various types of patients, including homosexual patients and those engaging in extramarital sex. "Physicians must identify their own weaknesses and at least present a neutral attitude to the patient while asking questions" about sexual behavior. It is also important that we not let our "body language" reveal "value judgments."

The Jewells seem inconsistent in that they evidently don't mind expressing their value judgment that value judgments regarding these sexual behaviors are improper in a medical setting.

* * * * * * *

Dr. A. Kenneth Fuller, writing in a question and answer section of Medical Aspects of Human Sexuality (Feb. 1991, p. 25) tells us of a proposed new sexual disorder - "paraphilic coercive disorder" - which is said to describe some rapists or would-be rapists. The "disorder" would include a six month or greater history of "fantasies and sexual urges involving sexual contact." Understandably, those suffering from such disorders might be expected to act on their urges, more than once.

It should be interesting to observe the collision between the liberal feminist agenda item against rape and the liberal agenda item medicalizing sin. No one

can live consistently with an ungodly philosophy.

* * * * * * *

Letters to The Lancet (October 19, 1991, pp. 1010-1011) pass along data maintaining that Dutch doctors assist in the suicide of 386 people a year, kill 2,318 at their request, and kill 1,030 patients without their explicit and persistent request. Euthanasia and assisted suicide deaths constitute 2.9% of all deaths in the Netherlands, and 54% of Dutch doctors have participated in these deaths.

* * * * * * *

In the AAPS News, March, 1991, we are given the formula for determining physician Medicare fees:

$$MFS = \{[PW \times PW_i] + [OH \times OH_i] = [M \times M_i]\} CF$$

PW is the physician work component of the RBRV

PW_i is the physician work index

OH is the overhead component of the RBRVS.

OH_i is the overhead index.

M is the malpractice component.

M_i is the malpractice component .CF is the monetary conversion factor.

Your task is to find patient satisfaction in the formula.

* * * * * * *

Offering an alternative to "a meat market proposal" that patients be allowed to sell their organs for transplantation, B.D. Colen proposes a "national organ draft." Explaining his plan in the Medical Tribune of April, 4, 1991, he proposes that all of us be tissue-typed at birth. When the time comes to take one of us off a respirator, the hospital will be required to notify the National Organ Draft data bank and we will be stripped of useful parts. Unless you initiate action to seek "conscientious objector" status, the presumption would be that your "brain dead" body belonged to the state.

Your task is to find the patient in this plan. I left my heart in San Francisco. Try Des Moines for my bones, Tampa for my liver, Rochester for my lungs ...

* * * * * * *

Intercessors for America notifies us that there is a "move underway to place

sonogram machines in crisis pregnancy centers." The hope is that the view of unborn baby may convince pregnant women of the humanity of the infant even when other information won't. The machines are expensive — about $30,000. For more information regarding the machines write: Sound Wave Images, 2422 Harness, Union Lake, MI 48387, or call (313) 360-0743.

* * * * * * *

Two physicians in Vienna, speaking to each other: "What really bothers me is the role we complacently preempt. The human body is our human body. Medicine is our medicine. It's like a carpenter looking with a proprietary air on all lumber and regarding carpentry as his property. To get away with this we draw on the ancient priestcraft. We dress mysteriously, we have our special costumes. We have our own language, our own magic gibberish. We have had laws passed to protect the omniscience to which we pretend. We protect one another like members of a priestly fraternity. We foster the belief that we are a mystery. The hold we have on people is their own fear, pain, terror, and ignorance. And we, too, are ignorant. We can say only that we know more than they know. We are pitifully ignorant." [Taken from Morton Thompson's The Cry and the Covenant (London: Heinemann, 1951, p. 126), a novel about Ignaz Philipp Semmelweis.]

* * * * * * *

Dr. Jennifer Schneider tells us that sex addicts are "unable" to change their sexual practices, exhibiting "compulsivity" which is the "loss of the ability to choose freely whether to stop or to continue." She identifies shame as "a major issue of sex addicts." [Postgraduate Medicine, 90, Nov. 1, 1991, pp. 171-182.] Taking the lessons into practice, a publication of a treatment center for alcohol and drug dependency tells us that "addicts are caught in a well of shame because for them it is no longer a matter of choice."

"The Lord is righteous, He is in her midst, He will do no unrighteousness. Every morning He brings His justice to light; He never fails, But the unjust knows no shame." Zeph. 3:5.

The Durham Declaration

We have received a copy of the Durham Declaration to United Methodists On Our Church and   Abortion.
It is signed by more than two hundred God-fearing United Methodists.

The declaration divides into a section of belief, followed by a con fession of sin and a pledge. It is too lengthy to reproduce here, but some excerpts may provide an appreciation of the document:

"...Abortion is testing our church today as deeply as slavery tested our church in the nineteenth century. Abortion is stirring up great confusion and exposing deep conflicts in our community of faith. This condition continues, in part, because the United Methodist Church has not addressed the problem of abortion theologically. Our church has been content to debate abortion with the merely political terms that American society has made available. This is an insufficient response to an historic test.

"...Contemporary culture insists that we own our bodies and that we have a right to do with them whatever we want. However, we United Methodist Christians declare that this is false. We believe that we are not our own. We do not own our selves or our bodies. God owns us. 'It is he that made us, and we are his.'

"...We believe that caring and providing for one another includes welcoming children into the family of the Church. As members of the Body of Christ, we know that children -- those who are hidden in the womb and those who are held by the hand, those who are labeled 'unwanted' and those we are called 'wanted' -- are gifts from God... And we conform to the example of the early church, which, though living in the midst of a pagan empire that casually practiced abortion and abandoned children (usually to slav ery, prostitution, or death), helped to provide refuge for unwanted little ones and their needy parents.

"...We confess that we have rebelled against God. We have rejected the light of Christ and turned to the darkness of the world. We have denied -- by thought, word, and deed -- that we belong to God.

"We confess that we have often compromised the Gospel by submitting to the seductions of society. We have exchanged the message of salvation in Jesus Christ for a false message about human potential. We have capitulated to extreme self-involvement and self-interest. Neglecting the call to discipleship, we have treated matters related to marriage, sex, and children as if they were merely lifestyle questions. We have lived as if the church is simply another voluntary association of autonomous individuals ... Fearing division, we have removed abortion from the concerns of our church's mission. Thereby our church has reduced the abortion problem to private choice and to just another issue for partisan politics.

"...We pledge, with God's help, to practice and to teach a sexual ethnic that adorns the Gospel. Christian discipleship includes, though it is not limited to, the ordering of God's gift of sexuality. Sexual discipline requires, at a minimum, 'fidelity in marriage and celibacy in singleness.' According to Biblical teaching, sexual relations outside the boundaries of 'fidelity in marriage and celibacy in singleness' are manifestations of sin that call for repentance and reconciliation. This ordering is a part of the excellent way of Christian discipleship. It stands over against the jungle of modern sexuality, which is most evidence in our society's inability to hold men sexually accountable.

"Biblically based sexual discipline should be directly and consistently advocated -- by our church's bishops, district superintendents, clergy, parents, church schools, publishing programs, colleges and universities, hospitals, children's homes, boards, and agencies -- among United Methodist children, youth and adults. In addition, the church should teach the responsibilities for men and women that accompany sex. The church should condemn sexual promiscuity.

"We pledge, with God's help, to teach our churches that the unborn child is created in the image of God and is one for whom the Son of God died. This child is God's child. This child is part of God's world. So the life of this child is not ours to take. Therefore, it is sin to take this child's life for reasons whether of birth control, gender selection, convenience, or avoidance of embarrassment.

"We pledge, with God's help, to call our church's boards and agencies to end their support of pro-choice political advocacy and also to develop ministries that support women in difficult pregnancies.

"...We pledge, with God's help, to encourage United Methodist-related hospitals to adopt medical ethics guidelines which are protective of the unborn child and mother.

"We pledge, with God's help, to consider how our church should best apply discipline to her members who reap profits, small and large, from the advocacy and performance of elective abortions.

****

The full text may be obtained by sending a self-addressed, stamped envelope, with $1, to:

Rev. Paul T. Stallsworth
Creswell United Methodist Church
Route 1, box 272 A
Creswell, NC 27928

Weariness Among the Physicians

Marvin Olasky, Ph.D.

*Dr. Olasky is Associate Professor of Journalism at the University of Texas at Austin and Senior Fellow with the Capital Research Center in Washington, D.C. He is the author of seven books, The following article is from a history of abortion which he is currently writing, tentatively entitled, **The Containment of Abortion, 1652-1962.** .*

Within state and local medical societies, the crucial turning point on abortion often came not in the 1960s but during the first third of the century, as more doctors told stories like the following three by Robert Ferguson of Charlotte, North Carolina:

ø A few years ago there came under my observation a young woman in her first pregnancy and vomiting severely, who had made up her mind that she would not carry the pregnancy to fruition. She was taken to the hospital by her family physician with whom I saw her in consultation. The mother was on hand and took charge of the case. All questions addressed to the patient were answered by the mother ... this patient had another consultant called in and was curetted immediately.[1]

ø The first year I started out to practice, on a Sunday morning, a beautiful young woman wearing many large diamonds appeared at my office and told me her troubles, the same old story, and said she had to have an abortion. I told her that was not my line of work and she would have to look elsewhere. She insisted and said she did not know where to go and if it was the fee that held me back all I would have to do would be to state my price, that she did not care what it cost, she was going to get rid of it. Although I was several thousand dollars in debt for my education I told her that a million dollars would not influence me in the least and that has been my stand ever since I got my diploma. Most doctors are importuned many times each year to produce these abortions of convenience and, inevitably, some succumb.[2]

ø About two years ago a lady on whom I had previously operated sent her daughter of 14 years to my office to examine on account of persistent nausea. The girl was three months pregnant and I asked her mother over the telephone to come to my office. She, like all the others, wanted to know what she could do to get rid of it — said it just couldn't be permitted to go on. I told her the law and that there was nothing I could do. She said she did not expect that I would do anything for her but thought I might tell her of some doctor who would help her out. I told her I did not know of any such. She remarked that she would go the rounds till she found one. A short time later she visited my office and informed me that she had found a doctor in Charlotte who produced an abortion on her daughter. I asked her the point blank question what he charged and she said he charged $500, and while that was a big fee, she did not mind anything to get her daughter out of trouble.[3]

Although many doctors were performing abortions, the leadership and rhetoric within local medical societies tended to be anti-abortion, and in city after city during the century's first three decades, local leaders called meetings to discuss ways to fight abortion.

These meetings developed a typical pattern, beginning with the opening remarks by a theologian who examined religious and ethical issues. In Toledo, for example, doctors in 1905 assembled to hear Reverend F. Heirmann, S.J., criticize an abortionist who had said, "I would as leave kill, if necessary, an unborn child as a rat."[4] Heirmann then posed the question: "Whether abortion is murder or whether the human embryo must be considered a person who has a right to life?"[5] He quoted scientific studies showing the unborn child to be human life from the moment of conception, and told the assembled doctors that "the positive law of God" showed them how to react in the face of that knowledge. Heirmann also suggested explicit language: "Instead of resorting to big

Latin compounds, foeticide, infanticide, let us use the strong and powerful Anglo-Saxon, child murder, murder of the unborn ..."[6]

Next on the typical agenda came an estimate of abortion incidence, with commentary by a local medical opponent of abortion. For example, in 1904 Dr. Charles Bacon told the Chicago Medical Society that at least ten to thirteen percent of all pregnancies nationwide ended in induced abortion.[7] Bacon pleaded with fellow doctors to oppose abortion, since "The right to life is the most fundamental right of an individual."[8] Bacon acknowledged that some said the unborn child's dependence on a mother reduced its rights, but he suggested that such thinking would lead to infanticide, since a baby "needs the breast and the care of the mother for a long period ... This human being is just as much an independent being at the beginning of its intrauterine life as after it has reached a condition of extrauterine viability."[9]

Tunes of "Onward, medical soldiers" spluttered to a halt, however, when local district attorneys or lawyers were called upon. For example, W.S. Carroll, an assistant district attorney for Erie County, told the Erie County Medical Society in 1908 that "under common law abortion was homicide or manslaughter ... but the modern law does not look upon the offense in such an atrocious light."[10] Anti-abortion laws were virtually "a dead letter," Carroll reported, with no recent cases of offending physicians or midwives being jailed or even having their licenses revoked. Evidentiary hurdles, he observed, were significant; a doctor, called to attempt to repair part of the damage caused by abortion, could not testify about anything the woman told him unless she explicitly answered a series of questions acknowledging her words to be a dying statement. Dying declarations *were* admissible in criminal (although not in civil) cases, but a doctor who attained such information while treating a patient was not allowed to communicate anything that "shall tend to blacken the character of the patient without her consent."[11]

Local officials told doctors that if an anti-abortion case was not developed precisely, evidence would not hold up in court. At one medical convention, St. Louis attorney Earnest Oakley reminded doctors that statements by a dying woman to a doctor were not admissible in court, unless she said the required words: "I am going to die ... I have abandoned all hope of recovery."[12] Oakley told doctors that they must prompt such statements by asking women hard questions, or else give up all hope of convicting an abortionist. Other officials also strove to lower expectations. M.O. Heckard, Registrar of Vital Statistics in Chicago Department of Health, spoke of "a girl from one of our best families who has made a mistake."[13] Heckard asked whether he should "report this matter to the proper inquisitorial officers, and have the distress of the relatives advertised, who are already bowed down with grief and shame." He said he would "if there were any possibility of bringing the criminal to justice," but argued that this would not happen:

The evidence is destroyed. If the physician does his duty to the law, makes this report directly to the Coroner, can he expect another call from that family or their immediate friends? And it is not every physician in the city who can afford to sacrifice a family under such circumstances. What can he do?[14]

Frustration showed in the words of attorneys such as prosecutor Fletcher Dobyns:

There are approximately from six to ten thousand abortions produced in this city each year; there are something like two hundred deaths from that evil each year. We can count on the fingers of one hand the convictions for criminal abortion that have been secured during the last half dozen years ... In one case, the physician who took the stand for the defense said it would be impossible for a doctor, even after curetting the parts, as he said he did, to say whether it was fetal tissue ... Another physician took the stand and showed how the same condition could have existed from something else, and that death could have resulted from other cause or causes.[15]

J.M. Sheean, attorney for the Medico-Legal committee of the Chicago Medical Society, similarly said, "The decisions and enactments on our statute books are but reflections of the public conscience ... The law as it stands if further advanced than apparently the public demand for its enforcement would require..."[16] An article in the *Providence Medical Journal* in 1903 reported the "First conviction for Abortion in the State of Rhode Island," but in doing so showed "the difficulties encountered in the effort to convict for criminal abortion in Rhode Island."[17] The convicted offender was a long-time abortionist with a record of previous cases dismissed, and in this case a strong ante-mortem statement and ample evidence of abortion as the cause of death made conviction possible. Even so, the sentence of the abortionist was only two years.

After hearing from law officials at local and national meetings, doctors repeatedly bemoaned the difficulty of enforcement. Dr. Henry D. Holton of Vermont told the American Academy of Medicine, "I have seen a good deal of trouble in securing conviction and have experienced it in trying to convict men whom I know, and everybody had a sort of common knowledge, were guilty, but to get the legal evidence was practically impossible."[18] Dr. Edward T. Abrams of Dollar Bay, Michigan, told fellow AMA members in 1908, "For the past two years I have been a member of the Michigan legislature and also chairman of the committee on public health of that body." During that time, he said, he had been unable to find a way to make abortionist arrest and conviction more likely. In response to one law-tightening proposition, Abrams reported, "I was assured by the best authority in our state that there would be no more powerful inducement for the concealment of abortion than to make a woman a party to the criminality of the act, because it will destroy absolutely the method of getting evidence."[19]

Doctors such as Charles Bacon of Chicago argued that prosecutors could be successful if more physicians cared deeply enough about abortion to take abortionists to court and not let them off the hook. Bacon complained that few doctors put up with

the many disagreeable annoyances attendant upon fighting abortion: the loss of time resulting from attendance at the Coroner's and the Grand Jury and finally at the trial... attacks

to be expected from the defendant's attorney... the enmity of the friends of the accused midwife or physician is a factor that will cause many to hesitate to do anything that promises no return except loss of time and money, and worry and annoyance.[20]

Bacon cajoled his fellow doctors to try harder, but he acknowledged,

Ordinarily it is very difficult to get satisfactory evidence against a professional abortionist. The relatives or others interested in the case are generally very anxious to prevent any publicity for obvious reasons, and even in case of the death of the mother it is frequently impossible to get any member of the family to take action in the matter.[21]

Dr. W.H. Wathen of Louisville suggested that doctors "ostracize any man who will produce a criminal abortion," but such unity seemed unlikely.[22]

Even Dr. Rudolph Holmes, who had led Chicago's successful campaign against abortion advertising in newspapers, fell victim to the spiritual depression that seemed to creep over anti-abortion physicians. He had told the Chicago Medical Society that it must maintain vigilance, for the ads "undoubtedly will reappear in a new guise..."[23] And yet, when that even happened in 1910 exactly as Holmes had predicted, he seemed close to despair. Holmes noted that abortionists, denied newspaper advertising space, were printing more business cards and distributing them through brothels and rooming house landlords. He reported that Chicago abortionists had their own legal department, with witnesses

on tap and ready to swear that "the young woman had an operation elsewhere and the doctor was merely performing a life-saving operation."[24] Holmes described the working methods of an abortionist who managed to stay out of jail year after year:

The cardinal principle of their actions is never to perform an operation with a witness present; her companion is rarely if ever allowed in the room. If discovery is made it is her word against his; if she dies he stands alone. A very popular way is for two or more operators to work in harmony; one will make all the arrangements for the procedure, and then when all is ready another will slip in and do the work.[25]

Holmes also complained that regular doctors were performing or commissioning abortions. He spoke of three kinds of abortionists: The young doctor "inveigled into committing his first offenses in his pressing need for money"; the established physician "who largely is engaged in ethical practice but who systematically relieves his patients in order that he may hold his families;" and the full-time abortionist, often recruited by established doctors to handle their "dirty work."[26] Holmes noted that doctors in good standing in their local and national societies performed abortions, and that their colleauges knew of the practice but were "too weak-kneed to take aggressive action for their expulsion." He also saw governmental complicity, and asked, "What can you expect when a member of our legislature is backing financially and politically one of the most notorious abortion hospitals in Chicago?"[27]

What apparently pushed Holmes

into despair was the sense that he was virtually all alone. He wrote,

I have come to the conclusion that the public does not want, the profession does not want, the women in particular do not want, any aggressive campaign against the crime of abortion. I have secured evidence. I have asked different physicians, who either had direct knowledge of the crime against the prisoner before the bar or who could testify as to the general reputation, to come and testify. They promised to come, but when the time for trial is at hand no one appears. On the other hand, so-called reputable members of our Chicago Medical Society regularly appear in court to support the testimony of some notorious abortionist.

Holmes complained that, "it is not possible to get twelve men together without at least one of them being personally responsible for the downfall of a girl, or at least interested in getting her out of her difficulty." His conclusion was that "legislation is not needed, at least, in Illinois. We have as good a law as perhaps can be made. It is the enforcement of law that is needed."[28]

Other doctors were angered by silence among societal leaders from other spheres. Walter Dorsett in 1908 told the AMA's Section on Obstetrics and Gynecology that "the clergy do not seem to be at all concerned. Few sermons are preached from the pulpit for fear of shocking the delicate feelings of a fashionably dressed congregation ..."[29] He complained that medical students were not being told about the "enormity of the crime, and that many "yield(ed) to the temptation."[30] Women con-

templating abortion, according to Dr. Edward A. Weiss, then saw "the apathy toward induced abortion on the part of their neighbors, physicians, and the world at large ..."[31] Everyone thought "lightly of the offence" and knew that the law was seldom enforced.

Dr. M.S. Iseman in 1912 presented one of the earliest twentieth century pictures of hopelessness concerning abortion. In New York City, he wrote, "embryonic humanity has no more sanctity nor protection than the rats which infest its docks."[32] Regular M.D.s were the leading practitioners: "So general is the demand and so common the practice, that in the competition for the traffic the ordinary criminal operator has been practically driven out of the business by the highly skilled and respectable members of the medical profession." Well-connected women could gain permission for "therapeutic abortions" from those brilliant specialists of the art, the gynecologists, whose philanthropic and unfailing tomahawks are whetted for every embryo daring to stray within the confines of a woman's clinic."[33]

Iseman described progressive era New York as a mecca for abortion. "While the local traffic is as much as the thousand or more abortion specialists can attend to," he wrote, "the outside contingent is simply enormous, and during the season it is difficult to say which is the stronger attraction for the lady visitors to the metropolis — the horse-show, the opera, or the gynecologist."[34] He reported that, "The laws against the crime of abortion are no more enforced in the great state of New York than the Revised Statutes of the United States are enforced in China. Out of the scores of thousands committed every year, in some years not a

single indictment follows. According to the report of the Secretary of State on the statistics of crime for the ten-year period 1895-1904, there were only nine convictions in the entire State, of which two were in New York City.[35]

Iseman then took his readers on a city-by-city tour of abortion in America. Based on statistics concerning recorded childbirths and estimates of officials, he claimed there were 4,000 induced abortions in Washington, D.C., each year.[36] "It is current opinion that the swift-flowing sewers, and even the convenient and silent Potomac itself," were convenient disposal sites for aborted unborn children and killed newborns: "The fact, however, that in 1908 the bodies of 86 of these rash intruders were found abandoned and thrown out upon the streets in the parks of the city indicates that in some circles the dog or the coroner is preferred to the drains."[37] During the five-year period from 1905 to 1909, thousands of abortions resulted in only nine indictments for abortion, and three convictions — not enough to do more than to slow down slightly the traffic to abort.[38] In the District, Iseman wrote, abortion referrals were made even in the "booths of the hairdressing parlors, the sanctums of the dressmaker, and the boudoir of the milliner, and what information cannot be obtained in these directories can be readily learned from the chambermaid or 'wash lady.'"[39]

Other large cities were no better, Iseman reported. Enforcement was rare; for example, in Atlanta in 1911, "after years of suspended animation, the police made a solitary arrest for the crime of abortion ..." That was not enough to deter abortionists who hired agents to distribute advertising cards in hotels.[40] Iseman concluded that, "except in the formal letter of the statute books, the sanctity which nearly twenty centuries of Christianity has conferred upon the unborn human being is repudiated."[41]

The repudiation of that sanctity also made it easier to broaden indications for therapeutic abortion. "it seems that the wisdom of this can be scarcely questioned," Dr. Frank Higgins argued as early as 1904, because even though some doctors might "perform abortion in many unnecessary cases, it is believed that this will not be true to any large extent ..."[42] In the past, Higgins continued, doctors would induce abortion "only when the patient [was] suffering from such grave disease that her life is in eminent peril," but now many believed that the "termination of pregnancy is entirely justified to prevent the advance of what might later prove to be a fatal disease."[43] Other doctors also discussed therapeutic abortion. Charles Jewett in 1908 wrote that induced abortion was commonly accepted when it could "interrupt morbid processes that threaten to cripple permanently important mental and physical functions." He reported the contention that "melancholia may be taken as an indication for abortion if the woman's condition is manifestly growing worse."[44] Charles Bacon noted in 1910 that Illinois law allowed therapeutic abortion only to save the life of the mother, but "As a matter of fact almost all therapeutic abortions are done to save the health of the mother."[45]

Edward A. Weiss, a Pittsburgh obstetrician, was a persistent critic of lenient standards for therapeutic abortion. He contended in 1913 that "life of the mother" exceptions in state laws were "so flexible that fre-quently the slightest indisposition of the mother is used as pretext and the life of the fetus is terminated with the conscience-satisfying excuse that it was necessary to preserve the life of the mother."[46] Weiss went on to argue that abortion was too common, because students were taught to think of it as a first resource:

It is the exceptional teacher and writer on obstetrics and diseases in women that properly instructs his students on this important subject; more often the contrary is true and his lectures abound with reference and explicit directions as to when and how pregnancy should be terminated.

Weiss, contending that many unborn children were dying unnecessarily, hit hard at the standard teaching: "Is it any wonder then that the student who graduates from the classroom with little of no moral instruction goes forth to follow in the steps of Herod in the slaughter of the innocent?"[47] He argued, "If the unborn child had attorney to represent it at the courts of justice there would be a higher regard for its life ..."[48] A decade later, at a meeting of obstetricians and gynecologists, Weiss still was insisting that "therapeutic abortions" were too common. He asked, "Is it any wonder that so many abortions are being performed by the laymen and the quack, when we, as a profession, give them so much leeway and encouragement?"[49]

Physicians' estimates of the efficiency of law went along with their sense of how much law could accomplish. In 1917 Dr. G.D. Royston questioned 51 women who admitted 82 illegal abortions (30 self-induced, 20 done by physicians, 20 by midwives, 12 by drugs) and concluded that nothing would "deter a woman once determined to interrupt her pregnancy."[50] That same year Dr. John Murphy of New York complained that abortionists often dispatched patients to city hospitals confident in the belief that the patients would not be pressed to reveal the source of their affliction: "City hospitals are unwitting abettors of the abortionist ... safe havens for what I might term criminally sick women."[51] Murphy wrote of how he recently asked one patient if a doctor had "sent her to the hospital, and she answered, 'No one, I always come here after my abortions ... And I've told a number of my friends about it.'" Murphy concluded that the hospital "now seems to be a branch of the devil's workshop."[52]

The coming of the "Great War" raised questions about what Americans were fighting for. Dr. Robert McNair wrote in 1918 of "a strong indication of the standing of the criminal abortionist in modern society today, when it is considered how quietly and gracefully his practice is ignored."[53] McNair told of how one abortionist was "cornered, literally red-handed," and arrested, but was soon free and "allowed to roam at large in accordance with his own sweet will. The reason, it would seem, is quite simple, expressed in two words — public sentiment." The United States in the world war was fighting for a "world wide democracy," McNair commented, "but until we look more carefully to correcting the principles that must serve as the foundation to this great social order of progressive democracy, etc., there is serious danger of history repeating itself in the social conditions of ancient Rome ..." McNair concluded that "Huns and the Vandals came from without to pillage and destroy; in reality and it was afterward found out, that the Huns and the Vandals were within the walls of the eternal city."[54]

Complaints continued in the 1920's as Dr. Palmer Findlay of Omaha, after estimating that one in five or six pregnancies was ending in induced abortion, wrote of how hard it was "to convince the lay public that life begins at the moment of impregnation ..."[55] Findlay wrote that "Not one in a thousand [abortionists] is ever held accountable for the crime he commits, "due to difficulties of evidence and reluctance to file complaints. Dr. N.W. Moore similarly noted, "notwithstanding our most drastic laws, the criminal is rarely convicted. If a guilty physician is placed on trial there is very often some sympathetic doctor-friend in his community ready to throw a mantle of charity around him."[56] When the Obstetrics Society of Philadelphia in 1923 discussed ways to limit abortion, no new answers were forthcoming; Dr. Edward Schumann called abortion "an evil which has existed through all time and will continue to exist" with the only hope of limitation "more drastic laws" and "moral training of young people."[57] In the discussion that followed, Dr. John McGlinn said, "We should not ask the Legislature for more laws: we have more laws than we need at the present time and will only have another that will not be enforced because you cannot make people good by legislation."[58]

Doctors who forgot that legislation is education, and stated the question that way — can *laws* make people good? — sometimes gave up when they saw that laws could not. At a symposium in 1908, Dr. Rachell S. Yarros of Chicago insisted "You can not enforce laws ... with which the public has little sympathy. Even

if we could enforce anti-abortion laws the problems would not be solved."[59] At that symposium Dr. J.H. Carstens of Detroit held out little hope for the power of law as long as individuals thought "there is nothing earnest in this world. That it is just made for them and for their pleasure, and everything that interferes with that pleasure they object to and try to do away with ... we shall never accomplish much by law."[60]

And yet, some doctors understood that the law did deter some abortions and save some unborn lives, and that persecution of a few abortionists sent many more running for cover, at least temporarily. In 1927, for example, Dr. E. A. Ficklen of New Orleans argued that hopes for "total abolition of the practice" could not be met, for in 25 states, over a ten-year period, only 44 abortionists were convicted.[61] Ficklen explained why so few convictions were obtained under a Louisiana law that had been tightened in 1919: "In many instances there was a moral certainty of the guilt of the accused, but ... drastic changes in criminal law with the requirements for evidence very much reduced would be necessary before we could expect more convictions."[62] Ficklen concluded that those changes would not be forthcoming, since the community was divided on abortion. And yet, he did not conclude that current laws, although porous, were worthless. Laws that could not put abortionists in jail could at least restrict their practice.[63]

As early as 1906 some medical leaders who saw partial success as failure spoke of abandoning anti-abortion laws. Those who were pro-abortion then began to take advantage of such weariness. Dr. Henry Marcy argued in the Journal of the

American Medical Association that "the product of early impregnation is of so little importance that abortion will not be serioiusly established as a criminal offense.[64] Maximillian Herzog closed one meeting of the Chicago Gynecological Society by opposing the idea of treating abortion at all stages as murder: "To look on an embryo four weeks old as a human being seems to be an exaggerated view."[65] Furthermore, Herzog saw doctors as god-like and argued that even dying declarations should not be allowed in court, since the physician's authority should outweigh a judge's: "Whatever is confided to a physician is not to be divulged in court under any circumstances. The relations of physician and patient ought to be those of absolute confidence."[66]

Dr. William Robinson, who became a leading spokesman for abortion, told the Eastern Medical Society in 1911 that some unmarried women were right to abort their children, and wrote in 1915 that "The evil of abortion is one of the most terrible evils in our society," but only because of its danger to women.[67] Once he saw the problem as one of avoiding unnecessary risk at the hands of a quack, Robinson was able to conclude that "Under our present social and economic conditions the professional abortionist, much we may despise and condemn him, has more than once proved a real benefactor, in preserving the sanity, the health and the life of a frantic young woman and frantic family."[68]

By the early 1930's there was more such talk, and three different positions on abortion had emerged among physicians. On the left Robinson had become openly pro-abortion; he argued that infanticide (under the guise of accidental suffocation or drowning, medical overdose, exposure to cold, or simple abandonment) still was frequent, and that "the legalizing of abortion" would solve the problem.[69] Robinson stated that it was "better to permit the removal of a few inanimate cells" than to have an "unwanted" child born. On the other end of the spectrum from Robinson was Dr. Matthew Liotta, who insisted "on the rights of the unborn child as a human being from the moment of its conception ..."[70] Liotta based his condemnation of abortion squarely on biblical grounds: "The commandment, 'Thou shalt not kill,' binds all men."[71] He saw his fellow physicians as accomplices:

... Never before in all past ages has there been such merciless killing of innocent, helpless and unborn human beings as is going on at the present time.

Atheistic "knowledge" and technical skill were fighting biblical morality, Liotta argued: "It is all very well to know science. What is most needed is the art or skill which enable one to apply the principles of science in a manner pleasing to God."[72]

Many physicians, however, seemed to be in the middle. Robert Ferguson of Charlotte, for example, saw abortion as killing but wanted to be "compassionate." The changed understanding of compassion was evident when Ferguson told of a 14-year-old pregnant girl and asked, "Should not we as organized bodies of medical men apply to the Legislatures of the various States for relief for these unfortunate young girls?" After all, Ferguson argued, "Conceptions of right and wrong change from time to time, and theology, jurisprudence and medicine present radical differences on various points in different countries."[73] He proposed that "The medical profession should work to the end that certain changes might be made in our National and State laws that would permit the prevention of the attaching to our girls of 14 years of age and under the stigma of having borne and illegitimate child."[74] By 1930 the inevitability of induced abortion was assumed. and articles in medical journals debated the effectiveness of conservative or radical post-abortion treatments of women without suggesting ways to avoid that choice in the first place.[75]

At least in hindsight, a reading of hundreds of abortion-related articles in medical journals from the first third of the century shows that when anti-abortion doctors tried to come up with effective "rationalistic" appeals, they sometimes emphasized arguments that had immediate usefulness but would, as it turned out, backfire later on. Rudolph Holmes, for example, proposed that "Arguments concerning the danger of having the operation done are to my mind more effective than too strong presentation of the moral aspect..."[76] However, as abortion became physically safer for the mother, the downplaying of morality began to hurt. So did the tendency of some to decree that religious concerns should play no part in the abortion debate. Although a Cleveland doctor, Rolande E. Skeel, complained after one discussion of "a very unfortunate thing indeed that a theological viewpoint has been allowed to enter that which should be a calm scientific consideration of a medical viewpoint," calm examinations apart from biblical presuppositions tended to lead to more abortions.[77] This was particularly true as — in the words of Dr. J.D. Roberts — "parents of illegitimate children, prompted by the anxiety of the situation with disgrace and ostracism before them, "pleaded with doctors to find them "any path out of the difficulty, regardless of law and morals."[78]

Sigmund Zeisler of the Chicago Gynecological Society proposed another method of approach that would haunt the anti-abortion movement. Zeisler wrote, "Whenever a moral question comes up for consideration, I always like to fall back on the old Kantian categorical imperative which is about as follows, 'Always act thus, that the motive underlying your actions may furnish the principle for a general law.'"[79] The categorical imperative for an abortionist, Zeisler wrote, meant

that everybody should commit abortion and that every pregnant woman should allow or consent to the abortion. What then would become of this world? ...That anything should ever become a general practice which would result in the total annihilation of the human race cannot be contemplated with degree of ease of mind. Hence it is self-evident that abortion is wrong, that it really needs no discussion from the moral point of view.[80]

Such an argument would not be compelling in later years when ideas of "overpopulation" became popular.

Some arguments did not take so long to turn around. Dr. Wilbur Krusen, in an echo of spiritualist thinking, argued that it "is the right of every child to be well-born," yet "many an embryo is launched even upon an ante-natal career with a justifiable grievance."[81] Five years later Dr. James P. Warrbasse was arguing that the Child should not force itself upon parents that do not want it. It is so apt to find its self in an uncongenial atmosphere that three are caused to suffer where two were happy before ... Were the unconceived child to speak it might say, 'Let me be created in love and born only as a gift to parents whose hands are held out with loving welcome to receive me. Spare me from the hostile frown of my creators.' A babe is so important a thing that it is only deserving of loving parents...

From there it was only one small step to aborting the "thing" to save it.[82]

Other attempts to make anti-abortion arguments without regard to theology also have a modern pro-abortion ring. Dr. Allen Gilbert wrote in *Pediatrics* that "Individual self-consciousness does not occur until the 2nd or 3rd year of life. Only then can the child say, 'I am.' Until then the child has the 'possibility of personality."[83] Gilbert stated that the possibility occurs with conception, so abortion should not be allowed: "a life *in utero* is sacred in that it represents the possibility of self-consciousness..."[84] But others would take that statement of "possibility" as an opportunity to treat the unborn child as sub-human.

What many of these arguments had in common was their pragmatism. Dr. J. D. Roberts of North Carolina complained that the abortion-prone were not listening to doctors:

Speak with as much authority as we may, urge as we have done for ages past as a profession, frown upon the practice, condemn it as iniquitous, censure the perpetrators as criminals, murderers; remonstrate with them with all our force, still ... the God-given edict from

Sinai's Mount 'Thou shalt not kill' is disregarded [by] the people of a corrupt and profligate time.[85]

Roberts noted that many doctors, either out of frustration or their own religious beliefs were moving away from moral appeals and speaking against abortion on utilitarian grounds. Increasingly, the anti-abortion house appeared to be built on sand. The utilitarianism was reflected in early twentieth century popular medical encyclopedias; unlike their late nineteenth century predecessors, those that contained anti-abortion warnings generally stood only on utilitarian ground. For example, *The Household Physician: A Twentieth Century Medic* warned that "various womb complaints are the usual accompaniments" of abortion, and capable of "ruining the future life or usefulness of the woman."[86] *The Century Book of Health* "warn[ed] women of the folly and danger" of abortion, and contended that "death frequently results from the employment of such means as are necessary to produce abortion."[87] But with the maternal death rate in abortion about two percent, desperate women outside of marriage could possibly take the chance.

Utilitarianism was so dominant that some medical books even had titles such as *The Human Machine: Its Care and Repair*.[88] Other popular books had only brief mentions of abortion. Edgar Maryott's *The New Medical World* simply noted that "Miscarriages criminally procured are to be deprecated, and any man or woman carrying on such unrighteous business should be dealt with as a base criminal."[89] A monstrously-long book such as *Health Knowledge* (1,525 pages) discussed suppression of menses, and — in the style of an

earlier century — recommended use of Cotton root, aloes, and other medication.[90] In all of those 1,525 pages just nineteen words specifically commented on abortion: "Criminal abortion means that the womb was emptied intentionally. This is caused by taking drugs, or opening the womb."[91] Emphases on illegality and danger to the woman proved to be weak later in the century; once utilitarian thinking became supreme the battle, in the long run, was lost.

"We are apt to grow sluggish, we are apt to go a little with the tide," Dr. George Phillips had warned in 1896.[92] Three decades later, Dr. W.C. Bowers observed that "pressure is brought to bear on every physician from the day he opens his office till the end of his life, to have him commit abortion." Bowers said, "If he loses sight of the criminality of the affair, and the moral responsibility he takes, he is sometimes inclined to aid people who seem in very distressing circumstances, but if he ever does he has started down the hill."[93]

REFERENCE NOTES

1. Robert Thrift Ferguson, "Abortion and Abortionist," *Southern Medicine and Surgery*, Vol. 93 (December, 1931), p. 889.
2. Ibid.
3. Ibid., p. 892.
4. Rev. F. Heirmann, "Ethical and Religious Objections to Criminal Abortion," paper read before the Academy of Medicine of Toledo and Lucas County, January 27, 1905; *Toledo Medical and Surgical Reporter*, Vol. 31 (1905), p. 233. Heirmann was president of St. John's College.
5. Ibid., p. 234.
6. Ibid., p. 235. Heirmann noted that killing in "just wars" and self-defense, as capital punishment for crimes committed, was allowable.
7. C.S. Bacon, "The Duty of the Medical Profession in Criminal Abortion," symposium before the Chicago Medical Society, November 23,

1904; *Illinois Medical Journal*, Vol. 7 (1904), p. 18.

8. Ibid.

9. Ibid., p. 19. Bacon also opposed euthanasia: a person should not be deprived of life, Bacon said, even if "he be diseased, unconscious, worthless or for any reason whatever unless the State represented by its judicial officers decides that he has forfeited his life by his crimes and rendered its extinction necessary for the welfare of the state."

10. W.S. Carroll, "The Rights of the Unborn Child," *The Pennsylvania Medical Journal*, vol. 13 (1909-1910), p. 936. Carroll stated that the woman who had an abortion done upon her was not guilty under the statute particularly related to abortion.

11. Carroll, p. 941.

12. Earnest F. Oakley, Jr., "Legal Aspects of Abortion," *American Journal of Obstetrics and Gynecology*, Vol. 3 (1922), pp. 37-41.

13. Dr. M.O. Heckard, symposium remarks in the *Illinois Medical Journal*, Vol. 7 (1904), p. 42.

14. Ibid.

15. Ibid., pp. 40-41.

16. Ibid., p. 37.

17. *Providence Medical Journal*, Vol. 4 (1903), pp. 57-59.

18. Discussion at 1907 meeting of the Academy, *Bulletin*, Vol. 8 (1907), p. 347.

19. *Journal of the American Medical Association*, Vol. II (1908), p. 960.

20. Bacon, p. 21.

21. Ibid., p. 21.

22. *Journal of the American Medical Association*, Vol. III (1908), p. 957.

23. Minutes of the Chicago Medical Society, Vol. 17, October, 1905-June, 1907.

24. Dr. Rudolph Holmes, "The Methods of the Professional Abortionist," *Journal of Surgery, Gynecology and Obstetrics*, Vol. 10 (1910), p. 542.

25. Ibid., p. 543. Holmes added, "In Boston, a coterie of some four or five abortionists adopted this method — the operator would enter the room masked. One of these men confided in a lawyer that he and his associates were doing like 800 to 1,000 a year."

26. Ibid., p. 542.

27. *Journal of the American Medical Association*, Vol. II (1908), p. 960.

28. Holmes also placed hopes on education: Young people "will know facts and will live accordingly. Many now make themselves believe that there is no life until the movements are felt. When the false teaching in this respect is put aside good will be accomplished." Holton similarly concluded, "I believe it is a matter of education to a great extent."

29. Walter B. Dorsett, "Criminal Abortion in its Broadest Sense", *Journal of the American Medical Association*, Vol. II (1908), p. 957.

30. Ibid.

31. Dr. E. A. Weiss, "Some Moral and Ethical Aspects of Foeticide," a paper read at the Annual Meeting of the American Association of Obstetricians and Gynecologists, Toledo, September 17-19, 1912; *American Journal of Obstetrics*, Vol. 67 (1913), p. 78.

32. M.S. Iseman, M.D., **Race Suicide** (New York: The Cosmopolitan Press, 1912), p. 140.

33. Ibid.

34. Ibid., p. 141.

35. Ibid., p. 143.

36. Ibid., p. 152.

37. Ibid., p. 153.

38. Ibid., p. 158.

39. Ibid., pp. 153-154.

40. Ibid., p. 199.

41. Ibid., p. 155.

42. Dr. Frank A. Higgins, "The Proper Indications and Methods for the Termination of Pregnancy," paper read at American Medical Association's 1904 Meeting, Section on Obstetrics and Diseases of Women, in the *Journal of the American Medical Association*, Vol. 43 (1904), p. 1531.

43. Ibid., p. 1531.

44. Charles Jewett, "Indication for Artificial Abortion in the First Three Months of Pregnancy," *New York State Journal of Medicine*, Vol. 8 (1908), p. 113.

45. *Journal of Surgery, Gynecology and Obstetrics*, Vol. 10 (1910), p. 548.

46. *American Journal of Obstetrics*, Vol. 67 (1913), p. 79.

47. Ibid.

48. Ibid., pp. 74-75.

49. *American Journal of Obstetrics and Gynecology*, Vol. 3 (1922), p. 46.

50. G.D. Royston, "A Statistical Study of the Causes of Abortion," *American Journal of Obstetrics and Diseases of Women and Children*, Vol. 76 (1917), p. 582.

51. John C. Murphy, "Are Municipal Hospitals Unwitting Aids to Abortionists?" *The Medical Times*, Vol. 45 (April 1917), p. 103.

52. Ibid.

53. Robert McNair, "Status of the Abortionist in the Modern Social Order," *New York Medical Journal*, Vol. 107 (March 16, 1918), p. 503.

54. Ibid.

55. Palmer Findlay, "The Slaughter of the Innocents," *American Journal of Obstetrics and Gynecology*, Vol. 3 (1922), p. 35.

56. N.W. Moore, "Abortion, Crimial and Inevitable," paper read before the Kentucky State Medical Association, October, 1922, *Kentucky Medical Journal*, Vol. 21 (1923), p. 332. Moore added, "Many places offer help, and when an unmarried woman becomes pregnant and consults me as to how to dispose of her case, I refer her to one of these institutions."

57. Dr. Edward A. Schumann, "The Economic Aspects," *The American Journal of Obstetrics and Gynecology*, (1924), p. 485.

58. Ibid., p. 486.

59. *Journal of the American Medical Association*, Vol. 48 (1908), p. 548. She added, "Many women say that if they had a little support from the man, they would not think of having an abortion performed."

60. Ibid.

61. E. A. Ficklen, "Some Phases of Criminal Abortion," paper given before the Orleans Parish Medical Society, March 28, 1927; in *New Orleans Medical and Surgical Journal*, Vol. 79 (1926-1927), pp. 884-893.

62. Ibid, p. 886.

63. Other means of restriction also could be useful. Dr. Edwin B. Harvey of Boston, for example, argued for containment by stripping known abortionists of their medical licenses. "The whole business of medical practice is curative, treating diseased persons for the purpose of mitigation of cure," Harvey noted: "What disease is the abortionist trying to alleviate or cure?"

64. Henry Marcy, "Education as a Factor in the Prevention of Criminal Abortion and Illegitimacy," *Journal of the American Medical Association*, Vol. 47 (1906), p. 1889.

65. *Journal of Surgery, Gynecology and Obstetrics*, Vol. 10 (1910), p. 550.

66. Ibid.

67. Dr. William Robinson, **Fewer and Better Babies, or the Limitation of Offspring** (New York: Critic and Guide, 1915), p. 121.

68. Robinson, p. 133. Robinson also cited (pp. 224-225) a European pro-abortion literature that was springing up.

69. William J. Robinson, "Abortion and Infanticide," *American Medicine*, Vol. 39(1933), p. 70. He expanded on these ideas in his book, **The Law Against Abortion** (New York: Eugenics Publishing Co., 1933), which will be discussed in chapter eleven.

70. Matthew A. Liotta, **The Unborn Child** (New York: Liotta, 1931) preface.

71. Ibid., pp. 9, 12-13. Liotta wrote, "God's punishments are meted out to everyone who recommends or makes use of any method that will cause an abortion."

72. Ibid., pp. 11-12.

73. Robert Thrift Ferguson, "Abortion and Abortionist," *Southern Medicine and Surgery*, Vol. 93 (December, 1931), p. 889.

74. Ibid., p. 892.

75. H.C. Hesseltine, "Indications for the Treatment in Abortions," *Journal of the Iowa State Medical Society*, Vol. 20 (1930), p. 406.

76. Rudolph Wieser Holmes, M.D., "Criminal Abortions; A Brief Consideration of its Relation to Newspaper Advertising — A Report of a Medico-Legal Case," *Illinois Medical Journal*, Vol. 7 (1905), p. 30.

77. *American Journal of Obstetrics*, Vol. 67 (1913), p. 81.

78. J.D. Roberts, "Criminal Abortion," *Carolina Medical Journal*, Vol. 46 (1900), p. 135. Roberts asked that educational efforts by doctors continue, but that the vice be condemned from the pulpit; he had heard that done only once, "tho' more murders are annually committed in this way than all others combined."

79. Sigmund Zeisler, "The Legal and Moral Aspects of Abortion," remarks at the 1910 meeting of the Chicago Gynecological Society, printed in the *Journal of Surgery, Gynecology and Obstetrics*, Vol. 10, p. 539.

80. Ibid., p. 540.

81. *Therapeutic Gazette*, Vol. 34 (1910), p. 162.

82. James Warrbasse, "Let Me be Created in Love," in **Critic and Guide,** and Robinson, pp. 244-245.

83. Dr. J. Allen Gilbert, "The Advent of Self-Consciousness and Its Relation to the Crime of Abortion," *Pediatrics*, Vol. 13 (1902), p. 296.

84. Ibid., p. 298.

85. J.D. Roberts, p. 131. Roberts noted that Christian teachings were being overlooked as pagan ideas came back into vogue.

86. **The Household Physician; A Twentieth Century Medic** (Boston: Woodruff, 1909).

87. **Century Book of Health** (Springfield, Mass: King-Richardson, 1912) pp. 486-487.

88. **The Human Machine: Its Care and Repair** (Topeka: Herbert S. Reed, 1905).

89. **The New Medical World** (Springfield, Mass.: Hampden Publishing, 1906), p. 531.

90. J.L. Corish, **Health Knowledge** (New York: Domestic Health Society, 1919), p. 69.

91. Ibid.

92. George A. Phillips, "Criminal Abortion: Its Frequency, Prognosis, and Treatment," *Maine Medical Association Medical Transactions*, Vol. 12 (1895-1897), p. 308.

93. Fernald, p. 64.

The Case for Routine Neonatal Circumcision

James L. Fletcher, Jr., M.D.

Dr. Fletcher is a graduate of Vanderbilt University School of Medicine and completed a residency in Family Medicine at the University of Connecticut School of Medicine. After practicing in Sparta, Tennessee, and Atlanta, Georgia, he joined the faculty of the Medical College of Georgia in Augusta, where he is Associate Professor of Family Medicine.

Routine neonatal circumcision is the most commonly performed operation in the United States. Annually from one to one-and-a-half million baby boys lose their foreskins in the neonatal period. Circumcision has a long history of acceptance in this country and did not begin to face any serious opposition until about the 1950's when an anti-circumcision movement began to surface. Since that time, this group of opponents has grown in numbers and in vehemence so as to exert significant social and medical influence in some areas, notably the West Coast. It is the purpose of this paper to show that there is substantial medical evidence to support the practice of routine neonatal circumcision.

Circumcision is an ancient surgical procedure. It supposedly arose independently in many parts of the world. It is depicted on the tomb of Egyptian King Ankh-Mahn, circa 3,000 B.C.[1] As far as the western world is concerned, the origin and justification for neonatal circumcision can be traced to the Bible and the Jewish patriarch, Abraham.[2] The United States stands in rather stark contrast to most of the rest of today's world. In the United States today about 4 out of 5 boys are circumcised, whereas the rate of circumcision is falling in most of the rest of the world, and especially in Europe where the rate of neonatal circumcision is typically much less than 10%.[1,3]

The Medical Fuss

Official medical flack aimed at circumcision may be traced to 1971 when the American Academy of Pediatrics, which typically claims to represent practicing pediatricians in the U.S., stated: "There is no valid medical indications for circumcision in the newborn."[4] They re-affirmed this stance in 1975, and in 1978 the American College of Obstetricians and Gynecologists threw their official weight behind this position. Whatever else these statements meant, they had two very practical results. First, they encouraged a lot of physicians, and especially young physicians in training, to begin attempts to talk parents out of circumcising their infants (I can well remember that pressure when I was a resident physician in the late 1970's). Second, insurance companies listened, and a number of them have begun to refuse to pay for routine circumcision. Thus this medical/political statement against circumcision has had a rather significant impact.

The Natural History of the Foreskin

It is not until shortly before birth that the fetal prepuce, or foreskin, begins to separate, and in most cases the foreskin is not readily retractable at the time of birth. Thus, in the typical neonate, it cannot be pulled back over the bulbous tip of the penis (glans penis). In his classic study of the natural history of the foreskin, Gairdner[5] showed that only about 4% of newborn boys will have a retractable foreskin. By a year of age, the number has risen to 50%. By 4 years of age, it is 90%, but that still leaves 10%. In fact, in his study, Gairdner showed that in a series of 200 boys, age 5 to 10 years, fully 6% of them did not have a retractable foreskin.

What are the medical consequences of partially retractable or unretractable foreskins? Phimosis or paraphimosis may occur. Phimosis is a stenosis (tightening) of the preputial opening so that the foreskin cannot be retracted. Paraphimosis is a condition where the opening of the foreskin is pulled back over the glans but gets "stuck" there and cannot be moved distally again. This leads to swelling and a very uncomfortable penis. Balanitis, infection and inflammation of the glans penis, and posthitis, infection and inflammation of the foreskin, can occur separately or concomitantly as balanoposthitis. Studies show that from 5 - 14% of boys who are not circumcised as newborns will later require circumcision for phimosis, paraphimosis or recurrent balanoposthitis.[1,6]

But why should we consider routine neonatal circumcision of all boys? There certainly are some males who should not be circumcised, at least as newborns.[7] Should we not just wait for subsequent problems such as balanoposthitis to develop and treat them when they appear? Is there any scientific rationale for recommending newborn circumcision as a general policy?

Penile Problems: A Closer Look

As noted, the three most common penile problems uncircumcised boys and men might develop are phimosis, paraphimosis, and balanoposthitis. Balanitis is commonest in young boys 2 to 5 years of age. Fewer than 4% of boys will be affected by this problem, yet when we consider the total number of young boys in the United States, its significance cannot be ignored. Most boys have only a single episode.[8] Phimosis has a peak incidence in older boys, quite possible after recurrent episodes of balanoposthitis, usually between the ages of 6 to 10 years.[9]

Providing a temporal perspective, Ferguson and colleagues in New Zealand[10] followed prospectively a group of 146 circumcised and 445 uncircumcised boys from birth to 8 years of age, documenting episodes of balanitis, meatitis, posthitis, "sore penis," phimosis, inadequate circumcision, and postoperative infection. After one year of age the uncircumcised children had a higher rate of problems: 17.2% vs. 6.5% (statistically significant at the .01 level).

What about penile problems in older men? How do they relate to circumcision status? Some California investigators[11] published a two-part study. The first portion was a cross-sectional evaluation of 398 men presenting to a dermatology clinic for a variety of problems. The doctors checked them all for balanitis and found it to be present in 28. Among these 28, 18% were circumcised, 82% were uncircumcised; thus there was about a five-fold greater risk of the disorder among the uncircumcised men. They also found that in patients with co-existing diabetes, balanitis occurred in about one of three uncircumcised patients; there were no circumcised diabetics who had balanitis. The retrospective second part of the study examined 67 circumcisions performed over a 3-year period. Twenty-nine percent of these operations were for recurrent balanitis, 44 percent for phimosis. Diabetes was again very frequent in the group circumcised for balanitis. Thus older men also have penile problems, especially uncircumcised and diabetic men. (Perhaps, we'd be wise to circumcise all future diabetic males at birth — if only we knew who they were.)

Yet, it must be conceded, there are complications of neonatal circumcision. As the anti-circumcision movement has grown, there has been press coverage of so-called circumcision "disasters." In reality, serious complications are quite infrequent. Various studies suggest an overall complication rate of somewhere between 0.06 and 0.6%.[1,6] Infection, bleeding and failure to remove an adequate amount of foreskin are the most common. Significant bleeding is said to occur in about 1% of circumcisions; this is usually minor and can be controlled with minor hemostatic procedures. True disasters, like necrosis of the glans penis, are really quite rare, although they have been greatly discussed by the media. Death as a complication is almost unheard of. Perhaps 4 deaths have occurred in the U.S., one of which was a ritual circumcision performed at home by a non-physician. In recent reports from 500,000 patients in New York City and 175,000 in U.S. Army Hospitals, there were no deaths associated with circumcision. Details on other serious circumcision complications have recently been published,[6,12] and are not notably frightening.

Thomas Wiswell, a neonatologist now at Walter Reed Hospital, has done extensive research on circumcision vs. uncircumcision. In 1989 he published his evaluation of over 136,000 boys born in army hospitals; between 1980 and 1985 medical records were reviewed for complications related to circumcision status during the first month of life. Among the circumcised boys (over 100,000), he found 193 complications, or an overall rate of about 0.2%, and no deaths. Among the uncircumcised boys (nearly 36,000), there were 88 complications, or again a rate of about 0.2%, and two deaths.[12]

Breaking these complications down into specifics, among the circumcised boys, there were 83 who bled excessively after the procedure, most of whom required no sutures (stitches). Only 3 of these required transfusions; subsequently it was discovered that two of these three infants were classic hemophiliacs. The second most common complication was minor local infection (cellulitis), occurring in 60 infants. There were no deaths, and no loss of the glans or entire penis. Among the uncircumcised boys, urinary tract infections (UTI's) accounted for all the complications — 88 of them. Thirty-two of these 88 had concomitant bacteremia (blood poisoning), three developed meningitis, two developed kidney failure, and, as noted, there were two deaths. Thus, while the overall complication rates were about equal, complications were more severe in the group of uncircumcised boys in the first month of life. (The rate of UTI's among uncircumcised vs. circumcised boys was statistically significant at the 0.0001 level, the rate of bacteremia significant at the 0.0002 level.)

Urinary Tract Infections

Let us now focus upon the subject of UTI's among infant boys. Ginsberg and McCracken[13] initiated this controversy when, in 1982, they published their findings of a study of 100 infants, 5 days to 8 months of age, admitted to the hospital with their first UTI. The investigators wanted to discover what unusual characteristics these infants shared. They found a preponderance of UTI's among males during the first three months of life; 75% of the infections were among males vs. females, in marked contradistinction to what occurs in later childhood. Among the infant females infected, 45% of them had X-ray evidence of abnormal urinary systems, but only 7% of the boys did. Somewhat to their surprise, 95% of the infected boys were uncircumcised. This led the investigators to ask the question: Does uncircumcision increase the risk of UTI among infant males?

Subsequently, Dr. Wiswell picked up the investigative ball and ran with it. He and his colleagues at Brooke Army Hospital studied[14] nearly 5300 infants born over an 18 month period. Four hundred of these infants were evaluated sometime before 1 year of age for UTI (34 of the 41 infected were less than 3 months of age). They compared females to males, and circumcised to uncircumcised males. In this study there were 13 infections among females (a rate of 0.04%), 4 infections among circumcised males (a rate of 0.2%), and 24 infections among uncircumcised males (a rate of 4.12%) Thus, uncircumcised male infants had many more infections than both females (statistically significant at the 0.01 level), and circumcised males (a 20-fold difference statistically significant at the 0.001 level). The investigators concluded that circumcision might reduce meatal (penile urinary opening) bacterial contamination, and thus, subsequent infection.

In 1986 Wiswell and Roscelli[15] published a study involving a huge number of subjects. From 55 army hospitals world-wide they evaluated more than 400,000 infants born over a 10-year period, 1800 of whom (0.43%) subsequently developed a UTI during the first year of life. As these data were categorized, they found a rate of infection among females of 0.5%, found younger males more likely to be infected than females, and found that circumcised males had a rate of 0.11% infection vs. uncircumcised males with an infection rate of 1.12%. Uncircumcised boys accounted for only 10% of the study population, but for 26% of total UTI's and 71% of male UTI's. Thus, although they were a small proportion of the population, most of the UTI's were in this subgroup of uncircumcised males.

Hertzog[16] published another case-control study in 1989. She studied all males less than a year of age who had a urine culture as part of an evaluation of acute illness at Boston Children's Hospital during 1985-86. She defined cases as those who had greater than 100,000 bacterial per urine culture result; there were 36.

There were 76 controls, defined as those with less than 1,000 bacteria per culture result. The urine specimens were all obtained either by suprapubic tap (with a needle) or a catheter specimen. Thus these were "clean" specimens and not the typical "dirty" (contaminated) bag urines that are so often obtained in the physician's office or the emergency room and which are so prone to grow contaminant bacteria (which have nothing to do with a UTI). This investigator also analyzed demographics, including age, ethnic group, type of health insurance (as a proxy for socioeconomic status), and the method of obtaining a culture specimen. Her findings showed that all of the cases were uncircumcised, whereas only 32% of the controls were uncircumcised. This was highly statistically significant. She concluded that uncircumcision seems to be a highly significant risk factor for UTI in male infants up to one year of age. Her analysis also showed that regardless of the patient's ethnic group or socioeconomic status, the risk was still 39 times higher for uncircumcised boys to develop a UTI; thus she confirmed the work of Wiswell.

Finally, Crane and Gershel,[17] published a prospective study in 1990. This was an examination of 442 infants less than 8 weeks of age presenting to the emergency room with fever. Among these febrile infants, 33 (7.5%) of them had a UTI; two of these infants were bacteremic. The investigators found that 22 of the 33 UTI's were in males; 18 of the 22 infected males were uncircumcised. Again, they concluded that uncircumcised male infants are at higher risk of developing UTI's.

Looking at the UTI and circumcision data from a different angle, Wiswell and colleagues[18] noted that beginning in the late 70's, during the anti-circumcision "push," a decline in the frequency of circumcision occurred among male infants born in army hospitals. Wiswell asked the question: What happened to the incidence of UTI's in male infants during this period of a slight decline in circumcision? He showed that concomitant with a decreasing frequency of circumcision, there also occurred an increasing frequency of UTI's in male infants. Cause and effect are difficult to prove, but this data analysis was very suggestive that as fewer male babies were circumcised, more of them developed UTI's at a young age.

What about the microbiology and pathophysiology of UTI's in infants? Why should uncircumcised males get more UTI's? Wiswell and colleagues[19] posed the question: Is there a difference in the periurethreal flora, bacteria which grow around the urinary operning at the tip of the penis, in circumcised vs. uncircumcised infants? They cultured (for bacteria) 25 circumcised and 25 uncircumcised boys at ages 2 days, 2 weeks, and 2, 4, 6 and 12 months. They obtained both intraurethral (interior) cultures and circumferential (exterior) glans cultures. Results showed that uncircumcised boys had significantly higher colony counts (numbers of bacteria) at all ages except 12 months. And specifically, gram negative uropathogens were cultured more frequently from the urethras of uncircumcised boys as 2, 4, and 6 months of age. Wiswell's conclusion was that there is a difference in the flora of uncircumcised vs. circumcised boys 6 months of age and younger. The presence of a foreskin is associated with greater quantities of both periurethral bacteria and specific potential uropathogens.

Thus, the data supporting the hypothesis that uncircumcised male infants have a higher risk of developing UTI's is becoming overwhelming. What difference does it make? After all, we are living in the days of powerful antibiotics. Can't we just admit the unfortunate uncircumcised little boys who get UTI's to the hospital, treat them, and watch them recover? We could. But it turns out that there are some potential short-and long-term sequelae of UTI's in children.

The most serious short-term complication is death. In a recent study, Bonadio and colleagues[20] analyzed 91 cases of sepsis (blood infection) with *Escherichia coli*, the most common uropathogen. About one-third of these sepsis cases were secondary to a UTI among the affected children, nearly two-thirds of whom were less than 12 months old. Overall, one child in twelve with sepsis died. Thus UTI is not necessarily a benign affliction even with modern antibiotic therapy.

Regarding long-term sequelae, in a study done in Sweden, a small number of patients (30) were followed closely for a long time, 27 years. These were patients with focal renal scarring, as documented by intravenous pyelography (X-ray studies), related to pyelonephritis (kidney infection) early in childhood. The authors looked for high blood pressure and other complications of kidney damage. What they found after 27 years of follow-up was that one-tenth of these patients had developed end-stage renal disease. Seven patients had developed high blood pressure. Two of the 16 women had developed high blood pressure during pregnancy. Among 20 patients with no end-stage renal disease or renal surgery, all of them had a lower glomerular filtration rate, higher di-

astolic blood pressures, higher mean arterial pressures, and higher plama renin activity, vs. healthy age-matched controls. The Swedish investigators concluded that children with focal renal scarring due to early pyelonephritis have a higher risk of long-term kidney sequelae.[21]

We also know that long-term sequelae are significant in terms of the percentage of children they affect. We know that acute pyelonephritis early in life is associated with a greater risk of renal damage than infection later in life. We don't know why this is, but the younger the child, the greater the risk of significant damage. We know that 10-15% of infants with pyelonephritis will subsequently develop renal scarring. We know the incidence of high blood pressure in children with renal scarring is greater than 10%, and we know that scarring due to pyelonephritis is the commonest cause of hypertension in children.[21-24] Thus, early UTI's in children may have a significant effect upon their later health.

Sexually Transmitted Diseases

Let us turn our attention to sexually transmitted diseases (STD's). The conclusions we may draw regarding circumcision status and STD's are perhaps less convincing than those regarding UTI's. Taylor and Rodin[25] published a report evaluating 214 male clinic patients with genital herpes. They compared them to 410 randomly selected control patients, from the same London clinic, without genital herpes. The percentage of circumcision in the control group was double that in the herpes group; or turning it around the another way, uncircumcised men seeking care in this clinic had double the risk of having genital herpes as compared to otherwise similar circumcised patients (statistically significant at the 0.01 level).

A study from Australia, evaluating 848 men with STD's and 471 controls drawn from the same STD clinic population, demonstrated a significant association between the uncircumcised state and genital herpes, gonorrhea, candidiasis, and syphilis. In this study, patients were about 2.7 times more likely to contract herpes, 2.3 times more likely to have gonorrhea, 5 times more likely to have candidiasis (yeast), and over 5 times more likely to have syphilis if they were uncircumcised. These investigators found no increased associated risk for nonspecific urethritis, genital warts, chlamydia, crab lice, or scabies, however.[26] Other authors have published different conclusions regarding some of these same diseases.

In a study from Singapore, the authors were seeking etiologic agents of purulent penile ulcers among 80 patients. They isolated *Haemophilus ducreyi*, the causative organism of chancroid, from 18 men among the 80 that they studied. Only one of these men was Malayan; the remainder were Indian and Chinese. What did this mean? In Singapore the Malayan people, being mainly Islamic, circumcise their infants. Indians and Chinese do not. Therefore, the authors concluded that circumcision protects against chancroid, another STD.[27]

When the American Academy of Pediatrics reconvened their Task Force on Circumcision in 1988 and published an updated report, they stated: "Although published reports suggest that chancroid, syphilis, human papillomavirus, and herpes virus type 2, are more frequent in uncir-

cumcised men, methodologic problems render these reports themselves inconclusive."[28] Thus they granted that there was suggestive evidence relating the uncircumcised state to certain types of STD's, but were unwilling to say it was conclusive.

But what about *the* STD of our age: Human immunodeficiency virus (HIV) infection? A study from Nairobi, Kenya, published in 1988, showed that 11% of 340 men attending an STD clinic were HIV-positive. These men were categorized in terms of risk factors. Men with genital ulcers were about 7 times more likely to be HIV-infected. Uncircumcised men were about 2.7 times more likely to be HIV-infected. The authors showed that both uncircumcised state and genital ulcer history were risk factors independent of each other. They concluded, "Intact foreskin [uncircumcised state] may operate to increase susceptibility to HIV."[29]

In a subsequent prospective study, 8.2% of 422 men who had acquired an STD from prostitutes (African prostitutes with an 85% HIV positivity rate) seroconverted over a short followup period. Newly acquired infection was independently associated with acquisition of genital ulcer disease and being uncircumcised. The relative risk among uncircumcised men was over 8 times that of circumcised men. These authors implied that differences in the prevalence of genital ulcers and (lack of) circumcision practices may largely explain the significantly higher heterosexual transmission rates of HIV infection in Africa (vs. the West).[30]

These two studies and other similar data led Dr. Thomas Quinn, an oft-quoted epidemiologist from the National Institutes of Allergy and Infectious Diseases, to say this: "The

finding of increased HIV infectivity among uncircumcised African men suggests that circumcision should be advocated, just as we advocate condoms. We've got to do everything we can do decrease the rate of transmission of AIDS."[31]

Cancer of the Penis

In the United States a man's risk of developing penile cancer is rather small (about one in 600). Yet more than one thousand men are newly diagnosed with it each year, and the associated mortality rate is as high as 25 percent. Each year in the United States about 300 men will die of cancer of the penis. Penile cancer is typically located toward the tip of the penis (on the glans, the coronal sulcus, or the distal shaft), and the malignancy tends to be associated with lower socioeconomic class and poor hygiene. It is almost exclusively a disease of uncircumcised men.

In my research of the medical literature, I've been able to tally only 11 cases of penile cancer reported in men circumcised as neonates.[32-34] These men had, in some cases, rather unusual risk factors, such as antecedent penile trauma or exposure to potentially toxic agricultural chemicals. Nonetheless, these cases are the significant exceptions. The rule is that circumcision provides nearly perfect prophylaxis against penile cancer. In a study from Bombay, Paymaster and Gangadharan[35] examined nearly a thousand cases of penile cancer over a 22-year period. They found that the great majority of cases of penile cancer occurred among Hindus, Christians and Parsees, who never practice newborn circumcision. There were none among Jews (who were circumcised, of course, as newborns). Among Muslims, who in India circumcise their boys between ages of 3 and 12 years, they found an intermediate number of cases (12).

The reconvened Task Force on Circumcision of the American Academy of Pediatrics concluded this about penile cancer: "The decision not to circumcise a male infant must be accompanied by a lifetime commitment to genital hygiene to minimize the risk of penile cancer developing."[28] The question a reasonable physician must pose in response to this statement is how certain can one be that his or her newborn male patients will subsequently always practice scrupulous penile hygiene or never be sexually promiscuous? In fact, there is *no* experimental data to support the hypothesis that optimal penile hygiene (whatever exactly that is) averts the potential hazards of the uncircumcised state. Such studies, necessary support for anti-circumcision advocacy of hygiene for the prevention of penile complications, simply haven't been done.

Perhaps it is best said as Warner and Strassen wrote: "Neonatal circumcision would remove the voluntary aspect of personal hygiene programs. It would eliminate the need to monitor young boys for retractibility of their foreskins and prevent circumcision from having to be performed at a later age when it could be more dangerous and more traumatic."[1] Circumcision facilitates penile hygiene. Certainly, it is not that hygiene cannot be attempted in the uncircumcised state, but how often is it done properly?

Female Complications of Male Uncircumcision

Finally, let us turn to cancer in the female. The relationship of circumcision and uterine cervical can-cer has been hotly debated. Investigators of past years had noticed that Jewish women had a much lower incidence of cervical cancer. We know that cervical cancer in the female is related to STD's (especially human papillomaviruses and perhaps herpes type 2). We know such cancer is related to sexual activity at an early age, frequent coitus, promiscuity — common sense risk factors. We know that cervical cancer is virtually unknown in nuns and other virgins.

In 1981 Irving Kessler, an expert in gynecologic oncology, wrote that after several decades of observations and epidemiological investigations, cervical cancer does, indeed, behave as if it were an STD.[36] In an interesting study begun in 1973, he and his colleagues observed women married to men who had had previous wives who had developed cervical cancer. They traced 1762 case wives and 1493 control subjects. There were 54 case wives and 20 control women who developed cervical cancer, suggesting that women marrying men previously married to wives with cervical cancer incurred a nearly three-fold increase in the risk of cervical cancer. These males appeared to sexually transmit a risk factor for cervical cancer to coital contacts. We now suspect that this risk factor is human papillomavirus.

In a study from Puerto Rico where they have a central cancer registry, Martinez[37] studied the frequency of cervical cancer among wives of men with penile cancer. There were 889 cases of penile cancer observed over 22 years in this registry. Martinez chose 889 controls with different types of cancer (e.g., mouth, pharynx, esophagus, stomach) and matched them for year of diagnosis and age. He found 8 cases of cervical cancer among wives of men with pe-nile cancer (only 1.2 cases would have been expected). He found no cases among control wives. Again, this suggests a transmissable factor related to penile cancer in men and cervical cancer in women.

Conclusion

Thus I have attempted to demonstrate that routine neonatal circumcision is medically beneficial. It facilitates lifelong penile hygiene, which may in turn help prevent several other potentially serious, even lethal, health problems. Research clearly indicates that uncircumcised males have a greater incidence of penile problems (e.g., balanoposthitis), albeit usually of minor severity.[10,11,38] The mounting evidence overwhelmingly suggests that neonatal circumcision is a significant factor in prevention of early UTI's among boys,[12,20] UTI's which may lead to fatal sepsis or subsequent kidney problems and high blood pressure.[21,22] Although the research evidence is less conclusive, there appears also to be an association between being circumcised and the avoidance of many STD's, including HIV infection.[25-27,29-31] Neonatal circumcision is the nearly perfect prophylaxis against penile cancer.[32-35] (What other medical procedure may reap such an accolade?) Finally, women married to circumcised men are probably less likely to contract cervical cancer, although sexual practices are also extremely significant in this regard.[36-38]

So why should "the circumcision decision" continue to be problematic? There are two main reasons. First, it must be recognized that people may not approach circumcision by means of a rational decision-making process based on scientific data. For most parents, when it comes to circumcising their sons, social (and, yes, religious) concerns dominate.[39] Education by health care workers does not necessarily make a difference with parents either.[40] Historically in the United States, parental "irrationality" has favored continuation of majority circumcision.

The second reason is the intellectual opposition to circumcision, now well entrenched in organized medicine. Certain higher-visibility physicians have picked up the anti-circumcision banner and have waved it vigorously. Morgan's[41] scathingly critical essay typifies earlier opposition. He thinly veils his conclusion that circumcision is basically for unenlightened religious types. More recently, such published opposition has taken a more moderate "let's-wait-for-more-supportive-evidence" tone.[42]

And, of course, naysayers can always raise objections on seemingly reasonable grounds. They may object to the pain that accompanies the procedure. There is no real doubt that it is painful, but there is no significant evidence that such pain causes any longstanding problems for the circumcised boy. In addition, there are relatively simple means of assuaging that pain.[43,44] Furthermore, if post-neonatal circumcision is subsequently necessary for a medical reason, such a procedure is associated with greater risks of anesthesia, lost work time and wages, and probably with greater pain.[1] Objectors may complain of the risk of circumcision complications; as I have shown, this is a generally specious argument.[1,6,12] Finally, it may be argued, routine neonatal circumcision costs too much in an increasingly resource-scarce society. Cadman[45] and colleagues have raised this flag. Their focus, however, is very narrow: penile cancer prevention. They do not seriously address

prevention of other penile problems, UTI's STD's, etc. Furthermore, Warner and Strassen[1] and Wisewll[23] have a convincing case that routine neonatal circumcision would save health dollars.

After all of the salvos, point and counterpoint, have been fired, and the battlefield haze begins to lift, perhaps the real reason for circumcision opposition is revealed. The battle over circumcision is probably generated more by worldviews than by scientific data. In my opinion, the circumcision debate is yet another front in the civil war of values being waged in the United States today. On the one side we have traditional Judeo-Christian values; on the other, post-Enlightenment humanism/secularism. The very fact that the western practice of circumcision derives from the patriarch Abraham is an affront to those who would deny the validity of the holy Scriptures. Circumcision, to many moderns, is yet another embarrassing anachronism, similar to "Victorian" sexual mores, to be discarded.

I confess I also bring my bias with me. Some of the early medical studies of the relationship of circumcision to UTI's caught my attention. As I explored further, I began from the assumption that the God of the Bible would not command Abraham to perform a harmful surgical procedure upon Isaac, the child of the promise. It is my conclusion that the medical/scientific evidence supports this hypothesis.

To be sure, there are evangelical Christians who genuinely oppose routine neonatal circumcision. And, it must be stated, a Christian physician convinced of the merits of the procedure must not seek to force his viewpoint upon unwilling parents. Nonetheless, in 1992 it may be mini-

mally concluded that there is insufficient scientific evidence to advocate anti-circumcision. Neither does medical science provide a sufficient basis to attempt to dissuade parents who, for whatever reason, desire that their newborn son be circumcised.

ENDNOTES

1. Warner, E., Strassen, E., Benefits and risks of circumcision. *Canadian Medical Association Journal*, 1981, Vol. 125, pp. 967-976, p. 992.
2. Genesis 17:9-11, **The Holy Bible**.
3. Wallerstein, E., Circumcision: the uniquely American enigma. *Urologic Clinics of North America*, 1985, Vol. 12, pp. 123-932.
4. American Academy of Pediatrics, Committee on Fetus and Newborn. **Standards and Recommendations for Hospital Care of Newborn Infants**, 5th ed., Evanston, IL: 1971.
5. Gairdner, D., The fate of the foreskin: a study of circumcision. *British Medical Journal*, 1949, Vol. 2, pp. 1433 - 1437.
6. Anderson, G.F., Circumcision, *Pediatric Annals*, 1989, Vol. 18, pp. 208-213.
7. Contraindications to neonatal circumcision include age less than 24 hours, sickness, instability, prematurity, history of bleeding disorders, penile abnormalities (e.g., hypospadias), umbilical cord abnormalities, ambiguous genitalia, and presence of any staphylococcal infection. Parents of the child must provide written informed consent prior to the procedure.
8. Escala, J.M., Rickwood, AMK, Balanitis, *British Journal of Urology*, 1989, Vol. 63, pp. 196 - 197.
9. Rickwood, AMK.; et al., Phimosis in boys, *British Journal of Urology*, 1989, Vol. 52, pp. 147 - 150.
10. Fergusson, D.M., et al., Neonatal circumcision and penile problems: an 8 year longitudinal study. *Pediatrics*, 1988, Vol. 81., pp. 537 - 541.

11. Fakjian, N., et al., An argument for circumcision; prevention of balanitis in the adult. *Archives of Dermatology*, 1990, Vol. 126, pp. 1046 - 1047.

12. Wiswell, TE, Geschke, D.W., Risks of circumcision during the first month of life compared with those for uncircumcised boys, *Pediatrics*, 1989, Vol. 83, pp. 1011 - 1115.

13. Ginsburg, C.M., McCracken, G.H., Urinary tract infections in young infants, *Pediatrics*, 1982, Vol. 69, pp. 409 - 412.

14. Wiswell, T.E., Smith, F.R., Bass, J.W., Decreased incidence of urinary tract infections in circumcised male infants, *Pediatrics*, 1985, Vol. 75, pp. 901 - 903.

15. Wiswell, T.E., Roscelli, J.D., Corroborative evidence for the decreased incidence of urinary tract infections in circumcised male infants, *Pediatrics*, 1986, Vol. 78, pp. 96 - 99.

16. Herzog, L.W., Urinary tract infections and circumcision: a case-control study, *American Journal of Diseases of Children*, 1989, Vol. 143, pp. 348 - 350.

17. Crain, E.F., Gershel, J.C., Urinary tract infections in febrile infants younger than 8 weeks of age, *Pediatrics*, 1990, Vol. 86, pp. 363 - 367.

18. Wiswell, T.E., et al., Declining frequency of circumcision: implications for changes in the absolute incidence and male-to-female sex ratio of urinary tract infections in early infancy, *Pediatrics*, 1987, Vol. 79, pp. 338 - 342.

19. Wiswell, T.E., et al., Effect of circumcision status on periurethral flora during the first year of life. *Journal of Pediatrics*, 1988, Vol. 113, pp. 442 - 446.

20. Bonadio, W.A., et al., Escherichia coli bacteremia in children, *American Journal of Diseases of Children*, 1991, Vol. 145, pp. 671 - 674.

21. Jacobsen, S.H., et al., Development of hypertension and uraemia after pyelonephritis in childhood: 27 year follow up. *British Medical Journal*, 1989, Vol. 299, pp. 703 - 706.

22. Berg, U.B., Johansson, S.B., Age as a main determinant of renal functional damage in urinary tract infection, *Archives of Diseases of Children*, 1983, Vol. 58, pp. 963 - 969.

23. Wiswell, T.E., Routine neonatal circumcision: a reappraisal, *American Family Physician*, 1990, Vol. 41, pp. 859 - 863.

24. Schoen, E.J., The status of circumcision of newborns, *New England Journal of Medicine*, 1990, Vol. 322, pp. 1308 - 1312.

25. Taylor, P.K., Rodin, P., Herpes genitalis and circumcision, *British Journal of Venereal Disease*, 1975, Vol. 51, pp. 275 - 277.

26. Parker, S.W., et al., Circumcision and sexually transmitted disease, *Medical Journal of Australia*, 1983, Vol. 2, pp. 288 - 290.

27. Thirumoorthy, T., et al., Purulent penile ulcers of patients in Singapore, *Genitorurinary Medicine*, 1986, Vol. 62, pp. 253 - 255.

28. American Academy of Pediatrics, Task Force on Circumcision. Report of the task force on circumcision, *Pediatrics*, 1989, Vol. 84, pp. 388 - 391.

29. Simonsen, J.N., et al., Human immunodeficiency virus infection among men with sexually transmitted diseases: experience from a center in Africa, *New England Journal of Medicine*, 1988, Vol. 319, pp. 274 - 278.

30. Cameron, W.D., et al., Female to male transmission of human immunodeficiency virus type 1: risk factors for seroconversion in men, *Lancet*, August 19, 1989, pp. 403 - 407.

31. Quinn, T.C., as quoted by Marx, J.L., Circumcision may protect against the AIDS virus, *Science*, 1989, Vol. 245, pp. 470 - 471.

32. Leiter, E., Lefkovitz, A.M., Circumcision and penile carcinoma, *NY State Journal of Medicine*, August 1975, pp. 1520 - 1522.

33. Boczko, S., Freed, S., Penile carcinoma in circumcised males. *NY State Journal of Medicine*, November, 1979, pp. 1903 - 1904.

34. Rogus, B.J., Squamous cell carcinoma in a young circumcised man, *Journal of Urology*, 1987, Vol. 138, pp. 861 - 862.

35. Paymaster, J.C., Gangadharan, P., Cancer of the penis in India, *Journal of Urology*, 1967, Vol. 97, pp. 110 - 113.

36. Kessler, I.I., Etiological concepts in cervical carcinogenesis, *Gynecologic Oncology*, 1981, Vol. 12 (Supplement 2), pp. 57 - 524.

37. Martinez, I., Relationship of squamous cell carcinoma of the cervix uteri to squamous cell carcinoma of the penis: among Puerto Rican women married to men with penile carcinoma, *Cancer*, 1969, Vol. 24, pp. 777 - 780.

38. Herzog, L.W., Alvarez, S.R., The frequency of foreskin problems in uncircumcised children, *American Journal of Diseases of Children*, 1986, Vol. 140, pp. 254 - 256.

39. Brown, M.S., Brown, C.A., Circumcision decision: prominence of social concerns, *Pediatrics*, 1987, Vol. 80, pp. 215 - 219.

40. Herrera, A.J., et al., Parental information and circumcision in highly motivated couples with higher education, *Pediatrics*, 1983, Vol. 71, pp. 233 - 234.

41. Morgan, W.K.C., The rape of the phallus, *JAMA*, 1965, Vol. 193, pp. 123 - 124.

42. Poland, R.L., The question of routine neonatal circumcision, *New England Journal of Medicine*, 1990, Vol. 322, pp. 1312 - 1315.

43. Fontaine, P., Toffler, W.L., Dorsal penile nerve block for newborn circumcision, *American Family Physician*, 1991, Vol. 43, pp. 1327 - 1333.

44. Blass, E.M., Hoffmeyer, L.B., Sucrose as an analgesic for newborn infants, *Pediatrics*, 1991, Vol. 87, pp. 215 - 218.

45. Cadman, D., Gafni, A., McNamee, J., Newborn circumcision: an economic perspective, *Canadian Medical Association Journal*, Vol. 131, pp. 1353 - 1355.

The Corporeal Aspect and Procreative Function of the imago Dei and Abortion

Andrew A. White, M.D., M.A.T.S.

Dr. White is a 1978 graduate of the University of Michigan Medical School now in the private practice of family medicine in the North Shore of Boston. He also holds a Master of Arts in Sacred Theology from Gordon-Conwell Seminary.

The crucial question in the abortion debate is not when human life begins. Even many pro-choice advocates, from early on in the history of their movement, have quietly acknowledged that human life begins at conception. This after all had been the consensus of the medical community until Roe vs. Wade in 1973.[1] But in a strategy of deceit, well chronicled by Curt Young,[2] the reality of human life beginning at conception was carefully concealed from the public mind in order, as one pro-choice physician put it, "to separate the idea of abortion from the idea of killing." This physician did recognize that human life begins at conception but he also realized that killing innocent human life is intolerable to most people. So he, among others, believed a strategy of deceit was necessary until the new ethic of abortion was accepted - a new ethic that would recognize the relative value of post-conception procreative choice over immature human life.

The evangelical Christian will, of course, recognize that he must turn to Scripture to determine what is the value of human life at the earliest stages of its growth and development, i.e., from conception until birth, and what are responsible procreative choices. For the Christian the crucial questions are: (1) What value does God place on immature human life? (2) Does God ever give human beings the right to choose to take away an innocent human life once He has created it? (3) What are responsible procreative choices? While these questions have been looked at biblically from many different perspectives, my hope is that the same reflections on the nature and function of the *imago Dei* will add fresh insights to the abortion debate. In the process, a recognition of the corporeal aspect (which has been neglected by scholars of all theological persuasions) will be argued for.

The creation and procreation of man in the image of God and the command to protect that image is detailed in the book of Genesis in Chapters 1, 5, and 9. (The bold print and underlining to follow is to highlight passages which will be cited to argue for the procreative function of the imago Dei):

(Gen. 1:26) Then God said, "Let us make man **in our image** (*selem*), **in our likeness** (*demut*), and let them rule over the fish of the sea and the birds of the air, over the livestock, over all the earth, and over all the creatures that move along the ground." (1:27) So God created man **in his own image** (*selem*), **in the image** (*selem*) **of God** he created him; **male and female** he created them. (1:28) God blessed them and said to them, "**Be fruitful and increase in number; fill the earth** and subdue it. Rule over the fish of the sea and the birds of the air and over every living creature that moves on the ground."

(Gen. 5:1) This is the written account of Adam's line. <u>When God created man, he made him **in the likeness** (*demut*) **of God**</u>. (5:2) He created them **male and female** and blessed them. And when they were created, <u>he called them "man" [Adam]</u>. (5:3) <u>When Adam had lived 130 years, he had a son **in his own likeness** (*demut*), **in his own image** (*selem*); and he named him Seth.</u>

(Gen. 9:1) Then God blessed Noah and his sons, saying to them, "**Be fruitful and increase in number and fill the earth.** (9:2) The fear and dread of you will fall upon all the beasts of the earth and all the birds of the air, upon every creature that moves along the ground, and upon all the fish of the sea; they are given into your hands.

(9:3) Everything that lives and moves will be food for you. Just as I gave you the green plants, I now give you everything.

(9:4) But you must not eat meat that has its lifeblood still in it.

(9:5) And for your lifeblood I will surely demand an accounting from every animal. And from each man, too, I will demand an accounting for the life of his fellow man.

(9:6) Whoever sheds the blood of man, by man shall his blood be shed; for **in the image** (*selem*) **of God** has God made man.

(9:7) As for you, **be fruitful and increase in number; multiply on the earth and increase upon it.**"

In Genesis, two Hebrew words are used by the author to describe the relationship of man to his Creator, i.e., "image" (*selem*) and "likeness" (*demut*). In the Ancient Near East "image" primarily referred to the representative of something rather than its resemblance. The kings of the Ancient Near East, as representatives of the divine on earth, were called the image of God.[3] And these kings, when they could not be present in person, often left images (idols) of themselves in various cities and territories to represent their majesty and power.[4] "Likeness," on the other hand, is a more abstract term primarily meaning "similarity" or "resemblance." To be a divine likeness, then, is to have features analagous to God in some way(s).[5]

Scholars have pointed out that the two terms "image" and "'likeness" are synonyms which are used interchangeably in Genesis. But while synonyms always overlap in meaning and thus are often interchangeable, they may retain their primary sense.[6] Therefore if "image" and "likeness"

retain their primary sense, man created in the image of God is both God's representative and is like the God he represents.

Many OT scholars now recognize that man's corporeality is included in the concept of the image of God in the OT.[7] For a physical image, e.g., a statue or idol, is the most frequent meaning of "image' in the OT, as well as in contemporaneous extra-biblical literature. Contextual support for the thesis that corporeality is a significant ontological aspect of the image of God is readily apparent if our second thesis is correct, i.e., that procreation is only possible among corporeal beings. Further contextual support comes from a recognition of the creation of the *imago Dei* as male and female (primarily differentiated on the basis of physical attributes) and from a recognition that when the image of God is attacked in Gen. 9:6, it is corporeal man whose blood is shed. Some evangelical scholars, however, have been hesitant to accept corporeality as an integral aspect of the image of God.[8] For if man as a corporeal being is created in the image of God, an anthropometric deity after which the image is fashioned is one logical inference. Indeed, the creation of men and women in the image of a god or goddess in Babylonian culture often included a physical similarity between the created human being and the god or goddess.[9] However, there is another much more logical inference to the inclusion of the man's corporeality in the concept of the image of God in Israelite religion; namely, man is a "transcription of the eternal, <u>incorporeal</u> Creator in terms of temporal, <u>bodily</u>, creaturely existence [emphasis mine]."[10] God, in His essence, is both invisible and incorporeal; however, man (God's image) is visible and corporeal. But while it is true

that God in His essence is both invisible and incorporeal, God Himself (not just His image) can appear in the visible form of the *shekina*, in the bodily form of an angel, i.e., the angel of the Lord, and in the corporeal form of a human being in Jesus of Nazareth (see also Genesis 18 and 32 for OT examples of God in corporeal form). Therefore, since God Himself can appear in such visible and even corporeal forms, corporeality as a part of the nature of the image of God should not be rejected on theological grounds. Indeed, given the evidence for the prominence of the concept of man's psychosomatic unity in ancient Israelite anthropology, the exclusion of the corporeal from the nature of the image of God seems highly unlikely. In short, **the ontological aspect of the *imago Dei* includes man's corporeality.** While aspects of man's nature other than corporeality are likely to have been included in the concept of the image of God, e.g., various mental and spiritual faculties, few commentators agree on what those aspects are. For there is little if any extra-biblical or OT evidence to support most speculations.

The immediate context of Genesis suggests <u>the ways in which men and women function as the *imago Dei*</u>. Many commentators have pointed to representative rule over lower creation as one way in which man is like God (see especially Gen. 1:26-28). God rules over all of creation, visible and invisible. Men and women are His representative rulers in the visible realm and like God rule, but only over lower creation.[11]

In contrast to acceptance by many scholars of corporeality as an ontological aspect and representative rule as a functional aspect of the *imago Dei*, few scholars, if any, have done more than intimate that **procreation** is another way in which men and women function as the image of God. "Might there be in procreation," Henri Blocher says timidly, "a reflection of divine creation?"[12] Support for the thesis that procreation is a way that men and women function as God's image follows:

1) An anology between creation and procreation is clearly implicit in Gen. 5:1-3. "When God created man, he made him in the 'likeness' of God ... When Adam had lived 130 years, he had a son [Seth] in his own 'likeness,' in his own 'image.'..." In commenting on this passage, Meredith Kline says, "Clearly we are being advised that there is a similarity between these two processes [creation and procreation], both of which result in products like their authors. Adam's fathering of a son provides a proper analogy to God's creating of man and the relationship of Seth to Adam is analogous to man's relationship to his Maker.[13] Through procreation, then, men and women resemble God in His creative activity.

2) In the same context where it is announced that man is created in the "image"/"likeness" of God (Gen. 1:27 and 5:1,2), the author also announces that God created them male and female. According to Gordon Wenham, the expression "male and female" highlights the sexual distinction within mankind[14] and Claus Westermann says, "The human race is God's creation as male and female. There can be no human existence apart from this existence in two sexes. ... As God's creation, the human race receives a blessing. That blessing is primarily, as with the animals, fertility. Through procreation, conception, and birth the blessing produces the chain of generations ... after the Creation story in Chapter 5."[15] Thus the creation of the image of God as male and female naturally points to procreation as a function of the image.

3) In Gen. 1:28 the command to "be fruitful and increase in number and fill the earth" immediately follows man's identification as the "image of God" (1:27). Likewise in Gen. 9:6 man's identification as the "image of God" is contained within a literary inclusion that opens (9:1) and closes (9:7) with the command "be fruitful and increase in number and fill the earth." Thus the command to procreate is associated with the image of God. Indeed the relationship of the various sections of Gen. 9:1-7 becomes more intelligible when the procreative function of the image of God is recognized as the unifying theme. The postdiluvian remnant of mankind is reminded of its commission to procreate (9:1,7), a commission which naturally follows man's creation in the image of God (9:6). This commission, however, goes beyond the act of procreation itself to procreation's purpose. For if images of God are to increase in number and fill the earth, not just be fruitful, they must provide sustenance to their offspring (9:3). Beyond this, their offspring must be protected from both man (9:5b,6) and beast (9:2,5a). This protection is grounded in the sanctity of life in general (9:4) and in the sanctity of the life of man, who is created in the image of God, in particular (9:5,6).

4) Further contextual support for the significance of the association between procreation and the image of God in Gen. 1:27, 28 is offered by Warren Gage who sees an analogy between man's commission to "fill the earth and subdue it" (1:28) and God's subduing and filling the original creation in Genesis 1. "During the first three days," says Gage, "God is depicted as subduing the chaos of the original creation, bringing about an ordered cosmos. During the final three days God is depicted as filling the heavens and earth, the former with starry hosts and the latter with all manner of life. ... The work of man, as he is commissioned by his Creator, is a mirror of the divine activity in Genesis 1. Man is commanded to fill the earth and to subdue creation. ... Thus in his work of filling and subduing ... man is commissioned in the image of his Maker."[16]

5) As we have seen above, in the OT the theme of procreation is associated with the image of God. In the NT the language of procreation is associated with the image of God. For example, in the same context in which the "Son" (Col. 1:13) is called the "image (eikon - the Greek equivalent of selem in the Septuagint) of the invisible God" (1:15), He is also called the "firstborn over all creation" (1:15). The idea of the image of God made a word associated with procreation, i.e., "firstborn," appropriate. However, the hymnodist (Col. 1:15-20 is a hymn honoring the Son) was careful to choose a word which in the appropriate setting could refer to supremacy in rank through the exercise of the privilege of primogeniture. Likewise

in Hebrews, the "Son" (1:3,5), through whom God made the universe, is said to be "the exact representation of His being" (1:3); and in the same context He is called God's "firstborn" (1:6). Now it could be argued that the idea of sonship is what makes the word "firstborn" appropriate in both Colossians 1 and Hebrews 1. But, of course, the language of sonship is also a part of the language of procreation. Interestingly, in many ancient Babylonian and Egyptian texts the idea of sonship is associated with that of image.[17] Luke, in his genealogy of Jesus, may have consciously recognized this ancient association between sonship and image. For the Lucan genealogy of Jesus, which reflects the Genesis 5 genealogy of Adam (where, as we have seen above, Adam is created in the likeness of God even as Seth is created in the likeness/image of Adam), calls Adam "the son of God" even as Seth is "the son of Adam" (Luke 3:37). Finally in Jas. 3:9, in the same verse in which the author identifies men as "made in the likeness of God" he calls God "Father." In the two other places where the author of James calls God "Father" there is a reason for so doing clearly identifiable in the immediate context, i.e., in 1:17 God is the "Father of the heavenly lights" and in 2:27 the "Religion that God our Father accepts" includes looking after "orphans" (see Ps. 68:5 where God is said to be "A father to the fatherless"). In 3:9 the reason for calling God "Father" is because all those "made in the likeness of God" are in some sense children of God our Father (though many are also in very real sense the children of the devil - see for ex-

ample John 8:44). In brief, the language of procreation, specifically "firstborn," sonship and paternity is associated with the concept of the image of God even in contexts where procreation is not primarily in view.

6) In the NT the theme of recreation, which is closely linked conceptually to the theme of procreation, is associated with the image of God. The new man, who has been raised with Christ, is being made new again in knowledge in the "image (*eikon*) of his Creator" (Col. 3:10, also see Eph. 4:24 where the new man is [re]created to be like God in true righteousness and holiness.) In commenting on Col. 3:10, F.F. Bruce recognizes the association between recreation and the image of God and the link between recreation and procreation when he says, "Christ-likeness is being reproduced more and more in the life of the believer."[18] And Bruce is right, for Paul says that the Son is the "firstborn" among many brothers who are destined to be conformed to His "image" (*eikon*, Rom. 8:29).

There is then strong support for the thesis that **men and women function as the *imago Dei* not only through representative rule over lower creation but also through procreation.** One objection that could be raised to our thesis is the fact that procreation does not distinguish man from lower creation while man alone is created in the image of God. Thus our thesis needs a little refinement. Men and women function as the image of God not only through representative rule over lower creation but also through **procreation of divine likenesses**.

IN SUMMARY, God is the invisible, incorporeal Creator of His visible, corporeal image. Ontologically, corporeal human beings are the image of God. Functionally through procreation, men and women are God's representatives for creating His image and are like God in their ability to produce likenesses of themselves which when traced back to the origin of man are likenesses of God. Men and women also function as the *imago Dei* through representative rule. But representative rule is, of course, dependent on procreation of divine likenesses. For through procreation the earth is filled with representative rulers. Thus the command to fill the earth and subdue it is a command to extend the kingdom of God through procreation and to establish God's reign over all the earth through representative rule.

In the light of the above discussion, it is not surprising that God has pronounced the sentence of capital punishment on all murderers as their just retribution (Gen. 9:6). For murderers so devalue the image of God that they choose to destroy it. And to devalue the image of God, God's representative ruler and likeness, is to devalue God Himself. God will not, indeed cannot, ignore such an assessment of His worth.

In addition to destroying and devaluing the image of God, the murderer is acting in a way that is completely antithetical to responsible functioning as the image of God. Murder is, in other words, directly contradictory to one of the functions which our nature as those created in the image of God calls for, namely procreation. By destroying and devaluing the image of God and by functioning in a way so contradictory to human nature as the image of God, the murderer forfeits his right to life.

The recognition of an ontological aspect of the *imago Dei* in corporeality safeguards **the sanctity of all human life**. A purely functional definition of the *imago Dei* would not afford such safeguards. For many people do not function as the image of God. Sometimes people do not function as the image of God for ethically neutral reasons. For example infants and children because of immaturity are unable to constructively rule over lower creation and infertile couples are unable to procreate. Many other times people do not function as the image of God for immoral reasons, as in environmental pollution and the illegitimate use of birth control. However, regardless of the reason people do not function as the image of God, they are still by nature the image of God as long as they are living human beings. And as long as they are living human beings they are to be afforded the protection of Genesis 9.

The fetus is an example of a living human being who is not functioning as the image of God for ethically neutral reasons. The fetus cannot constructively rule over lower creation or procreate. However, the fetus is by nature the image of God. For while some have denied the "personhood" of the fetus, no rational medical experts have denied its corporeality. Abortion is recognized by all rational medical experts to be the destruction of human life. Therefore, to abort is to destroy and devalue the image of God. And as noted above, to destroy the image of God is to devalue God Himself.

If murder is directly contradictory to functioning as the image of God, to procure or to perform an **abortion** is the paramount example of such contradictory behavior. For in abortion, the destruction of human life is carried out at the very time when bringing forth life by completing the act of procreation (an act which began with sexual intercourse) is our responsibility as those created in the image of God. Abortion, then, is a particularly heinous crime, since in one and the same act we both destroy and devalue the image of God and we reject our procreative function as the image of God.

The prevalence of abortion in modern America is clear evidence that the ethical aspect of the image of God is lost, at least in part. Unregenerate men and women no longer have true knowledge of the Creator (Col. 3:10) and are unrighteous and unholy (Eph. 4:24). Imagining themselves to be gods, rather than the image of God, they are no longer satisfied to rule constructively over lower creation. Instead they participate in a reign of destruction directed against the very likenesses of God. And rejecting their procreative role to fill the earth with divine likeness, they even go so far as to attack God's image-bearers at a time in their lives when their createdness is their most prominent characteristic. The creature could hardly be in more open rebellion against his Creator.

Only if men and women are recreated in the image of the Son will the ethical aspect of the image of God be restored. And the results of that recreation will be new men and women who live lives true to their nature. As God enables them, these recreated men and women will extend the kingdom of God through procreation. Being conformed to the image of God's Son, they will establish God's reign over all the earth through representative rule and that reign will include protecting the image of God wherever they find it.

SPECIAL CREDITS

*Credit is due to
Gregory Beale, Ph.D.,
John J. Davis, Ph.D., and
Gordon Hugenbrger, Ph.D.,
all of whom teach at
Gordon Conwell Theological Seminary,
for their helpful suggestions.*

ENDNOTES

1. Unfortunately, as recently as 1989 one evangelical physician confused matters regarding the issue of when human life begins by suggesting that it begins at implantation. See Arden Almquist's article entitled "When does Human LIfe Begin?" in the *Christian Medical and Dental Society Journal*, Winter, 1989, pp. 12 - 15. My letter to the editor was not accepted but a number of convincing rebuttals to Almquist's position were printed in the letters to the editor in the 1990 Summer volume of the *CMDS Journal*, pp. 16-20.

2. Young, Curtis J., **The Least of These**, 1983, pp. 21 - 32.

3. Wilson, S.G., "New Wine in Old Wineskins: Image of God." *The Expository Times*. September, 1974, pp. 356.

4. von Rad, G., **Theological Dictionary of the New Testament**, 1964, Vol. II, p. 392, and Blocher, H., **In the Beginning**, 1984., p. 81.

5. Johnson, S.G., *op. cit.*, p. 356 and Blocher, H., *op cit.*, p. 85.

6. Silva, M., **Biblical Words and their Meaning**, 1983, pp. 121-125. It will become apparent that this author does not accept James Barr's thesis that *demut* defines and limits the meaning of *selem* (summarized on pp. 161, 162). Rather, we believe that *selem* and *demut* are complementary terms - synonyms that overlap but have distinguishable primary senses which have been retained.

7. For examples see Jacob, E., **Theolo-**

gy of the Old Testament, 1958, pp. 166ff., von Rad, G., **Old Testament Theology,** 1962, Vol. 1, pp. 144ff., Eichrodt, W., Theology of the Old Testament, 1967, Vol. II, pp. 122ff. This author does not agree with all the ways in which these scholars argue for corporeality as an aspect of the image of God. That all three of these well-respected OT scholars recognized corporeality as an aspect of the image, however, is highly significant.

8. For example, see Wenham, G., **Genesis 1-15,** 1987, p. 30.

9. Eichrodt, W., *op. cit.,* p. 122.

10. Kidner, D., **Genesis,** 1967, p. 51.

11. For example see Clines, D., "The Image of God in Man," *Tyndale Bulletin,* 1968, especially his brief summary on p. 101.

12. Blocher, H., *op. cit.,* p. 93. In commenting on Genesis 1:26,27 and 2:21f, Kline says, "...biblical revelation thus intimates that this creating of man is a kind of divine authoring analogous to human procreation."

13. Kline, M., **Kingdom Prologue,** 1989, p. 30.

14. Wenham, G., *op. cit.,* p. 33.

15. Westermann, C., **Genesis: A Practical Commentary,** 1987, p. 11.

16. Gage, Warren, **The Gospel of Genesis,** 1984, pp. 31,32.

17. Blocher, H., *op. cit.,* p. 89.

18. Bruce, F.F., **The epistles to the Colossian to Philemon and to the Ephesian,** 1984, p. 146.

Editor's Note

In the Summer, 1990, issue we presented some practices of Dr. Paul Glanville in Arizona who has been experimenting with some radical departures from certain medical orthodoxies. One of his departures was to have his patients keep their own medical records. The idea has begun to become almost irresistible to me. In a recent week I found that I had to devote literally hours to answering demands for copies or other use of patients' medical records. Attorneys want information, necessitating the filing of the patient's authorization and picking out the information which related to the accident in question. Meals on Wheels wants confirmation that a patient has chronic disease in order to qualify for their services. Life insurance companies plunder through past histories. Visiting nurses and physical therapists send information to be included. Worst and commonest of all, medical insurers want "copies of all visits from June, 1989, through January, 1992," or the like. They are looking for pre-existing conditions that will allow them to refuse to pay the patient. Some may just be looking to string out the interval before they have to pay in order to hold on to the money a bit longer. For any physician whose bills are few but relatively large, the costs of retrieving, copying, and filing the records constitutes a small percentage of the entire bill. For physicians who deal mostly with outpatients and do not do big ticket procedures, such costs constitute a substantial portion of the total bill.

What a patient sees as the cost of "medical care" is increasingly the cost of the *administration* of medical care. The physician takes the blame. How might patients respond differently if they were made aware of the massive plundering being done by third parties in their records? We were interested to find some of Dr. Glanville's reasoning echoed in the *Journal of Medical Ethics,* Vol. 17, 1991, "Medical records: practicalities and principles of patient possession."

****

Impetus appears to be building behind a movement to outlaw the corporal punishment of children, first in schools, then elsewhere in public, and finally in homes. Family practitioners, pediatricians, and all medical personnel who are subject to mandatory reporting requirements of child abuse are being steadily indoctrinated into the view that spanking, *per se,* is abuse, "outmoded," and unnecessary. As Christians who are mindful of the Biblical injunctions teaching this method as a part of child rearing, our initial reaction is often misguided. The opponents of corporal punishment usually cite "studies" of the supposed bad effects of corporal punishment, or of the effectiveness of alternative methods. We are wont to answer with studies of our own selection. While it is possible to debate the issue on such grounds, it is a strategic error not to challenge the opponent's implicit assumption that the matter is a scientific one. What God has revealed about training children, *cannot,* be made more true by citing scientific studies. Revelation is not tested by experience. Experience is tested by revelation. Deciding the issue requires everyone to begin from certain beliefs taken as true without proof -- on faith. Scientists have faith, for example, that there are regularities in the universe which can be observed, that their observations are veridical, and that their formulations can capture the essence of a relationship. That a scientist may choose to omit revelatory information from God as valid doesn't prove that it is of no relevance; it merely demonstrates that he *assumed* that it was of no relevance. Assumptions are not proof, and we need to remind our opponents of that.

(Additional Editor's Note on page 92:26.)

Pastor's Column

The Reverend Byron Snapp

Rev. Snapp holds a B.A. from King College and an M.Div. from Reformed Theological Seminary. He is assistant pastor of Covenant Presbyterian Church and prinicipal of Covenant Christian School in Cedar Bluff, Virginia.

Murder Begets Murder

Sometimes God especially allows the news to be providentially interconnected. During the week of January 19 the news media gave birth to the fact that infants between birth and one year of age are in the most rapidly growing group of murder victims. FBI statistics, according to the media, reveal that 131 infants were slain in 1973. Two hundred and sixty-four were slain in 1990. This increase represents slightly more than one hundred percent. No other age group doubled during this time period.

Several things in this report should spark our interest. First, the news was reported during the week when attention is focused on the abortion issue. January 22 has become the day to have pro-life rallies throughout the United States.

Secondly, in God's providence, these statistics began with the base year of 1973. January 22, 1973, was the historic day in which the Roe vs. Wade Supreme Court decision was announced. Thus, the taking of unborn human life became legal in the United States. Since that date, close to 30 million lives have never been allowed, by their mother's wish, to see the light of day. The cynic might reply, in light of these millions, "What is another couple of thousand deaths by murder who are only a few months older than those aborted infants?"

It should come as no surprise that we have seen a rise in the murder rates of infants following the Supreme Court's ruling in Roe vs. Wade. (Murders of children in age groups 1 - 10 dropped when 1973 figures are compared with 1990 statistics.) The Court decision, when viewed in the light of Scripture, shows the cheapness of human life. If a life is cheap before it is born, can we expect it to gain value after birth?

Clearly the Bible teaches that human life exists from the moment of conception. King David was inspired to write that he was conceived in sin. (Psalm. 51:5) From the moment of his conception he was a human and a sinner. We think of John the Baptist who leaped in his mother's womb when pregnant Mary entered the house of his parents. Certainly, John was far more than a mass of tissue or just an appendage of his mother. I also am reminded of the Lord Jesus Christ within Mary. Surely, He was a living Person, taking on flesh during those months, while remaining fully God. Would John leap because a mass of tissue had entered the room? Scarcely! Spirit-filled Elizabeth clearly recognized Mary as "the mother of my Lord" (Luke 1:43) even though Jesus was several months from birth.

The Church needs to speak as clearly as the Bible speaks in regard to human life existing from conception. Passages such as Psalm 139:13-16 and Jeremiah 1:5 also provide additional support for this teaching. Many of today's youth will not get this teaching anywhere else.

Secondly, the Church must also clearly teach that sin has consequences. We are easily deceived into thinking that we can sin in isolation. Sin can exist in one action alone without anything or anyone else being affected. A sin seldom exists by itself. A sinful thought leads often to sinful words and deeds. Sinful deeds often are the forerunner of even greater sinful actions.

Society deceives itself into thinking that legalized abortion will not have any effect on the living. Reports continue to surface on the dire physical consequences that have resulted in many mothers after the abortion of their children. As the recent media report gives evidence, the lives of the newly born are in increasing danger.

While the report does not no state, we can imagine that many of these infants are killed by a parent or a close friend of the parent. Of course, it is the mother (the baby's close relative) who must consent to an abortion if the baby is unwanted.

Naturally "authorities" blame the environment -- single parent homes, the inner city structure, etc. -- for these deaths. Even in this blame we see a consequence of sin. A denial of God means sin does not exist. Yet evil continues. Rather than blame man, the sinner, the blame is wrongfully place on the impersonal environment. Even the authorities must admit that not every single parent of a newborn kills that baby nor do all inner city infants die. the problem is not one's environment. It is the problem of one's heart. As others have said, "The heart of the problem is the problem of the heart."

Certainly many physicians are not blind to the consequences that flow out of sinful activity. Such sinful actions can have great effects on our bodies, our families, and our society as a whole.

Let us hope and pray that our churches will wake up and point out more often that we do not sin in individual isolation. Our nation sorely needs to hear the connection between consequences and the sin that spawned them.

Editor's Note

Casually, we say we watch "the news" on television. Not quite. We watch *a* news -- someone's *selection* among all the possible reportable data, perhaps with a certain spin on it. Recently, our state welfare agency was investigated in the death of a teenager who had been placed in foster care. The girl choked to death while being held in restraints at a state facility. The investigation was reported on the inside of the second section of the newspaper. Front page news, however, was of a similarly retarded young male who was badly injured in a fire. He was alone in a house, chained to a wall. He was found dangling from a window at the limit of his chain. In the case of the burned man, the same agency was considering charges against his family, though the family stated it had sought assistance from the agency in managing the man's violence, to no avail. The agency may judge the family, but a family has little recourse against the agency, which after all, is just suffering from the same conditions that exist in society. Is the point to catch the family?

****

The National Hospice Organization has issued a policy statement regarding assisted suicide and euthanasia, strongly opposed to both practices. Among the quotable portions of the statement: "Euthanasia could become a penalty for being too sick, too isolated, or too poor." "...clinicians have the right to have their own beliefs and values. Patients are not the only moral agents in this process. Ethical decisions are bilateral, not unilateral."

Population Control

Franklin E. Payne, Jr., M.D.

*Dr. Payne is Associate Professor at the Medical College of Georgia. He is author of **Biblical/Medical Ethics, Making Biblical Decisions,** and **What Every Christian Should Know about the AIDS Epidemic.***

"And God blessed them; and God said to them, 'Be fruitful and multiply, and fill the earth...'" (Genesis 1:28a). This command is one of the "Creation Mandates" of Genesis 1,2. Today, the great debate about this passage is whether or not the earth has been "filled." That is, has the population of the earth reached the level at which its resources are inadequate to meet the needs of all people on earth?

The answer that gets the most attention today is that the earth's population has indeed reached or exceeded that level. Many Christians believe this answer. However, the overwhelming evidence is that the earth's resources and man's technology is quite capable of supporting many times the present six billion people on earth. Some of that evidence follows.

First, Colin Clark estimates that the world could sustain 35 billion people on the "overconsumptive" American diet and 100 billion on an "adequate" Japanese diet. Historically, famines have six causes: war, the prevention of cultivation, the willful destruction of crops, defective agriculture, government interference by regulation and taxation, and currency restrictions.

The continuing famine in Ethiopia is an example. For centuries, Ethiopian farmers had stored food after good harvests to provide for years of bad harvests. However, by government decree such storage was labeled "hoarding" and disallowed. Families were relocated and commercial marketing of food was forbidden. And, many other governmental "changes" disrupted a fairly efficient system of food production and supply that severely aggravated (if not caused) this continuing famine.

Second, productivity is not necessarily limited where people are closely populated. Taiwan, while two-thirds the size of Switzerland but with sixteen million people, has the second highest standard of living in Asia (behind Japan, another densely populated country).

Third, food production has increased more rapidly than the population on a world-wide basis. Even in the United States where large surpluses of food are produced almost every year, *more* could be produced were it not for government controls. But, politics is not the only problem. Worldwide, the average work day varies from 45 minutes to seven hours. Surely, there is a great deal more time for greater production!

Thus, in Creation God gave mankind abundant natural resources to provide for the needs of a planet "filled" with people. In addition, He has given mankind an ingenious mind that is capable of utilizing those resources, provided man is willing and is free to pursue such development.

Why, then, is overpopulation rhetoric so appealing? The answer has to do with short-term vs. long-term costs, apparent consensus of expert judgment, population as a cause of pollution, judgments about people's rational use of resources, one-sided news media exposure, and hidden agendas that include increasing government control and an elite power structure.

Population statistics indicate that 2.2 children per married couple is necessary to *maintain* population at current levels. Thus, the logical conclusion is that couples who are able to have children should be "fruitful" with 3 or more to continue to "multiply" within God's Creation Mandate. This number should also be adequate statistically to fill the void of those who are physically unable to bear children.

These children will themselves become the resources to feed themselves and others. As long ago as the 18th century, Adam Smith recognized the surest sign of a healthy economic order was continued population growth. As children "multiply," their needs of children (food, shelter, clothing) increase, and economic expansion occurs. (This reality is certainly a message to the United States in the 1990's with its abortion rate and stagnant economy.)

In addition, an expanding number of children are necessary to provide for the needs of their parents. In the United States, an inordinate burden is being placed upon productive workers because the abortion of one in three pregnancies for 18 years has greatly limited present and future workers.

Population growth creates new economic opportunities and markets. Such growth expands markets, making investments more attractive by reducing risks and increasing total demand for goods and services. Larger numbers of people lead to proportional economies that make large public investments such as highways, bridges, railroads, irrigation systems, and ports less expensive on a per-person basis.

Finally, we must believe God. Every mention of the bearing of children is described in positive terms (e.g., Psalms 127:3-5). This Biblical affirmation of children coupled with the Creation Mandate provides the authority to override any scientific objections to population control. And, God never limited or abrogated that affirmation or mandate. As pointed out, however, the greater scientific evidence points to more-than-sufficient resources to meet a growing population. And likely, God will either terminate history before actual overpopulation occurs, or He will continue to give man the ingenuity to stay ahead of population needs until His Second Advent.

BIBLIOGRAPHY

1. Beisner, C., **Prospects for Growth: A Biblical View of Population, Resources, and the Future**, 1990.

2. Davis, J.J., **Evangelical Ethics**, 1985.

3. Payne, F., **Making Biblical Decisions**, 1989.

4. Simon, J. **The Ultimate Resource**, 1981.

Guest Editorial

Joseph K. Neumann, Ph.D.

FORCED CHARITY:
The Increasing Use of Licensing Regulations to Accomplish Government Objectives.

Licensing regulations somewhat similar to those of today have existed at least since 1200. Licensing is a growing civil governmental activity that restricts the practice of an occupation to individuals approved by the state. Others practicing the occupation outside the scope of government approval may be punished by fines and/or jail sentences. Licensing is different than registration or certification procedures that are less restrictive and frequently administered by private organizations.

Licensing is almost invariably sought by the occupational groups themselves "for the public welfare." However, since the middle of this century it has become increasingly clear that licensing advances not the general populace, but the establishment of the professional group being licensed. Licensing has been criticised for the following reasons:

1. **Economic Limitations**: Licensing regulations restrict the right of individuals to make a living.[1] People with little or no economic resources are less likely to be able to meet licensing requirements. Further, licensing increases the fees for services, generally making services less available for purchase. Since licensing functionally provides a monopoly for individuals in the licensed occupations, groups as diverse as physicians, lawyers, photographers, barbers, psychologists and house painters have all sought to be licensed by the state.

2. **Mediocrity**: Licensing procedures effectively encourage a state-enforced, institutionalized mediocrity.[2] Detailed standards are set by older, powerful members of an occupational group and imposed upon those entering the profession. Diversity decreases as new entrants seek to conform and go about the business of earning a living for themselves and their families.

3. **Ineffectiveness**: Licensing regulations are not even effective at doing what they are purportedly designed to do, "protect the public."[3] Licensing as a measure of competence does not correlate with actual professional performance. The state may occasionally remove an incompetent practitioner. However, studies fail to find any general beneficial effect on performance for the public regardless of the occupational group.

4. **Unbiblical Principles**: Licensing exists because we tolerate the application of unbiblical principles in such areas as free market honesty, contract making, and equality of opportunity.[4] Licensing serves to increase the power of the state at the cost of individual freedom. The state becomes a false god bestowing rewards and punishments as it seeks obedience to its humanistic objectives. Proverbs 13:15 clearly warns Christians and the societies in which we live that "the way of the unfaithful is hard."[5]

H.M. Holzer's following paper[6] does a wonderful job of expanding these criticisms to the area of current government health policy. In America, licensing regulations have repeatedly been used to enforce political policy. Evangelist Samuel A. Worcester and others were imprisoned for over a year when they refused in the 1830's to stop unlicensed preaching to the Cherokees[7] as the state of Georgia sought to gain jurisdiction over Cherokee territory. Licensing regulations were used earlier this century to enforce various loyalty or non-communist political stances. Such licensing restrictions have largely been eliminated. Holzer now raises the specter of licensing restrictions being used to enforce conformity to governmental political policy in another area, health care objectives.

Increasing health care expenses and demands place overwhelming burdens on already strained government health programs. Holzer focuses on such health care issues and several recent West Virginia and Massachusetts court decisions. For example, physicians in Massachusetts who treat Medicare patients are not allowed to bill the patient for the difference between what the government pays and what the service is worth. Physicians who do not accept such conditions may lose their licenses. Thus, the licensing standard has shifted from purported "fitness" requirements to the willingness to perform services in accordance with state health-care cost containment policies. This forced, unbiblical "charity" was justified, in part, by the fact that licensing is a state-granted monopoly given to physicians and thus service conditions may be regulated by the government. According to such a principle, there is no reason to think that any licensed health care providers could not be forced to meet other state-perceived "needs" (e.g., working in the state national guard, performing surgery on HIV-positive patients) or risk losing their licenses. Professor Holzer has done an outstanding job of describing this alarming abuse of state power.

REFERENCES

1. Gellhorn, W., **Individual Freedom and Governmental Restraints**, Greenwood Press, Westport, CT, 1968, pp. 105- 151.

— Dorsey, S., Occupational Licensing and Minorities, *Law and Human Behavior*, Vol. 7, pp. 171 - 181, 1983.

— American Association of Retired Persons. *Unreasonable Regulation — Unreasonable Prices*. Report prepared by the AARP Consumer Affairs Section, Washington, D.C., 1986.

2. Friedman, M., **Capitalism and Freedom**. University of Chicago Press, Chicago, pp. 137 - 160, 1982.

— Fretz, B.R., & Mills, D.H., **Licensing and Certification of Psychologists and Counselors: A Guide to Current Policies, Procedures, and Legislation**. Jossey-Bass, Washington, D.C., 1980.

3. Gross, S.J., **Of Foxes and Hen Houses: Licensing and the Health Professions**. Quorum, Westport, CT, 1984.

— Rethans, J.J., Sturman, F., Drop, R., van der Vleuten, C., & Hobus, P., Does Competence of General Practitioners Predict Their Performance? Comparison Between Examination Setting and Actual Practice. *British Medical Journal*, Vol. 303, pp. 1377 - 1380, 1991.

4. Neumann, J.K., Licensing of Health Care Professionals From a Biblical Perspective. *Journal of Biblical Ethics in Medicine*, Vol. 22, No. 2, pp. 21 - 26, 1988.

— Neumann, J.K., A Theological Perspective on the Licensing of Helping Professionals. *Journal of Psychology and Theology*, Vol. 17, No. 3, pp. 252 -6 22, 1989.

5. Neumann, J.K., Thompson, W., & Woolley, T.W., Evangelical Vs. Liberal Christianity: The Influence of Values on the Nonclinical Professional Decisions of Social Workers. *Journal of Psychology and Christianity*, Vol. II, No. 1, pp 57 - 67, 1992.

6. Holzer, H.M., The Physician's License: An Achilles' Heel? *The Journal of Legal Medicine*, Vol. 12, pp. 201 - 220, 1991.

7. Hutchins, J., The Trial of Reverend Samuel A. Worcester. *Journal of Cherokee Studies*, Vol. 2, No. 4, pp. 3567 - 374, 1977.

The Physician's License: An Achilles Heel?

Henry Mark Holzer, J.D.

Henry Mark Holzer, Professor of Law at Brooklyn Law School and a constitutional litigator, currently represents physician groups in Massachusetts and West Virginia.

Reprinted from *The Journal of Legal Medicine*, Vol. 12, pp. 201 - 220, 1991, by permission of Hemisphere Publishing Corporation, a member of the Taylor and Frances Group.

INTRODUCTION

Greek legend tells of Achilles, foremost of the Trojan War heroes, who was brought down by an arrow that struck his one vulnerable spot. There is a modern-day parallel, making physicians practicing in the United States today vulnerable to the power of the government in a way that few have noticed. Through each state's abuse of the power over medical licenses, private physicians may be made virtual servants to state-perceived medical care needs. Today, those needs transcend caring simply for the elderly, indigent, and other customary beneficiaries of state-provided health care services — by far.

News travels fast in a small town, and so the man who needed hernia surgery declined to be tested for the acquired immunodeficiency syndrome virus. The hospital ran the test anyway, and allegedly the results became common knowledge among the physicians of the hospital, the only one in the county serving the low-income population. No one would operate on the man. They told him to seek surgery in San Francisco, several hours to the south.

"We get phone calls like this from patients around the country," says Norman Nickens, coordinator of the Lesbian/Gay/AIDS Unit of the Human Rights Commission of the City and County of San Francisco. "I just got a call from someone in West Virginia *who could not find a local doctor to see him.*"[1]

The evidence is now overwhelming that government at all levels, in an attempt to fulfill the role of self-appointed guarantor of the well-being of its citizens, insists on more and more health care for an ever-increasing pool of beneficiaries. Because of antidiscrimination statutes and interpretations of medical ethics, those beneficiaries now include HIV-positive patients. Concomitantly, there is a decreasing public ability to finance, and a diminishing professional willingness to provide, that care.

I. Health Costs and America's Physicians

At the beginning of 1990, the Bipartisan Commission on Comprehensive Health Care, created two years earlier by Congress to recommend legislation on health care issues,[2] issued a report calling for an $86.2 billion program that would provide not only health insurance to each and every American who needed it, but long-term nursing care as well.[3] (One remembers the early estimates of how much it was going to cost the American taxpayer to fund the Savings & Loan bailout.) This $86.2 billion was not the program's cost for a decade nor even for several years. The $86.2 billion price tag was estimated at the requisite funding for just a single year. The total Federal share of the health insurance and nursing homes programs was to cost $66.2 billion a year. Expanded nursing home care for elderly people with low and moderate incomes for others with severe disabilities would take $42.8 billion of the $66.2 billion. "The remaining $23.4 billion in Federal money would provide health insurance for those who do not already have it."[4]

Approved by the Commission by a narrow margin, Representative Fortney H. Stark, D-Cal., candidly admitted that "[w]ithout a way to pay for it, [the idea] is a non-starter. ... It is legislatively dead."[5] Even the Commission's Chairman, Senator John D. Rockefeller IV, recognized that "[w]e are not dealing with the world's easiest problem."[6] To put it mildly! Lacking are both material and human resources, a problem universally recognized.

In an article that appeared in the *New York Times* in early 1990, focusing on the Massachusetts experience, it was observed that as much as physicians in 49 states may complain about how much they are regulated, it could be worse. They could be working in Massachusetts, where regulation of practices and fees are the most extensive in the country. But that degree of regulation is not without cost. The *Times* noted further:

> The American Medical Association estimates that more than 10 percent of doctors in private practice have left the state since 1985; the figure may be as high as 30 percent in some specialties, although a special state commission says the figures are difficult to determine. ... Last year Massachusetts convened a special Physician Supply Commission to study the problem. That was in part to respond to legislators' claims that constituents in some areas were having trouble finding physicians and to claims by hospitals in some parts of the state that they could not fill their staffs. ...[7]

Massachusetts is not alone in trying to provide the maximum amount of health care for the least amount of money. Another current example is West Virginia, where the state pays the health care costs of virtually all

of its public employees. Caught in the same bind as Massachusetts and other states — with commitments to provide health care vastly outstripping actual and potential funding through taxation — West Virginia shifted a substantial portion of its health care costs to the shoulders of the states' physicians. Not only did West Virginia enact a law, like Massachusetts, against "balance billing,"[8] but it went even further in an effort to provide as much medical care for as many people at the least possible cost to the state.

A close examination of the West Virginia legislation offers a meaningful insight into the nature of the threat that American physicians now face through their licenses. The Omnibus Health Care Cost Containment Act was born in the Office of the Governor, with identical versions being submitted virtually simultaneously to the House and Senate. The House bill (H.B. 2707) was introduced on March 21, 1989 and immediately referred to the Finance Committee. The bill was never considered thereafter by the Finance Committee, and the House bill went nowhere.

The Senate version, S.B. 576, eventually became law. Filed "By Request of the Executive," on March 20, 1989, the bill cleared both Houses of the West Virginia legislature in about one month and was promptly signed into law. As a statement of public policy, certain legislative "Findings" were incorporated into the statute, virtually replicating the Governor's rationale for adopting the legislation. The legislative findings and purposes are set forth below:

(1) That a significant and ever-increasing amount of the state's financial resources are required

to assure that the citizens of the state who are reliant on the state for the provision of health care services and payment thereof receive such, whether through the public employees insurance agency, the state medicaid program, the workers' compensation fund, the division of rehabilitation services or otherwise;

(2) That the state has been unable to timely pay for such health care services;

(3) That the public employees insurance agency and the state medicaid program face serious financial difficulties in terms of decreasing amounts of available federal or state dollars by which to fund their respective programs and in paying debts presently owed;

(4) That, in order to alleviate such situation and to assure such health care services, in addition to adequate funding of such programs, the state must effect cost savings in the provision of such health care;

(5) That it is in the best interest of the state and the citizens thereof that the various state departments and divisions, involved in such provisions of health care and the payment thereof cooperate in the effecting of cost savings; and

(6) That the health and well-being of all state citizens, and particularly those whose health care is provided or paid for by the public employees insurance agency, the state medicaid program, the workers' compensation fund and the division of rehabilitation services, are of primary concern to the state.

(b) This article is enacted to provide a framework within which the departments and divisions of state government can cooperate to effect cost savings for the provision of health care services and the payment thereof. It is the purpose of the Legislature to encourage the long-term, well-planned development of fair, equitable and cost-effective systems for all health care providers paid or reimbursed by the public employees insurance agency, the state medicaid program, the workers' compensation fund or the division of rehabilitation services.[9]

This statement of legislative purpose clearly indicates that the *raison d'etre* for West Virginia's Omnibus Health Care Cost Containment Act was to shift part of the cost of medical care from the state to someone else. Basically, there were two candidates — the taxpayers generally, or physicians in particular. In this regard, the legislative history contains a "smoking gun."

Although in the House Finance Committee no transcript of the proceedings is made, a staffer takes notes. On April 4, 1989, S.B. 576 was referred to subcommittee, and the next day the bill was discussed in the full committee. There, a witness named Phil Reale, representing the Governor, conceded, as the "Findings" quoted above make quite clear, that S.B. 576 was actually a budget bill: "[T]axes can't be raised again to take care of the problem."

West Virginia tried to solve its "problem" in three ways:

1. By allowing state agencies that provide health insurance coverage to "cap" payments to health care providers for services rendered to the formers' beneficiaries. In other words, when the state paid its employees' medical bills, the physicians would receive pre-set amounts. There would be no sums paid in excess of what the state "schedule" provided.
2. By prohibiting "balance billing." No matter how much the physician believed his or her services to be worth, no matter the ability and willingness of the patient to pay, the state's payment was all that the health care provider could receive.
3. A so-called "take-one-take-all" provision was enacted, requiring that the providing of services to any one state beneficiary necessitates the providing of services either to every other one who wants medical care, or to a certain number of Medicaid patients (probably 15% of the physician's total patients). This means that a West Virginia physician was given the choice of either refusing to see many patients or, in order to continue treating them, accepting as patients an unlimited number of state medical care beneficiaries.

In sum, West Virginia has placed the state's physicians in a vise. Having undertaken to pay the medical bills of thousands of state employees who are the patients of private physicians, West Virginia has substantial power over those health care providers. Through the use of the three means just discussed, the state has used that power to purchase low-cost medical care at the physicians' expense.

II. The Physician's Achilles Heel

As clever as the West Virginia Legislature may have been in shifting to the shoulders of the states' physicians much of its self-imposed burden to provide health care for virtually all of its public employees, an even more Machiavellian scheme has been hatched, predictably, by Massachusetts. There, the legislature has implemented a sure-fire device through which that state — and any other state — can satisfy much of its self-chosen commitment to provide near-universal health care not only at a reduced or low cost, but perhaps even at no cost at all.

The device involves tying the physician's license to practice medicine to a personal obligation to serve state-designated health care beneficiaries. In other words, as a condition of practicing medicine, the physician must serve the needs of those selected by the state, at a price determined not by the physician and the patient, but by the state.

The story of how "license servitude" became law in Massachusetts, and the response of Worcester's distinguished internist Dr. Leonard J. Morse, has an important bearing on not only the problem confronting the nation's physicians, but on its solution. In a 1986 article appearing in *Massachusetts Medicine*,[10] Dr. Morse explained that, as a condition of granting or renewing a license, the 1986 statute prohibited physicians who accepted Medicare from "balance billing." In other words, Medicare assignment was to be mandatory.

This was not a new idea in Massachusetts. Two years earlier, the Board of Registration in Medicine, of which Dr. Morse was then Secretary, had been lobbied to make mandatory Medicare assignment a condition of licensure. The Board rejected the idea, and the legislation was proposed soon thereafter.

Dr. Morse provides an insider's view of how the Massachusetts Legislature was lobbied.

The atmosphere at the Health Care Committee hearing was overwhelmingly supportive ... Senior citizens were transported to Springfield for a day's excursion, and two television stations covering the hearing remained until the late morning, documenting only the proponent's testimony. Viewers of the evening news saw only one side of the issue, because opponents were not heard until late in the hearing.[11]

Also lobbied was the Massachusetts Medical Society, whose 204th annual meeting was actually disrupted by members of the Massachusetts Senior Action Counsel and the Cape Cod Alliance for the Elderly, in support of the legislation.[12]

The lobbying succeeded, making every Massachusetts physicians' license subject to mandatory Medicare assignment. Expressing the feelings of many Massachusetts physicians, Dr. Morse's article in *Massachusetts Medicine* concluded by indignantly stating that "as a practicing physician in Worcester for the past 24 years, I consider the passage of mandatory Medicare assignment a travesty of Justice and an affront to a noble profession."[13]

Dr. Morse's final words explained the rationale for the stand he had taken:

I could not in good conscience continue to participate as a member of the Massachusetts Board of Registration in Medicine, despite the fact that I considered my appointment to the Board an honor, giving me the privilege to serve not only the citizens of our state, but the members of a dedicated profession.[14]

Dr. Morse's principled stand squarely framed the issue. Like West Virginia, Massachusetts had sought to satisfy lobby-demanded, state-perceived health care needs by shifting the government's cost burden not to taxpayers in general, but to physicians in particular. Unlike West Virginia, however, or any other state so far, Massachusetts had backed-up that shift with a threat to the physicians's license.

A. The Law of Professional Licensing

To understand fully the meaning and implications of the Massachusetts license servitude law, it is necessary to review the constitutional foundation upon which professional licensing laws rest.

Medical licensure laws were originally enacted in the United States during the late 19th and early 20th centuries as a matter of public necessity. Protecting the public against quackery, commercial exploitation, deception, and professional incompetence required legally enforceable standards for entrance into and continuation in the medical profession. The states' medical practice acts therefore specified both ethical and educational requirements for physicians — requirements relating to personal character, scientific education, and practical training or experience.

The early licensure statutes reflected the recommendations of the Flexner Report on medical education published in 1910. This report initiated efforts to raise the standards of medical school admission, instruction, and curriculum, to

place these schools under the jurisdiction of universities, and to provide full-time faculty and adequate facilities for teaching and clinical experience. The incorporation in medical licensure laws of requirements which proprietary schools could not meet resulted in the closing of "diploma mills," as the inadequate medical schools of the time were called.[15]

Ironically, the seminal precedent sustaining the constitutionality of state professional licensing laws was established in a case originating in West Virginia.

In 1882, the state had enacted a law requiring every medical practitioner to obtain a certificate from the state board of health attesting that the applicant had graduated from a "reputable" medical college or, alternatively, had practiced medicine continuously in West Virginia for 10 years prior to March 8, 1881, or "that he has been found, upon examination by the board, to be qualified to practice medicine in all its departments"[16]

The "practice of, or the attempt by any person to practice, medicine, surgery, or obstetrics in the state without such certificate ... was a misdemeanor punishable by fine or imprisonment, or both, inthe discretion of the court." [17]

In the case of *Dent v. West Virginia*,[18] the defendant was indicted under this West Virginia statute for unlawfully practicing medicine. He pleaded not guilty, and the prosecution and defense agreed to the following facts.

[T]he defendant was engaged in

the practice of medicine ... at the time charged in the indictment, and had been so engaged since the year 1876 continuously to the present time, and has during all said time enjoyed a lucrative practice, publicly professing to be a physician, prescribing for the sick, and appending to his name the letters, "M.D.;" that he was not then and there a physician ... that he has no certificate, as required by [the law] but has a diploma from the "American Medical Eclectic College of Cincinnati, Ohio;" that he presented said diploma to the members of the board of health [but they refused to grant him the certificate] because, as they claimed, said college did not come under the word "reputable," as defined by said board of health; that if the defendant ... should be prevented from practicing medicine it would be a great injury to him, as it would deprive him of his only means of supporting himself and his family.[19]

Dent claimed that the statute was unconstitutional because it interfered with his vested right to practice medicine. The trial judge rejected this argument and Dent was convicted.

Eventually, the case reached the Supreme Court of the United States, which enunciated legal principles that have informed the subject of professional licensing from that day to this. Rooting its decision in the state's power to provide for the general welfare of its citizens, especially securing them "against the consequences of ignorance and incapacity, as well as of deception and fraud,"[20] the court upheld the West Virginia law. It emphasized that the state had a right to be concerned with the putative physician's skill and learning, and knowledge of such things as "the remedial properties of vegetable and mineral substances."[21] As the Court said in closing: "[T]he law of West Virginia was intended to secure such skill and learning in the profession of medicine that the community might trust with confidence those receiving a license under authority of the state."[22]

That *Dent* stands for the proposition that states have the power to license professions in the public interest, and that the state's interest is in protecting its citizens from unskilled practitioners, is not open to doubt. Nor is it open to doubt that until Massachusetts went looking for a way to save itself health care money, the Dent principle, for the most part, had been interpreted to limit licensure criteria to those associated, either directly or indirectly, with skill and learning.[23] In modern times, this proposition was underscored by the Supreme Court of the United States in *Schware v. Board of Law Examiners*,[24] where Justice Black equated "good moral character of proficiency" with "high standards of qualification." In other words, the tenth amendment to the Constitution of the United States reserved to the states the power to legislate in furtherance of health, safety, welfare, and morals, and the states have exercised that power by, among other things, requiring that medical licensees, and other professionals as well, be qualified — that they demonstrate a sufficient level of knowledge and skill so that their patients may act in reliance thereon, thereby reducing the potential that patients would be injured by quacks.

B. The Challenge to Massachusetts License Servitude

Putting aside the important question of whether the state's imprimatur on a professional's skill and learning, let alone his or her moral fitness, is the best way to protect the public from incompetents, the qualification criteria traditionally has been the only requirement imposed on the medical license. Thus, prior to the two Massachusetts cases discussed below, derision and/or incredulity probably would have greeted the suggestion that an architect's licensing board could require that architects draw blueprints for a low-cost housing project, free of charge. Or that a plumber's licensing board could require plumbers to install pipes and fixtures, free of charge. Or that licensed undertakers bury the indigent without cost. Or that licensed bowling alleys provide free frames. Or licensed liquor stores free wine.

Similarly, it would have appeared unimaginable that all physicians in Massachusetts who treated federal Medicare patients could be required, under penalty of losing their state licenses, to accept as the fee for services rendered only what Medicare reimbursement provided, and not a nickel more, regardless of the patients' ability and willingness to pay. But that is exactly what Massachusetts has done, and the significance far transcends what has happened in the Bay State.

As Dr. Morse's resignation noted, Chapter 475 of the Massachusetts Act of 1985 now provides that the state licensing authority, the Board of Registration in Medicine,

shall require as a condition of granting or renewing a physician's certificate of registration, that the physician, who if he agrees to treat a beneficiary of health insurance under Title XVIII of the Social Security Act, shall also agree *not to charge to or collect from such ben-*

eficiary any amount in excess of the reasonable charge for that service as determined by the United States Secretary of Health and Human Services.[25]

In other words, if a Massachusetts physician treats a patient over 65 years of age, the physician receives what the Medicare schedule allows for that housecall or procedure, or whatever, regardless of the physician's needs, regardless of the patient's ability and willingness to pay, and regardless of whatever mutually agreeable arrangements the physician and a patient otherwise may have made.[26]

Not surprisingly, the license servitude statute was challenged in the United States District Court for the District of Massachusetts by the Massachusetts Medical Society and the American Medical Association. The case was entitled *Massachusetts Medical Society v. Dukakis.*[27] To understand the court's decision, it is first necessary to highlight important aspects of the federal Medicare system.

Under Medicare, physicians receive payment for the medical services that they provide on the basis of a "reasonable charge" established by the Department of Health and Human Services (HHS). Eighty percent of that "reasonable charge" is paid by the Medicare program, and the patient is obligated, at least in theory, to pay the balance of the physician's charge.[28] Actually, the federal act contemplates either of two methods of payment. First, the physician can agree to accept what is referred to as "assignment" — meaning that the physician will take as payment in full, no matter what the patient owes, the "reasonable amount" that HHS has established, 80% of that

charge payable by Medicare and the remaining 20% payable by the patient. Or the physician can bill the patient directly for the services provided. The patient is then reimbursed by Medicare for 80% of the "reasonable charge." Obviously, the physician's actual charge to the patient can be more than the "reasonable charge," in which case the patient is personally responsible for (a) the remaining 20% of the "reasonable charge" and (b) however much more the physician has billed over the "reasonable charge." "The physician practice of charging an amount greater than the reasonable charge is called 'balance billing.'"[29]

It is in this context that the Massachusetts license servitude law needs to be understood. As a prerequisite to obtaining or keeping a license to practice medicine in the state, the Massachusetts statute prohibited balance billing, forcing the physicians to take Medicare assignment and to collect 100% of what HHS determines is a "reasonable charge." This "reasonable charge" may be far less than what the medical service is worth, far less than what the physician wants, far less than what the patient is able to pay, and far less than what the physician and patient would have voluntarily arranged between themselves had they been free to do so.

The Massachusetts Medical Society (MMS) and the American Medical Association (AMA) understood this point very well. In their federal court attack on the constitutionality of mandatory Medicare assignment, the core of their argument was articulated as follows:

> Chapter 475 is ... unconstitutional because it violates the due process clause of the Fourteenth Amendment. This

clause requires that any condition on professional licensure "must have a rational connection with the applicant's fitness or capacity to practice ... It forbids any condition that is not directed to protecting "against the consequences of ignorance and incapacity" or "deception and fraud."[30]

In elaborating upon this point, the MMS and the AMA contended that the statute clearly imposed a condition on the license, but one that had no relation either to competence or character. But what about the cases cited by the Commonwealth in support of its core argument that the mandatory assignment condition on the license advanced certain legitimate governmental policies? The MMS and the AMA were able to distinguish some and turn others to their advantage.

For example, the MMS and the AMA noted that *Nebbia v. New York*[31] was an economic regulation case that in no way implicated the requirement of competence to practice a profession. Other of the Commonwealth's cases[32] were similarly distinguished as either not involving professional licensing or ultimately resting on the requirement of competency. According to the MMS and the AMA, not only did the Commonwealth's United States Supreme Court citations provide no support for the constitutionality of Massachusetts' mandatory assignment license condition, but neither did the four Massachusetts cases upon which the Commonwealth relied.[33]

The MMS's and the AMA's last major point was an important one — because the right to pursue a learned calling has always been recognized as more "protectable" than engaging in trade or business activities, social goals that limit the former must be more important than those that inhibit the latter.[34] That being so, the MMS and the AMA observed that the Commonwealth had made no connection between the mandatory assignment condition on the license and the Massachusetts physicians' competence to practice medicine.

Substantively, the plaintiffs had lucidly defined the issue, and their constitutional arguments were cogent and compelling — but to no avail. Despite these arguments, the United States district judge decided that the mandatory Medicare assignment condition was constitutional. Let us examine the court's reasons.

At the very beginning of that portion of the district court's opinion dealing with the license servitude issue, the judge succinctly stated the positions of each party: the MMS and the AMA were arguing that "[i]n order to pass constitutional muster ... the Act must bear a rational relationship to a physician's *fitness or capacity to practice.*' Defendants disagree that this is the appropriate standard, arguing that it is necessary only for the Act to bear a rational relationship *to a legitimate state purpose.*"[35] Obviously, the latter standard was very much broader, and thus considerably easier for the State of Massachusetts to satisfy.

After considering various precedential decisions of the United States Supreme Court and elsewhere, the court seemed to be drifting in the state's direction:

[I]t may be that the defendants' proposed "rational relation to a legitimate purpose" standard is the correct one. If

this is so the Act must be upheld. The containment of medical costs for the elderly is plainly a legitimate concern of the Commonwealth. It is also plain that the legislature could reasonably determine that requiring physicians not to balance bill their Medicare patients was a means of addressing that concern, and that the licensure process was an effective mechanism for enforcing that prohibition. *I conclude that the reliance of the legislature on the legislative facts that medical care costs are a serious problem for the elderly and that conditions on licensure are an effective means of obtaining physician compliance with state regulation is well within the bounds of rationality required by ordinary due process scrutiny.*[36]

In other words — and this is the least remarkable aspect of the decision — if the test for assessing the constitutionality of Massachusetts' mandatory Medicare assignment was a rational relation to a legitimate purpose, as the state argued, rather than grounded in fitness or capacity to practice, as the MMS and AMA argued, the Act passed constitutional muster because helping the elderly with their medical bills is a worthy goal.

The more remarkable aspect of the court's decision, however, was what followed. What if the MMS and the AMA were correct? What if the appropriate test to be applied to the Act was not mere rational relation to a legitimate purpose (that is, helping the elderly with their medical bills), but rather whether the Act had a rational relation to a physician's fitness or capacity to practice? The court held that it would not make

any difference. Even if rational relation to fitness or capacity was the proper standard, the constitutional challenge must fall.[37]

In other words, even if the conditions imposed on a physician's license must be related to fitness or capacity to practice, including the traditional criteria of education, experience, and good moral character, mandatory Medicare assignment is sufficiently so related.

It was, of course, one thing for the district judge simply to assert this startling conclusion, but another for him to offer any support for it. What follows may seem to be an unduly lengthy quotation, but it is offered because four paragraphs constitute virtually everything that the judge had to say to buttress a decision that not only imposed a significant servitude on the physicians of Massachusetts, but opened the door to endless other servitudes on them and on their medical colleagues throughout the United States.

Nothing in the case law of conditions on professional licensure attributes to "fitness or capacity to practice law" the narrow definition advocated by [the MMS and the AMA]. Nor would such a definition ... be consistent with the broad powers which states hold to determine for themselves how best to promote the welfare of their people. Even if, under the Due Process Clause, a state may only require of a licensee that which is related to fitness or capacity, it must be sure that the state has some latitude in choosing what it considers to be necessary *indications of fitness and capacity.* However narrow or broad that latitude may be, I conclude that the power to require those licensees who choose to treat a particularly needy segment of the population to do so for limited fees lies within that latitude. Stated another way, *I conclude that the legislature's determination as a matter of legislative fact that the provision of cost-contained services to the elderly is a necessary part of what it means to be fit and capable to practice in this state is not outside the bounds of what the Due Process Clause permits.* A strong analogy to that legislative choice lies in the requirement that lawyers serve some clients at little or no charge. The requirement to perform *"pro bono"* work or to accept without compensation a court-appointment to represent a needy client has been upheld numerous times by various courts. [The MMS and the AMA] distinguish this line of cases by pointing out that lawyers have unique responsibilities as "officers of the court." But in this context, I conclude that this distinction between lawyers and physicians is without significance ... As are lawyers, doctors are entrusted with the performance of a special role. As do lawyers, they "enjoy a 'broad monopoly ... to do things other citizens may not lawfully do.'" As with lawyers, the state has a special interest in protecting its citizens by regulating those who fill that monopolistic role. In sum, I conclude that the choice of the state legislature to designate the provision of cost-contained services to the elderly as a condition of licensure does not offend the Due Process Clause, *even if that clause requires that such conditions reasonably relate to fitness or capacity to practice.*[38]

The essence of the court's conclusion is startling, transcending even the license servitude issue that was being decided. In effect, the United States District Court for the District of Massachusetts was deciding that: because physicians receive a "monopoly" from the state to practice medicine, they can be made to perform any service required of them by the state; performance of that service can be made an encumbrance on their licenses; and their failure to perform that service manifests unfitness and lack of capacity to practice medicine. In other words, with the license to practice medicine comes the duty to serve state-dictated goals. Today that means caring for the needy. Tomorrow, who knows?

C. Pressing the Challenge to License Servitude

Undeterred, the MMS and the AMA appealed the district court's ruling to the United States Court of Appeals for the First Circuit.[39] Although they did not challenge the underlying altruist, collectivist, statist principles that underlay the district court's decision, they did continue to hammer away at the idea that anything but fitness was the criterion for medical licensure, let alone that fitness included the willingness to serve the needy.

In the United States Court of Appeals, the MMS and the AMA tracked the arguments that they had made in the district court: although statutes regulating mere occupations can be upheld if they have a rational relation to a legitimate state interest, laws creating licensing conditions must be justified on the basis of fitness or capacity. The plaintiffs also added a powerful critique of the lower court's opinion upholding the

constitutionality of mandatory Medicare assignment. The district judge erred, they contended, in several important respects. First, he was mistaken about mandatory assignment's alleged social goal of regulating fees to the needy because Medicare is not a need-based program but rather a program for the elderly of whatever means. Second, he was equally mistaken in attempting to rely on cases that have upheld the requirement that lawyers provide *pro bono* representation to indigent criminal defendants, because physicians can not be analogized to officers of the court and because the medical needs of elderly patients are not analogous to the constitutional rights of criminal defendants.

The court of appeals disagreed.

MMS ... argues that the Massachusetts ban on balance billing violates the due process clause of the fourteenth amendment because it deprives doctors of the "liberty" to practice their profession. The Massachusetts statute makes a doctor's promise not to balance bill a condition of obtaining a license. ... Moreover, the Massachusetts Board of Registration in Medicine has stated that it will impose sanctions for any violation of the law "that are commensurate with the severity of the violation" ... — sanctions that may include a reprimand, censure, fine, or suspension or revocation of license. *** MMS argues that the condition that Massachusetts imposes on medical licenses — a promise not to balance bill is not rationally connected with a doctor's "fitness or capacity to practice" medicine. *In our view, however, this "promise" simply amounts to rule. It is a rule* *that forbids balance billing. And, there is nothing irrational about a state's saying that a physician, entering the profession, must promise to follow the rules.* Nor is it irrational to say that a physician who seriously violates the rule — who commits a violation that is "commensurate with" the penalty of license revocation — is not "fit" to practice medicine. For these reasons, the judgment of the district court is Affirmed.[40]

The court of appeals simply held that the "condition" not to balance bill was a mere "rule," and that rules had to be followed. Nothing more was offered by the court of appeals to justify its decision. "Rules" are "rules," no more, no less.

The MMS and the AMA arguments in the federal appellate court were well reasoned, as they had been in the district court, and based on solid consitutional principles. Skill and learning — "fitness," if you like — traditionally had been the sole criteria for granting and renewing a license to practice medicine, and for good reason — to protect the patient from quacks. Yet, the political organs of the Massachusetts government (the legislature and the governor), and now both the federal trial and appellate the courts in that state, had decided that fitness alone was no longer enough. Thus, protecting patients was not all that the state, in its magnanimity, could do for them. Other patient-oriented goals could be accomplished by holding hostage the physician's license to practice medicine. In sum, the patient's needs — this time, for less costly medical care — could and should be satisfied at the expense of the physician.

But if that were true — if the physician's license to practice medicine was to be held hostage to the financial needs of the patient — then to what could that license not be held hostage? Could Massachusetts, or any state, for that matter, require physicians, as a condition of obtaining or renewing their licenses, to spend one day each week in a leper colony? Or in a maximum security prison? Or in the state national guard? Or, indeed, satisfying any state-perceived "social need," like performing surgery on HIV-positive patients?

Sadly, the answer may be yes, based on the principles articulated in the *Massachusetts Medical Society* decision, which the Supreme Court of the United States refused to review. In a way, the decision in that case should not have been surprising. The groundwork had been laid shortly before in a case decided by the Massachusetts Supreme Judicial Court.

D. Failure of the Challenge Foretold

In the 1984 case of *Walden v. Board of Registration in Nursing*,[41] registered nurse Nancy L. Walden received an application for license renewal from the Massachusetts Board of Registration in Nursing. Among other things, the application required that she certify under penalties of perjury that, to the best of her knowledge and belief, she had filed all state tax returns and paid all state taxes required under law.[42] Because nurse Walden refused to certify that she was not a tax evader, the Board declined to process her application for license renewal. She sued, lost at trial, and appealed to the Massachusetts Supreme Judicial Court.

Just as the MMS and AMA would argue a year later in the Mas-

sachusetts federal district court, and later in the circuit court, Walden had contended in the state court that professional licenses could be made dependent only on fitness, not on collateral purposes that the state thought were important to accomplish. Anticipating what the MMS and AMA would contend later, here, in part, is what Walden argued. "The Supreme Judicial Court has also long recognized 'the right to enjoy life, liberty and the pursuit of happiness is secured to everyone under the Constitution of Massachusetts' and that 'this includes the right to pursue any proper vocation to obtain a livelihood.'"[43]

Walden argued further that such a blatantly coercive statute did not deserve judicial deference, and that the Massachusetts' high court had in the past struck down legislation not rationally related to a legitimate governmental end.

[T]he oath requirement is a blatantly coercive legislative enactment undeserving of judicial deference. Where legislation such as this impacts so harshly upon protected liberty and property interests, the Court is *obligated* to determine whether the enactment impermissibly infringes upon such interests. In such an instance, "it is precisely the function of the judiciary under substantive due process, when conventional ideals and government action significantly and seriously diverge, to reassert the primacy of the ideals." A. Bickel, *The Least Dangerous Bunch*, 23-38 (1965). There should be no hesitation to similarly invalidate the Disputed Law, as there is no "real and substantial" relation between the tax oath and either the state's interest in tax collection nor in the good character of its licensed nurses. As has been argued previously in this Brief, any true tax outlaw would have absolutely no aversion to falsely attesting to the oath. Realistically, the declaration cannot be said to bear a reasonable relationship to the prevention of tax avoidance. *See Coffee-Rich, Inc. ...* [Legislative 'regulations must be reasonable in their nature, directed to the prevention of real evils and adapted to the accomplishment of their avowed purpose.'"][44]

If the license condition had nothing to do with the government's legitimate interest in tax collection, according to Walden it had even less to do with nursing.

Although the Superior Court strained to link the Disputed Law to the state's interest "in employing citizens of good character" ... [Footnote omitted] there is neither record evidence nor ready inference that licensees who have complied with tax laws have better or worse character than those who have not and/or that the Legislature was the least bit concerned with that notion when it enacted REAP, an unabashed effort aimed purely at increased tax collection. ... Although the state may certainly regulate nursing, in ways already mentioned in this Brief, to condition the practice of nursing upon a certification of compliance with state tax laws makes no more sense than to condition the right to drive a car on the highways upon the filing of census information, or the right to vote on the payment of speeding tickets. Thus, the Dis-

puted Law infringes impermissibly upon the Appellant's constitutionally protected liberty and property interests in pursuing her profession and maintaining her license.[45]

Walden's arguments were constitutionally solid, and the Massachusetts' license servitude condition that affected her was even more remote from fitness than would be mandatory Medicare assignment. Yet, in language that would anticipate the result in the *Massachusetts Medical Society* case the next year, the Massachusetts Supreme Judicial Court flatly rejected Walden's claim that the state-demanded tax probity certification had nothing whatever to do with her fitness to be a nurse. Although the court recognized that Walden was arguing "that because occupational licensing is involved, [the law] must have a rational basis related to her profession or her practice of it,"[46] and although it recognized that "[t]here is language in *Schware* ... which tends to support [Walden's] claim that the rational basis for regulatory legislation must relate to her competence to practice nursing,"[47] Massachusetts' highest court was unpersuaded. Even if the *Schware* decision meant what it seemed to say, according to the Supreme Judicial Court, "the fact that a licensee of the Commonwealth, at least a nurse, had knowingly failed to comply with the tax laws of the Commonwealth could be treated rationally as an anti-social act demonstrating unfitness to carry on a responsible profession in which adherence to other laws is required."[48]

CONCLUSION

The *Massachusetts Medical Society* and *Walden* cases teach a hard les-

sion, and send a strong, unequivocal message to the physicians not only of Massachusetts, but throughout the nation: while fitness remains the core requirement for the granting and renewal of a professional license, as surely it must, now, expressly according to *Walden* and implicitly according to *Massachusetts Medical Society*, "anti-social acts" are to be synonymous with "unfitness." "Anti-social acts" like refusing to spend one day a week practicing in a leper colony? Or in a maximum security prison? Or refusing to join the state National Guard? Or doing anything else that the state might deem socially useful?" LIke refusing to perform surgery on HIV-positive patients.

The American Medical Association certainly does not think so, having in 1982 gone on record as opposing any conditions on a physician's license except fitness: "The Council believes that licensure laws should be related solely to physician competence and that licensing boards should be charged with responsibility for matters relating to competence. The boards should not be charged with responsibility for accomplishing other state objectives, including health care cost containment for the elderly.[49]

Unfortunately, the "other state objectives" sought to be accomplished by legislatures are not going to end with health care cost containment for the elderly (many of whom, it should be noted, are more affluent than the physicians who treat them). For example, at about the same time that mandatory Medicare assignment as a condition for licensure came to Massachusetts, a bill was introduced in that legislature attaching the same conditions for Medicaid patients. Although it did not pass, the idea behind the bill was exactly the same as the idea upon which mandatory Medicare assignment rests, and idea now validated constitutionally by both the highest federal and state courts in Massachusetts: the physicians' license to practice medicine is held in servitude to state-perceived medical needs.

Given that those needs are growing larger every day, as the Bipartisan Commission report discussed above makes clear, it is only a matter of time until other states latch on to the idea that they can "solve" their perceived health care needs not by politically unpopular and often unacceptable method of raising taxes generally, but rather by increasing the servitude of America's physicians. Their licenses will then become a yoke by which they will be pulled toward state-dictated medical servitude. Eventually, more and more of America's physicians will refuse to practice as mere handmaids of government. Actually, that is already happening.

My patients ask me why, after six years in the private practice of neurosurgery in the Boston-North Shore area, I am leaving to practice elsewhere. I tell them that the many assaults physicians in Massachusetts have to endure has left me with no other choice. In the past six years, the number of neurosurgeons practicing in Massachusetts has dropped from more than 120 to less than 80. Few physicians choose to move to Massachusetts to begin a practice, despite the fact that the Boston medical community has always held a position of world prominence.

***

However, the overseers of medicine in Massachusetts tend to treat physicians as though they are antisocial, amoral incompetents who need to be controlled like circus animals.

***

Fortunately, one of the things that is still permitted for Massachusetts physicians is the right to leave and practice elsewhere. I will miss my patients.[50]

So will they all.
And, surely, will we miss them.

ENDNOTES

1. Holzman, *AIDS Fear Alters Surgeon's World*, Insight Magazine, Oct. 15, 1990, at 52 (emphasis added).
2. The Commission was called the "Pepper Commission," after its then-Chairman, Florida Senator Claude Pepper.
3. Tolchin, Panel Says Broad Health Care Would Cost $86 Billion a Year, *N.Y. Times*, Mar. 3, 1990, at 1, col. 1. Obviously, the recipients of that care would include AIDS sufferers.
4. *Id.* at 9, col. 1.
5. *Id.* at 1, col. 1.
6. *Id.*
7. Rosenthal, Some Point to Massachusetts as Extreme of Regulation, N.Y. Times, Feb. 19, 1990, at A13, col. 1
8. "Balance billing" refers to the amount billed by a physician to a patient that constitutes the difference between the physician's actual charge and the reimbursement received from Medicare. 1989 W. Va. Acts, ch. 16, art. 29B, 16-29-D-4.
9. *Id.* 16-29-D-1
10. Morse, Why I Resigned from the Board, *Mass. Med.*, Mar./Apr. 1986, at 13-14.
11. *Id.* at 14.
12. *Id.*
13. *Id.*
14. *Id.*
15. Forgotson, Roemer, & Newman, *Licensure of Physicians*, 1967 Wash, U.L.Q., 249.
16. W. Va. Code, ch. 93, 9 (1882).
17. *Id. See* Dent v. West Virginia, 192 U.S. 114, 117 (1889).
18. 129 U.S. 114 (1889).
19. *Id.* at 117-18.
20. *Id.* at 122.
21. *Id.* at 123.
22. *Id.* at 128.
23. Thus, state imposed requirements relating to education and even experience are clearly within the police power. Although requirements of "character and fitness" (*see* Schware v. Board of Law Examiners, 353 U.S. 232 (1959), arguably go too far when the criteria are skill and learning, the former requirements have been updated as rationally related to the latter. The excuses given for citizenship and residence requirements have been based on the notion that somehow United States citizens and state residents make better licensed professionals. Those requirements are now gone. *See In re* Griffiths, 413 U.S. 717 (1973) and Supreme Court of New Hampshire v. Piper, 470 U.S. 274 (1985). Even less defensible is Idaho's requirement, for example, that prior to a physician's licensure or the renewal of a license, malpractice insurance must be in place. Nevertheless, in passing on the constitutionality of Idaho Code section 39-4206(6) (1975), the Supreme Court of Idaho stressed that, similar to the protection afforded patients by the state requiring that the physician possess a certain level of skill and learning, the malpractice insurance requirement provided "protection to patients who may be

injured as a result of medical malpractice ... " Jones v. State Bd. of Medicine, 97 Idaho 859, 555 P.2d, 399, 408 (1976).

24. 353 U.S. 232, 239 (1959).

25. Mass. Gen. L. ch. 112, 2 (1985) (emphasis added). The *Association of Retired Persons Bulletin* of September 1990 reported at page six that "[m]ore states are placing tighter limits on the amount doctors can charge their Medicare patients." According to AARP, Pennsylvania, Massachusetts, and Rhode Island have prohibited balance billing and a new law will "bar doctors in New York from billing patients more than 15 percent in excess of Medicare's approved rate. That amount will drop to about 10 percent by 1993." AARP also reported that "Vermont and Connecticut bar doctors from charging low-income beneficiaries more than Medicare's approved rate. Other patients may be charged up to the federal limit, which, as previously noted, will next year cap the amount that physicians may bill in excess of the approved rate at 25 percent."

26. A thorough, painstaking search and analysis of the statutes and rules governing medical licenses in each of the other 49 states has failed to reveal anything even remotely similar to the license servitude imposed on the physicians of Massachusetts.

27. 637 F. Supp. 684 (D. Mass. 1986).

28. "The reasonable charge is calculated by HHS on the basis of the physician's own 'customary charge' for that service as well as the 'prevailing charge' in the locality for similar services. 42 U.S.C. sec 1395u(b)(3). 42 C.F.R. 405.502(a)." *Massachusetts Medical Soc'y*; 637 F. Supp. at

686.

29. *Massachusetts Medical Soc'y*; 637 F. Supp. at 686. *See supra* note 8.

30. Plaintiff's Reply Memorandum of Law in Support of Request For Declaratory Relief, at 33, Massachusetts Medical Soc'y v. Dukakis, 637 F. Supp. 684 (D. Mass. 1986).

31. 291 U.S. 502 (1934).

32. North Dakota State Bd. of Pharmacy v. Snyder's Drugstores Inc., 414 U.S. 156 (1973); Ferguson v. Skrupa, 372 U.S. 726 (19630; Williamson v. Lee Optical Co., 348 U.S. 483 (1973); Minnesota Ass'n of Health Care Facilities, Inc., v. Minnesota Dep't of Pub. Welfare, 742 F.2d 442 (ith Cir. 1984); Whitney v. Heckler, 780 F.2d 963 (11th Cir.), *cert. denied.* 479 U.S. 813 (1986); Massachusetts Nursing Ass'n v. Dukakis, 726 F.2d 41 (1st Cir. 1984); American Medical Ass'n v. Heckler, 606 F. Supp. 1422 (S.D. Ind. 1985).

33. The MMS and the AMA argued that the four Massachusetts cases cited by the defendants confirmed that a condition on licensure must bear a relationship to "capacity or fitness." Walden v. Board of Registration in Nursing, 395 Mass. 263, 479 N.E. 2d 665 (1985), involved a certification that the applicant for licensure had paid his or her taxes. Raymond v. Board of Registration in Medicine, 387 Mass. 708, 433 N.E. 2d 391 (1982), concerned the illegal possession of unregistered weapons. Feldstein v. Board of Registration in Medicine, 387 Mass. 339, 439 N.E. 2d 824 (1982), dealt with Medicaid fraud. Levy v. Board of Registration in Medicine, 378 Mass. 519, 392 N.E. 2d 1036 (1979), involved grand larceny. In all these cases, the Supreme Judicial

Court stressed that the conduct that triggered licensure sanctions demonstrated the licensee's lack of fitness or capacity to practice.

34. In support of this proposition, the MMS and the AMA cited Hampton v. Mow Sun Wong, 426 U.S. 88 (1976), Truax v. Raich, 239 U.S. 33 (1915), and Silver v. Garcia, 760 F.2d 33 (1st Cir. 1985). Also cited was Stalland v. Board of Bar Examiners, 530 F. Supp. 155 (D.S.D. 1982).

35. *Massachusetts Medical Soc'y*, 637 F. Supp. at 703 (emphasis added).

36. *Id.* at 706 (emphasis added).

37. *Id.*

38. *Id* at 706-07 (emphasis added) (citations omitted).

39. Massachusetts Medical Soc'y v. Dukakis, 815 F.2d 790 (1st Cir. 1987).

40. *Massachusetts Medical Soc'y*, 815 F.2d at 797 (emphasis added).

41. 395 Mass. 263, 479 N.E. 2d 665 (1985).

42. *See* Mass. Gen. L. ch. 62C, 49A (1984).

43. Brief for Plaintiff-Appeallant, Supreme Judicial Court of Massachusetts, Walden v. Board of Registration in Nursing, 395 Mass. 263, 479 N.E. 2d 665 (1985).

44. *Id.*

45. *Id.*

46. *Walden*, 479 N.E. at 671.

47. Id.

48. Id. at 672 (emphasis added).

49 Counsel on Medical Education, *The Report on Medical Licensure*, 259 J.A.M.A. 1994, 1999 (1988).

50. Kornel, *Why M.D.'s Leave: One Physician's Tale*, The Boston Herald, Sept. 12, 1990, at 39 (emphasis added).

Book Review

The New Medicine: Life and Death after Hippocrates

by Nigel de S. Cameron
(Crossway Books, Wheaton, IL, 1992),
192 pp. $1195

Reviewed by David W. Hall

Nigel de S. Cameron has provided the American medical community with one of the finest recent treatises on medical ethics. Cameron (now at Trinity Divinity School) has been one of the leaders among biblical ethicists in the UK. Now in this book, he traces the consequences of jettisoning the Hippocratic approach to medicine. His beginning chapter presents and expounds this Oath, which has been in the descendancy for the past few decades. Cameron vividly warns the reader of the consequences of such abandonment, as well as the inferiority resulting from replacing Hippocratic medicine with the New (relativistic) Medicine. As C.E. Koop in the Forward summarizes, "How will patients be served in the future? That's what this book is all about: the rise and fall of Hippocratic medicine. Where *should* we go? Where *will* we go?" (p. 16). This book is a warning to the public of what happens when medical personnel are no longer anchored by covenanted ethical norms.

Cameron acquaints the reader with the rise of Hippocratic medicine, and is helpful when he points out that the "Hippocratics were a minority, a reforming movement whose distinct professional and ethical characteristics came ultimately to dominate the development of the western medical tradition" (p. 38), at least until the 20th century. He views medicine as a *professio* or a 'calling' (p. 53), and consistently asserts the inextricable relation between underlying faith and ethical practice, for example, "Only if medicine is narrowly conceived in terms of technique - a set of skills, a matter of expertise - could this be so. If, by contrast, medicine is actually constituted by its commitment to a set of values, then the dropping of those values marks the beginning of the end of medicine itself" (p. 12). Lamenting the loss of the Hippocratic framework of values, he suggests "that after Hippocrates - when medicine departs from the values of the Oath and ceases to be Hippocratic - it looses something essential to its character; in fact, it begins to cease to be 'medicine' at all" (p. 23). Rather, Cameron asserts that all medicine is fundamentally value-driven, and ineradicably theological. He contends that Hippocratic practice, even if founded by pagans, is theistic, and resulting in the twin values of philanthropy and the sanctity of life (p. 64). This medical ethicist is clear when he heralds, "The displacement of its covenantal structure leaves the Oath a naked ethical code" (p. 62), so intrinsic is the vertical dimension to the ancient oath.

The third chapter describes the most blatant example of the forsaking of Hippocratism, in a chapter which frighteningly portrays the thought and practice of Nazi medicine. In this "stark occasion in the western medical tradition when the profession turned its back on the Hippocratic legacy" (p. 69), we can see what to expect from New Medicine, if unleashed from some sufficient, transcendent covenant. It is painful, eerie, and threatening to read about some of the experiments and medical abuses by the Nazis, all under the name of progressive medicine. Further, the consequent answer to such was the 1948 Geneva Declaration, which is "a pallid affirmation made by the Physician in the presence of man alone ... its only reference points are horizontal. The act of displacing an oath with a declaration bears powerful witness to the secularising of western medical tradition" (p. 86). In sum, what is needed is a "transcendentally medical faith" with a covenantal structure (p. 87). The difference between the two approaches is stated by Cameron: "The Hippocratic Oath, with its transcendental, covenantal structure, holds firmly together as an integrated whole. The Declaration of Geneva is a series of ethical assertions which invite amendment and revision" (p. 87). Indeed, such is the degenerative history of medicine since 1948. Moreover, Cameron laments, "By abandoning the transcendent and covenantal character of the Oath, those ... have turned the principles of medical ethics into one long composite motion to be debated year on year at representative medical assemblies." (p.88).

In his four chapter, Cameron chronicles the most dominant feature of post-Hippocratic medicine as the "progressive marginalization of those who are weakest and most powerless in the clinical situation" (p.92). In this chapter and the next, he treats abortion and euthanasia as exhibits of this characteristic. These chapters are supplemented by the author's knowledge of and reporting on the legal *status quaestionae* in various western countries (p.108). His alternative in the final chapter, "Paternalism and Pluralism," is a call for a return to concern for the patient's healing, and not mere relief of suffering, subjectively measured. Borrowing from Thomas Kuhn, Cameron urges the medical practitioner to rally "back to the future," by once again assuming a reformist and minoritarian paradigm, until the day can be recaptured. The Appendix sets for a positive statement of the necessary anthropology and theology of healing to support these.

This book is well-researched, well-documented, and the author is quite plausible in his appropriation of history, theology, and medical ethics. While at times, the British thoroughness may irritate American readers, this work is supplemented with flashes of stylistic brilliance, for example when Cameron writes, "In fact, we see in the negative aspects of the Oath's moral injunctions (as in the Ten Commandments) sophistication that is born of realism" (p. 65), or in reference to the Geneva Declaration, that it "read as a lament to a lost medical tradition" (p.86).

This is a fine, well-conceived contribution to the debate. I only have one question about it, and that is the critical dependence on a pagan Oath. This book, while helpful, also raises the larger apologetic question about a Christian's reliance on non-Christian sources. Is this a form of medical evidentialism, seeking common ground in an ancient pagan Oath? If so, the thesis is apologetically questionable. Yet, even this question should not prevent one from benefiting from a fine work. It could even have been more strongly supported if the author had sought to relate the Hippocratic Oath to the OT covenantal form, which only predated the Oath bh by c. 200 years. It could even be discovered that the Hippocratic Oath, so covenantal in character, is precisely so in that it is a pagan version, or a heresy, of Old Testament covenantal outworkings. This book is as good an explanation as I've read of the Hippocratic oath in service of a Pro-life ethic.

Letter to the Editor

Dear Editor,

The recent JBEM article by Greg Rutecki and John Geib, "A Time to Be Silent..." (Vol. 5, No. 4), was quite interesting. The paper focused on the Biblical justification for confidences ("secrets") as well as some Biblical limits of confidentiality. Protection of life, for example, is given as a clear reason to "break" confidentiality, at least with those most intimately concerned with the case.

I, and perhaps other readers, would be interested in the authors' comments concerning other cases that are not related to immediate physical abuse or life-threatening issues. For example, a health care worker is counseling and/or providing other assistance to an individual who professes to be a Christian with a regular but infrequent sinful behavior pattern (e.g., shoplifting). The worker clearly counsels the individual and offers to obtain other Biblical counseling assistance. The client does not change the sinful pattern over a substantial period of time. In addition, the individual refuses to allow the health care worker to talk to anyone else about the situation. Would verses such as Matthew 18:15-17 indicate that the health care worker must eventually "break" confidentiality and inform the individual's pastor/elder/deacon?

Joseph K. Neumann, Ph.D.
Mountain Home, TN

The author's reply:

In the practice of Biblical counsel, any attempt to balance "silence" and "speech" (Eccl. 3:7) requires individual situations be framed in a spiritual awareness of the goal desired. Scripture itself reveals that goal as follows, "Brothers, if someone is caught in a sin, you who are spiritual should restore him gently" (Gal. 6:1a).

In the consideration of sins which do not involve threat to life (e.g., "shoplifting"), the authors feel that other attempts at restoration are indicated ("gently"). The counselor can strongly urge the counselee to use his/her pastor, elders and biblical accountability group as arbiters who can successfully illuminate the necessary spiritual truths (Matt. 18:15-17). As a later resort to the counselor can break the counseling relationship in an attempt to bring the counselee to repentance/restoration.

We both feel strongly that the injunction to silence in counseling situations can only be broken and Biblically justified by a threat to life.

Serving Him,

Gregory Rutecki, M.D.
John Geib

Editor's Note

The article entitled "Population Control" by Franklin E. Payne, Jr., M.D., which appeared in the Winter, 1992 issue, was reprinted from *Encyclopedia of Biblical and Christian Ethics*, Thomas Nelson Publishers, Inc., with permission.

AIDS:
The Moral, Medical, and Spiritual Challenge

Harold O.J. Brown, S.T.M., Ph.D.

Dr. Brown is Forman Professor of Ethics in Theology at Trinity Evangelical Divinity School in Deerfield, Illinois.

Paper presented at a symposium entitled: Crisis in Medicine: Toward Biblical Solutions, which was held at Emmanuel Presbyterian Church, Wilmington, Delaware, on October 11 & 12, 1991.

When I was invited to take part in this conference, I proposed to address myself to the future relationship between AIDS and the ongoing euthanasia movement, often denominated the "death with dignity" or "natural death" movement. Death as a consequence of AIDS — almost invariably from so-called "opportunistic infection" is very seldom dignified, as both medical personnel and clergy who have had contact with AIDS patients know all too well. In order to obtain a more decent *exitus lethalis*, euthanasia in various forms is sought and practiced: however, this is not "natural death."

In the area of AIDS therapy and research, events are succeeding one another with bewildering rapidity. In proposing to deal with the phenomenon of AIDS and euthanasia, I assumed that two factors would be very significant: first, the incredibly heavy burden that a relatively small number of AIDS patients would place on the health care and insurance systems of our countries;[1] second, I assumed that the fact that AIDS has been very largely transmitted by means of activities that may be illegal (drug use, in some cases, prostitution) and/or considered immoral and unnatural by large segments of the population would lead to increasing moral and emotional pressure on public authorities to "do something" to contain the problem and to limit the damage that it was causing.[2]

Instead, I discovered that there is — in the United States at least — considerable pressure on insurors and health maintenance organizations (HMO's) virtually to ignore the fact that AIDS is a specific disease with a highly distinctive etiology and very high intensity of care requirement and cost, in other words, not merely to treat it as any other disease, but almost to act as though it did not exist. For example, although evidence of prior health problems is universally considered by insurors and in many cases leads to "rating" — i.e., to increasing the charges for coverage and/or to reducing the benefits to the insured — in several U.S. jurisdictions where AIDS is heavily represented, such consideration is prohibited by law:

California:
Results of a blood test for antibodies to HTLV-III virus shall not be used for the determination of insurability.

Reference: Cal. Health & Safety Code, 199.21(f) as amended by A.B. 488, effective April 4, 1985.

Florida:
Results of HTLV-III antibody tests, conducted at state established blood testing sites, cannot be used to determine insurability.

Reference: Fla. Stat. Ann. 381.606 (1986).

District of Columbia:
D.C. Law 6-132, effective August 7, 1986, in part: Sec. 4

Prohibited Actions.

(a) An insuror may not deny, cancel, or refuse to renew insurance coverage ... because an individual has tested positive on any test to screen for the presence of any probable causative agent of AIDS, ARC (AIDS-related complex), or the HTLV-III infection, ... or because an individual has declined to take such test.

(b) (1) In determining whether to issue, cancel, or renew insurance coverage, an insuror may not use age, marital status, geographic area or residence, occupation, sex, sexual orientation ...

for the purpose of seeking to predict whether any individual may in the future develop AIDS or ARC. (d) No life insurance policy or contract shall contain any exclusion, reduction, or other limitation of benefits related to AIDS, ARC, HTLV-III infection, or any disease arising from these medical conditions, as a cause of death.[3]

Additional sections of the D.C. Law prohibit insurors from requesting any individual to take the HTLV-III antibody test and prohibit asking whether an individual has taken such a test. Further, for five years from the law's effective date, insurors may not consider AIDS in setting premium rates.[4]

If one bears in mind the fact that insurors regularly inquire about dangerous sports, such as parachute jumping, auto racing, and scuba diving, and frequently write exclusionary clauses into their contracts with respect to incidents that may occur in consequence of such activities, legislation of the District of Columbia type must certainly appear extraordinary.

With respect to my second assumption, to the effect that moral and emotional pressure would be put on public authorities with regard to "high risk activities" and those who engage in them, I had anticipated that Christians and their churches would be challenged to rise to the defense of HIV-infected persons and of those engaging in or suspected of engaging in high risk activities. Instead, we discover that AIDS is characterized as " challenge to rethinking" by theologians such as Prof. Volker Eid of the Roman Catholic Theological Faculty of Bamberg (Germany). Prof. Eid

writes: "In our case, rethinking means to come to terms with the fact of the deadly threat of AIDS, to come to terms with the plight of the affected, caused by AIDS. And it also means to come out from among our traditional customs of attributing guilt and of prejudice."[5]

Eid writes, "Guilt is an undeniable fact in the life of every man," but he is very concerned that in connection with AIDS, even the merest suggestion of guilt, sin, and repentance is to be avoided: "As to the mention of Jesus' liberating association with guilty persons in our ecclesiastical and theological talk about the theme of AIDS, one must make it very clear that even when we exercise the greatest restraint, we might create the following impression: 'It is true that by your sexual behavior you have laid guilt upon yourselves in some way or other; nevertheless, we are going to help you.'"[6]

Other theologians are even more emphatic in taking the phenomenon of AIDS as a reason — or pretext — to write in justification of male homosexuality, or of homosexuality of both varieties. Thus Pastor Hans-Geor Wiedemann, who holds a law degree as well as a degree in theology, writes with what I would describe as aggressive candor:

"If the Mene, tekel of AIDS should once again bring homophobia to the point that homosexual and bisexual lovers are stigmatized as lepers, then the credibility of the church will be at stake if it remains silent about it. The church gains credibility only then, when it not only involves itself on behalf of AIDS patients, but also makes it plain: homosexual lovers are as close to God — or as far from him — as everyman, as every man and every woman. Practically, the church

will have to prove this not only by accepting Christians who practice homosexual love as members, but also as full-time workers, without reservation. The church could also raise up a standard by not withholding its blessing from loving homosexual couples who wish their partnership to be blessed in a service of worship."[7]

The title of Wiedemann's essay, "The Church and Homosexual Love in the Age of AIDS," makes it plain that the author considers AIDS an incentive to justify homosexuality and make it acceptable, far from raising a warning finger.

Even former United States Surgeon General C. Everett Koop, M.D., who as a confessing Christian in the Reformed tradition accepts the biblical strictures regarding homosexual conduct as the inspired Word of God and therefore considers homosexual relations sinful, is extremely cautious about saying anything that directly stigmatizes homosexuality as such in his many warnings about AIDS:

"The Surgeon General's report describes high risk sexual practices between men and between men and women. I want to emphasize two points: First, the risk of infection increases with increased numbers of sexual partners — male or female. Couples who engage in freewheeling casual sex these days are playing a dangerous game. What it boils down to is — unless you know with *absolute certainty* that your sex partner is not infected with the AIDS virus — through sex or through drug use — you're taking a chance on becoming infected. Conversely, unless you are *absolutely certain* that you are not carrying the AIDS virus, you must consider the possiblity that you can infect others.

"Second, the best protection against infection right now — barring abstinence — is the use of a condom. A condom should be used during sexual relations, from start to finish, with anyone you know or suspect is infected."[8]

From a logical perspective, one could fault former Surgeon General Koop for his use of the terms *absolute certainty* and *absolutely certain*. Even in the case of a long-standing, faithful marriage relationship, no woman whose husband has been out of her sight even briefly can be sure that he has not had a relationship in which he contracted the AIDS virus; indeed, the same thing can be said about a man, for although he may be completely faithful to his wife, he cannot know with absolute certainty that she has totally refrained from the kind of extra-marital contact that might make her an HIV-carrier. If we think of a couple that is contemplating marriage, a test for HIV antibodies taken before marriage could prove that a prospective spouse was uninfected three months prior to the test, but would not reveal an infection closer to the test date. For a period, the State of Illinois where I reside required HIV antibody tests prior to issuing a marriage license. One result was that many couples fled to neighboring states, where such a test was not required, to marry. Dr. Koop obviously pressupposes — and has explicitly written and said this elsewhere — that many people, from their teen years onward, will move rather quickly into an intimate sexual relationship with a person whom they do not know well and/or have not known for a long time.

To turn from Dr. Koop's medical advice to the "pastoral" counseling of nominal Christians with whom he would not be likely to be much in sympathy — but with whose practical counsel he does not seem to differ significantly — we read in a set of "guidelines" prepared for confirmation candidates (average age 15- 16) in Dusseldorf, Germany:

"8. In the future (!?) the following principles are to be observed:

a) It is important to talk openly with future sexual partners about sexuality — also about what one has already experienced in this area.

b) "Going to bed together" should be preceded by a longer period of getting acquainted. 'Disco behavior' is frivolous and generally frustrating."[9]

The German clergy, like Dr. Koop, seem to assume a fairly high level of sexual contacts and a multiplicity of partners. If one makes this assumption, then the "protection" that both recommend — the prophylactic or condom — is hardly a sure defense. It is particularly surprising to hear the Surgeon General *accept* the idea of sexual relations with one whom one *knows* to be infected, subject to the use of a condom. As one military doctor in the United States commented on the use of condoms: "If the 'partner' is uninfected, the condom is pointless; if the 'partner' is infected, it is an unacceptable risk."

Dr. Koop endorses the selective use of condoms, the Dusseldorf pastors the generalized use. If one were to apply Immanual Kant's principle of universifiability ("Act only upon the maxim that you can wish to be universally accepted") to the Dusseldorfer suggestion, it is evident that a consequence would be the rather rapid disappearance of the human race. Pastor Wiedemann polemicizes against "the reduction of sexuality to procreation,"[10] but what we are confronting here is the absolute separation of sexuality from procreation.

Questioned by this writer at a lecture given at Wheaton College, Wheaton, Illinois, on February 22, 1990, concerning the impression that Dr. Koop was using the term "monogamy" — which traditionally meant a life-long marrige between one man and one woman — to refer also to an exclusive sexual relationship between two men, the former Surgeon General replied, in effect, that for him and his wife, monogamy means monogamous heterosexual marriage, but that given the state of our knowledge about homosexuality, for others it might mean something different.

Even more vigorous in his denunciation of putative ecclesiastical reactions to AIDS than Wiedemann is psychologist Dr. Siegfried Rudolf Dunde, who also has a theological degree. Dr. Dunde fulminates against "hate" as a reaction to AIDS, and charges that AIDS turns hatred for the disease into hatred for the diseased. He also designates nonconformity, disgust, and freedom of pleasure (*Lustfreiheit*) as "mechanisms of hatred" (*Haßausloser*) which stimulate in Christians — at least in the kind he dislikes — "joy over the fate of those who are 'different.'"[11] Dunde thus overlooks all the efforts of more moderate theological voices such as Eid to show concern, sympathy, and love for AIDS victims, despite the fact that attitudes such as Eid's seem to this observer to be far more typical of the Christian response to AIDS than the kind of malicious "joy" that Dunde claims to see. Indeed, AIDS has functioned as a *Haßausloser*, but as a mechanism to inspire hatred of the church and Christian moralists (as well as morals). The church could plausibly be saying to most AIDS sufferers, if not "Serves you right!", then at least "You brought it on yourself." Instead,

Dunde as well as many AIDS activists and other critics of traditional Christianity seem to be enraged at the church as though the church were responsible for the fact that AIDS has appeared on the scene as a kind of fulfillment of Paul's warning in Romans 1:27. Most Christian observers, conservative as well as liberal, are quick to state that they do *not* regard AIDS as the "penalty" for homosexual conduct to which Paul refers. Nevertheless, because it is in Romans, and the church preaches and teaches from Romans, it seems almost as though the chuch is held responsible for AIDS, and for this reason is made the target of condemnation and even of hatred. Before AIDS, the traditional tendency of the church to condemn homosexual conduct was more or less ignored by homosexual activists, whereas now they are calling on the church to repent and to disavow its previous "homophobia." With regard to the hidden implication that the church in some way wished AIDs upon those who disregarded its moral teachings, one can only quote the familiar French proverb, cited by Professor Jerome Lejeune of Paris thus:

"Seul Dieu peut vraiemment pardonner; l'homme pardonne parfois; la nature ne pardonne jamais."

I. THE MORAL CHALLENGE

The moral challenge of AIDS to the Christian community as well as to medicine and health care providers is directly tied to the undeniable and yet vehemently disputed intimate tie between AIDS and male homosexuality, and especially with the frequency promiscuity, and exotic nature of much male homosexual activity. This tie is denied over and over again, in various ways, by refer-

ence to the increasing ratio of intravenous drug users to male homosexuals among the HIV-infected, by reference to the rising number of HIV-infected women and babies, by reference to the situation in Africa, where homosexuality is relatively rare but AIDS is sadly widespread among heterosexuals. Over dinner in Basel, Switzerland, a young medical graduate, a Christian, informed the writer that male homosexuals no longer constitute the largest percentage of new AIDS patients in Switzerland. That melancholy distinction now belongs to "Fixer," i.e., to intravenous drug abusers.[12]

The fact that the AIDS virus can be contracted by a variety of means, and that it has spread widely in Africa where there is little homosexuality, does not alter the fact that in almost every case in the West, new infections can uniformly be traced back to original infection through male homosexual conduct.

Although homosexual behavior and individuals with a primarily or exclusively homosexual orientation have always existed, both Christianity and Judaism have strongly condemned homosexual acts. Inasmuch as the original carriers and disseminators of the HIV in the West were unaware that they were carrying and spreading such a disease, they should not be subject to criticism for doing so. However, inasmuch as the conduct in which they engaged had been subject to moral reproach *before* it became known how much such conduct contributed to the epidemic, it is bizarre that it is precisely AIDS that has led to increased tolerance of male homosexuality and to increasing sympathy for those who engage in it. Before any compelling connection between homosexuality and the spread of disease could be shown,

homosexuality was disapproved; once the connection became inescapably evident, it was accepted. It is as though cigarette smoking, which was subject to some moralistic criticism before its connection with lung disease was established, had suddenly become respectable once its role in causing lung cancer and other disorders was definitely demonstrated. This is, of course, precisely not what happened. Cigarette smoking has become the subject not only of medical admonitions and warnings — sometimes couched in rather grisly terms — but also of general moral disapproval and social intolerance. It is evident that something strange is going on here. "The [AIDS] epidemic has created strong allies for gay people in the parents, friends, and loved ones of those who have died and are dying of this disease ... it is not possible to observe the courage of people with AIDS and their friends and lovers who are caring for them without developing a great respect."

There is apparently a confusion of categories here. Observers such as S.R. Dunde claim that Christians and others are motivated to hate those who are sick rather than the sickness. Instead, in the above citation Jim Foster observes that the misery, suffering, and courage of the sick has moved outsiders not only to love and accept them, but also to accept their conduct.[13] Lung cancer continues to claim more victims than AIDS, and a high percentage of lung cancer patients are or were cigarette smokers. Do we hear cries for legislation to protect the rights of cigarette smokers? Quite the contrary, at least in the United States.

Do we even hear expressions of sympathy for victims of lung cancer, emphysema, and other smoking-related disorders? Certainly not. Do we hear expressions of satisfaction that lung cancer is found among those who have never smoked? Indeed not. In this connection it is also relevant to note that lung cancer is not contagious, and that the lung cancer patient cannot infect others, neither via sexual intimacy nor in any other way.

Traditionally Christianity has called upon its adherents to hate the sin while loving the sinner. Most Christians, dealing with the HIV-infected and with AIDS patients, make an effort to do this. Sensitive observers such as Professor Eid of Bamberg warn them that they must do all that they can to avoid any suggestion of moral disapproval, not to mention condemnation.[14] Militant advocates of the homosexual cause, such as Dr. Dunde, demand that all barriers, scruples, and reservations be not merely dropped but repented and actively repudiated, and the San Francisco Health Commissioner Jim Foster rejoices that a disease which is primarily carried and spread by homosexual activity, that is to say, by active homosexuals, is creating not merely sympathy for these who suffer in consequence of their "life-style," but even for the "life-style" which lies at the root of their suffering, and for their right and the right of others to pursue it and to advocate it as they see fit. There is certainly a difference between saying to the AIDS victim, "You should have known better: you brought this on yourself," true though that may be, and saying to others, to those who have not yet embraced the "life-style" or contracted the virus, "Take heed, lest ye likewise perish."

Defenders of homosexual activity and of homosexual rights, such as Pastor Hans-Georg Wiedemann, previously cited, often speak in terms of homosexual love, although it is frequently hard to interpret brief, casual relationships as love. To interpret particular homosexual acts as expressions of love does not set aside biblical injunctions that apply to them, nor, to the extent that such acts are prohibited by civil law, does love produce immunity to legal action and penalties. Nevertheless, to evoke the idea of love certainly can produce a measure of understanding and sympathy among non-homosexuals, as Pastor Wiedemann demonstrates.

The earliest data gathered on AIDS, even before it was at all well understood, brought out its connection with male homosexuality: it was originally called Gay-Related-Immune-Disorder (GRID).[15] It was originally suggested that the new element responsible for the appearance of a hitherto-unknown malady "was an unprecedented level of sexual promiscuity that had developed among a subgroup of homosexual men in New York, San Francisco, Los Angeles, and some other large urban centers since the late 1960's."[16] In other words, it became evident early on that GRID, later AIDS, was associated not merely with male homosexuality, but with a high degree of promiscuity as well as with certain specific practices. Homosexuality as an expression of a deep same-sex emotional relationship was not the cause, although the phenomenon of deep same-sex emotional relationships was and is often evoked to secure sympathy and approval for homosexual conduct. Homosexual activists, even in the morbid atmosphere of the AIDS epidemic, claimed not the right to sex within relationships, but the right to sex as such. Thus Dennis Altman writes in *AIDS in the Mind of America:* "The growth of gay assertion and a commercial gay world meant an affirmation of sex outside of relationships as a positive good, a means of expressing both sensuality and community ... I do not think it is too fanciful to see in our preoccupation with public sex both an affirmation of sexuality and a yearning for community, which may be one of the ways we can devise for coming to terms with a violent and severely disturbed society."[17]

No moral code, past or present, with which this writer is familiar, has ever extolled sexual activity as such, without respect for relationships, responsibilities, self-control, or discipline. This means that the advocacy of homosexual freedom and rights, which has so paradoxically intensified in the course of the AIDS epidemic, implies a categorical repudiation of all aspects of every human moral code that deals with sexual conduct, and, indeed, by implication, of the very existence of such moral codes. The vehement language of writers such as Altman ("a violent and severely disturbed society") and Dunde (Haßausloser") indicates a massive, categorical repudiation of the existing social order and of all the edifying concepts and traditions that have gone into its creation. The demand for the legitimization of homosexual love and its associated activities clearly involves a repudiation of the tie between sexuality and reproduction and implies a rejection of the idea of natural law (as does that other modern social pestilence, abortion on demand). However, as we have seen, Altman — and others with him — go beyond demanding acceptance of homosexual relationships and demand the affirmation of generalized and even public sex as such. Altman's book was published in 1986, three years after Professor Luc Montagnier's identification of the AIDS virus, and two years after the American researcher Robert Gallo made the same discovery.

The moral challenge connected with AIDS is this: to hate the sin while showing compassion and concern for the sinner. As St. John writes in his First Epistle, "If anyone should sin, we have an advocate with the Father, Jesus Christ the righteous, and he is the propitiation for our sin ..." These "comfortable words," as the Prayer Book communion liturgy calls them, follow the admonition, "If we confess our sins, he is faithful and just to forgive us our sins, and to make us clean from all iniquity" (I John 2:1-2, 1:9). To fail to acknowledge sin as sin, or, even worse, to insist that it is not sin at all, but a higher good and a natural right, is to forfeit the possibility of forgiveness, and with it the offer of salvation and eternal life.

II. THE MEDICAL CHALLENGE

AIDS has confronted the medical community, health care providers and insurors with a series of challenges. Among the most immediate is this: how to pay the costs of AIDS. According to a study prepared for the Centers for Disease Control, by 1991 AIDS cases would number 68.63 per 100,000, and would account for approximately 12% of all costs, direct and indirect, of illness in the United States. Estimates of the number of future AIDs cases vary widely: it is assumed that virtually 100% of HIV-infected persons will ultimately proceed to full-blown AIDS, barring other fatal developments, unless a means of treating the cause is found soon. Estimates of the number of HIV-carriers are simply guesses based on the number of diagnosed AIDS patients. If we take the frequently-mentioned figure of 1,500,000 HIV-carriers among the U.S. population,

and take the median cost estimate for 1991 from the C.D.C. data, $10,900 per AIDS patient, we arrive at the figure in 1991 dollars of $164,400,000,000 for current HIV-carriers. Needless to say, such a figure cannot be exact. Nevertheless, it is evident that the cost of providing medical care for those individuals already carrying the human immunodeficiency virus will be immense.

The euthanasia movement in many countries, for the moment, is concentrating on persons in a "vegetative" state, with an emphasis on "cost containment" as well as on "mercy" for the patients. It may be left to physicians or others to determine when a person's "quality of life" no longer justifies the expenditures involved in keeping him alive. Thus David Thomasma, director of the Medical Humanities Program at Loyola University Stritch School of Medicine in the Chicago, Illinois, suburb of Maywood, writes: "Medicine should aim at reconstructing life sufficiently to sustain other values ... When these human values can no longer be sustained because of the physical condition of the patient, then a decision should be made for euthanasia on the basis of the patient's or surrogate's request."[18] Few modern writers are suggesting that the cost of terminal care should be the decisive factor, but when "inducing or bringing about death" is described by Thomasma as "a virtuous and moral act, especially if it is done in conjunction with the wishes of the patient," it is apparent that the physical and emotional misery of late-stage AIDS patients, which will increase together with both individual and total health care costs as the number of terminal AIDS cases rises, will push more and more people to begin implementing this "virtuous and moral" act.[19] A recent survey in the Maryland Jour-

nal of Contemporary Legal Issues cites extensive similarities between the presentations of euthanasia advocates in the United States today and those of the physicians who endorsed and implemented Nazi Germany's euthanasia program in the 1930's.[20] According to information in that survey, currently one in six deaths in the Netherlands is caused by active euthanasia, although the death certificates almost always specify death by "natural causes."[21]

The combination of physical and emotional misery and sometimes mental disability, burgeoning terminal care costs, the ever-present if often unreasonable fear of infection to care givers, and the certainty of ultimate if often delayed death will surely push more and more of those who think like Thomasma, Daniel Callahan, and others cited in the just-referenced survey by Rita Marker, et al., to encourage and perhaps ultimately to insist upon "virtuous and moral" acts to induce death.

Medical researchers, encouraged by substantial government funding in the United States, are energetically pursuing the task of finding ways to treat or cure AIDS in the HIV-infected and to prevent future infections, even among those who insist on continuing high-risk behavior. Most authorities seem to think that it will be quite some time before such efforts bear significant fruit. Surely we have to reckon with AIDS as a very significant source of increasing pressure on the health care systems of the world. The pressure may be accentuated by the perception that most AIDS victims have contracted the disease through conduct widely held to be reprehensible or even degenerate, which could conceivably lead much of the population to begrudge huge expenditures on their behalf. Although — as indicated earlier — almost all authorities, medical, moral, theological, legal, and otherwise, vigorously repudiate the suggestion that AIDS victims should be held responsible for their condition, and especially not in a way that would permit society to reduce its care and concern form them, the danger that this may happen cannot be excluded. (Lest there be any doubt, this writer vigorously *opposes* any such reduction.)

In the previous section, it was suggested that AIDS may have the effect of causing society, government, and the churches to accept patterns of conduct previously condemned, in spite of the fact that they facilitate the spread of the dread disease. Now it appears that the consequences of AIDS could push society towards the acceptance of euthanasia, voluntary and involuntary, which naturally would be extended to situations in which AIDS is not involved.

In addition to the very clear challenge posed by euthanasia, there are two other significant issues directly related to the medical response to AIDS: the question of whether it is related to homosexuality in a specific way, and the question of whether medical advice in the area of AIDS prevention can reasonably be expected to be effective as long as it continues to avoid the type of moral admonitions that used to be implied in terminology such as "deviance" and "degeneracy."

In the early days of the AIDS phenomenon it was called, as noted above, Gay-Related-Immune-Deficiency. Before the discovery of HIV by Luc Montagnier and Robert Gallo, various theories proposed that the immune deficiency was caused by an overloading of the body's immune defense mechanisms in consequence of intrusive exposure through frequent, highly promiscuous sexual encounters, to vast number of bacterial, viral, and parasitic organisms as well as to semen. For various reaons, there has been a marked tendency to distinguish AIDS from "infections of homosexual men," as is done, for example, in the text, *AIDS and Infections of Homosexual Men*, to which reference has already been made. Parts I, II, and III of this textbook discuss "sexually transmitted diseases," but precisely not AIDS, which is considered separately in the balance of the book.[22]

Researcher Joseph A. Sonnabend writes, "It was assumed that HIV was directly responsible because of its tropism for CD4 lymphocytes coupled with the acceptance that the loss of this lymphocyte subset is the hallmark of AIDS ... [but i]t has also yet to be explained how infection of a small number of CD4 lymphocytes can account for the widespread abnormalities observed in AIDS."[23] The burden of Sonnabend's study is to raise the question: Has the discovery of the HIV too rapidly diverted attention from a very real possibility that it is the homosexual life-style that *released* the HIV — now known as the direct agent causing AIDS — from harmless latency to pursue its virulently destructive course? In other words, should male homosexuality, especially in its more extreme forms, be stigmatized as life-threatening even more vigorously than is now being done, by all but universal consent, for cigarette smoking?

The final "medical" question is this: Is it medically and morally responsible, in the light of what we know and are learning about AIDS, to continue to treat AIDS-related conduct, especially in the sexual realm, as though it were on the one hand natural and totally uncontrollable, and on the other could easily be rendered safe by the use of a thin latex barrier, the much-lauded condom? Those wishing to avoid syphilis, gonorrhea, and other venereal diseases were not told, "Use a prophylactic," but rather, "Shun prostitutes." This writer in adolescence and young manhood never once encountered a physician, Christian, Jewish, or other, who would suggest that patronizing prostitutes was more or less all right provided one provided onself with a proper condom. At that time, syphilis and gonorrhea were already treatable and curable. AIDS is not, and probably will not be for some time to come. What makes it possible for genuinely spiritual physicians at the top of their profession, such as Dr. Koop, to talk the way he does about AIDS, not approving homosexuality, but, as it were, praising by faint damns?

III. THE SPIRITUAL CHALLENGE

"And the rest of mankind, who were not killed by these plagues, did not repent ... and they did not repent of their murders nor of their sorceries nor of their immorality nor of their thefts." Rev. 9:20-021, N.A.S.B.

In the ninth chapter of the Apocalypse, St. John speaks of three plagues which kill off one-third of mankind. Dr. Jonathan Mann of the World Health Organization has uttered a series of such dire predictions concerning AIDS that one could well envisage it as one of the apocalyptic plagues. While Dr. Mann and other public health officials are preoccupied with the genocidal potential of AIDS, this writer has attemp[ted to draw attention to the perverse and paradoxical potential of this disease to change morals, categorically separating sex from procreation and even from relationships, definitively overturning Hippocratic standards and replacing them with a utilitarian ethic of euthanasia, and otherwise subverting the society of those whom the plagues do not carry off. Until the present time, the reaction of much of the society and of part of the church has been that described in Rev. 9:21, namely, "They did not repent."

There are other areas to which one could direct attention: AIDS has dramatically changed the tone and quality of discourse and education concerning sex. Former Surgeon General Koop sprinkled remarks concerning anal sex from the pulpit of Wheaton College's Edman Chapel. Whether or not this was good or necessary, it certainly represented a departure. In the *Surgeon General's Report*, "Education concerning AIDS must start at the lowest grade possible ... The threat of AIDS should be sufficient to permit [he really means "require" — H.O.J.B.] a sex education curriculum with a heavy emphasis on prevention of AIDS and other sexually transmitted diseases."[23] Dr. Koop's oft-repeated insistence that he is — or was at the time — the Surgeon General, not the Chaplain General — cannot obscure the bizarre situation in which one of the United States' most celebrated evangelical figures, indeed one strongly in the Reformed tradition and a long-time associate of the late Francis Schaeffer, distinguishes between "needle sharing" (not mentioned in Scripture), which he says "must be avoided," and homosexual conduct (prohibited in Scripture), which he contends can be "responsible."[24]

The covenant relationship between one man and one woman, known as marriage, is a very fundamental aspect of divine creation. Two of its essential features are the guarantee of legitimacy (or paternity) in children, and the promise of fidelity in sexual relationships.

As John Davidson argues in the most recent *Human Life Review*, abortion destroys the solid compact of marriage in a devastating way. His argument is interesting: the social function of marriage in all societies, is to hold men to know and care for their own offspring. Without marriage, with so-called free love, no man could know with confidence that any woman's child is his. It is indeed marriage that enables a man to have *his own* children. Abortion on demand — with the provision, so often reaffirmed up to the present, that no man, husband, lover, father, friend — may interfere with or hinder the woman's absolute right to an abortion, marriage can no longer function as an institution to secure or guarantee a man's right to children.

A recent German proposal speaks of a woman's right to "self-determined pregnancy." Of course, no woman alone can determine can determine to be pregnant. What this means, of course, is self-determined abortion and, ultimately, the absolute negation of the man's right to descendants. Sexual relations, biblically speaking, are not limited to reproduction — but they are closely allied to it, both in Scripture and in the ordinary order of nature. Abortion breaks the compact. The progressive legitimization of homosexual acts further shatters all correspondence between sex and reproduction.

Inasmuch as homosexuality by its nature is sterile, to legitimize homosexual behavior as equivalent to heterosexual is to equate the moral value of being born with being not being born, of being with non-being, of living with dying.

Recent developments — in Switzerland, a new sexual code making homo- and heterosexuality equal in the eyes of the law, in the USA a paper approved by the U.C.C. defending the "rights" of homosexuals and bisexuals as well and as fully as those of married heterosexuals — makes the rupture of the covenant between spouses, between fathers and sons, between generations all too evident. And, when the rupture between generations at the beginning of life is patent, the rupture at the end is evident as well.

Sexuality should not be limited to reproduction, but it ought to be self-evident that reproduction and family are two of the most essential ends of created sexuality. Much of the moral code of Scripture has practical relevance for health and well-being. Nothing reveals the danger of ignoring God's laws — and the laws of nature — more dramatically than AIDS. Can it be, in the declining years of our century, and perhaps of our civilization, and perhaps even of world history, that the very thing that ought to be a warning will become the pretext for ignoring both nature and reason as well as God, and for plunging full steam into the very maelstrom that destroys? Is AIDS the stimulus that will cause our society, like that of ancient Rome, to merit Paul's judgment: "Thinking themselves wise, they became fools" (Romans 1:22)?

ENDNOTES

1. See William Carroll, "AIDS-Related Claims Survey: Claims Paid in 1986," in James Vculek, ed., **AIDS One. Legal, Social & Ethical Issues Facing the Insurance Industry**, (Chatsworth, CA: NILS Publishing Company, 1988), pp. 395 - 406.

2. See Robert Fulton and Greg Owen, "AIDS: Seventh-Rank Absolute," in Inge B. Corless and Mary Pittmann-Lindeman, eds., **AIDS, Principles, Practices, & Politics. Reference Edition** (New York: Hemisphere, 1989), pp. 314 - 317.

3. Paschal, Richard J., "Statutory Restrictions on Life Insurance Underwriting of AIDS Risk With Emphasis on Restrictions in the District of Columbia," in Vculek, *op. cit.*, pp. 72 - 73.

4. *Ibid.*, p. 73.

5. Eid, Volker, "Aids — eine Herausforderung zum Umdenken," in Christel Becker-Kolle, Ed., **Schwarze Angst. Leben mit AIDS** (Stuttgart: Quell, 1989), p. 57.

6. *Ibid.*, p. 74.

7. Wiedemann, Hans-Georg, "Die Kirche und die homosexuelle Liebe im Zeitalter von Aids." in Becker-Kolle, *op. cit.*, p. 111.

8. Statement by C. Everett Koop, M.D., Wednesday, October 22, 1986, in Corless and Pittman-Lindeman, *op. cit.*, p. 196.

9. Becker-Kolle, *op. cit.*, p. 221.

10. Wiedemann, *loc. cit.*, p. 109.

11. Dunde, Siegfried Rudolf, "Der Haß gegen die Infizierten," in Becker-Kolle, *op. cit.*, pp. 113 - 128.

12. Conversation with Marcel Kraft, M.D., July 31, 1991. Statistical data to confirm this were not available to the writer. American commentators have frequently confused the percentage increase among IV drug users as a high-risk group with the absolute number of new cases. In the United States the greatest rate of increase is among drug abusers, but the largest number of new victims is still drawn from among practitioners of male homosexuality. Interpretation of the statistics is made more difficult by the fact that many who practice male homosexuality are also IV drug users, and by the fact that although the group classed as "bisexual" is often separated from "homosexuals" for statistical purposes, it is plausible to think of that the vast majority of infected *bisexuals* contracted the virus through their male homosexual contacts.

13. Foster, Jim, "Impact of the AIDS Epidemic on the Gay Political Agenda, in Corless and Pittman-Lindemann, *op. cit.*, p. 531.

14. Cf., f.n. 5 above.

15. Murphy, Julien S., "Women with AIDS: Sexual Ethics in an Epidenic," in Corless and Pittman-Lindemann, *op. cit.*, p. 337.

16. Sonnabend, Joseph A., "AIDS: An Explanation for Its Occurrence among Homosexual Men," in Pearl Ma and Donald Armstrong, eds., **AIDS and Infections of Homosexual Men**, 2nd ed., (Boston: Butterworth, 1989), p. 452.

17. Altman, Dennis, **AIDS in the Mind of America** (New York: Anchor/Doubleday, 1986), cited by Jim Foster in Corless and Pittman-Lindemann, op. cit., p. 527.

18. Thomasma, David, "The Range of Euthanasia," in *American College of Surgeons Bulletin*, Aug., 1988, pp. 4 - 5.

19. *Ibid.*, p. 10.

20. Marker, Rita L., Stanton, Joseph R., Recznik, Mark E., and Fournier, Keith, A., "Euthanasia: A Historical Overview," in *Maryland Journal of Contemporary Legal Issues*, Vol. 2, Issue 2, Summer, 1991, pp. 257 - 298.

21. *Ibid.*, pp. 295 - 296.

22. Cf., f.n. 16 above.

23. *Ibid.*, p. 450.

24. The *Surgeon General's Report* is reprinted in Vculek, *op. cit.*, pp. 376-395; see esp. pp. 392, 380.

Pastor's Column

Health Insurance: Some Decisions To Be Made

The Reverend Byron Snapp

Rev. Snapp holds a B.A. from King College and an M.Div. from Reformed Theological Seminary. He is assistant pastor of Covenant Presbyterian Church and principal of Covenant Christian School in Cedar Bluff, Virginia.

Whew! I've just learned the new monthly rates for my health insurance policy. The monthly premiums for my 80/20 $500 deductible policy will be a little over $600. Changes in my prescription card means more money out of my pocket for prescribed medicine. I am only in the 40 - 50 age bracket. What will the rates be twenty years from now?

The church can provide some Biblical principles that will help each of us to be better prepared to make the critical decisions we may face in the midst of serious illness. The church should help financially as funds are available and the need arises. Yet with burgeoning medical costs money is not always available. What then?

We must remember that there is a time to die (Ecc. 3:2). Our days are numbered by God (Ps. 90:10-12). He who has determined our boundaries (Acts 17:26) and knows the number of hairs on our head (Mt. 10:30) has determined before the foundation of the world the day of our death. God sovereignly works all things out according to His will (Eph. 1:11). As this Biblical truth is proclaimed and, by God's grace, believed, the Christian can take great comfort. This acceptance does not mean we reject medical resources and technology. It does mean we use them wisely.

We live in an age in which medical technology allows people to often put off the fact of their mortality a little while longer. Yet, death will inevitably come, unless Christ returns first.

Thus the pastor, officers, and the laymen must ask in the midst of illness, "What is the price of life?" Life is important. It is God-given. God has placed us in this world, at this time, for a purpose. Facing a long term, serious illness we may well ask if part of our life is also faithfully to glorify God in death soon.

The Christian, while loving life, need not fear death. It is but a passage to heaven itself. Thus, the pastor must remind his hearers of the reality of death and the need to be spiritually prepared for it by repenting of sin and trusting in the finished work of Christ alone for salvation.

Secondly, when deciding on treatment for what is, humanly speaking, terminal illness, serious questions must be asked.

(1) Will this treatment bankrupt my family and my estate? Will, after years of work and saving, I have no capital to pass on to my children and their families as they begin their careers?

(2) What is the probability of improvement, remission, or cure assuming the insurance company and I pay the hundreds of thousands of dollars that this treatment and all the other cost that it entails?

(3) Have my goals in life been met? Who is sick? A child fighting a disease with a young body and a young immune system might well live a normal life span if expensive treatment is used. A young adult may have the goal of raising his/her children if at all possible and decide to endure painful and expensive treatment to gain as many months or years of life as possible. An older adult whose children are grown may decide to accept treatment or forego it depending on family needs, treatment involved and the pain to be endured.

The situation with each individual is entirely different. Thus, the answers will always vary from person to person. Yet we must be ready to face reality and ask medical personnel tough questions. Such questions need to be thought through from time to time. As part of its teaching ministry the church can greatly facilitate the facing of serious illness by an individual or family member by providing some Biblical guidelines such as have been mentioned. So often an individual is so stunned by news which blood work or a biopsy reveals that the person tells the doctor to do whatever can be done. Sometimes that decision may not be the best option given the suffering involved, short additional life span, or expenses.

Such teaching can be done through the preached word, Sunday School classes, or a Bible study perhaps led by someone in the medical field.

(Continued on page 56)

Birth Control

Franklin E. Payne, Jr., M.D.

Dr. Payne is Associate Professor at the Medical College of Georgia. He is author of **Biblical/Medical Ethics,** **Making Biblical Decisions,** *and* **What Every Christian Should Know About the AIDS Epidemic.**

Modern concepts of "birth control" have gained considerable social acceptance because of the movement started by Margaret Sanger early in the 20th century. Its goals advocated that "procreation of the diseased, the feebleminded, and the poor be stopped." Today, that movement exists as "family planning," formally represented by the international organization of Planned Parenthood whose agenda is anti-Christian, anti-family, and pro-abortion!

By contrast, God's direction for His people in Scripture is clear. He is intimately involved with the formation of unborn children (Psalm 139:13-16). "Children are a gift of the Lord" and a "reward"; "a full quiver" of them is a "blessing" (Psalm 127:3-5). God plans the lives of people even before they are born (Jeremiah 1:5). Even salvation is "for you and your children" (Acts 2:39).

Thus, God expects and will bless families with children. *The modern couple who is physically able to have children has no Biblical justification to choose to be childless.* Moreover, to "be fruitful and multiply" (Genesis 1:28), is not only directed at Christians, but also to non-Christians since it was given before the Fall of mankind (Genesis 3) and after the Great Flood (Genesis 9:1).

With this background, stewardship of procreation (birth control) is neither endorsed nor prohibited by Scripture. Man's responsibility is not just to let "nature take its course," but consciously to order his life toward the fulfillment of the divine plan. Thus, the number of children that a couple has and the timing of their birth is permissible, *as long as other Biblical principles are not violated.* As seen above, the Biblical emphasis is on large families. Given the fact that 2.2 children per couple are necessary to maintain the current world population (ZPG or Zero Population Growth), more than 2 children per family seems a reasonable goal, especially since 20 percent of married couples are physically unable to have children.

Some circumstances seem to allow for timing of birth. A child too early in one's marriage may not be wise (Deuteronomy 24:5). Successive pregnancies may be too hard on some women with physical problems. Family income may be believed insufficient to provide for many children. (However, most estimates of needed resources for raising children are greatly exaggerated.) Completion of higher education requirements seems a sufficient reason for a *short* postponement of children. Inherited genetic disease *may* be a reason not to have children, but medical and spiritual counseling is necessary because this area is quite complicated.

However, this control cannot be argued to extend to unmarried women and men. Fornication and adultery are severely condemned by God (Exodus 20:14; I Corinthians 6:15-20). The use of birth control to prevent one consequence of these sins is not ethically acceptable (Romans 3:8).

BIRTH CONTROL METHODS

Birth control methods generally fall into two types: those that prevent fertilization of the egg (conception) and those that prevent implantation of the fertilized egg into the uterus (abortifacient). Since God says that individual human life begins at conception (Genesis 4:1; Psalm 51:5; Matthew 1:20), abortifacients are not an ethical choice. These methods include surgical abortion by various means and at various stages of fetal development, the intrauterine contraceptive device (IUD), the "mini pill" (containing a progestin only), subcutaneous injection of estrogens and progestins, the "morning after" pill (a high dose of estrogen or progestin), and the new French abortifacient, RU-486.

Coitus interruptus is the oldest form of contraception. Onan's punishment for this act was for his failure to fulfill his levirate obligation, not the act itself (Genesis 38:8-9). Thus, *coitus interruptus* is morally acceptable, but practically is not reliable as it requires considerable discipline for the man.

The rhythm method is the only form of birth control acceptable to Roman Catholic teaching, but also common to Protestants. It is specifically endorsed by the Apostle Paul for specific occasions and *by mutual consent* (I Corinthians 7:5). With some modern adaptations such as temperature monitoring and testing of vaginal mucous, the prevention of pregnancy by this method has been greatly enhanced. However, its reliability and difficulties in practical application limit its efficacy.

Other morally acceptable forms of birth control include the use of condoms, diaphragms, cervical caps, and spermicides (foams and jellies), usually used together in various combinations. There are only minor problems such as proper fitting and irritation associated with these methods, but again their ability to prevent pregnancy is limited by the efficacy of the methods themselves and their practical implementation before and during sexual passion.

Breast feeding has a feedback mechanism that can prevent ovulation. As a single form of birth control, it may be the least reliable. However, it will decrease the incidence of pregnancies in sexually active women who nurse their babies.

The most effective and most controversial form of birth control among Christians today is the birth control pill (oral contraceptive).

Generally, they contain both an estrogen and a progestin. Their primary method of action is to prevent ovulation. Secondary actions include the prevention of sperm moving to an egg (if ovulation does occur) and alteration of the lining of the uterus to prevent implantation (if ovulation and fertilization occurs). While much has been made of potential side effects of the "pill," women who do not smoke and are under 35 years of age appear at little risk of serious side effects. The pill even has positive effects to prevent ovarian cancer, benign breast disease, ectopic pregnancy, and other problems common to women.

The controversy rages over the question, "Are oral contraceptives abortifacients?" On the negative side, if ovulation does occur in women using oral contraceptives, it is rare (probably in the range of 1 in 250 cycles). Further, the likelihood that sperm can survive the hostile uterine and tubal environment created by the hormonal effects to reach the egg is remote.

On the positive side, millions of women on the pill make for a large number of potential abortions (non-implantation), despite the rarity. For example, one can postulate that 1 in 1000 cycles will result in conception. But 10 million women will have 130 million cycles (28 days) each year, resulting in 130,000 abortions at this supposed rate. A consistent pro-life position (that individual human life begins at conception), then, would appear to reject this position.

In the final analysis, the almost 100 percent efficacy of the birth control pill must be weighed against the potential (not proven) for abortion of a fertilized egg. If pregnancy must be absolutely prevented and sterilization is not an option, then another method should probably be chosen. If, however, pregnancy needs only to be statistically delayed (the vast majority of cases), then other methods ought to be chosen.

The last two forms of birth control involve surgery: tubal ligation and vasectomy. While many of these procedures can be reversed with the microsurgical techniques available today, a decision for one or the other should only be made with the serious intention to renounce future pregnancies. Whether tubal ligation or vasectomy is chosen involves many factors that can only be made within the context of individual marriages.

BIBLIOGRAPHY

1. Davis, J.J., **Evangelical Ethics**, 1985.
2. Payne, F., **Making Biblical Decisions**, 1989.
3. Provan, C., **The Bible and Birth Control**, 1989.

Pastor's Column

By The Reverend Byron Snapp

(Continued from page 54)

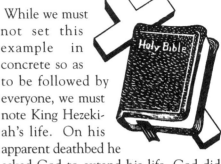

While we must not set this example in concrete so as to be followed by everyone, we must note King Hezekiah's life. On his apparent deathbed he asked God to extend his life. God did. Those additional years were some of the worst in his life as he foolishly showed the Babylonians all his wealth. God told him he would remove the kingdom from his household (II Kings 20). Additional days and years of life will not always be better for us.

Thirdly, according to James, sick members can call on the elders to come and pray and anoint them with oil (James 5:14). This can be done while one is under a doctor's care. After all, God must be behind every successful treatment and recovery from any disease. Through prayer the matter is committed by the church to God. Healing may or may not come. Again, this is a practical way in which the church can be involved.

I have no solution to the escalating medical costs and insurance premiums. Yet the involvement of the church in providing Biblical teaching on the reality of death, God's sovereignty, and realistic questions to consider can well make a difficult situation somewhat easier to face. ∎

Critically Ill:
The Family and Health Care

Bryce J. Christensen

Reprinted from The Family in America, a publication of The Rockford Institute Center on the Family in America, May, 1992, Vol. 6, No. 5, by permission. The Family in America is published monthly by The Rockford Institute, 934 North Main St., Rockford, IL 61103-7061.

Health care has pushed itself to the top of the national agenda in recent months. In January of this year, Democratic leaders convened a "Town Meeting" on health care in 285 sites around the country. At these town meetings, voters saw a specially prepared video depicting current provisions as wholly inadequate. "We need change, dramatic change," House Speaker Thomas S. Foley (D-WA) says in the tape. Sponsors of the meetings presented three different plans for guaranteeing health care to all Americans. In one option, Medicare would expand to cover all citizens; in a second plan, health care for all Americans would be covered under a new nationalized system, comparable to that found in Canada and many European countries; in a third option (called "play or pay"), the federal government would require all employers either to offer health insurance to their employees or to pay into a national government system for caring for uninsured Americans. Proponents of these systems seek not only to provide all Americans with health care, but also to impose some restraint on runaway health care costs.[1] Total national health expenditures rose from $74 billion in 1970 to $604 billion in 1989.[2] Real per capita spending on health care has climbed more than five times faster than productivity over the past two decades.[3] The

rise in health-care costs paid by government has been even steeper, from $28 billion in 1970 to $190 billion in 1986. The expenses of a single government program — Medicare — have risen from just $7.6 billion in 1970 to $102 billion in 1989.[4] To date, policymakers have achieved only meager success in their efforts to contain costs through price controls, health maintenance organizations, and physician review. National health-care costs are projected to rise to $1.5 trillion by the year 2000 and to a staggering $2 trillion by the year 2030.[5]

As pressures grow for a political resolution to the crisis in medical spending, some analysts now believe that the problem cannot be properly understood without considering significant changes in American family life. Although only individual Americans can decide how to order their family lives, a growing body of research reveals that such decisions profoundly affect how much of the nation's wealth must be spent on medical care.

Evidence linking health and family life is not hard to find. Writing recently in Social Science and Medicine, Catherine K. Riessman and Naomi Gerstel observed that "one of the most consistent observa-

tions in health research is that married [people] enjoy better health than those of other marital statuses." Riessman and Gerstel noted that "this pattern has been found for every age group (20 years and over), for both men and women, and for both whites and nonwhites."[6]

In a paper presented to the American Public Health Association, Charlotte A. Schoenborn and Barbara F. Wilson reported in 1988 that in a national survey "married persons had fewer health problems than unmarried persons." The researchers further suggested that the "surge in divorces" in recent decades has imposed "hidden health costs on the American population."[7]

"A HEALTHY ESTATE"

Nor is there anything peculiar to this century or this country about the link between marriage and health. In a genealogical study of upper-class Europeans during the 16th, 17th, 18th, and 19th centuries, Sigismund Peller established that "mortality of married men always has been more favorable — especially in the age below 50 — than that of bachelors." Although Peller found relatively high morality rates among married women during the 16th and 17th centuries (due in large part to deaths in childbirth), he found that mortality rates improved dramatically for married women over the centuries while mortality rates for unmarried women under age 50 improved more slowly.[8] William Farr noted a fairly consistent link between marriage and mortality in a study focused on mid-19th century France. Probably because of deaths in childbirth, Farr did find higher death rates among married women than among unmarried women aged 20-25. Among women over age 30 and among men over age 20, Farr documented a significantly lower mortality rate among the married than among the unmarried. "Marriage is a healthy estate," Farr concluded. "The single individual is more likely to be wrecked on his voyage than the lives joined together in matrimony."[9]

In much more recent studies published in 1987 and 1990, demographers at Princeton University have documented the same pattern. In the 1987 study, the researchers analyzed "a range of cultures (Sweden, Japan, England, and Wales, and the United States whites)" and found that "in all cases, despite any differences in marriage behavior that may exist, married persons experience lower mortality rates" than single, divorced, and widowed peers. The Princeton team then broadened their survey to 26 developed countries ranging from Austria to New Zealand to Singapore. Across all of those cultures, the results were similar: "It is clear that in developed countries married persons of both sexes experience a marked mortality advantage relative to single individuals."[10] In the 1990 study, Princeton investigators established that in 16 industrialized countries, unmarried men and women suffered from higher death rates than married men and women. The researcher concluded that their

findings "strengthen previous speculations about the importance of marriage in maintaining health and the increased stresses associated with both the single and the formerly married states." These findings may be of growing relevance in the years ahead because "for the majority of countries [studied] ... as well as for both genders, the excess mortality of each unmarried state (relative to married persons) has increased over the past two to three decades."[11]

Poor health among the unmarried often translates into huge hospital bills, since the unmarried do not have spouses to care for them at home. In a two-year study at the University of Michigan, researchers monitored the health of 165 men and women all aged 55 and over, after their hospitalization for various chronic conditions. The investigators observed that the unmarried men and women suffered from "worse health overall" than the married and spent "far larger fractions of time in the hospital (34.1 percent vs. 16.0 percent.)"[12]

And although studies usually find that marriage confers a greater health benefit upon men than upon women, wedlock clearly fosters good health among women, too. In a 1990 study supported by the National Institutes of Aging and the National Institute of Mental Health, researchers found that among women ages 40-64, those who were married enjoyed a significant health advantages over those who were unmarried and that those who were mothers were healthier than those without children.[13]

Researchers are still trying to clarify the reasons for the linkage between marriage and good health. In a study published in 1962, Joseph Berkson admitted that "powers of

explanation seem to fail" when trying to account for the fact that death rates run consistently higher for singles than for marrieds and higher for the divorced than for singles, not only overall but for "such diverse disease groups as heart disease and cancer, arteriosclerosis and benign neoplasms, suicide and appendicitis, peptic ulcers and tuberculosis, nephritis, accidents, and bronchitis."[14]

Debra Umberson shed more light on the subject in a study published in 1987. She found that mortality rates ran consistently lower for parents than for adults who are not parents and for the married than for the unmarried because marriage and parenthood both exert a "deterrent effect on health-compromising behaviors" such as excessive drinking, drug use, risk-taking, and disorderly living. By providing a system of "meaning, obligation, [and] constraint," family relationships markedly reduce the likelihood of unhealthy practices.[15]

Further evidence of the relationship between divorce and poor health habits comes from John Clauson of the University of California at Berkeley. Clauson's research leads him to believe that both divorce and smoking may be traced to a common personality profile. According to Clauson, young people with "planful competence" (people who are "thoughtful, self-confident, and responsible") tend to avoid both divorce and smoking, while young people evincing little planful competence tend to become heavy smokers early in life and to divorce in subsequent years."[16]

Yet health habits alone cannot fully account for the health-enhancing effects of marriage. In a study recently completed at Ohio State

University, researchers compared the health of separated or divorced men with that of married men who were carefully matched in economic and occupational circumstances. Nor were the two groups distinguishable by "even marginal differences in health-related behaviors." Yet the researchers found that the divorced and separated suffered poorer health and had "poorer cellular immune system control" than their married peers.[17]

LIVING LONGER

Researchers in Sweden have reported similar findings. Looking at the health statistics for about 8,000 middle-aged Swedish men, the researchers found a mortality rate of 9 percent among married men over a period of approximately ten years compared with a mortality rate of 20 percent among single men during the same period. Even after taking health habits and occupational class into account, the researchers established that "death from causes other than cancer and cardiovascular disease was strongly associated with marital status."[18] These findings deserve particular scrutiny because the Swedish marriage rate is now the lowest in the industrialized world, while the Swedish rate of family dissolution is perhaps the hightest.[19]

In a study in 1982, Jukka T. Salonen found the same pattern among Finnish men. Even after results were statistically adjusted to account for tobacco use, cholesterol levels, and blood pressure, this study showed that an unmarried middle-aged man was more than twice as likely as a married man to die from various diseases, including ischaemic heart disease, and cerebrovascular disease.[20]

Clearly, the effects of marriage upon health are not limited to any changes that wedlock may cause in health habits. (Harold Morowitz of Yale University concludes that "being divorced and a non-smoker is slightly less dangerous than smoking a pack or more a day and staying married." adding facetiously that "if a man's marriage is driving him to heavy smoking, he has a delicate statistical decision to make."[21] Many researchers now explain the health benefits of marriage as a consequence of social support. Evidence from a longitudinal study in Alameda County, California, suggests that marriage is one type — albeit a particularly important type — of "social network tie" affecting health. In their analysis of the Alameda County data, researchers for the National Institute of Aging find that marital status assumes "primary importance" in determining mortality rates among those less than 60 years old.[22]

In 1989, Swedish epidemiologists corroborated the insights gained in Alameda County Study, by finding "an independent association between marital status and all-cause mortality" among Swedish adults.[23]

Social ties also apparently account for the pattern identified by Ofra Anson in a recent analysis of data collected in the National Health Interview Survey. Anson found that single women living alone spend more days sick in bed and suffer more chronic conditions than do women living with husbands. Single women living with unrelated persons likewise suffer worse health than married women, but not as bad as that of singles living alone. But those women reporting the worst health are unmarried mothers: compared to other groups of women, unmarried mothers visit doctors more often, spend more days sick in bed, and are hospitalized more often.[24]

In 1989, researchers at Columbia University classified almost two million deaths occurring in 1986 according to the cause of death and according to the likelihood that such deaths might have been prevented or delayed by "formal" care (the kind of care received by physicians or other professionals), "informal" care (the kind of care received from family members or friends), or some combination of formal and informal care. The results revealed that for both men and women, for both blacks and whites, for almost every age group, marriage provides protection against early death. The protective effect of marriage appeared most pronounced for types of death that can be delayed or prevented chiefly through informal care. Most of the causes of death included in this category were chronic diseases such as diabetes, cirrhosis, asthma, and hypertensive heart disease. For this category, the mortality rate of unmarried white males aged 35-54 ran an astounding 390 percent higher than for their married peers. Among white females, the mortality rate for this type of death ran 200 percent higher for unmarrieds aged 35-44 and 120 percent higher for unmarrieds 45-54, compared to married women of the same ages. A parallel but less dramatic pattern appeared among blacks.[25]

In a recent examination of the relationship between marriage and cancer — the nation's second leading cause of death — epidemiologists at the Michigan Cancer Foundation could find no consistent relationship between cancer and marital status (although a statistical relationship between marriage and lower cancer rates could be discerned for a few specific types of cancer such as cancer of the buccal cavity among black and white males and among black females; lung cancer among blacks of both sexes; and cervical and ovarian cancer for females of both races). However, the authors of this study did note evidence that "marriage influences survivorship among cancer patients," even if it does not prevent its occurrence.[26] Indeed, in a study conducted in 1987 in New Mexico, researchers found that unmarried victims of cancer are more likely to go untreated for cancer than married victims and even if treated are still less likely to survive than married victims. "The decreases in survival [among cancer victims] associated with being unmarried are not trivial," the researchers noted.[27]

Stressing that "married people live longer and generally are more emotionally and physically healthy than the unmarried," Robert H. Coombs of the UCLA School of Medicine laments that "the therapeutic benefit of marriage remains relatively unrecognized."[28]

Most of the research on the physical health effects of divorce has focused on adults, not children. But parental divorce does appear to put children's health at risk. In *The Broken Heart: The Medical Consequences of Loneliness* (1979), James Lynch of the University of Maryland cited evidence that parental divorce not only causes mental neurosis, but also helps foster "various physical diseases, including cardiac disorders" later in their lives.[29] In a national study in 1985, researchers found that, children of divorced parents suffered significantly worse health than the children of intact marriages. The authors of the study concluded that "marital status is related to health status of all the family members, including both parents and children."[30]

SICK CHILDREN

In 1988, researchers examined two health surveys conducted by the National Center for Health Statistics, finding that "single mothers report poorer overall physical health for their children." The authors of the study explain their findings by noting that many unmarried mothers live in poverty, so exposing their children to greater health risks, and that a disproportionate number of single mothers are young and therefore more likely to bear an illness-prone premature infant. The Rutgers researchers also uncovered evidence that unmarried mothers are more likely than married mothers to exaggerate the health problems of their children.[31] Indeed, Finnish health authorities at the University of Tampere find that children from broken homes are significantly more likely to require medical attention from psychosomatic symptoms than children from intact families.[32] But most health problems among children in single-parent households are not psychosomatic. In a paper presented in 1990 before the Population Association of America, Deborah Dawson reported that in a national survey, "the overall health vulnerability score was elevated by 20 to 40 percent" among children living with never-married, divorced, and remarried mothers, compared to children living with both biological parents.[33]

Like divorce, illegitimacy appears linked to harmful — often fatal — health problems for children. In a study completed in 1987, researchers at the National Center for Health Statistics found that compared with married mothers, unmarried women run "a substantially higher risk of having infants with very low or moderately low birth weights." Low birth weight defines one of the best predic-tors of infant mortality. The NCHS researchers believe that marriage exerts no "direct causal influence on the outcome of pregnancy," but argue that a life course that includes marriage is likely to be healthier than one that does not. (Unmarried mothers, are, for example, more likely to smoke than married mothers.)[34]

Divorce and illegitimacy also affect the future health of children by increasing the likelihood that they will engage in premarital sex or that they will use tobacco, alcohol, or illegal drugs. In recent studies in the United States and Canada, researchers have shown that, compared to teens from intact homes, adolescents from nonintact families are more likely to engage in premarital sex and to use tobacco, alcohol, and illicit drugs.[35] Such teens appear especially vulnerable to diseases (including AIDS) caused by tobacco, by sexual contact, and by dirty drug needles.

In another recent study highlighting the importance of family life on children's health, researchers at Stanford Center for Chicano Research discovered that Mexican-American children are remarkably healthy, significantly more healthy than Puerto-Rican children, even though Mexican-Americans are just as impoverished as Puerto Ricans and have much less access to medical care than Puerto Ricans. In trying to explain this "unexpected" pattern, the researchers rate a significant difference in family life: "Puerto-Rican families are ... more likely to be headed by a single parent than Mexican-American families, who have a percentage of two-parent families similar to that of non-Hispanic whites.[36]

American policymakers and concerned citizens can hardly ignore the apparent linkage between family dissolution and poor health at a time of high divorce and illegitimacy rates and of low and falling marriage rates. The American divorce rate has risen more than 40 percent since 1970, by almost 250 percent since 1940.[37] Perhaps 40 percent of marriages formed in the 1980's are headed for divorce. On the other hand, the rate for first marriages among women ages 15-44 has dropped more than 35 percent since 1970; one American in eight now remains unmarried for life.[38] Partly because of a sharp drop in marital fertility, the proportion of the nation's children born out of wedlock has soared. In 1960, only one birth in twenty was illegitimate. In 1985, over one-fourth of all births were out of wedlock.[39]

The health costs associated with this national retreat from family life are not only the burden of individual households, but of the taxpayers. Largely because of the rise in illegitimacy, taxpayers now pay the birth costs for one infant in seven. Because of illegitimate children are born prematurely with alarming frequency, they often require special surgery, mechanical respirators, isolation incubators, and other costly medical care paid for out of general hospital funds and the public purse. In a 1984 study at the National Center for Health Services, analysts found that divorced women were not only less healthy than married women (despite the fact that "the divorced population is somewhat younger than the married"), but that divorced women are more likely than married women to rely on public assistance for health care.[40] Likewise, in their study in 1988 on single motherhood and children's health, researchers at Rutgers commented that unmarried mothers and their children "disproportionately constitute a population which is chronically dependent on the state for basic necessities, including health care."[41]

The erosion of family life not only drives up the nation's future medical bills, it also reduces the number of future taxpayers who can pay those bills. Policy analyst Ben Wattenberg identifies the trend toward fewer, later, and less stable marriages as a primary reason for a national fertility rate which has languished below replacement levels for more than a decade.[42] Wattenberg indeed believes that the "birth dearth" could cause Social Security system to fail early in the next century if — as many predict — the Social Security trust fund is combined with the Medicare trust fund.[43]

Family disruption and depressed fertility not only erode the tax base, these developments also create higher public costs for the institutional care of the sick and elderly. In 1977, Lynch reported that Americans were paying "uncounted billions of dollars" to care for divorced and single people who stay in hospitals longer than do married people suffering from the same illnesses.[44] American taxpayers also face rising costs of institutionalizing elderly persons because of childlessness and family dissolution. In RAND Corporation studies published in 1988 and 1990, Peter Morrison warned that trends in American family life may make it difficult to care for the rising number of elderly Americans. He noted that because of high divorce rates, "the care spouses traditionally have provided each other in old age will be far less available" in the decades ahead. The birth dearth will further exacerbate the difficulty of caring for the elderly. "Early next century when baby boomers grow old," Mor-

rison writes, "they will have few adult children to fill the role of caregiver, because they produced so few offspring." And while the working woman's need for paid child care has received a great deal of attention, the plight of the working woman's elderly parents has received less consideration. Pointing out that "by tradition, adult daughters have provided elderly parents with home care," Morrison anticipates a "demographic scenario" in which "elderly Americans long on life expectancy may find themselves short on care where it matters most — at home."[45] Researchers from Vanderbilt University anticipated "intergenerational conflict" provoked by the increasing costs of providing nursing-home care for aging Americans without children able or willing to care for them in their homes.[46] In 1989, annual public expenditures for nursing-home care already stood at over $25 billion.[47] Because of the profound effects of marriage and family life upon health-care costs, the public debate over how to meet those costs cannot proceed very far without addressing these issues. That debate is already heating up.

Writing recently in *The New Republic*, Phillip Longman argued that "medicare is going broke" because of the aging of the population and the declining American birth rate. "Without fundamental changes, Medicare won't be able to meet the needs of today's middle-aged Americans and their children," Longman reasons, warning that under current policies "the trade-off between health care for the young and the old will become increasingly stark and unavoidable."[48] Formerly chief of staff at the White House under President Lyndon Johnson, James R. Jones predicts that unless current trends can be checked, federal spending on health care could consume 20 percent of every American worker's taxable income by the year 2009. Under such a crushing tax burden, younger Americans would find it hard to avoid "a sizable decline in their future standard of living." Jones, therefore, calls for "no less than rethinking our notion of health care entitlement from the bottom up."[49] Fundamental rethinking may account for the rediscovery of family responsibilities by some public-health officials. Richard Morse of Kansas State University sees "some movement, at present, to deny welfare or Medicaid to those individuals whose families cannot prove they are unable to perform that responsibility."[50] Alexa K. Stuifbergen of the University of Texas at Austin likewise believes that "policymakers are increasingly looking to the family as a hedge against the rising cost of health care services."[51]

This rediscovery of family responsibility for health care raises vexing questions, however, in our era of "no fault" divorce and stigma-free illegitimacy. If (as many Americans believe) the government should not "impose values" by promoting any particular lifestyles, it is then just to impose the collectivized *costs* of repudiating values undergirding marriage and child rearing? If the relationship between family life and public health-care costs is acknowledged, how can a modern welfare state avoid political warfare between lifestyles?

THE FAMILY VS. THE STATE

Further, Americans need to ask whether personal freedom or family integrity can survive a statist assault on illness. From Plato to B.F. Skinner, utopians have regarded the family as a regressive social unit and therefore an obstacle to the creation of the ideal state. In one of the great anti-utopian novels of this century, *Brave New World* (1932), Aldous Huxley depicted a regime of hedonistic totalitarianism in which the state has conquered sickness - and destroyed the family. In the climactic episode, a "Savage" who has not been programmed by state psychologists protests against a world in which marriage and disease have disappeared together. Dismayed that he cannot marry because marriage has disappeared as an institution, the Savage protests also against the engineered healthiness of the world. "I don't want comfort," the Savage insists. Claiming "the right to be unhappy," the Savage also affirms "the right to grow old and ugly and impotent; the right to have syphilis and cancer; the right to have too little to eat; the right to be lousy; the right to live in constant apprehension of what may happen tomorrow; the right to catch typhoid; the right to be tortured by unspeakable pain."[52]

Some Americans may regard the Savage's tirade against an imaginary utopia as irrelevant to circumstances in the United States. Others will point to evidence that even in its limited attempts to mitigate uncertainty and suffering, the welfare state has weakened family life. A former Fulbright scholar in Sweden, a country with an exceptionally well-developed welfare system, David Popenoe has gone so far as to suggest that "the inherent character of the welfare state by its very existence help[s] to undermine family values or familism — the belief in a strong sense of family identification and loyalty, mutual assistance among family members, and a concern for the perpetuation of the family unit." Popenoe points out that although many of Sweden's welfare programs "began with the goal of helping families to function better," over time "the very acceleration of welfare-state power weakened the family still further."[53]

To the degree that American policymakers do expand the health services available from the welfare state, they likewise run the risk of weakening the family. Anthropologists Glynn Custred and Andrei Simic note the "circular relationships ... in which the state is increasingly called upon to fill the void created by the erosion of the family's primary functions, and in so doing further aggravates the situation."[54] In pointing to what might be taken as an example of this "circular relationship," Stephen Crystal documents the difficulty federal officials have encountered in trying to reverse a previous policy of paying the nursing-home costs of elderly parents with adult children. Though financially able children once covered such costs, many affluent Americans now resist the notion that they are responsible for their aging parents. "It's hard," observes Crystal, "to unscramble an omelet."[55]

No easy resolution to the health care crisis appears possible. Marriage and family life foster good health; yet, Americans are in retreat from family life. In any case, Americans rarely chose to accept or avoid the commitments of marriage and family in order to control their health-care costs. If Aldous Huxley saw clearly, then the capacity to make family ties actually requires a willingness to accept risks, including health risks. Even the development of private, non-government forms of health insurance may signal a movement away from reliance upon the family.

Aside from the cultural effects of the welfare state and health insurance, contemporary observers have another reason not to dismiss too hastily the protest of Huxley's Savage against a world devoid of disease and marriage. More than a few scholars have traced the current decline of family life to changes in religious and moral attitudes.[56] These changes themselves may be partly attributable to the greater power of and greater reliance upon modern medical technology. For centuries, Christians and Stoics regarded the contemplation of death as an important moral and spiritual exercise. Relatively few Americans now engage in this exercise. "Everything ... goes on," writes French historian Philippe Aries, "as if neither I nor those who are dear to me are any longer mortal. Technically, we might admit that we might die .... But really, at heart, we feel we are nonmortals."[57] "Death," writes Aries elsewhere, "has become a taboo, an unnameable thing .... In the 20th century, death has replaced sex as the principal prohibition."[58] Aries further believes that "advancements in therapeutics and surgery" have fostered death denial: "Everyone acts as though medicine is the answer to everything .... Caesar must die one day, [but] there is absolutely no reason for oneself to die."[59]

It is beyond the scope of this essay to assess fully the causes and consequences of the invisibility and denial of death — except as a histrionic spectacle in violent movies and television shows. However, the pervasive shift in attitudes toward death does signal a cultural shift of more than trivial importance to anyone trying to understand contemporary family life and medical care.

America's retreat from family life is the consequence of many diverse cultural trends, most of them beyond the direct control of policymakers in

a liberal democracy. American government officials are now asked to cope with the rising medical costs created by family dissolution; yet, by collectivizing those costs, these officials help cause further erosion of family ties. It is a dilemma sure to unsettle the nation in the decades ahead.

ENDNOTES

1. Clifford Kraus, "Democrats Begin Health Offensive," *New York Times*, 5, January, 1992, p. A8.
2. Bureau of the Census, *Statistical Abstract of the United States: 1991*, 11th ed. (Washington: U.S. Government Printing Office, 1991, table 136.
3. James R. Jones, "Aging and Generational Equity: When Past, Present and Future Converge," *The Internist*, January 1989, p. 6.
4. Bureau of the Census, *Statistical Abstract of the United States: 1991*, table 136.
5. Jones, "Aging and Generational Equity," (see note 3), 7.
6. Catherine K. Riessman and Naomi Gerstel, "Marital Dissolution and Health: Do Males or Females Have Greater Risk?" *Social Science and Medicine* 20 (1985): 627.
7. Charlotte A. Schoenborn and Barbara F. Wilson, "Are Married People Healthier? Health Characteristics of Married and Unmarried U.S. Men and Women," paper presented at American Public Health Association, Boston, Massachusetts, 15 November 1988, pp. 3,4,9,15.
8. Sigismund Peller, "Studies on Mortality Since the Renaissance," *Bulletin of the History of Medicine* 13 (1943): 435 - 441 and 21 (1947): 73 - 99.
9. William Farr, "Marriage and Mortality," in *Vital Statistics: A Memorial Volume of Selections from the Reports and Writings of William Farr* (London, 1885; rpt. Metuchen, NJ: The Library of the New York Academy of Medicine/ The Scarecrow Press, 1975), 438 - 441.
10. Ellen S. Kisker and Noreen Gold-

man, "Perils of Single Life and Benefits of Marriage," *Social biology* 34 (1987): 135 - 140.
11. Yuaureng Hu and Noreen Goldman, "Mortality Differentials by Marital Status: An International Comparison," *Demography* 27 (1990): 233 - 250.
12. Lois M. Verbruggs and Donald J. Balaban, "Patterns of Change in Disability and Well-Being," *Medical Care* 27 Supplement (1989); S138-S147.
13. Pamela K. Adelmann, "A Causal Analysis of Employment and Health in Midlife Women," *Women and Health* 16 (1990): 5 - 17.
14. Joseph Berkson, "Mortality and Marital Status: Reflections on the Derivation of Etiology from Statistics," *American Journal of Public Health* 52 (1962): 1318 - 1329.
15. Debra Umberson, "Family Status and Health Behaviors: Social Control as a Dimension of Social Integration," *Journal of Health and Social Behavior* 28 (1987): 309 - 316.
16. John A. Clausen, "Health and the Life Course: Some Personal Observations," *Journal of Health and Social Behavior* 28 (1987): 337 - 344.
17. Janice K. Kiecolt-Glaser, *et al.*, "Marital Discord and Immunity in Males," *Psychosomatic Medicine* 50 (1988): 213 - 229.
18. Annika Rosengren, Hans Wedel, and Lars Wilhelmsen, "Marital Status and Mortality in Middle-Aged Swedish Men, "*American Journal of Epidemiology* 129 (1989): 54 - 63.
19. See David Popenoe, "What Is Happening to the Family in Sweden?" *Social Change in Sweden*, No. 36, Swedish Information Service, December 1986, pp. 1 - 7.
20. Jukka T. Salonen, "Socioeconomic status and risk of cancer, cerebral stroke, and death due to coronary disease and any disease: a longitudinal study in eastern Finland, "*Journal of Epidemiology and Community Health* 36 (1987): 294 - 297.
21. Morowitz quoted by James L. Lynch in **The Broken Heart: The Medical Consequences of Loneliness** (New York: Basic Books, 1977), 45 - 46.
22. Teresa E. Seeman *et al.*, "Social Net-

work Ties and Mortality Among the Elderly in the Alameda County Study," *American Journal of Epidemiology* 126 (1987): 714 - 721.

23. Bertil S. Hanson *et al.*, "Social Network and Social Support Influence Mortality in Elderly Men," *American Journal of Epidemiology* 130 (1989): 100 - 111.

24. Ofra Anson, "Living Arrangements and Women's Health," *Social Science and Medicine* 26 (1988): 201 - 208.

25. Eugene Litwak *et al.*, "Organizational Theory, Social Supports, and Mortality Rates: A Theoretical Convergence," *American Sociological Review* 54 (1989): 49 - 66.

26. G. Marie Swanson, Steven H. Belle, and William A. Satariano, "Marital Status and Cancer Incidence: Differences in the Black and White Populations," *Cancer Research* 45 (1985): 5883 - 5889.

27. James S. Goodwin, et al., The Effects of Marital Status on Stage, Treatment, and Survival of Cancer Patients," *Journal of the American Medical Association* 258 (1987): 3125 - 3130.

28. Robert H. Coombs, "Marital Status and Personal Well-Being: A Literature Review," *Family Relations* 40 (1991): 97 - 102.

29. Lynch, **The Broken Heart** (see note 21), 78 - 80.

30. John Guidubaldi and Helen Cleminshaw, "Divorce, Family Health, and Child Adjustment," *Family Relations* 34 (1985): 35 - 41.

31. Ronald Angel and Jacqueline L. Worobey, "Single Motherhood and Children's Health," *Journal of Health and Social Behavior* 29 (1985): 38 - 52.

32. Hilleui Aro, *et al.*, "Psychosomatic Symptoms Among 14 - 16 Year Old Finnish Adolescents," *Social Psychiatry* 22 (1987): 171 - 176.

33. Deborah A. Dawson, "Family Structure and Children's Health and Well-Being: Data From the 1988 National Health Interview Survey on Child Health," paper presented at the annual meeting of the Population Association of America, Toronto, May, 1990.

34. Joel C. Kleinman and Samuel S. Kessel, "Racial Differences in Low Birth Weight," *New England Journal of Medicine* 317 (1987): 749 - 753.

35. See Susan Newcomer and J. Richard Udry, "Parental Marital Status Effects on Adolescent Sexual Behavior," *Journal of Marriage and the Family* 49 (1987): 235 - 340; Rhys B. Jones and D. Paul Moberg, "Correlates of Smokeless Tobacco Use in a Male Adolescent Population," *American Journal of Public Health* 78 (1988): 61 - 63; Jean-Francois Saucier and Ann-Marie Ambert, "Parental Marital Status and Adolescents' Health-Risk Behavior," *Adolescence* 18 (1983): 403 - 411; William J. Doherty and Richard H. Needle, "Psychological Adjustment and Substance Use Among Adolescents Before and After a Parental Divorce," *Child Development* 62 (1991): 328 - 327; Richard H. Needle, S. Susan Su and William J. Doherty, "Divorce, Remarriage, and Adolescent Substance Use: A Prospective Longitudinal Study," *Journal of Marriage and the Family* 52 (1990): 157 - 159; Denise Kandel and Emily Rosenbaum, "Early Onset of Adolescent Sexual Behavior and Drug Involvement," *Journal of Marriage and the Family* 52 (1990): 783 - 798.

36. Fernando S. Mendoza *et al.*, "Selected Measures of Health Status for Mexican-American, Mainland Puerto-Rican, and Cuban-American Children," *Journal of the American Medical Association* 265 (1991): 227 - 232.

37. Bureau of the Census, *Statistical Abstract of the United States: 1989*, p. 85; Bureau of the Census, *Historical Statistics of the United States: Colonial Times to 1970* (Washington: U.S. Government Printing Office, 1976), 1:64.

38. Arthur J. Norton and Louisa F. Miller, "Marriage, Divorce, and Remarriage in the 1990's" paper presented at the annual meetings of the American Public Health Association, Atlanta, Georgia, November 1991; Bureau of the Census, *Statistical Abstract of the United States: 1991*, table 128.

39. Bureau of the Census, *Statistical Abstract of the United States: 1991*, table 93.

40. Marc L. Berk and Amy K. Taylor, "Women and Divorce: Health Insurance Coverage, Utilization, and Health Care Expenditures," *American Journal of Public Health* 74 (1984): 1276 - 1279.

41. Angel and Worobey, "Single Motherhood and Children's Health" (see note 31), 49.

42. Ben J. Wattenberg, **The Birth Dearth** (New York: Pharos, 1987), 124 - 126.

43. Wattenberg, **The Birth Dearth** (see note 42), 68 - 70.

44. Lynch, **The Broken Heart** (see note 21), 209.

45. Peter A. Morrison, "The Current Demographic Context of Federal Social Programs," N-2785-HHS/NICHD, The RAND Corporation, September 1988, pp. 9 - 12; Peter A. Morrison, "Demographic Factors Reshaping Ties to Family and Place," The RAND Corporation, June 1990, P-7650.

46. Wayne A. Ray, *et al.*, "Impact of Growing Numbers of the Very Old on Medicaid Expenditures for Nursing Homes: A Multi-State Population-Based Analysis," *American Journal of Public Health* 77 (1987): 699 - 703.

47. Bureau of the Census, *Statistical Abstract of the United States: 1991*, table 142.

48. Phillip Longman, "Deathbed Politics," *The New Republic*, 30 March 1987, pp. 18 - 20.

49. Jones, "Aging and Generational Equity," (see note 3), p. 8.

50. "Interviews: Richard L.D. Morse, Ph.D.," *Family and Community Health* 9 (February 1987): 85.

51. Alexa K. Stuifbergen, "The Impact of Chronic Illness on Families," *Family and Community Health* 9 (February 1987): 50.

52. Aldous Huxley, **Brave New World** (1932; rpt. New York: Harper & Row, 1969), 160 - 163.

53. David Popenoe, **Disturbing the Nest: Family Change and Decline in Modern Societies** (New York:

Aldine de Gruyter, 1988), 237 - 239.

54. Glynn Custred and Andrei Simic, "Modernity and the American Family: A Cultural Dilemma," *International Journal of the Sociology of the Family* 12 (1982): 163.

55. Stephen Crystal, **America's Old Age Crisis: Public Policy and the Two Worlds of Aging**, (New York: Basic, 1982), 13.

56. See Pitirim Sorokin, **Social and Cultural Dynamics: A Study of Change in Major Systems of Art, Truth, Ethics, Law, and Social Relationships**, rev. and abridged ed., (1957; reprint, New Brunswick, NJ: Transaction, 1985), 700 - 702.

57. Philippe Aries, **Western Attitudes Toward Death** (Baltimore: Johns Hopkins University Press, 1974), 106.

58. Philippe Aries, "The Reversal of Death: Changes in Attitudes Toward Death in Western Societies," in **Death in America**, ed. Philippe Aries, *et al.*, (Philadelphia: University of Pennsylvania, 1975), 140.

59. Aries, The Reversal of Death" (see note 56), 140.

The Institute for Creation Research (ICR) has settled its federal lawsuit against the California Department of Education on terms very satisfactory to the Institute. The Department of Education and, especially, its Superintendent Bill Honig, had tried to shut down the graduate school operated by ICR. The lengthy list of stipulations declared by the judge included "that a private postsecondary educational institution may teach the creation model as being correct provided that the institution also teaches evolution." *While the Institute chooses to teach evolution so that its students will understand this common, erroneous dogma, it remains a shame that the state mandates that a private graduate school must teach error.*

From a recent issue of **Parenting** magazine, Penelope Leach gives us some reasons to quit spanking children as a means of discipline. Included among them is that "almost everybody agrees that it's wrong for people to settle arguments or impose their will on each other with blows." We are further told that "physical punishment used to be an accepted part of all relationships that gave one individual legitimate authority over another — master over slave, servant or wife; officer over enlisted man; law enforcer over lawbreaker. But that has all been consigned to the history books by a society that prides itself on universal human rights." *Almost everyone but God (II Sam. 7:14, Prov. 22:15, Prov. 13:24).*

The Rutherford Institute (P.O. Box 7482, Charlottesville, VA, 22906-7482) is planning to file lawsuits against state school systems in California and Massachusetts "for allowing condom distribution to students in tax-payer funded public schools ... without parental permission or involvement." *Schools are inherently religious in that their curriculum and methods must depend upon empirically unprovable presuppositions which are taken on faith. In a "pluralistic" state, Christians can expect increasing difficulties with public schools. We need a strategy to recover all of the aspects of the education of our children, not only the egregious departures of pluralism.*

"One of the continuing fascinations of clinical medicine is the inability of any physician, no matter how experienced, to predict with certainty the course of disease ... Medicine, like no other profession, continues to make its practitioners humble." Arthur W. Feinberg, "The Evaluation of Amaurosis Fugax," *Hospital Practice*, April 30, 1992, p. 57.

The *Christian Brotherhood Newsletter* (P.O. Box 832, Barberton, Ohio, 44203) had been publishing the medical needs of its Christian subscribers for years in order that they may assist one another with the expenses attendant to illness. [See the Fall, 1989, issue of this journal.] Nondrinking, nonsmoking Christian subscribers who are faithful in their church attendance send checks directly to one another, after the Newsletter has verified the expenses and participation according to the plan the subscribers choose among themselves. One check per year goes to the newsletter publishers for their service. Though the activity is clearly planful Christian charity, the insurance commissioners of several states are trying to move against the *Newsletter* to prevent it from being circulated in their states, charging it with being a "pyramid scheme" in which the latecomers will be suckered into paying the bills of the earlier subscribers. *We have statist housing, education, and medicine. Having done so well in those endeavors, the state now wants a monopoly on charity, notwithstanding the fact that funds collected under coercion (taxes) are, by definition, not charity (II Cor. 9:7). Will churches which take up offerings to indemnify a loss suffered by someone need a state insurance commissioner to oversee the collection plate after it is passed? As for a "pyramid scheme," the pot calls the kettle black. What, after all, is Social Security but one massive involuntary pyramid scheme?*

In the February, 1992, issue of *Good Housekeeping,* we read how a woman discovered that her shoplifting was "an addiction." Through group support by telephone with Shoplifter's Anonymous and counseling she came to understand the psychodynamics of her shoplifting and changed her behavior. Nowhere in the article does the author acknowledge the sinfulness of her behavior. The issues she dealt with were internal and horizontal, but there was no sense of her "vertical" responsibility before God. *The public is heeding the medical profession's medicalization of sin. We are providing a capacious vehicle for mankind to bypass God's Law and his offer of forgiveness in Christ.*

The Americans with Disabilities Act, says Jim Brady, "can usher in the dawn of a new age for Americans with disabilities. If we get the printed words off the pages of the statute books and into the hearts and actions of the people." The press secretary to Ronald Reagan who was severely wounded in the assassination attempt on the president was thus quoted in "The Independent," a publication of Walton Rehabilitation Hospital.

Whereas outward morality can be legislated, inward morality cannot be achieved by Congressional ink. See II Corinthians 3:3, Jeremiah 31:33 and Hebrews 8:10. Christians should not seek to use State coercion to accomplish ends for which the State is not charged by God to accomplish. Palingenesis is not something the civil state can or should attempt. The Americans with Disabilities Act may create a severe backlash against the very persons it is intended to help.

Editor's Note and Letters to the Editor

"Advanced directives" such as living wills, a "will to live," and durable power of attorney for health care are explained in a brochure available from The Christian Life Commission of the Southern Baptist Convention (901 Commerce, #440, Nashville, TN, 37203-3696). The straightforward brochure, entitled "The sanctity of Human Life: A Time to Live, A Time to Die: Advance Directives and Living Wills" is particularly suitable to inform patients or church members about these options and as the title implies is written from a strong sanctity of life position.

Letters to the Editor

Dear Editor:

Franklin Payne's article on Birth Control [Spring, 1992] was a good attempt to survey this subject which has only recently become of interest to Protestant ethicists. When one examines his article, however, one notices that it breaks itself in two. The first section traces a Pro-natalist position from the Scripture; the second section jumps into a stewardship-centered Pro-birth control direction. I would suggest that a number of Payne's points do not follow from his premises. Let me give some examples:

1. At one point Payne rightly argues that there is "no Biblical justification to choose to be childless." Yet a paragraph later he suggests that birth control is "neither endorsed nor prohibited by Scripture." You can't have it both ways (which is just what modern couples want). Since we don't know the future, the day to day, month to month, year to year, birth control practices of young couples for the first 5 (7, 10, 15 ???) years of marriage offer a *de factor* choice for childlessness.

2. Though I agree with Payne's view that Scripture is for large families, it seems that a family size of 3 is pulled out of the thin air in order to be a kind of compromise between Pro-natalist and Pro-birth control positions.

3. Payne also mis-uses Scripture at one point. He argues that "A child too early in one's marriage may not be wise" and then cites Deut. 24:5 which implies the very opposite. "If a man is recently married, he must not be sent to war or have any other duty laid on him. For one year he is to be free to stay at home and bring happiness to the wife he has married." Knowing human nature, that happiness would certainly include conjugal bliss; and by the end of a year at home it is highly probable that one child, or possibly 2, might be conceived.

I appreciate his attempt to come to grips with this difficult topic. But I think the cultural ramifications of the Bible are at odds with our habitual view of "control" on this issue.

Yours in Christ,

James L. Sauer, Director of Library
Eastern College, St. David's, PA

Dr. Payne replies:

I find Mr. Sauer's letter distressing -- not because he differs with me, but because he criticizes without offering alternatives. My goal in the article was to offer practical guidelines *within Biblical principles*.

I challenge him to come to real solutions to the dilemma that h e creates for modern couples who choose to pursue higher education. Would he have them not consider marriage until they have finished their education (somehow controlling the raging hormones within)? Would he have them engaged (i.e., moderate their passion for each other) until years of education are finished? Would he have them use no birth control and still continue their education *with children* and all the accompanying problems of working parents, child-rearing, studying, etc.? Would he have every couple bear as many children as possible, i.e., 10 - 20 over a possible 30 years of fertility? If so, he is placing a Pharisaical load (Matthew 23:4) on modern couples.

(Continued on page 92:90)

Questions Surrounding the Withdrawal of Artificial Hydration and Nutrition from Patients in a Persistent Vegetative State

Daniel E. Deaton, M.Div., M.A.R., Th.M.

Dr. Deaton is serving as chaplain at the Naval Hospital in San Diego where he is a member of the bioethics committee. He holds the M.Div. and M.A. degrees from Gordon-Conwell Seminary and a Th.M. from Princeton Theological Seminary.

In 1950, Rita Greene was working as a nurse at Washington, D.C., General Hospital when whe contracted tuberculosis from one of her patients. She then became a patient at the hospital where she was treated for about one year. On October 25, 1951, the day before she was to be released, Greene suffered a cardiac arrest and lapsed into a persistent vegetative state (PVS). Since that day, she has lain motionless and unconscious in room 5221 of D. C. General, where she has been kept alive through artificial hydration and nutrition (AHN) administered by private duty nurses who also turn and bathe her. She is believed to be the longest surviving PVS patient in the United States.[1]

The American Academy of Neurology defines PVS as:

> "...a form of eyes-open permanent unconsciousness in which the patient has periods of wakefulness and physiological sleep/wake cycles, but at no time is the patient aware of him- or herself or the environment. Neurologically, being awake but unaware is the result of a functioning brainstem and the total loss of cerebral cortical functioning."[2]

This total loss of cerebral cortical functioning may have been caused by a variety of insults to the brain. Among thse are "nutritional insufficiency, poisoning, stroke, infections, direct physical injury, or degenerative disease."[3] PVS patients are incommunicative, cannot experience pain, and are incontinent of urine and stool.[4]

It is not clear how many patients, like Rita Greene, are victims of PVS. Neither is it known what it costs for the life-sustaining technology and care to keep these patients alive. Estimates range from 5,000 to 25,000 PVS patients in the United States at any given time, with the costs of uncomplicated PVS care ranging from $2,000 to $10,000 per month per patient, depending on the site (home, hospital, or chronic care facility), type of nutrition (enteral or parenteral) and the region of the country where the care is provided.[5] The one area of agreement is that the number of PVS patients is growing and will probably continue to grow with the advancement and application of trauma care and high-technology medicine.

The care and management of PVS patients raise significant ethical questions. These involve the reliability of the diagnosis of PVS and the possibility of recovery, the definition of death, the issue of whether AHNM should be considered as treatment or care, the burdensome costs and consequences of such care, and the question of when, if ever, it is ethically acceptable to terminate AHN of a PVS patient. The aim of this paper is to bring these issues under scrutiny from the point of view of Christian ethics.

Affirmations and Presuppositions

In order to consider the issues outlined above, I offer the following framework of affirmations and presuppositions which I believe form a valid (though not exhaustive) grid through which to view these (and some other) problems in medical ethics.

1. *Human life is made in the image of God and is a gift as a trust from Him.*

God assigns value to human life. He gives it and He takes it away. We are the stewards of our lives, and we are held accountable by Him for the choices we make all through life and not just at its end stages. To choose death by suicide or "euthanasia" is a fundamental rejection of this first affirmation.

2. *Death is a reality because of the entrance of sin into the human race.*

Death is an enemy to be fought even though for the Christian death has been transformed into the entrance to a glorious eternity. Nevertheless, there is a time to die and there exists no duty pointlessly to prolong dying. Physical longevity is not the supreme value to be increased at all other costs.[6]

3. Treatments may legitimately cease when there is no benefit or reasonable hope for the patient's recovery.

Proper medical treatment is not always to be equated with maximum treatment. Care in the forms of comfort and company must always be given to those with no natural hope of recovery, but not that which only prolongs the dying process. Treatment that is very costly, unusual, dangerous, difficult, or which causes serious or painful side effects disproportionate to any clearly curative benefits may be discontinued.[7]

4. Patients have the right to refuse treatment when they are competent to do so, and their legally appointed surrogates may do so for them when those patients become incompetent or voiceless.

This is not to accept the so-called "autonomy" of the patient.[8] It is to recognize the individual's personal responsibility to make informed decisions about his or her own care. This right is relative to other concerns and is not a right to ruin one's health or to cease ordinary curative treatments which have a reasonable hope for success. The patient, or his or her legally appointed surrogate, has the right to free and informed participation in medical decisions affecting him or her when there are alternative treatments.[9]

5. All decisions to continue or forego

any particular treatment depend on the patient's present condition and the best objective medical determination on the part of the physician or physicians making the diagnosis.

Paul Ramsey suggests the term "medically indicated" best describes appropriate care.[10] It is not based on "quality of life" judgments or notions about what life is "meaningful." The issue is the "comparison of treatments to determine whether they are likely to be beneficial in any way other than prolonging dying."[11]

6. The same treatments that were potentially life saving when begun, can, after further medical diagnosis, become means for aimlessly prolonging dying.

The dying patient may at times need to be protected from relentless medical intervention when such intervention was begun with the expectation of a cure but over time was determined to be futile. The same standard of "comparison of treatments" given above applies also to the decision to continue curative treatment or discontinue its use.[12] The initiation of treatment, whether in an emergency or non-emergency setting, does not imply or require its continued use. Information that was unavailable at the initiation of treatment or the deterioration of a patient's condition may be factors that allow for withdrawal of "life support" or other forms of treatment.[13]

7. Decisions to treat or cease treatment are not infallibly made. Where the prognosis is uncertain, or different courses of treatment or non-treatment are recommended by the care givers, responsible third parties not involved in the treatment should be consulted.

This affirmation applies especially to decisions made on behalf of voice-

less patients or incompetents who must depend on surrogates to make these difficult decisions for them.

8. In situations where the correct course of treatment or non-treatment is unclear, the application of the Golden Rule ("Do to others as you would have them do to you" Luke 6:31) is appropriate.[14]

This is not an endorsement of "situation ethics" or a subjective method of making decisions by some nebulous appeal to "love." It is merely the recognition that God commands us to act on behalf of others in a manner consistent with how we would like to be treated. When we are not morally obligated to take a given course of action, we should be guided by our wishes for ourselves.

9. Food, air and water by natural routes are necessary means of the preservation of life and may not be denied to any patient.[15]

Food and water taken through the mouth and air breathed on one's own are not forms of medical treatment to be withheld from anyone. The deliberate withholding of food and water from someone who is capable of ingesting them in order to hasten his or her death is immoral.

AHN and the PVS Patient

With the above affirmations and presuppositions in mind, the possibility of withdrawal of AHN from certain PVS patients may be considered by posing and answering several questions.

1. How reliable is the diagnosis of PVS, and what is the likelihood of recovery from it?

The primary methods of diagnosis

of PVS involve careful and extended clinical observation of the patient along with laboratory studies. PVS patients will show "no behavioral response whatsoever over an extended period of time."[16] No voluntary action or behavior is observed in a PVS patient. He or she awakens and sleeps cyclically, but shows no behavioral evidence of being able to respond in a learned manner to external events or stimuli. Despite appearances of alertness at times, PVS patients "repeatedly fail to demonstrate coherent speech, evidence of comprehension of the words of examiners or attendants, or any capacity to initiate or make consistently purposeful movements."[17]

In addition to behavioral observation, positron emission tomography is used to determine the metabolic rate for glucose in the cerebral cortex. In PVS patients, such a rate is greatly reduced to a level inconsistent with consciousness or the capacity to experience pain.[18] Brain imaging tests (CT scans) sometimes also reveal lesions or cortical atrophy, depending on the cause and duration of the condition.[19]

Taken together, the above diagnostic criteria provide a very high degree of certainty in the diangosis of PVS. The more difficult issue is the determination of the permanence of the state. This depends on the nature of the brain injury, the age of the patient, and the period of time the loss of cognitive function has already lasted. Both the American Medical Association and the American Academy of Neurology agree, however, that once PVS has lasted three months, recovery of consciousness is very rare and the condition can reliably be considered permanent.[20]

Patients under 40 years of age have the best possibility of regaining consciousness, although the likelihood is still very small.[21] The American Medical Association's Council Report on PVS concludes:

Even in young persons who have experienced head trauma, a conservative criterion for the diagnosis of PVS would be observed unawareness for at least 12 months. Cognitive recovery after 6 months is vanishingly rare in patients older than 50 years. If the handful of reported occurrences of cognitive recovery in patients with PVS are divided by the total estimated number of PVS cases in this country, the odds of recovery are less than 1 in 1000. The risk of prognostic error from widespread use of the above criterion is so small that a decision that incorporates it as a prognostic conclusion seems fully justifiable.[22]

Based on the above, I conclude that the diagnosis of the permanence of PVS is reliable, though not infallible. After a patient has been in PVS for one year, the possibility that he or she will recover seems to be statistically minute. Those diagnosed to be in a permanent PVS due to atrophy of or severe physical trauma to the cerebral cortex may be judged to be beyond the possibility of natural recovery of consciousness.

2. Should the definition of death be expanded to include those diagnosed to be in a permanent PVS?

Some ethicists have suggested that the definition of death be changed from a whole-brain death criterion to the criterion of the "permanent loss of sentience."[23] Under this definition, further treatments of patients diagnosed in permanent PVS would not be required, since

such patients would be considered dead as persons even though their bodies were biologically alive.[24]

Although this would solve the dilemma of AHN of PVS patients, I do not think it is a wise approach. A person without sentience is still a person, although a very ill one. To make a distinction between a person and his or her body opens the possibility of further redefinition of death to include, perhaps, those who have limited capacity for awareness such as Alzheimer's sufferers or severely retarded persons. It is wiser to define death as "the irreversible loss of heart, lung and brain function — to make each a necessary criterion and all three together the sufficient criteria for declaring someone to be dead."[25]

No one "recovers" from the above defined state of death. Those who have suffered temporary or permanent loss of sentience ought not to be considered among the dead.

3. Can AHN ever accurately be considered as treatment?

This difficult question has been debated widely and forcefully. At first glance, it would seem that AHN should be placed in the category of ordinary palliative care never to be denied anyone. Those who take this view maintain that to withhold hydration or nutrition even when it must be administered artificially is to kill the patient deliberately by dehydration or starvation.[26]

Such a view carries much weight yet seems to ignore the very obvious parallels between AHN and other mechanical interventions such as respirators, dialysis machines and even antibiotic therapy.

The most common methods of AHN are the nasogastric tube (threaded through the nostril and into the stomach), the gastrostomy tube (surgically inserted into the stomach), the jejeunostomy tube (surgically inserted into the small intestine), and the intravenous (IV) line into the bloodstream (seldom used for the long term AHN needed for PVS patients. All of these devices are invasive, require supervision of highly trained personnel, are accompanied by risks and side effects (e.g., infection, bleeding, diarrhea, electrolyte imbalances, pneumonia, fluid overload, etc.) and are costly.[27] Unlike the giving of a cup of water or bowl of soup, these feeding procedures can reasonbly be viewed as medical treatments not ethically and unequivocally mandated for every patient.

For the vast majority of patients, AHN is a very beneficial temporary therapy allowing for the treatment of medical problems when the taking of food and water by natural routes is not possible. AHN also allows time for the clarification of diagnosis over a longer period as in the case of PVS patients. The presumption should therefore always favor the initiation of AHN in patients for whom death is not irreversibly imminent. However, the initiation of AHN does not imply or require its continued use irrespective of its efficacy for the recovery of the individual patient.

4. When may AHN be withdrawn from a PVS patient?

The decision to cease treatment by AHN ought never to be taken lightly. The PVS patient is totally dependent on the judgments of others for his or her care and is among the most vulnerable in our society. The focus should always be on the patient.

It should also be noted that a decision permitting the withdrawal of AHN does not make it morally obligatory. Respect should be given to families and care-givers who conscientiously object to the withdrawal of AHN and they should never be required to act against their consciences. Families willing to accept the burdens and costs of indefinite AHN should be permitted to move the PVS patient to a facility where such treatment can be carried out.

With those observations in mind, AHN of PVS patients may be ethically withdrawn when there is no natural and reasonable hope that the patient will recover. When a PVS patient is reliably known to be in an irreversible condition, treatment is no longer medically indicated since it is no longer of benefit to him or her.

A conservative and prudent method of determining irreversibility would be to require a team of neurologists who have previously not been involved in the diagnosis or treatment of the patient to examine him or her after he or she has remained in a PVS for a period of at least one year. Using the diagnostic criteria outlined in question one above, the team may determine, with certainty[28] in some cases and overwhelming probability in others, that the individual will not recover from the PVS.

The family or legally-appointed surrogate for the patient may then decide whether or not to withdraw AHN on the basis of the patient's known wishes, their own informed judgment, or the application of the Golden Rule. Such a decision need not be made hastily and should reflect, if possible, the unanimous view of the immediate family if they

are making the decision. In any case, the family is not under obligation to continue useless or futile application of AHN. It may be withdrawn, not because of some "quality of life" judgment, or by defining the patient as already dead, but because it offers no benefit toward the recovery of the patient. In these narrowly defined situations AHN can be seen as serving aimlessly to prolong dying for patients in whom there is no reasonable and natural hope for recovery.

5. Since death results from withdrawing AHN, isn't this a form of euthanasia, and a painful one at that?

The issue of pain is irrelevant to the PVS patient, since those in PVS lack the cortical function needed to experience pain. However, the accusation of euthanasia is a serious one to which a plea of "not guilty" is entered.

It should be noted that certain other medical treatments are withdrawn in some circumstances despite the fact that death will result as certainly as with the withdrawal of AHN. Among these are renal dialysis, blood transfusions, respirators, etc. In these cases it should be acknowledged that the underlying disease or injury that initially required the life supportive treatment is the cause of death and not the withdrawal of treatment which has been deemed useless. The withdrawal only seems to be the cause of death. Death would have invariably occurred had the treatment not been initiated in the first place. Withdrawal of life support affects the *timing* of the death, but is not the cause of it.[29] The intent of withdrawal is not to cause death but to cease treatments that offer no reasonable curative benefit. Death follows as a result of the patient's fatal pathology.

6. *Doesn't the withdrawal of AHN from certain PVS patients open the door for the withdrawal of AHN from other groups of patients?*

The possibility of abuse of any principled ethic always exists but in this case the danger is particularly acute. Because of this, Daniel Callahan has questioned the withdrawal of AHN even when it might be ethically legitimate in order to preserve a "moral emotion" and "repugnance against starving people to death."[30] Daniel Avila, Staff Counsel for the National Legal Center for the Medically Dependent and Disabled, has suggested that withdrawing AHN will lead to death by lethal injection.[31]

While I acknowledge the legitimate concerns and fears of the "slippery slope" to euthanasia, this danger can be guarded against without requiring treatments whose only effect is a pointless prolonging of dying for an irreversibly and incurably ill patient.

It is essential that both law and medical practice distinguish between those patients whose cortical function is totally and irretrievably lost and other persons who may have minimal or severely impaired consciousness.[32] The principle of the sanctity of human life would require a most vigorous protection of the latter group.

The position of this paper affirming the withdrawal of AHN from some PVS patients is not based on a "quality of life" ethic that might jeopardize other patients' right to life. It is based on the *curative futility* of the treatment, not the quality of the PVS patient's life.

Given the present diagnostic reliability as I understand it, I have proposed a waiting period of one year (instead of three months as the American Academy of Neurology suggests) for the determination of whether a PVS patient is known to be in an irreversible unconscious condition. This proposal is designed to make certain that the patient's unconsciousness is not temporary, and that there are no lingering remnants of sentience. This one-year period is admittedly a conservative precaution designed to prevent premature withdrawal of life support and defend against the intrusion of "euthanasia" where the diagnosis is uncertain.

SUMMARY AND CONCLUSIONS

The vast number of life-sustaining treatments available today forces us to be part of exceedingly difficult decisions about our own dying and death of our loved ones. These agonizing decisions require our best ethical judgments as we apply the unchanging word of God to the ever changing circumstances and dilemmas of the modern world. Knowing our fallibility we seek God's wisdom while depending on His grace when we fail to apply His truth accurately to all the facets of each problem.

Because of my intentional focus on the individual patient, I have not discussed related issues such as the emotional and financial burdens falling to the *families* of PVS patients. While I have eliminated these considerations as the *ground* for the withdrawal of AHN, they are important concerns. The pointless prolonging of dying through AHN in patients who are completely and permanently unconscious unquestionably generates profound emotional pain for the families as well as

immense financial burdens.

When these financial responsibilities cannot be met, they fall to the public sector, adding to the costs of health care and increasing public debt. Rita Greene, who was mentioned at the beginning of this paper, has been sustained in a PVS for over forty years with the costs of her care at D.C. General (a public hospital) covered by a workers' compensation claim.[33] These and related issues need to be debated and studied from an ethical standpoint before financial considerations bring about the rationing of health care merely on the basis of utilitarian or cost/benefit theories.

The withdrawal of AHN from anyone, even the permanently unconscious, may seem to be a cruel and insensitive act. Yet in his book *The Patient as Person*, Paul Ramsey suggests that permanently unconscious patients may be among those few patients who are "irretrievably inaccessible to human care."[34] He writes:

If there are cases of neglect and defect of care for the dying, there may also be not an excess but a now useless extension of care. Acts of charity or moving with grace among the dying that now communicate no presence or comfort to them are now no longer required.[35]

If that is so, we can properly withhold AHN in the narrowly defined cases I have described without fear of weakening the responsibility to protect and save human life, and without being accused of callous indifference to the patient in a permanent PVS.

Persons with total loss of cortical function are incapable of suffering hunger, sensing comfort or experiencing companionship. It is strange logic indeed that would require one to give to a patient what he or she cannot receive. Such actions may produce psychological benefit for the care giver, but they are matters of complete indifference to the patient.[36]

By focusing on the *patient*, we can do what is appropriate for him or her while avoiding the useless and costly extension of treatment when there is no hope of recovery.

ENDNOTES

1. McCormick, Brian, "Not Enough Data on Lives, Costs," *American Medical News*, January 7, 1991, p. 23.
2. Executive Board, American Academy of Neurology, "Position of the American Academy of Neurology on Certain Aspects of the Care and Management of the Persistent Vegetative State Patient." *Neurology*, Vol. 39, Jan. 1989, p. 125.
3. Council on "Scientific Affairs and Council on Ethical and Judicial Affairs, "Persistent Vegetative State and Decision to Withdraw or Withhold Life Support," *JAMA*, Vol. 263, Jan. 19, 1990, p. 427.
4. *Ibid.*
5. McCormick, *op cit.*, p. 23. See also Ronald E. Cranford, "The Persistent Vegetative State: The Medical Reality (Getting the Facts Straight)," *Hastings Center Report*, Vol. 18, February/March, 1988): pp. 27-32.
6. Frame, John M., **Medical Ethics: Principles, Persons and Problems**, Presbyterian & Reformed Publishing Company, 1988, p. 66.
7. Ramsey, Paul, **The Patient as Person**, Yale University Press, New Haven, 1970, pp. 122-123.
8. I refer here to chapter three of Tom L. Beauchamp and James F. Childress, **Principles of Biomedical Ethics** (New York: Oxford University Press, 1989). The authors, following John S. Mill, define autonomy in a way

that overrides other legitimate safeguards to the prevention of suicide and the protection of human life.
9. Ramsey, Paul, **Ethics at the Edges of Life**, Yale University Press, New Haven, 1978, p. 157.
10. *Ibid.*, p. 168.
11. *Ibid.*, p. 178.
12. *Ibid.*, p. 272.
13. Withdrawl of life support or other treatment may seem to be the cause of the patient's death, when in fact such treatment was only delaying the dying process brought about by the injury or disease afflicting the patient. The perception that withdrawal of treatment causes death may prevent the legitimate termination of useless treatment.
14. Payne, Franklin E., "Counterpoint to Dr. Davis on the Brophy Case," *Journal of Biblical Ethics in Medicine*, July, 1987, pp. 59-60.
15. Report of the Heroic Measures Committee, Presbyterian Church in American General Assembly, 1989.
16. Executive Board, American Academy of Neurology, p. 125.
17. Council on Scientific Affairs and Council on Ethical and Judicial Affairs, p. 427.
18. Executive Board, American Academy of Neurology, p. 125.
19. Council on Scientific Affairs and Council on Ethical and Judicial Affairs, p. 427.
20. Executive Board, American Academy of Neurology, p. 126.
21. In 1981, a Japanese team of Neurosurgeons did a five-year follow-up study of 110 PVS patients and found that 73% of them had died in that period. Only 5 of the 110 were considered recovered at all. Of the 5, three could not comunicate or move about. The remaining 2 recovered their cognitive abilities to a large degree. It should be noted that this study was done before some of the present diagnostic tools were being used. See K. Higashi, et al., "Five Year Follow-up of Patients With Persistent Vegetative State," *Journal of Neurology, Neurosurgery, and Psychiatry* Vol. 44, 1981, pp. 552-554.
22. Council on Scientific Affairs and

Council on Ethical and Judicial Affairs, p. 428.
23. See, for example, Daniel Wikler, "Not Dead, Not Dying? Ethical Categories and Persistent Vegetative State," *Hastings Center Report*, Vol. 18, February/March, 1988, pp. 41-47.
24. A good critique of this approach is offered by John M. Stanley, "More Fiddling with the Definition of Death?" *Journal of Medical Ethics*, Vol. 13, 1987, pp. 21-22.
25. Frame, John M., **Medical Ethics**, p. 61.
26. One writer calls this a "cowardly version of euthanasia" and compares it to the practice of Phoenician crucifixion. See John M. Dolan, "Death by Deliberate Dehydration and Starvation: Silent Echoes of the Hungerhauser," *Issues in Law and Medicine*, Vol. 7, Fall, 1991, 173-197.
27. See Bernard Lo and Laurie Dornbrand, "Understanding the Benefits and Burdens of Tube Feedings," *Archives of Internal Medicine*, Vol. 149, September, 1989, pp. 1925-1926. Clinical aspects of AHN are also discussed in an article by Katie Maslow, "Total Parenteral Nutrition and Tube Feeding for Elderly Patients: Findings of an OTA Study," *Journal of Parenteral and Enteral Nutrition*, Vol. 12, September/October, 1988, pp. 425-432.
28. In the case of a patient in whom atrophy of the cerebral cortex is evident, it is certain that natural recovery of sentience is impossible. Such certainty may also be possible in cases of severe trauma to the brain where the brainstem remains intact.
29. Holst, Lawrence, E. "Withholding Nutrition and Hydration: Some Old and New Questions," *The Journal of Pastoral Care*, Vol. 45, Spring, 1991, p. 12.
30. Callahan, Daniel, "On Feeding the Dying," *Hastings Center Report*, Vol. 13, October, 1983, p. 22.
31. Avila, Dan, "Establishing the Link Between Death by Starvation and Death by Lethal Injection," *Life Cycle*, Vol. 113, April, 1991, p. 8.

(Continued on page 80)

An Overview of Scriptural Principles as They Apply to Selected Current Life Issues

Robert Fleischmann

Mr. Fleischmann is the national director of WELS, Lutherans for Life.

In the course of human history various issues rise to the surface of public consciousness. Oftentimes those are life threatening maladies that victimize a population, such as war, famine, and pestilence. In recent times, however, citizens of the United States have become embroiled in social concerns of life and death in the issues of abortion, infanticide, suicide and euthanasia. These and related *life issues* touch not only public policy but reach deep into the thoughts, convictions, and morals of every citizen.

We must acknowledge the morality shifts in our society that have invited the changes in attitudes toward life issues. The constitutional dictates on individual liberty have received greater attention in the past 25 years. The result has been a shift in the acceptance of what has formerly been thought to be abhorrent behavior. This is especially evident in the arena of life issues. Today the thought of ending one's own life or the life of others is more acceptable than ever before.

Nevertheless, in Ecclesiastes we read, **"What has been will be again, what has been done will be done again; there is nothing new under the sun."** (Ecclesiastes 1:9). People were killing unborn babies in ancient times, and they kill them today. People were allowing some newborn children to die by exposure centuries ago, and it is allowed today. People have always resorted to self-murder because they have lost purpose and value. Historical records reveal an almost cyclical pattern of societies establishing subjective criteria for who can continue to live and who must die.

Throughout the ages Christians have made their voice known — louder at some times, softer at others. I would be so bold as to suggest that the liberalization of legal killing laws in these United States has come, in part, because the Christian voice has been too soft on these important issues. Before a Christian can consider activism in any issue, however, he must clearly understand God's word and will in these matters. While God does not provide answers for every question we encounter in life he does give us clear principles so we might make knowledgeable and God-pleasing decisions.

I will examine what I see as six major Biblical principles that apply to decision-making in life issues. From those principles I will suggest a few applications to specific life issues questions. The first point that must be clearly understood, however, is that ...

PRINCIPLES ARE DISTINCT FROM APPLICATIONS

The two words that are used frequently in Christian ethics are principles and applications. Principles are fundamental doctrines or assumptions based upon an established authority. In our instance, all valid principles are derived from the authoritative Word of God.

Applications are built from one or more principles and adapted to a particular circumstance. While the principles are unchanging, a change in circumstances may call for the application of different principles. The important point here is that the principles are absolute in their nature. Changing circumstances will vary the pertinent principles. Circumstances, however, do not determine the course of action. The principles determine the course of action.

While this appears to be a quibbling with semantics it is an important distinction to make when wrestling with life issues. The first Biblical principle which guides us in making life issues decisions makes this clear.

Principle #1:

Truly right deeds and decisions can only be made by the Christian from a heart of faith, regardless of its

perceived outcome.

Often the time to act in a life issues circumstance is a crisis. Something unexpected has happened and emotions are running high. The natural response will most likely not be the correct response.[1] The circumstance, and not religious conviction, appears often to be the determinant for the decision or action to be taken. In ignorance we may want to blot out all the confusing facts and simply say, "I'll let God take over from here." It sounds noble but such a philosophical approach (called consequentialism) is not always reliable and certainly not Biblical.[2]

Another typical response is legalism. "Our church says we shouldn't have abortions so it is always wrong." Or, "my pastor said you shouldn't withdraw nutrition and hydration, therefore we will not do it." While in most circumstances these might be the *correct* postions to take, if they are not rooted in faith, they are not God-pleaseing. Formalistic solutions in which circumstances dictate actions only serve to encourage obedience without thought and ultimately civic righteousness without faith. Without faith there is no *truly right* decision.[3]

With the motive to be from faith we can now consider the specific principles that speak of life and death.

Principle #2

God alone has the right to initiate and terminate life.

When we sit down with a young couple planning to get married, more and more of them are walking into the office with a *plan* for their married life. In two years they will buy a house, in three years they will replace the car and in the fourth year they will have a child. Without burying ourselves in the subject of effective and ineffective birth control methods almost without exception one of two things happen: (1) a baby comes way ahead of schedule, or (2) when the scheduled moment arrives for this addition to be made to the family, nothing happens.

While God extends to humans the intelligence (and possibly the self-discipline) to know when and how to have and not to have children, he nevertheless reserves to himself the right to initiate life.

Scripture abounds with references supporting this fact. We first see that Biblical writers pair the terms of conception and birth together.[4] Secondly, David gives a powerful testimony that man is accountable for sin not only from birth but from conception.[5] Some call the unborn child a blob of tissue or part of the mother's body. One cannot overlook the fact, however, that nowhere in Scripture does God hold a part of the mother's body accountable for sin, nor does he hold a blob of tissue accountable for sin. He only holds people accountable for sin. One should also note that the Hebrew word for conceived is related to the word for burn suggesting that the Hebrews recognized that conception was closely tied with the passionate act of intercourse.[6]

The New Testament also addresses the personhood of the unborn. Luke used terminology that clearly reflected a conviction that children inside and outside of the womb are persons. In Luke 18:15 he uses the Greek term, BREPHOS, to describe the babies, or little children, that were being brought to Jesus.[7] Luke, in 1:41 and 1:44 reveals that Elizabeth, the mother of John the Baptist, certainly recognized that she had a BREPHOS within her, as any other mother would bring her BREPHOS for the blessing of Jesus.[8]

God's prerogative to end life is clearly his as the Creator of life. His absolute authority over life and death is clearly portrayed in his words of Deuteronomy 32:39, *"See now that I myself am He! There is no god besides me. I put to death and I bring to life, I have wounded and I will heal, and no one can deliver out of my hand."* The Christian's submission to God in all things is rooted in the knowledge of God as the author of life and death.[9]

God's defense of his authority over life and death and the high value he places on human life can be seen in the words following the Flood. In Genesis 9:6 we read, *"Whoever sheds the blood of man, by man shall his blood be shed; for in the image of God has God made man."* God has just completed authorizing man to eat of plant and animal life. When it came to human life, however, that was a different story. While man can take plant and animal life he is not to take human life. In fact, so repulsive is it to take human life that the highest price, a human life, was to be paid for the crime.

Without delving into a lengthy study of capital punishment and war we should acknowledge that God does authorize the taking of human life in these two instances. But even in such circumstances such acts had to be done on the authority of God and not on one's own accord. I find it significant that God establishes an Old Testament civil code to correspond to the moral law which preserves human life. That civil code recognized there may be accidental loss of life. It established a procedure to assure that the loss of life was an accident and that another loss of life might not occur.[10] I believe that civil law gives further evidence of God's high value placed on human life.

Today arrogance has led man to believe that he may circumvent

God's authority over life and death. Mixing sperm and egg in a petri dish, the ability to alter the genetic make-up of life, and the ability to observe and somewhat control fetal development in the womb has given man a sense of power and control over his own destiny, and the destiny of others. Using God-given intellect man evaluates one life against another. Looking at physical and mental maladies that may exist he ignores the possibilities for Christian love and sacrifice and presumes for himself the right to play God and to determine who lives and who dies.

We see indications of this mentality in high places of the scientific community. Following the U.S. Supreme Court decision to legalize abortion Nobel laureate, Dr. James Watson,[11] expressed the opinion that *"If a child were not declared alive until three days after birth, then all parents could be allowed the choice only a few are given under the present system. I believe this view is the only rational, compassionate attitude to have."*[12] Because prenatal testing for fetal handicaps was an expensive and relatively rare procedure he wanted to give parents the legal opportunity to "dispose" of their child should he or she not have the "normal" physical or mental faculties.

As shocking as Watson's statement appears, subsequent revelations show that others had bought into that reasoning. Two doctors at the Yale-New Haven Hospital reported that 43 children died from withheld or withdrawn treatment. They acknowledged that though some would have died eventually, if treated others would have lived.[13]

The much publicized case of Baby Doe in 1982 focused attention on the practice of allowing children to die based upon quality of life standards.[14] While the U.S. Department of Health and Human Services

jumped in to put an end to such activity some medical profssionals defended their actions and boldly reported of their activites. One published report covered in detail the selective killing program in an Oklahoma hospital of spina-bifida patients. The article notes that a quality of life formula was developed and applied to patients resulting in the death of half of those with spina-bifida.[15]

The killing of the incompetent and defenseless in our society not only reflects a growing loss of reverence for the Creator, but it also reflects a loss of purpose to life. That is why another important principle to keep in mind is the recognition that life has a purpose.

Principle #3:

The purpose of life is to glorify God by coming to and growing in faith and to then share that faith with others by our words and examples.

The all-encompassing mission of life is to give God the glory.[16] Intimately tied to giving glory to God is the first principle that I outlined, namely, truly right deeds and decisions can only be made by the Christian from a heart of faith, regardless of its perceived outcome. In other words, giving glory to God is first an act of faith, not of works. That must be stated because one otherwise would attach inordinately greater value to one's physical and mental abilities to "perform for the glory of God" when, in fact, the purpose of life is rooted upon the invisible trait called "faith."

This in no way denies the truth that James wrote.[17] Faith not only produces good works but the believer is compelled to do so.[18] Scripture does not provide us with an "all-inclusive" list of good works. It does,

however, testify that good works are rooted in faith and are consistent with the will of God. What may be good works for one person may be beyond the capabilities of others.[19] The purpose God assigns to life is regardless of its enhanced or diminished quality.

Life is clearly a time to come to faith. It is a one-time opportunity.[20] Ignorance in this point is a root cause in the decline of values that we face today. As people gather around themselves a great number of teachers to tell them what their itching ears want to hear they seek an eternity without hell and life that gives you second chances. There will always be a following for the concept of reincarnation. People will always be attracted to religions without a hell. And one or the other of these notions yield a mentality that encourages the taking of human life — after all, what is there to lose?

Illustrative of this point was the backlash that resulted when the Catholic bishop warned New York Governor Mario Cuomo that he stood in danger of hell should he persist in his public position for abortion rights. Commenting on the incident Senator Patrick Moynihan brushed it off. He felt that Governor Cuomo didn't have to worry about gong to hell. In his own words, "Not many people any longer believe in hell." Representative Charles Rangel went a step further by saying, "I think that Governor Cuomo will be able to hold his own here as well as with St. Peter on Judgment Day. He'll just need a couple of minutes to explain it."[21]

Recognizing the attacks made on the Christian and his faith the believer is not content to sit idly by until his faith has been diminished and destroyed. Instead, he will do all he can to nurture that faith.[22] The Christian will avail himself of the means of grace and receive the continued assurance of his forgiveness.[23]

Consistent with Christian love and the purpose of life to come to faith is the corresponding desire to bring others to faith. The clearest testimony to this point is the Great Commission. It is in light of that commission that all other commands regarding our relationships with others take on a specific mission. Christ told us to *let your light shine before men, that they may see your good deeds and praise your Father in heaven.* (Matthew 5:16) Since only believers glorify God[24] there is a presumption that when "letting your light shine" the Christian does so to bring others to faith in God so they might, in faith, glorify him.[25]

As one considers what is at stake with this purpose in life, he will not lightly dismiss every opportunity to accomplish this mission. Our vanity may tempt us to think we can accomplish this only through our persuasive speech, hard work, and special skills. In reality, however, God uses us as instruments to accomplish his task of bringing others to faith. And, while we may have some attractive skills, the fact of the matter is that God uses us even when we can't uses our skills. If we see ourselves as instruments and not causative agents in bringing about the faith of others it changes our attitude about how we look at misfortune and hardship that inflicts our lives and the lives of those we love. God can use us, regardless of our great abilities or lack of impressive abilities. Regardless of the quality of our life we can still serve God's purpose for life. This brings us to our next principle.

Principle #4:

God demonstrates in his word that while there may be different qualities of life, he extends to all human life an inherent value, being the object of his love and plan for salvation.

God's first demonstration of value placed upon human life was seen in the creation of all things. Man, out of all creation, received that special distinction of being made "in the image of God."[26] God testified that in man was a value that far exceeded any other aspect of his creation. Though man lost that perfect image of God at the fall into sin he nevertheless remained the object of God's attention and special protection above all other created beings.[27]

The consistency of this high value placed upon human life by God is clear from the plan of salvation. Our lives became worthless because of sin. Sin made us unable to please God and earned for us only a justly deserved condemnation in hell.[28] God, however, placed upon man an inherent value. In ethical circles we would call this the quantitative value of human life. Despite the depravity of man before the sinless God there was nevertheless an intrinsic value that sustained God's love and commitment to us. The price he paid to secure our lives eternally is the greatest testimony of God's inherent value he places upon life.[29] God sacrificed his own Son so you and I might be the righteousness of God.[30]

God so values human life that he did not pick the healthy, wealthy and wise as the objects of his salvation. Nor did he pick the poor and unfortunate. The sacrifice he made for sin was universal. Christ died for us all.[31]

Because of this display of highest value for the eternity of all human life it should not surprise us that he is concerned for the earthly life of all people. David was in awe over God's concern for man who seemed so insignificant in the scheme of all things.[32] Peter realized that God does not have favorites in his love for people.[33] Christ was the visible proof of God's love for the unlovable.[34]

As we see God's providence for all people[35] it stands as an example of the high value we should also have for human life. As God has shown love and respect for all human life so ought we. We also should not play favorites.[36] The diminished quality of one's life does not mean that person deserves less love, compassion, and attention. In the eyes of God it certainly is of no lesser value.

Society today approaches life from a qualitative perspective. It compares lives and makes judgments over which life is of a higher quality and which is of a lower quality. I am not prepared to condemn that outright. Scripture readily acknowledges various degrees of quality in human life. From lame Mephibosheth to blind Bartimaeus, we find many examples where the qualitative value of human life is greatly diminished. Never once, however, is it grounds to end a life. Never once is that grounds for showing less love and concern. In fact, a diminished quality of life has been grounds for showing greater love and concern.[37]

The need to show equal concern for all life, recognizing that while its quality may differ all life has inherent value, brings us to the question of suffering.

Principle #5:

While suffering is the result of living in a sinful world, the believer faces it knowing God can use it to display his power, strengthen the sufferer's faith and to provide an avenue for the faith of others to be put into action.

Suffering is an undeniable part of

life in this world. It is clearly testified that suffering is a part of life as we seek to enter the kingdom of God.[38] The disciples rejoiced at suffering for Christ.[39] and Paul suffered as an apostle of Christ.[40] Life in this world of sin means suffering for all of us.[41]

As we face suffering, however, we do so with our purpose for life in mind — that is to give God the glory. God uses our suffering as a means to give him glory. As the disciples pondered the great sins that may have caused a man's blindness Christ used that man's malady to give glory to God, and left no doubt about it.[42] The Apostle Paul used his suffering as a cause to give God glory.[43]

Suffering that comes to our life may be an opportunity God has given us to give him glory. We are all familiar with the passage that says, "But in your hearts set apart Christ as Lord. Always be prepared to give an answer to everyone who asks you to give the reason for the hope that you have. But do this with gentleness and respect," (1 Peter 3:15). Why is anyone going to ask you about the hope that you have? This admonition presumes there is something about the way we are living or coping that is going to prompt someone to ask us how we retain hope.

When we face suffering our response to our predicament is observed by others. When we stand at the side of a suffering loved one or at the casket of a deceased loved one people watch how we react. Paul admonished, *Brothers, we do not want you to be ignorant about those who fall asleep, or to grieve like the rest of men, who have no hope.*" (1 Thessalonians 4:13) A hopeless response will not prompt people to ask you the source of your strength. God can use your suffering to help others.

Suffering, however, is also therapeutic for our own faith. Paul observed that suffering produces a spirit of perseverance.[44] Peter observed that suffering has a way of making us think about God.[45] Hasn't our suffering physically or emotionally many times driven us to our knees before God? When a loved one falls seriously ill we run to God's Word seeking an answer because we know he is the author of life and death. When suffering inflicts our lives we long to hear words of comfort from Scripture to assure us that all is well between us and our God, whom we may face soon.

We must acknowledge, however, that suffering may not be an obvious chance for a person to give glory to God. One's supposed state of incompetence may make suffering of little therapeutic value for one's faith. It still, however, may serve a purpose as an outlet for the faith and love of others. As Christ described the final scene of judgment he described events of misfortune used by believers to show their faith and love.[46] Paul admonishes us that the misfortune of others is to be our concern and something that we should respond to.[47]

The account of the Good Samaritan has always been an easy battle cry to get involved in life issues. One aspect of the story that is seldom examined, however, is the suffering of the man in the ditch. Christ says very little about him. What possible value could there be in his misfortune? It provides the opportunity for the faith and love of others to shine through. The fact that it didn't on the part of the priest and rabbi was to their discredit. His suffering, however, did give an outlet to the compassion of the Samaritan whose example has been an inspiration for millions.

Sometimes the suffering newborn child or the incompetent adult lying in an irreversible coma hooked up to artificial nutrition and hydration is there to be an outlet for our love. Maybe we are holding on to the purse strings so tightly that all we see are dollars going down the drain. If so, the lesson here may be soul-saving by releasing our grip on that which we can't take with us. Perhaps the suffering is to bring a fractured family together. And yes, perhaps it is meant to polarize a family for the ultimate protection of a soul or many souls.

God does not tell us the purpose for all things but he invites our trust.[48] Suffering is a great intrusion on the dream of all people to have a problem-free life. Sufferings are continual reminders for us to have a consistent and Scriptural view of death, confident of what it will bring and the liberation that will be ours.

Principle #6:

A Christian will recognize that sin brought death into this world but Christ changed the nature of death. The Christian longs for death and the paradise it brings with Christ, but he will seek to retain life as a time of faithful service to God until it is clear God wants to take him out of this life.

In a sense death is an unnatural intrusion on life. Death was not part of the order of creation. Man and woman were created to live forever. The violation of God's command, however, has brought death into the world. Today we consider it a natural part of life (like taxes). Because of sin all face death.[49]

God, however, through his son, Jesus Christ, changed the nature of death for the believer. No longer is it something to be feared in ignorance.[50] In fact, it is something we can actually long for.[51]

While Christ has won the victory over death and it is something we can look forward to, it is not, however, something for us to pursue. The principles regarding God as the author of life and death make that point clear. Even Paul, who longed for death, saw life as a time of service.[52]

As Christians, we may emphasize service to God as a part of living. Confidence in God assures us of victory in dying. The story of our victory over death through Christ is a doctrine of comfort. It is the assurance we have as we carry out our purpose in life to give God all glory. It is the confidence in knowing that when our work here is finished there is a reward earned by Christ waiting for us in Heaven.

As I mentioned in the opening, this generation dwells on individual liberty and self-determination. People will, in the name of a right to choose, end the life of an unborn child. In the name of autonomy people wil legally declare that regardless of what others may gain from their suffering they don't want to go through with it. In the name of self-determination people have endangered not only their own lives (and souls), but also the lives of others.[53] Exercising their autonomy people will remain silent about what is right.

God's Word also encourages the practice of autonomy. That practice, however, is always to be hemmed in by the dictates of God. We will make decisions, but not to suit our personal philosophies and goals, but always to reflect the will of God. This world will undoubtedly continue its hellbent path to judgment. As it does Christians need to speak loudly and clearly the truths of God's Word with their own lips and by their own actions. In closing the words of Paul to Timothy are a reminder of what we face and the reponse that is necessary:

"In the presence of God and of Christ Jesus, who will judge the living and the dead, and in view of his appearing and his kingdom, I give you this charge: Preach the Word; be prepared in season and out of season; correct, rebuke and encourage — with great patience and careful instruction. For the time will come when men will not put up with sound doctrine. Instead, to suit their own desires, they will gather around them a great number of teachers to say what their itching ears want to hear. They will turn their ears away from the truth and turn aside to myths. But you, keep your head in all situations, endure hardship, do the work of an evangelist, discharge all the duties of your ministry." (2 Timothy 4:1 - 5)

ENDNOTES

1. "The sinful mind is hostile to God. It does not submit to God's law, nor can it do so." (Romans 8:7) and "For what I do is not the good I want to do; no, the evil I do not want to do — this I keep on doing." (Romans 7:19)
2. Consider on the one hand where Gamaliel's consequentialism was correct, *"Therefore, in the present case I advise you: Leave these men alone! Let them go! For if their purpose or activity is of human origin, it will fail. But if it is from God, you will not be able to stop these men; you will only find yourselves fighting against God."* (Acts 5:38-39). But on the other hand the consequentialism of those around the cross was incorrect, *"He saved others,"* they said, *"but he can't save himself! He's the King of Israel! Let him come down now from the cross, and we will believe in him."* (Matthew 27:42)
3. "Without faith it is impossible to please God." (Hebrews 11:6)
4. Adam lay with his wife Eve, and she *became pregnant and gave birth* to Cain." (Genesis 4:1) and "So in the course of time Hannah *conceived and gave birth* to a son. She named him Samuel." (I Samuel 1:20)
5. Surely I was sinful at birth, sinful from

the time my mother conceived me." (Psalms 51:5)
6. The Hebrew word used here for *conceived* is the Piel perfect of *yichem*. It is derived from the word *chemah* which means *hot*. The Hebrew understood conception to be related to the heat of passion in intercourse and not to some other later parts of the pregnancy. See Genesis 30:41 and Genesis 31:10 for the infinitive absolute of this word.
7. People were also bringing *babies* to Jesus to have him touch them. When the disciples saw this, they rebuked them. (Luke 18:15)
8. When Elizabeth heard Mary's greeting, the *baby* leaped in her womb, and Elizabeth was filled with the Holy Spirit. (Luke 1:41) and "As soon as the sound of your greeting reached my ears, the *baby* in my womb leaped for joy." (Luke 1:44)
9. "My times are in your hands; deliver me from my enemies and from those who pursue me." (Psalm 31:15)
10. "This is the rule concerning the man who kills another and flees there to save his life — one who kills his neighbor unintentionally, without malice aforethought. For instance, a man may go into the forest with his neighbor to cut wood, and as he swings his ax to fell a tree, the head may fly off and hit his neighbor and kill him. That man may flee to one of these cities and save his life. Otherwise, the avenger of blood might pursue him in a rage, overtake him if the distance is too great, and kill him even though he is not deserving of death, since he did it to his neighbor without malice aforethought. This is why I command you to set aside for yourselves three cities." (Deuteronomy 19:4-7)
11. Dr. Watson, together with Francis Crick, won the Nobel prize in 1957 for discovering the double helix in DNA. Today Dr. Watson is head of the Human Genome Project, a $3 billion project funded by tax dollars through the National Institute of Health established to map out the complete genetic structure of the human species. It is hoped that this

will enable the scientific community to identify potential genetic defects and lead to cures for such diseases as cystic fibrosis, sickle cell anemia, and others. The project is expected to take 10 - 12 years and has raised many ethical concerns over how this knowledge will be used.

12. *Prism*, May, 1973.

13. *New England Journal of Medicine*, October 25, 1973.

14. *Baby Doe* was born on Good Friday in 1982 in a Bloomington, Indiana, hospital. He had an opening between his feeding and breathing tube which was repairable. Baby Doe, however, also had Down Syndrome. In consultation with their doctor and pastor the parents determined that their child would not lead a *quality* life because of his retardation and for that reason refused to have the corrective surgery on his throat. This meant that Baby Doe could not consume food or water. Despite numerous legal attempts Baby Doe died, legally, six days later of dehydration and starvation.

15. *Pediatrics*, October, 1983.

16. "So whether you eat or drink or whatever you do, do it all for the glory of God." (I Corinthians 10:31)

17. "In the same way, faith by itself, if it is not accompanied by action, is dead." (James 2:17)

18. "For we cannot help speaking about what we have seen and heard." (Acts 4:20)

19. God gives various physical, mental and spiritual abilities to equip a believer to help work in the church. *"It was he who gave some to be apostles, some to be prophets, some to be evangelists, and some to be pastors and teachers."* (Ephesians 4:11) He gives others varying financial abilities to support the Lord's work. *"But a poor widow came and put two very small copper coins, worth only a fraction of a penny. Calling his disciples to him, Jesus said, 'I tell you the truth, this poor widow has put more into the treasury than all the others.'"* (Mark 12:42-43) But whatever the financial, mental or physical predicament may be all that we do is to be by faith to the glory of God. *"We have different gifts, according to the grace given us. If a man's gift is prophesying, let him use it in proportion to his faith. If it is serving, let him serve; if it is teaching, let him teach; if it is encouraging, let him encourage; if it is contributing to the needs of others, let him give generously; if it is leadership, let him govern diligently; if it is showing mercy, let him do it cheerfully."* (Romans 12:6 - 8)

20. "Just as man is destined to die once, and after that to face judgment." (Hebrews 9:27)

21. Reported in a February, 1990, issue of the *New York Post*.

22. "Instead, speaking the truth in love, we will in all things grow up into him who is the Head, that is, Christ." (Ephesians 4:15)

23. "Consequently, faith comes from hearing the message, and the message is heard through the word of Christ." (Romans 10:17)

24. "That if you confess with your mouth, 'Jesus is Lord,' and believe in your heart that God raised him from the dead, you will be saved." (Romans 10:9) and "Therefore I tell you that no one who is speaking by the Spirit of God says, 'Jesus be cursed,' and no one can say, 'Jesus is Lord,' except by the Holy Spirit." (I Corinthians 12:3)

25. "Live such good lives among the pagans that, though they accuse you of doing wrong, they may see your good deeds and glorify God on the day he visits us." (1 Peter 2:12)

26. "Then God said, 'Let us make man in our image, in our likeness, and let them rule over the fish of the sea and the birds of the air, over the livestock, over all the earth, and over all the creatures that move along the ground.'" (Genesis 1:26)

27. "Whoever sheds the blood of man, by man shall his blood be shed; for in the image of God has God made man." (Genesis 9:6)

28., "for all have sinned and fall short of the glory of God." (Romans 3:23)

29. "For you know that it was not with perishable things such as silver or gold that you were redeemed from the empty way of life handed down to you from your forefathers, but with the precious blood of Christ, a lamb without blemish or defect." (1 Peter 1:18-19)

30. "God made him who had no sin to be sin for us, so that in him we might become the righteousness of God." (2 Corinthians 5:21)

31. "For God so loved *the world* that he gave his one and only Son, that whoever believes in him shall not perish but have eternal life." (John 3:16) and "He is the atoning sacrifice for our sins, and not only for ours but also for the sins of *the whole world*." (1 John 2:2)

32. "When I consider your heavens, the work of your fingers, the moon and the stars, which you have set in place, what is man that you are mindful of him, the son of man that you care for him?" (Psalms 8:3-4)

33. "Then Peter began to speak: 'I now realize how true it is that God does not show favoritism.'" (Acts 10:34)

34. "Great crowds came to him, bringing the lame, the blind, the crippled, the mute and many others, and laid them at his feet; and he healed them." (Matthew 15:30)

35. "He causes his sun to rise on the evil and the good, and sends rain on the righteous and the unrighteous." (Matthew 5:45)

36. "My brothers, as believers in our glorious Lord Jesus Christ, don't show favoritism." (James 2:1)

37. "Speak up for those who cannot speak for themselves, for the rights of all who are destitute. Speak up and judge fairly; defend the rights of the poor and needy." (Proverbs 31:8 - 9)

38. "We must go through many hardships to enter the kingdom of God." (Acts 14:22)

39. "The apostles left the Sanhedrin, rejoicing because they had been counted worthy of suffering disgrace for the Name." (Acts 5:41)

40. "Remember Jesus Christ, raised from the dead, descended from David. This is my gospel, for which I am suffering even to the point of being chained like a criminal. But God's word is not chained." (2 Timothy 2:8-9)

41. "I tell you the truth, you will weep and mourn while the world rejoices. You will grieve, but your grief will turn to joy." (John 16:20)

42. "'Neither this man nor his parents sinned,' said Jesus, 'but this happened so that the work of God might be displayed in his life.'" (John 9:3)

43. "But he said to me, 'My grace is sufficient for you, for my power is made perfect in weakness.' Therefore I will boast all the more gladly about my weakness, so that Christ's power may rest on me." (2 Corinthians 12:9)

44. "Not only so, but we also rejoice in our sufferings, because we know that suffering produces perseverance;" (Romans 5:3)

45. "For it is commendable if a man bears up under the pain of unjust suffering because he is conscious of God." (1 Peter 2:19)

46. "The King will reply, 'I tell you the truth, whatever you did for one of the least of these brothers of mine, you did for me.'" (Matthew 25:40)

47. "Do nothing out of selfish ambition or vain conceit, but in humility consider others better than yourselves. Each of you should look not only to your own interests, but also to the interests of others." (Philippians 2:3 - 4)

48. "Be still before the LORD and wait patiently for him." (Psalm 37:7) and "Be still, and know that I am God." (Psalms 46:10)

49. "Therefore, just as sin entered the world through one man, and death through sin, and in this way death came to all men, because all sinned — " (Romans 5:12).

50. "Brothers, we do not want you to be ignorant about those who fall asleep, or to grieve like the rest of men, who have no hope. We believe that Jesus died and rose again and so we believe that God will bring with Jesus those who have fallen asleep in him." (1 Thessalonians 4:13 - 14)

51. "I am torn between the two: I desire to depart and be with Christ, which is better by far;" (Philippians 1:23)

52. "I am torn between the two: I desire to depart and be with Christ, which is better by far; but it is more neces-sary for you that I remain in the body. Convinced of this, I know that I will remain, and I will continue with all of you for your progress and joy in the faith." (Philippians 1:23 - 25)

53. In a publication called *Withhold Treatment from Defective Newborn Children* the authors present an article entitled, *Giving the Hemlock: A Policy Proposal.* In it they point out that the right to self-determination is a fundamental "common law" right extended to all citizens. All citizens are also to be able to enjoy all rights. In the case of the incompetent they enjoy that right by proxy. As it specifically applies to children a parent is the proxy for the child. The authors observe that because all people, under the right of self-determination, can dictate their own medical treatment and even choose to kill themselves, then such rights should be enjoyed by the incompetent as well. They proceed to reason out that in the case of a *radically defective neonate* (i.e., severely handicapped newborn child) it would not be an unfair presumption that if the child were competent he would choose to refuse further medical treatment and suicide to end further suffering. The authors then argued for the parents' right, as proxies for the child, to choose suicide for the child.

ENDNOTES
(Continued from page 72)

32. Davis, John Jefferson, "Concerning the Case of 'Mr. Stevens'," *Issues in Law and Medicine*, Vol. 7, Fall, 1991, p. 241.

33. McCormick, Brian, "Not Enough Data on Lives, Costs," *American Medical News*, January 7, 1991, p. 23.

34. Ramsey, Paul, **The Patient as Person**, p. 161.

35. *Ibid.*, p. 162.

36. It might be argued by some that the mere receiving of the nutrition by the physical body is a good in itself without regard to the patient's consciousness. This would be true if there were any reasonable possibility that consciousness would be regained. Since that is not the case with patients in a permanent PVS, the mere maintenance of bodily life is futile. The maintenance of organic life is instrumental to the conscious personal life for which God created us. For a good treatment of this issue, see John Jefferson Davis, "Concerning the Case of 'Mr. Stevens'," *Issues in Law and Medicine*, Vol. 7, Fall, 1991, pp. 237 - 240.

The opinions expressed in this article are the author's and do not necessarily reflect the official positions or policies of the United States Navy.

Defining a Christian Doctor

Spiros A. Lazarou, M.D.

A graduate of University of Maryland Medical School, Dr. Lazarou has completed residencies in general surgery, and plastic and reconstructive surgery, and is now engaged in a fellowship in craniofacial surgery in Pittsburgh. He is Greek Orthodox.

This essay will outline some principles and concepts that would distinguish a Christian doctor's worldview from the current neopagan one. Though the theme is not completely developed some implications for one who wishes to practice medicine as a Christian should become clearer. In writing the following I make no pretentions that I am close to achieving this goal.

A Christian View of History

The Christian doctor does not practice in a vacuum. A brief description of his setting in its historical and eschatological light is in order.

The poison and tragedy of the Fall lies in the fact that Satan wrenched all things from their union and communion with God. He did not and could not create another world, a new man, a new language or anything new. The devil took the same man and the same words and made their reference point something other than the living God. Satan thus usurped God's design for man and things and converted them into instruments of evil.

The servants of God and those of Satan are alike in that they are both fallen image-bearers of God with the same urges, impulses, and language. However, if analyzed according to their presuppositions, one servant's reference point is the living God of the Bible with whom he has been restored to a living relationship; the other's reference point is himself. Both speak about God and salvation, love and hate, good and evil, health and disease but from two radically different reference points. Both men are made in the image of God and will live as prophet, priest and king but one does so to the glory of God and the other to the glory of man.[1]

In other words, Satan established a counterfeit kingdom. The Kingdom of God and the kingdom of Satan stand in opposition not primarily on moralistic grounds, but on where glory is given. The difference between the believer and the unbeliever is not one of degree but one of kind. Unredeemed man as the fallen image bearer of God is still acting as prophet, priest and king. But his basic impulse is to be as God, to build a city and make a name for himself; to build a kingdom on his own terms and to derive his identity apart from a relationship with the living God. He seeks to be autonomous. (Again, the unbeliever is also concerned with compassion, the poor, the homeless, etc. But, in the name of these things he has perpetrated monstrosities, e.g., Marxism. This is why the Kingdom of God begins in the hearts of men with repentance and faith.)

But, redeemed man, recreated man, restored man, as prophet, priest and king in Christ has rejected this autonomy. He now is able to continue, though imperfectly because of the continued effects of sin, the mandate given him in the Garden — to subdue the earth thereby establishing the kingdom of heaven on earth; to build the city of God thereby living in community; to live in love as self-sacrifice and thanksgiving, the life of liturgy, of sacrament. Thus, he redeems the culture from the effects of the Fall.

Jesus' concern was not merely the salvation of men's souls but the establishment of God's Kingdom which includes men's souls but is much more comprehensive. His concern includes the totality of existence — man and his entire habitat and culture. The Kingdom of Heaven is simply the restoration of all creation into union and communion with God. It is the referral of all things back to God. It is the future in the present. It is here, but not fully. It is the task of the Church, the body of Christ, to complete this work. The historical and eschatological dimensions of the Church — the entrance into the Kingdom — meet in the sacrament.[2] In its task of reconciling the world to God, the Church is involved in history but not simply as an activist. The Church sanctifies time by revealing its true significance and its consummation in the Kingdom as she refers all things to God — restoration.

One implication of all this is immediately clear. Science and medicine are not neutral with respect to God. God has interpreted all things with respect to Himself. Truth therefore exists (i.e., is perceived) when all things are seen in their right relationship to God. Modern science and medicine boast neutrality with respect to God (secularism) but this boast is untrue. The real issue is whether one adheres to the science of Christianity or the science of secularism.

The foregoing is the setting in which a Christian physician ministers. It should be obvious from the start that the Christian physician is involved in a conflict. Two kingdoms are locked in a life and death struggle. God ordained a titanic spiritual war in the Garden between the seed of the woman and the seed of Satan (Gen. 3:15). The continuous wars between Old Testament Israel and all other nations which are portrayed as the enemies of God are the types and shadows of New Testament Israel's (the Church) struggles against the forces of darkness (Eph 6:12).

Indeed, Christ did not come to bring peace but a sword (Matt 10:34), and Paul reminds us to live as soldiers at war (Eph 6:10-18). The Christian (physician) is *de facto* a soldier at war.

The Christian Mindset Presently

Having briefly described a Christian view of history, of reality, we must now add one more thing: a brief description of the Christian mindset presently.

Over the past few years there has been a renewed interest in religion, in "spirituality." Yet in the midst of this renewed interest in Christianity sin abounds. The values unremittingly opposed to Christianity are also on the increase. This startling situation is made possible because many Christians compartmentalize our faith, relegating it to one of life's many activities. Few of us are serious about our faith. We pray, worship, study the Bible, etc., But in the workplace with our colleagues and in the public square we do not speak candidly about what motivates our plans and policies — because we are in a secular environment. This tendency is augmented as Zizioulas points out, by a tendency in Orthodoxy, because of our emphasis on the eschatological, to disincarnate the Church. The danger here is that a mindset develops in which the Scriptures are not understood as having much to say in, for example, the fields of psychology or medicine or law, etc. This means an inevitable turning to nonchristian sources.[3]

On the other hand the dangerous tendency of the West is to historicize the Church, i.e., to emphasize the Church's role in the present as an activist body rather than as a manifestation of the *eschata* — the future in the present. Western theology tends to limit ecclesiology to the historical content of the faith — to the economy. The Church ceases to be a manifestation of the *eschata*, and ecclesial being and the being of God

are no longer organically bound. The Church is reduced to a "God-ordained" institution on equal footing with other such institutions (e.g., state, family). But the Church is more than this. It is the New Israel, the body of Christ, a new nation, a royal priesthood.

Either way, the result is an artificial dichotomy between the sacred and the secular. There are "Christian" topics or activities and then there is the world at large which we evaluate in secular terms. A spiritual schizophrenia results in which believers bounce between their secular and Christian mentalities as their conversation changes from the business to sanctification.

Such categorizing might be acceptable if Christianity were nothing more than a set of profound teachings. But Christianity asserts itself as the central fact of human history. The Creator of all things visible and invisible, of man himself, invaded the world in the person of Jesus Christ, died, was resurrected, ascended, and lives sovereign over all. Christianity is the central truth from which all behavior, relationships, and philosophy must flow. There is no sphere of life to which God has not spoken. Christianity bears on every aspect of life.

The modern "Christian" has succumbed to secularization. He accepts the morality, worship and spiritual culture of Christianity as religion but rejects the Christian view of life, the view that sets all earthly issues in the light of the eternal. As a result of this failure to apply truth to life, the secular mind-set enjoys a virtually unchallenged monopoly in the forum of public debate.

In March, 1986, the *Journal of the American Medical Association* published an article entitled "On the Death of Jesus Christ" which described the medical causes of Christ's death. The editors promptly received angry letters for publishing "religious" material. The article did not assert that Christ was resurrected, merely that he lived and was crucified. Few, if any, would discount this historical fact. Yet the hysterical response illustrates how defensive secularists can become when their monopoly on the mainstream of cultural communication is challenged.

The Object of Medicine

Disease, suffering, aging — dying, the growth of death in us — and death itself entered the world when sin entered the world; when man made his reference point something other than the life-giving, life-sustaining God (Gen. 2:17; Rom 6:23). Man in his state of sin and, thus, his state of decay, disintegration — man in his process of aging, ugliness, disease and death — this is the object of medicine.

Man's intellect, will and emotions have been corrupted and his body heads inexorably to decay and disintegration. God, however, in His infinite mercy ordained the healing ministry for He declares to the people, "I am the Lord your healer" (Ex 15:26). This is a ministry of life and healing — a ministry that is redemptive in its scope as it speaks to ameliorating the effects of the Fall and the curses therein. The pseudointellectuals of our time ignore the relationship of the Fall to suffering, sickness, and death. They have uncovered God's ordinary agencies such as bacteria, genes, cholesterol, and the like; but the authors of the Bible do not hesitate to ascribe to God the ultimate

cause as well as show its relationship to sin (Ex 4:11, Lev 26:16, Deut 28:21, Ps 107:17, 2 Sam 12:15, 2 Chron 26:20, Ps 103:3, I Cor 11:30). Modern man operates on the assumption that man is at least neutral morally, if not good. Implied is the notion that man does not deserve his suffering. But this assumption also strips suffering of its meaning and strips the cross of its victory.

At this point the issue of suffering needs to be addressed. The twin perspective of God as healer and afflicter, whether through the Devil (Job) or directly, is shown when Job speaks to the Almighty: "For He wounds, but He binds up; He smites but His hands heal" (5:18). However, this very same book shows that there is not an inevitable connection between individual sickness and personal wrongdoing. It is not that Job was sinless but that there was not a causal link between his illness and his sin. Jesus corroborates this in John 9:3 as does James in 5:14-16. [James says, "if."]

Our culture is preoccupied with suffering and death. Or, rather, it is preoccupied with the denial of it. Numerous institutions have sprouted to neatly hide it all — nursing homes, hospitals, hospices, funeral homes. All are unobtrusive, efficient, tidy. Man lives for the moment, the weekend. You only go around once ... go for it ... and the man of the hour, the man appointed to do something, to help, is the physician. It does not matter that the best epidemiologic studies have shown only a marginally beneficial effect of medicine on longevity and health. Many have previously addressed this. For false religion, whether secular or theistic, the final criteria is to help — thoroughly utili-

tarian. But for Christianity the final criteria is Truth. In the words of Schmemann, "The purpose of Christianity is not to help people by reconciling them with death, but to reveal the Truth about life and death, in order that people might be saved by this Truth."

An Orthodox Christian view of life which embraces a vision of the sacramentality of life and therefore of our suffering and death is paramount.

Sacrament is passage, transformation; not from the natural to the supernatural but from the old to the new. It is passage from the Kingdom of Man and death into the Kingdom of God and life, the world to come, into the very reality of this world and its life as redeemed and restored by Christ. And healing is a "sacrament" because its purpose or end is not health as such, the restoration of physical health, but the entrance of man into the life of the Kingdom, into the "joy and peace" of the Holy Spirit. In Christ everything in this world, and this means health and disease, joy and suffering, has become an ascension to and entrance into this new life, its expectation and anticipation.

In this world suffering and disease are indeed "normal," but their normalcy is abnormal. They reveal the ultimate and permanent defeat of man and of life, a defeat which no partial victories of medicine, however wonderful and truly miraculous, can ultimately overcome. But in Christ suffering is not "removed," it is transformed into victory. The defeat itself becomes a victory, a way, an entrance into the Kingdom, and this is the only true healing. Here is a man suffering on his bed of pain and the Church comes to him to perform the sacrament of healing. For this man as for every man in the whole world, suffering can be defeat, the way of complete surrender to darkness, despair, alienation and solitude. It can be dying in the very real sense of the word. And yet it can also be the ultimate victory of man and of life in him. The Church does not come to restore "health" in this man, simply to replace medicine when medicine has exhausted its possibilities. The Church comes to take this man into the Love, Light and Life of Christ. It comes not merely to "comfort" him in his sufferings. A martyr is one who beholds "the heavens opened, and the Son of Man standing at the right hand of God" (Acts 7:56). A martyr is one for whom God is not another — and the last — chance to stop the awful pain; God is his very life, and thus everything in his life comes to God, and ascends to the fullness of Love.

Suffering remains in this world no matter how far from it we run. Yet Christ says, "be of good cheer, I have overcome the world" (Jn 16:33). Through His own suffering, not only has all suffering acquired a meaning but it has been given the power to become itself the sign, the sacrament, the proclamation, the "coming" of that victory, the defeat of man, his very dying has become a way of Life.

The prescriptions for healing that God laid out in the Old Testament as well as the New affirm these truths. In Leviticus 13 and 14 the priest was appointed by God to diagnose and treat certain infectious diseases. It is beyond our scope to fully develop the significance of this legislation but a few points are in order.

Disease, like death, is an abhorrence to God, an abnormality, a product of the Fall, a reminder of our falleness. The law did not make an artificial distinction between physical well-being and spiritual vitality, exalting one at the expense of the other. It required that the true Israelite should be an integrated person whose spirituality involves all areas of his life. The real message of the legislation is that any type of uncleaness separates the believer from God. The leper would be cut off from spiritual fellowship with the covenant people and in a real sense would be without hope and without God in the world. Cure meant restoration to fellowship with his family and the whole community. Blood was shed as a part of the purifying ritual. Similarly, the shedding of Christ's blood on the cross reconciles man to God and makes it possible for the sinner to join the household of faith.

In James 5:14-16 the elder oversees the health problem. In both cases the primary function of the Church, as represented by the priest and the elder, is to place the disease in its proper light, i.e., its ultimate and/or proximate relation to sin, the protection of the community because of the infectious nature of disease/sin, the restoration of the covenant child to the community life and worship and fellowship with God. The spirit of the Old remains though the letter has passed away as the Old Covenants have been consummated in the New Covenant of Jesus Christ. The grace ineffable that is spurned today is that, in Christ Jesus, the ill have immediate recourse; immediate forgiveness, restoration, and reconciliation; immediate fellowship with the community and God. Here is the significance of the Sacrament of Healing. We pass from fallenness to exaltation; from defeat to victory; from disease and suffering to health and joy; from alienation to restoration. The sacrament that the Church performs merely encapsulates ceremonially the nature of the physician's practice as he ministers health to his patient.

A Definition of Health: The Objective of Medicine

At the most basic level is God's command to us to do all that we do to His glory (I Cor. 10:31). What does it mean to glorify God? In the Hebrew "glory" means "weight." We can't add weight to God since all that exists is His. Rather, it means to bring to bear the full weight of God's relationship to all things. Therefore, if I am to practice medicine to the glory of God I must do more than say that this is the case, for Christianity is not magic. Something does not glorify God because I say it does, regardless of my motivations. Rather, when I practice medicine in such a way that I apply biblical principles, that is, His Word, to fully bear on it, then I glorify God. We must therefore develop a Christian view of health.

Thus health is a wholistic concern. Jesus exemplified this and so does the language of Scripture. The Greek word translated "salvation" and that translated "healing" in many of Jesus' miracles is from the same root word "sozein." The truly saved man was saved inside and out.[4] Of the ten lepers that were healed, only the one that came back and gave thanks to God is said to be saved or healed. He was made whole. This wholeness is James' concern in his epistle 1:4.

As Jesus makes clear when He healed the paralytic brought down through the roof, true health is much more than the absence of disease. It begins internally with forgiveness of sins and a restored fellowship with God. It has to begin that way because disease and death entered the world when sin destroyed that fellowship. Christ's words corroborate the Old Testament. He alone had the power to forgive sin and restore the sinner.

In addition to the verb *sozein* noted above, the Bible uses *therapeusein* and *iasthai* as words for "heal." The former is used freely of Jesus' healing miracles. It is applied to healing diseases. Its root meaning is of "service," often of "worship" of God (Acts 17:25). The latter is also a general word for "heal" but unlike the former it is also used metaphorically of spiritual regeneration or restoration.

Since health has to do with the totality of creation — with the Creator himself — health cannot be equated merely with wellness or the absence of disease. If health in this wholesome, God-centered sense is our ultimate objective, then, by definition, we are declaring our "unhealth." So what does it mean for one to be healed of, say, a duodenal ulcer, depression, a broken marriage, a resolutely nursed grievance or a hurtful childhood memory?

Perhaps it would be helpful if we did not speak of healing so much as a cure. This would be appropriate within the primarily physical framework of much of our work. Indeed, today's healing is not aimed at the total man but cure of the disease. To announce the cure of a peptic ulcer would mean a restoration to function whereas to announce a healing would imply something more far-reaching — a restoration to purposeful living. We might say that the individual's

relationship to God has been revived. He now stands in a position to bring glory to God, having discovered a new zest for living as a responsible member of his parish, community, family, etc.

The Scriptures primarily address issues of health over and above cure. One might say what does it profit a man to have his cure and lose his soul? Christianity does not idolize life or comfort. Indeed, the way of love, of self-sacrifice, is to lay down one's life as our Lord did. the Christian does not sacrifice Truth for life. He does not steal or lie or do "everything" to save it. He does not bankrupt his family or pilfer public funds to maintain life at any cost. The Christian worships the living God and nothing else.

Christ, God incarnate, is the Great Physician. His healing ministry was part and parcel of His overall mission to God's needy world. Jesus came to reveal the Father through His words and His works. The comprehensiveness of Jesus' ministry is implied in His name. Jesus (Greek) or Joshua means deliverance from and to.

Jesus did not use the spells, incantations, conjurations, hypnosis, casting people into the deep sleep of "incubation," miracles of punishment, etc., that the Greek physicians of His day used. His healings were in the open and beautiful in their simplicity. Indeed, it is important to note the public nature of Jesus' healing. Almost all were done in full view of the community. This demanded a verdict from both the healed as well as the onlookers (Jn 20:31,31). The patient is restored to the community. The all-embracing nature of His healing of whole crowds, without comment many

times on the faith of the healed, convinces that His power over disease, and not individual faith, is the arbiter of recovery. This conceptualization is not to denigrate the importance of faith in the equation (Mk 5:34, Matt. 13:58).

Perhaps at this point it is worth noting that God — the Trinity — is a community. He is the one and the many. Man separated from God is separated from men and even divided in himself. He is man in isolation, alienation and death. True health begins in restoration to communion with God which manifests itself concretely in restoration to communion with the new humanity, the body of Christ.

Although Jesus' miracles were motivated by love and compassion we also have the dawning of a new age — the establishment of the Kingdom of God. His ministry was eschatological. He preached the Kingdom of God neither solely as a present reality nor exclusively as a future event. This is true of salvation/health in their broad dimensions. The Lord's casting out of demons predicts the Adversary's final defeat. His raising from the dead is a foretaste of the conquest of death. His healings anticipate the time when there shall be neither "mourning nor crying nor pain anymore" (Rev. 21:4). As a witness to this coming Kingdom, health and cures have dramatically improved in those nations where the Gospel has taken hold. The power of Jesus to restore true health has been entrusted to the Church, the body of Christ. True health involves the wellness of the total man and begins with repentance and restoration to fellowship with God.

Health and secularism

The unbeliever certainly understands health as a broad concept. The health industry is permeating every sphere of life and is the fastest growing industry despite the recession according to the *Wall Street Journal*. What are some of the forces propelling this?

Secularism is a worldview drawn from things "under the sun," to use Solomon's description. It interprets the temporal in light of the temporal rather than in light of the eternal and leads to pessimism and despair. Life becomes a treadmill of meaningless cycles. This interpretation is the form of today's Kingdom of Satan. As a counterfeit kingdom it corresponds to the Kingdom of God at every point. But the idolatrous nature of secularism, unlike its forerunners is insipid because the idols are not obvious to the naked eye.

The State takes on divine proportions in a world without God and the fallen image-bearers of God, cut off from any meaningful relationship with their Creator, will naturally look to the next "best" alternative for the solutions to their ills. The State is the only real option, and politics is the method of conjuring solutions from this many-tentacled deity. The State is the primary idol of power; our Father.

But there are other deities in secularism. An institution surrounding one of those deities is the "Church of Modern Medicine." This deity, the last enemy, is Death. We have already noted the culture's obsession with death. This fear of death catapults it into an idol and the physician is the man appointed to intercede on behalf of the patient. It is this fear of death that fuels the Church of Mod-

ern Medicine and the continuous expansion of the "health" industry. The institution of modern medicine and its priest, the physician, could not exist apart from the faith that modern man places in it.[5] This is evident in that few of the vast number of procedures performed and pills prescribed have ever been conclusively proven to be of benefit to health. If you ask, "Why?" enough times in medicine you eventually come to the Chasm of Faith.

As the culture moves further away from its Christian heritage, medicine as a ministry of life and health is being transformed into a ministry of death and exploitation. Modern medicine's definition of health is increasingly one that involves the complete disappearance of discomfort, suffering, pain, sacrifice. Having discredited the old God — the God of Life — as a cause of all our ills, modern medicine offers us a new God that can counteract all the pesky forms of life that inhabit our "quality of life," such as bacteria, viruses, genes, inconvenient fetuses, deformed or retarded children and old people.

Since the ultimate end of secularism is to exalt man, the modern physician sits on the pedestal of God and heals in his own name. He does not give due glory to God. To legitimize and further this new motif a new myth had to develop. On the surface, a myth is the illusion of an age or a culture whereby life and its origins are interpreted. As such the myth has an axiomatic truth to the age and is its criterion for judging and assessing reality.

But much more is involved in the concept of myth. A myth is the attempt of a culture to overcome history, to negate the forces and ravages

of time and to make the universe amenable and subject to man. Myth reveals a hatred of history. History shows movement in terms of forces beyond man and in judgment over man; is inescapably ethical, shows a continuing conflict between good and evil and clearly shows man to be the actor not the playwright and director. And this subjugation man hates. To fill a role he never wrote, to enter on stage at a time not of his choosing, this, man resents. The purpose man sets for himself in his myths is to end history, to make man the absolute governor by decreeing an end to the movement that is history. Where his myths acknowledge man's lot in history, man ascribes his sorry role, not to his depravity and sin, but to the jealousy of the gods. The goal of the myth more clearly enunciated in time, has become the destruction of history and the enthronement of man as the governor of the universe.

The means used by man to accomplish the goal of his myth is magic. The purpose of magic is the total control of man over man, nature and the supernatural. Whatever the form magic takes, this is its goal. Under the influence of Christianity, science escaped from magic. The purpose of science and medicine ceased gradually to be an attempt to play God and became rather the exercise of dominion over the earth under God. Redeemed man is God's vicegerent over the earth, and science is one of man's tools in establishing and furthering that dominion. For science to overstep that role is to forsake science for magic. The purposes of modern science are increasingly those of magic, the exercise of total control. Magic has thus again triumphed, and modern science is popular precisely because man today, wedded again to the world of myth, demands magic to overcome history, to eliminate the ethical struggle and to place man beyond good and evil, beyond judgment ... and death. On the whole, modern science has taken readily to this new role, and scientists and physicians are enjoying their new role as magicians to modern man.

Science thus has become magic, preoccupied as it is with the mystique of technique, ritual, precise formulations and a language of its own and is governed by myth. Indeed, what modern medicine holds increasingly more sacred are not human lives but mechanical processes and interventionist technological wizardry. This unhappy situation is made more difficult by the fact that the Church, frequently predisposed to accept contemporary mythologies, is today a particularly devout exponent of and adherent to the myth of the age, pockets of resistance from the remnant notwithstanding.

Within the context of this paradigm shift another principle has been imposed, the idea of progress. To this presupposition, Charles Darwin gave substance in his classical formulation of that myth which summed all the basic presuppositions of the modern spirit, the doctrine of evolution. Essential to this concept of progress was its anti-theological nature: it was a revolt from the sovereign and all sufficient God who by His predestinating will and eternal counsel brought all things to pass. The predestinating will of God is replaced by the predestinating will of nature. And in the next to the last paragraph of the *Origin of Species*, Darwin informs us that " ... as natural selection works solely by and for the good of each being, all corporeal and

mental endowments will tend toward progress toward perfection." This formulation, then, is the 'scientific' version of Romans 8:28, "For we know that all things work together for good to them that love God, to them that are the called according to His purpose." Thus, evolution must have the total scope of God's eternal decree with none of His existence, controls and requirements! Better a world without meaning than a world without God.

This belief, of course, is a recrudescence of the ancient concept of all life as a chain of being ultimately linked to God dynamically, in a scientific formulation. But the Kingdom of Satan has matured. The present formulation exposes man as the pinnacle — as God. Nature is god and as nature perfects man, man, the scientist, harnesses nature to conquer disease, death, man, finally even triumphing over nature itself only to spend eternity exploring space. The scientist becomes nature's tool to speed the process of man's perfected state. And the State is the essential means by which scientific man speeds along this process.

Church and state are distinct institutions when Christianity is strong. When this is not the case, the two tend to merge. In cultures where unbelief is high and statism is strong the Church of Modern Medicine is merged with the State — "socialized medicine" or "national health care." It is the State's work of benevolence — the Savior it provides its people. (Process and technology are the Holy Spirit, the instrument that mediates this salvation in our lives.) The State's current involvement in medicine cannot be dealt with here. However, suffice it to say that the State's poli-

tics of control, indoctrination, and conditioning could not occur without the sanction of modern medicine.

Man's calling is to exercise dominion under God over nature, to rule it, develop it, and exploit it under God and to His glory. Only regenerate man in Jesus Christ can do this. Fallen man is in captivity to his own nature and to the forces around him. Where men are not ruled by God they are ruled by tyrants. And the rise of evolutionary thinking has produced a world-wide rise of totalitarianism. Since man is no longer seen as a creation by God, he is becoming a creature of the total state, and the total state is determined to remake man in its own image. As a result man is now the primary experimental animal. People are alarmed at the use of animals in scientific experimentation. But the grim reality is that the primary experimental animal is man. Not only the mental health experts, but virtually every agency of civil government is today engaged in trying to remake man. When man, as in evolutionary thinking, is a product of nature, his being is determined by nature, and his psychology is passive, conditioned, a reflex action rather than a governing action.

Another way in which evolutionary thinking has altered the mind of man is with respect to responsibility. Whereas in Scripture the predestinating activity of God establishes liberty and responsibility, evolution strips man of it. His environment made him. Man is not a sinner but a victim. The means, therefore, of changing man is not regeneration, not moral responsibility and renewal, but changing his environment, which requires a Pavlovian world.

Thus, education ceases to be education; it becomes brainwashing and conditioning. Responsibility disappears. All becomes other's fault: father, mother, poverty, riches, little discipline, much discipline, etc.

This approach is consistent with the quality of life ethic. The doctor's responsibility becomes the removal of the circumstance that hampers the quality of one's life or that engender ill feelings. The assumption is that circumstances determine feelings and that feelings are the final criteria of truth and success. But, biblically, such is not the case. Feelings are our habituated responses to circumstances and are not the final criteria of truth or success. Our feelings about anything are ultimately the product of deeply ingrained beliefs. For this reason God does not call us to change our feelings but our thinking. He calls us to the renewing of our minds and obedience. As these changes take place the appropriate feelings will follow. For example, it is not a patient's small breasts that are making her feel bad about herself. Rather, it is her deepest convictions, the worldview by which she interprets the significance of her small breasts that produces her feelings.

Modern man assumes that he is basically good and consequently should not feel bad about himself. The Bible teaches something different. It teaches that man is a sinner living in rebellion to God and that evil is a product of sinful man's sinful choices. Jesus told the rich young man that no one but God is good. In Genesis 6:5, God tells us that every thought and inclination of man's heart is only evil all the time. Paul tells us in Romans 3:10 - 18 that no one seeks God, no one is good, no one is righteous. In other words

modern man should feel bad about himself. He is living in rebellion to God. He has estranged himself from God, the very source of his life, identity and significance. He has shaken his fist at God and lives to do his own thing. In its approach to the patient modern medicine promotes blameshifting and irresponsibility. Modern man then wonders why in the midst of unprecedented material wealth and liberty he feels so bad about himself.[6]

In pursuing this blameshifting course of medical practice, that is, the assumption that feelings are caused by circumstances, in addition to the broader implications of disengaging the Fall from its relationship to disease and death, the patient is completely stripped of any hope for a cure. The patient may be made to feel better for a while but, unfortunately, feelings change. Nothing substantive changes in augmenting breasts under these circumstances. And the patient is made dependent upon her doctor who ostensibly is the source of her well-being.

One thing is sure, when man makes an end (health) something that is the fruit of Godly living it becomes a destructive idol. Having rejected God's standards man is rapidly replacing a once objective and Christian concept of health with a destructive, materialistic one that cannot explain suffering and therefore give hope in the midst of it. Therefore, in attempting to eradicate suffering it is man that is being eradicated. Utopias cannot stand imperfection.

Conclusions

So, what does it mean to be a Christian doctor in light of the fore-

going? First, it means to be a Christian. It means that one is part of a transformed humanity whose reference point is the living God. It means revealing all things in their relationship to God, understanding all things in light of God's word, offering all things up to God and exercising dominion in His name. It means striving to please God in every sphere of life including our vocation which is our calling, our ministry. It means to go forth as soldiers and servants of a King with a vision for His Kingdom fully aware of the spiritual war and equipped with spiritual weapons: the Word and Spirit of God, faith, prayer, righteousness. It means to serve God by serving and loving your fellowman.

The Orthodox Christian physician does not function outside the context of his community as an independent agent. His work is his community's expression of Christ's love for the world. Similarly, the patient is reminded of his responsibility to others as appropriate. Indeed, the physician involves the community (his and his patient's) in the healing process; whether it be family, friends, counselors, priest, etc. Having been ordained to ministry through baptism, he functions as a priest pointing people, through the totality of his life and love, to Christ, yet providing aid even to those who may refuse Christ.

In this liturgical/sacramental approach to the ill the patient is brought from the loneliness and alienation that disease produces into victory, health and being as communion. We must serve our fellow man by listening to his complaints and ailments. We must serve by comforting him, teaching him about his illness, diagnosis, prognosis and treatments; but most importantly we serve by reminding him that there is no comfort outside of Christ. We advise and counsel and rebuke on occasion. We sometimes use drugs or other remedies, if they may benefit; but we use nothing without open thankfulness to God, asking for His blessing in its use. We seek daily to see God's hand in this world. We recognize that to ignore God's hand in the world is to deny Him. We treat the patient as fallen, a sinner in need of redemption far more than he needs our medicine. We remember that the patient has responsibility for himself before God, that we cannot force others to pay for his care and nor can he. We do all this and more in humility for we are not sustained by medicine but by God. God brings disease and health ultimately for His purposes. We are His agents. When by our silence we give the impression that we are the source of health we have acted arrogantly. In humility, we properly amass data, inquire, research, reevaluate ourselves that we may constantly be learning and improving ourselves for the sake of our patients. Above all, the love of Christ should overflow from us to our patients.

ENDNOTES

1. As prophet, man interprets all things in light of God's Word. As priest, he offers all things up to God. As king, he rules in God's stead as his vicegerent. (The unbeliever functions similarly in that he interprets all things in light of himself, offers up and does all things for himself and rules in his own name.)

2. Sacrament (*mysterion*) in Orthodox and early Church thinking is passage, transfiguration, transformation, restoration. This is the mystery now revealed by the Church. The differences between the western and eastern concepts of "sacrament" are radical and beyond the scope of this paper. Suffice it to say that in Orthodoxy the number of sacraments has no dogmatic significance. The whole Christian life is seen as a unity, as a single mystery or one great sacrament. Orthodoxy speaks of the sacramentality of life; of its transfigurement into the Kingdom of Heaven, the old to the new by the people of God — the new creations. The many major and minor blessings of the Church from baptism to a blessing for a farmer's tractor are simply actions revealing the entity blessed in its relationship to God; referring the person or thing to God; restoring all creation to union and communion with God; covenantally binding the person or thing to God the Father through the Son by the Holy Spirit.

3. An example of this is the language and psychology of feelings "high" vs. "low" self esteem that has also infected "Christian" counseling. These are unbiblical categories and set up false dilemmas. The Bible asks us to judge ourselves rightly. This judgment is an objective act because it is based on objective criteria. One's feelings may or may not be in accord with the objective reality. Feelings are our habituated responses to circumstances and are the product of our deepest convictions which is why God calls us to a renewed mind and

obedience. The appropriate feelings will follow. Additionally, the unbeliever, as a rebel against God, has no basis to feel good about himself. The believers joy rests in the objective fact of what God has done for him, who he is in Christ and other objective facts.

4. As I explain later, Christ's miracles had eschatological significance and are an icon of the Kingdom of Heaven.

5. The physician in all cultures has always been associated with the religious institutions of his day. Indeed, he has functioned as priest. This was true of Byzantine times as well. The hospital was mainly an institution of the Church and many, if not most, physicians were ordained as deacons or presbyters. The physician today is also a priest of modern paganism because medicine is a redemptive, a salvific activity. The lack of the traditional gods is what dupes modern man. Secularism's reference point is man, thus man is God.

6. One cannot imagine the upturn in health that repentance, faith and a renewed mind would produce simply in the change of feelings that would ensue. Modern man lives off a rich Christian inheritance and does not appreciate the benefits accrued in quantity and quality of life this has produced. In his landmark book, *The Health of Nations*, Dr. Leonard Sagan shows that the most important factor in health is a positive life and worldview, one that produces knowledge. Only where the Gospel of Jesus Christ has gone has this occurred.

BIBLIOGRAPHY

1. Palmer, B., **Medicine and the Bible**, The Paternoster Press, G.B., 1986.

2. Rushdoony, R.J., **The Mythology of Science**, New Jersey: Craig Press, 1967.

3. Kuhn, T.S. **The Structure of Scientific Revolutions**, Univ. of Chicago Press, 1962.

4. Robertson, O.P., **The Christ of the**

Covenants, Presbyterian & Reformed Publishing Co., 1980.

5. Schmemann, A., **The Eucharist**, New York: St. Vladimir's Seminary Press, 1962.

6. Schmemann, A., **For the Life of the World**, New York: St. Vladimir's Seminary Press, 1963.

7. Mendelsohn, R.S., **Confessions of a Medical Heretic**, New York: Warner Books, 1979.

8. Harrison, R.K., **Leviticus**, Illinois: Intervarsity Press, 1980.

9. Zizioulas, J.D., **Being As Communion**, New York: St. Vladimir's Seminary Press, 1985.

10. Constantelos, D.J., **Byzantine Philanthropy and Social Welfare**, Rutger's Univ. Press, 1968.

11. Sproul, R.C., **Tabletalk**, Ligonier Ministries, 1991.

12. Sagan, L., **The Health of Nations**, New York: Basic Books, 1987.

13. Maddox, R., Defining a Christian Doctor, *Journal of Biblical Ethics in Medicine*, 1991.

14. Rushdoony, R.J., **The One and the Many**, Virginia: Thoburn Press, 1978.

15. Stout, H., Economic Tradeoff, *Wall Street Journal*, Sept. 6, 1991.

Letters to the Editor

(Continued from page 92:66)

Contrary to his conclusion that my argument "breaks itself in two," I believe that it offers a wholistic solution (not "compromise") to the modern problems of higher education and sexual license within God's mandate to be fruitful and multiply. I have condemned voluntary childlessness. I have mandated "more than two children." Therefore, a couple cannot continue birth control for "5, 7, 15 ???" years as Mr. Sauer has speciously stated. And -- I have allowed for the Biblical fulfillment of sexual desires about which he has chosen to be silent.

I did not "pull out of thin air" a family size of three. Mr. Sauer chose to ignore the context and my actual words. I said "more than 2 children" which may be three or ten. Also, I gave that goal in the context of "multiplying" the earth's population.

As to Deuteronomy 24:5, Mr. Sauer has a good point to which I yield. However, the clear intent of the verse is the "happiness to the wife." The child that may be conceived is just one dimension of this happiness.

If Mr. Sauer and others are interested in a more complete development of my argument about birth control than I have been able to present here, I have written it in my book, *Making Biblical Decisions*.

Franklin E. Payne, Jr., M.D.

Dear Editors,

I have just recently become familiar with your journal. In reading the Winter, 1992, issue, I was very impressed with Dr. Andrew White's attempt at honing a definition of the *imago Dei* and applying it in a practical way to the issue of abortion ("The Corporeal Aspect and Procreative Function of the *imago Dei* and Abortion.")

I have become increasingly convinced through prayerful study that the proper understanding and application of the *imago Dei* is one of the central core principles in biomedical ethics. However, I do question how his definition of the image gives inherent value to the unborn fetus. Rather, he seems to imply an inherent value in the act of procreation and the process of childbirth. He does state that a fetus has inherent value in that adults "must provide sustenance and [protection of the fetus] from man and beasts" in their procreative quest to fill the earth. But this seems to stem from their value as potential procreators and not from their value as human beings in and of themselves.

He also states that a fetus has inherent value before birth because it "is by nature the image of God," but he does not define this nature or how it would give inherent value to the fetus. He states only that the fetus is "corporeal," but so is the woman who carried the child. Thus, the crux of the issue seems to be, "how can a full understanding of the nature of the *imago Dei* (as Corporeality and spirituality) give inherent value to an unborn baby and thus support a pro-life position.?"

Sincerely,
Doug Duffee, M.Div.
4th year medical student,
East Tennessee State University

Dr. White replies:

I was delighted that Mr. Duffee responded to my letter. An author is always happy when he discovers that at least one person, other than his mother, has read something that has taken him untold hours to research, reflect upon and finally write. Besides this rather egocentric pleasure the author is also pleased that Mr. Duffee has independently become convinced of the importance of the concept of the *imago Dei* to biblical medical ethics.

(Continued on page 92:108)

Pastor's Column

Shame

The Reverend Byron Snapp

Rev. Snapp holds a B.A. from King's College and an M.Div. from Reformed Theological Seminary. He is assistant pastor of Covenant Presbyterian Church and prinicipal of Covenant Christian School in Cedar Bluff, Virginia.

Shame. If there was a list of endangered words as there is of endangered species I believe shame would be on that list as a result of looking at our culture.

Recently, New York's highest court ruled that it is permissible for women to go topless in public as long as such action is not for lewd or commercial purposes. The case originated when several women in Rochester went topless at a picnic. They were arrested for indecent exposure. The women went to court. The court ruled that it is discrimination to allow men to appear in public without their shirts and not allow women the same exposure.

Perhaps there are those patients who still are ashamed for their doctor to examine certain areas of their bodies, even when those doctors are of the same sex. That is a needless concern, generally. Certainly, there are some unscrupulous physicians even as there are pastors. A recent report indicated that 9% of physicians have had sexual contact with their patients. As a part of their calling, doctors may well have to see areas of our bodies otherwise reserved for viewing by our marriage partner. Dr. Luke speaks of the woman with a hemorrhage in Luke 8:43ff. A visit to one of her many doctors could

well have required a pelvic examination. God made our bodes in such a way that medical viewing of various areas is a necessity. No clearer example can be given than the location of the birth canal. The Old Testament covenantal act of circumcision is also illustrative. Genesis 17:23 states that Abraham, at God's command, took Ishmael and his household male servants and circumcised them that day. While no longer covenantally required, circumcision remains a valid medical procedure.

Yet within society we are more and more seeing a move away from such shame. No doubt much of society's lack of shame can be traced back to the popularizing of the profaning of God's name by the media. Once this was accepted we have seen an increase of speech and activity that once would have resulted in shame in our society.

The reader of Scripture has to go no further than Genesis 3 to view shame. Following Adam's eating of the forbidden fruit we read: "Then the eyes of both of them were opened, and they realized they were naked; so they sewed fig leaves together and made coverings for themselves" (v.7). Later they "heard the sound of the Lord God as he was walking in the garden in the cool of

the day, and they hid from the Lord God among the trees of the garden" (v.8).

What was the reason for this hiding? They had sinned against a holy God and were conscious of that sin.

The sovereign God sought them out and confronted them with their sin and its consequences in their lives and upon all mankind who would descend from Adam and upon creation itself. Scripture then records that "The Lord God made garments of skin for Adam and his wife and clothed them" (v.21). Adam and Eve were unable to clothe themselves in such a way as to stand before the Lord God. Through God's actions they were taught that only God can provide proper clothing for man to stand before God. A substitute provided clothing for them in the Garden. A greater Substitute, Jesus Christ, would provide the proper clothing of His righteousness for all saved sinners throughout history.

Clothing is important for a sinful people. Clothing is a marked contrast to our otherwise naked condition before man and our actual, continuing nakedness before God. Due to their sin Adam and Eve could not bare their physical bodies to one another, for they could not bare their souls to one another. (Rather than confessing their sin to God, they blamed another for their sinful action.) When God came into the garden they sought the additional covering (or clothing) that the Garden provided (v.8). Yet, it was not enough. We are always naked before our ever-present God.

In Scripture, legitimate exposure of a woman's breasts is set within the context of marriage. In Prov. 5:18, 19 we read, "Let your fountain be blessed, and rejoice with the wife of your youth. As a loving deer and a graceful doe, let her breasts satisfy you at all times; and always be enraptured with her love." Song of Solomon records these words of the beloved regarding his wife: "Your two breasts are like two fawns, twins of a gazelle which feed among the lilies: (4:5). Nakedness is proper within the marriage relationship. A solid godly marriage is, of course, built on an open communicative relationship. Not only can the marriage partners be physically naked before one another, they are also to be willing to bare their souls to the one to whom they have become one flesh.

Our society continues to deny God and His Word. as a result sin against God is non-existent in the eyes of our decadent culture. It is therefore not surprising that we are seeing the increase of shamelessness. Once shameful acts are now committed openly and with increasing acceptance by many leaders in our society. Examples are many -- homosexual activity, legal abortion, living together outside the bonds of marriage, and the open looting during the recent riots in Los Angeles.

A culture which denies God will have little shame. Many physicians and medical personnel can attest that this has resulted in increased sexual diseases, treatment of which adds to spiraling medical costs. Of course, the effects extend beyond our physical bodies, touching every facet of our being in one way or another.

We often associate toplessness and nakedness with African or South American tribal females. As Christian missionaries enter these cultures and proclaim the Gospel of Christ, conversions occur by God's grace. The women then begin to wear clothing on their hips and chests. Why the change in dress? I believe it is in great part due to their regenerated understanding of their shameful position as a sinner before a holy God, not merely copying the dress of another culture.

We can continue to expect increasing shamelessness in our societiety until we by God's grace are ashamed of our sin and are turned by God-given repentance and faith to trust in and consciously serve the living holy God Who is the Final Arbiter in what is good and evil.

Letters to the Editor

Dear Editor:

Deaton's article in the summer 1992 issue entitled "Questions Surrounding the Withdrawal of Artificial Hydration and Nutrition from Patients in a Persistent Vegetative State" is a very good review of the topic. His biblical analysis should be helpful to Christians wrestling with this controversial issue.

He claims on at least three occasions, however, that his analysis is not based on "quality of life" judgments. This disclaimer is perhaps understandable because many have contrasted "sanctity of life" and "quality of life" as if they were mutually exclusive.

The practice of medicine is almost entirely about quality of life. Having a backache or a respiratory infection diminishes one's quality of life. The patient most often goes to the physician in an effort to improve his or her quality of life. Quality of life is a very personal and subjective assessment of the positivity or negativity of several attributes which characterize one's life.

Human life has inherent *value* which cannot be diminished by its greater or lesser quality. James Walter and Thomas Shannon address this from a Roman Catholic perspective in their book *Quality of Life* (Paulist Press, 1990) and conclude that "the so-called two ethics of life are not two but really one." The older ordinary/extraordinary distinction which has evolved into a "proportionality of benefits and burdens" discussion is really talking about quality of life judgments made by the patient or surrogate. This is inherent to the practice of and discussion about medicine and need not be avoided as if it were sacrilege.

Sincerely,

Robert D. Orr, M.D.
Director of Clinical Ethics
Loma Linda University Medical Center

Editor,

A Christian physician friend recently sent me a copy of the Summer 1992 issue of *Journal of Biblical Ethics in Medicine*. I must tell you that the concept of "advocating the Lordship of Christ in medicine" is most wel-

(continued on page 92:105)

William P. Teubl, M.D., of Rhinebeck, NY, has produced a brief essay on oral contraceptives for personal use, on why he no longer prescribes them. He intends the essay to be readable by non-Christians.

Moral Issues in Oral Contraception

When advising a patient, a physician must communicate the truth accurately and clearly. The physician's and patient's knowledge and preference result in a plan of action. Such a plan must be for the patient's good. A physician must not formulate or endorse a plan that he perceives to be of harm to the patient. A plan that involves risk is acceptable if the potential benefit to the patient outweighs the risk in the mind of both patient and physician.

Birth control may be of benefit to a sexually active couple who are not prepared for a child provided it does not violate their conscience. Abortion can be used as birth control, but it has been condemned because it does harm by taking a human life. Methods of birth control that act partly or entirely as abortifacients represent the same ethical dilemma as more invasive methods of abortion.

The incidence of conception in a woman using oral contraceptives is unknown, but recent data[2] indicates an ovulation rate of 4.7% on the low dose pill.[1] Older literature estimates the rate to be between 2% and 10%[3]. The likelihood of implantation given the histologic appearance of the endometrium is considered very low[4], therefore the conception rate is essentially the rate of ovulation times the chance of fertilization. For unprotected intercourse the fertilization rate is approximately 20%[5]. The effectiveness of cervical mucous changes in preventing fertilization has not been well studied, so sensitivity analysis is needed to estimate the range of possible conceptions. Given the foregoing a woman's chance of conception any given month is approximately 1% (4.7% X 20%), ignoring the role of cervical mucous changes. On oral contraception, a woman has 13 cycles per year. On the average, then, a woman will have one abortion every eight years she uses oral contraception (13 X 8 X 1%). A corollary is that on the average a physician induces one abortion per year for every eight women for whom he prescribes oral contraception. If cervical mucous changes were 90% effective in preventing fertilization, a physician would induce one abortion each year for every eighty women treated.

The statistics above are sobering for any physician or patient who is sensitive to minimizing harm. Even if oral contraception caused only one abortion every ten years in a given practice the moral argument against their use is strong. Using the above figures, if a physician prescribed for 160 women per year, he would cause eighty abortions over a forty year career. If cervical mucous was less than 90% effective, the figure would be higher. It is impossible to predict who would abort when.

Given the foregoing estimates and the availability of effective barrier methods and natural family planning a strong argument against the use of oral contraception can be made. Each physician has an obligation to weigh the perceived benefits to his patient against the harm just described. If as a result a physician's conscience does not permit him to prescribe oral contraception, he is obligated to inform his patients in an accurate, clear, and sensitive manner. Subsequently, he must develop a plan to phase out the use of oral contraceptives. Should a physician's conscience allow him to prescribe oral contraceptives, he is obliged to inform his patients of the abortifacient potential of the drug in question. Not to do so would be a denial of informed consent and would violate the conscience of patients who hold abortion to be morally unjustified.

In conclusion, the following statements appear to be justified:

1. A physician must be truthful with his patient.
2. Oral contraceptives are abortifacients.
3. A physician's conscience may prohibit him from prescribing oral contraceptives.
4. A physician prescribing an oral

contraceptive must inform his patients of its abortifacient potential.

The physician who operates under these conclusions with a clear conscience fulfills his obligation to seek the good of his patient.

ENDNOTE

1. Arguments developed are for the low dose pill, since they are most commonly used. The minipill and high dose pill require a somewhat different analysis.

2. Van de Vange, N., Second International Conference of the Society for Advancement in Contraception, Nov. 26 - 30, 1984.

3. Peel, J, and Potts, M., **Textbook of Contraceptive Practice**, Cambridge University Press, 1969, p. 99.

4. Guttmacher, A. "Prevention of conception through contraception and sterilization," **Gynecology and Obstetrics**, Carl H. Davis, ed., Vol. 1.

5. Tietze, C., "Differential fecundity and effectiveness of contraception," *Eugenics Review*, Vol. 50, 1959, p. 231.

* * * * * * *

Robert S. Jaggard, M.D., independent practitioner of private medicine in Oelwin, Iowa, sends information about the billing form he uses in his office, incorporating his answer to the intrusion of civil government.

PLACE of SERVICE is at the office unless otherwise specified. TIME listed is approximate number of minutes devoted to this service for this patient by Dr. Jaggard. FEE listed is that amount agreed upon by the patient and Dr. Jaggard as the proper payment for the doctor for this service. No real or implied contract exists between Dr. Jaggard and anybody else but the patient.

I have NO fee schedule. I use NO "code numbers." I use plain language that the patient understands. I do my best for the individual patient. ALL of my patients are Private Patients. Each private patient pays me the amount that the private patient decides is the proper amount to pay me for this service for this private patient on this occasion. I make suggestions, but the final decision as to the value of my service is up to the individual private patient. The amount of payment is listed in the right-hand column as the FEE. When this is paid, then that item is marked, "Paid," and dated, and that is the receipt.

If patients have private insurance, they can use this statement (or receipt) to submit THEIR claim to THEIR insurance company. Patients understand up front that I have NO contract with any insurance company, and I am not part of THEIR insurance contract, and it is up to the company to pay THEM in accordance with THEIR contract with THEIR company. My ONLY contract is with the patient.

Poor patients who do NOT smoke tobacco or drink alcohol are told that the service is available at "no charge." However, if they have cash for tobacco or alcohol, they have cash with which they can pay me.

Patients who have been trapped in the government tax-paid programs (such as "Medicare" and "Medicaid") are frankly told, up front, that I am NOT part of those political programs, because they do NOT allow the doctor to serve the patient, and they do NOT give the patient or doctor any right to make any choices in regard to treatment. Patients are informed that I will give them medical service at "no charge," but I can NOT help them get

any money from "Medicare" or "Medicaid." The big sign hanging in the office front window says, "PRIVATE MEDICINE." There is a sign on my front desk that says, "I am NOT a Government doctor." My policy has been (and still is) well publicized in the local newspaper.

I do NOT have to follow the "Medicare" rules because I am NOT part of their program, AND, neither are my patients. My service is available to patients at "no charge," so there is no possibility of reimbursement from Medicare (or supplemental insurance), so there is no reason to fill out a claim form. Also, my service is NOT "medically necessary." My service is helpful, and sometimes lifesaving, yes, but "medically necessary" is a political term that has no relationship whatsoever to scientific medicine. I have NEVER certified ANY care as being "medically necessary," and Medicare does NOT cover ANY care unless it is "medically necessary." Since there is "no charge," and it is not "necessary," my service is not involved with , and is not part of, the "Medicare" program.

To those patients who have Part B of Title XVIII, I explain that my service is available at No Charge, and, any money they pay me will NOT be reimbursed in any way by "medicare" or their supplemental insurance company. Patients who appreciate my service for them give me money to help pay the office expenses. I help them. They help me. We deal with each other in peace and honesty. We enjoy freedom together.

Teach Us to Number Our Days (Psalm 90:12).

Age And The Rationing of Medical Care: Use of a Biblical Valuation of Personhood

Gregory W. Rutecki, M.D. and John D. Geib, M.A.

Dr. Rutecki is Clinical Associate Professor of Medicine at Northeastern Ohio University College of Medicine. Mr. Geib is Instructor of Religion in the Department of Theology at Malone College in Canton, Ohio.

The unrelenting growth of health care spending in the U.S. has recently reached $738 billion per year, approximately 13% of the gross national product.[1] In comparison to other industrialized nations, this is 74 and 27 percent greater than the United Kingdom and Canada respectively. At the present pace, estimated costs for the year 2030 would peak at an astounding 26% of the GNP. In a pluralistic society such as ours any debate regarding cost containment confronts consumers who concomitantly demand immediate access to health services, state of the art technology and limited price. Former surgeon general of the U.S. C. Everett Koop predicts that cost reform may be possible by simultaneous submission to two of these demand but never with all three.[1] Thrust into this trilemma of cost containment is one potential solution: the rationing of medical care. Rationing has always been necessary but recently has passed from the consumers' control to newer forms of "third party" control such as the "gatekeeper" in health maintenance organizations or to a state or federal agency. And though rationing *per se* is controversial, a decreased distribution of medical services based only on advancing age seems to raise the hue and cry of Americans more than any contemporary subject in medical ethics.[2,3]

Two Questions Regarding Rationing

The first question one might ask about the proposed rationing of medical care to the elderly is why age alone would be chosen as a criterion for rationing. Discussion of the *raison 'd etre* of age-related rationing must present and develop evidence both that care for the aged is prohibitively expensive (especially for the "value" returned) and also that this cost will increase in the short term future.

Earlier in this century, Americans were predominantly young and medical care was therefore inexpensive with a focus on acute illnesses free of the costs of advanced technology. Today medical care has become an expensive proposition as Americans age and are beset with the more expensive chronic diseases. Furthermore, the final ten years of this century and the beginning of the next can be accurately described as the aging of America. By the year 2005, it is predicted that 35 million Americans will be older than age 65 and 50% of these older than age 75.[3,4] If present trends continue, 100,000 people could celebrate their 100th birthday that year.

The medical parallel of America's aging process is that costs per hospital admission in patients greater than age 66 increase progressively with age. Among the elderly, hospitalization costs for the same diagnosis are priced 50% greater in those older than age 85 compared to ages 66 to 71.[5,6] This "cost" is four times more than the average cost across "younger" age groups. Translated into 1987 dollars, 28% of the total Medicare allotment (22.7 billion dollars) reimbursed 6% of Medicare recipients who died that year. An even more startling fact is that these costs did not include nursing home expenditures which increase an additional 3 - 5 times for the "older" and are not reflected in the Medicare costs quoted above.

More importantly, this philosophy of rationing by age is not only based on dollar and cents but more significantly on an equitable and empiric search for the medical "value" of dollars spent.[7] This leads to the second corollary question: do the vast sums of money appropriated actually benefit the elderly in a verifiable reduction of morbidity and mortality? Unfortunately, further study of this question gives some very unsettling answers.

The medical expenses of the patients who die are the single greatest source of the age related rise in Medicare dollars spent. The expenses of older decedents are three to five times greater than the expenses of age matched hospitalized patients who survive.[5,6] Seventy-seven percent of the expense for Medicare patients occurs in the last 180 days of life and 30% in the last 30 days. These figures serve as a stunning example of the contemporary futility of "cure" motivated technology applied to the elderly. The annual medical costs for the elderly with certain diseases traditionally viewed as "terminal" (e.g., cancer) is $8,021, or $5,191 when a comorbid diagnosis is not simultaneously present.[5] At a minimum, these statistics suggest that a significant portion of the dollars spent reimburse a technology that may yield little value for the elderly in a qualitative lengthening of life. At a maximum, they seem to imply a misallotment of monies in unsuccessful end of life applications aimed at cure and not care.

In the secular arena, age as a criterion for rationing has received support from Callahan, Daniels, Lamm and Veatch, who are in a distinct minority.[3,8,9,10] Their arguments in favor of the rationing of medical care to the elderly have focused on utilitarianism (communalism over individualism) and prudence in spending (value-based rationing) as an attempt to achieve a more equitable distribution of dollars spent for medical care. This equitable distribution might resemble the Oregon "experiment" in which increased monies are spent on pre-natal care and less on the care of the elderly particularly if expensive technology (liver and cardiac transplants) is a spending choice.[11,12,13]

On the other hand, there has been a greater volume of literature in protest of the use of age as a criterion for rationing. (See references 2,14,15,16,17 for example.) It also appears that the general response of the Christian and Prolife Community voices a similar protest.[18,19]

This paper studies a Biblical perspective of age based rationing. The authors want to assess the Biblical view of aging, potential targets of rationing and equitable allotment of medical care in an attempt to find Biblical answers for Christians. Some form of rationing will likely occur in the short term future, *defacto* or otherwise, and we fear that the "target" group and method for selection of that group may involve a world view perspective foreign to Biblical ethics. Any decision by Christians concerning rationing or allotment must have a Biblical foundation which simultaneously addresses the valuation of persons both in eternal and temporal dimensions. Accordingly, we cite passages consistent with the concept that humans are both eternally and relatively valuable. This perspective will then be applied to individual situations and prayerfully submitted as an informed Christian response to the issue of medical care rationing based on age.

COMPARISON OF THE TEMPORAL AND ETERNAL VALUE OF HUMANS: BIBLICAL ILLUSTRATIONS	
The Eternal Value of Persons: Divine Intentions	**The Temporal Values of Humans: Biblical Reflections**
Eternal Life: Glorification and Sanctification God's eternal purpose is to glorify (conformation to the image of Christ) all those who have received Christ as Savior (Romans 8:18-39, I Cor. 15:45-49) Thus, each member of Christ's body is indwelt by the Holy Spirit, whose intent is to sanctify (renew progressively into the image of Christ and God) every individual member (2 Cor. 3:18-4:6)	Biological Life: Degeneration The realistic terminal span of human biological life is observed to be between seventy and eighty years (Psalm 90:10)
Chronological Life: Redemptive Equality Regardless of age, race, gender or class, God values humans enough to redeem (purchase from slavery to sin and death) those who believe in Christ with the price of Christ's life blood. (I Cor. 6:19-20, Gal. 3:26-29)	Chronological Life: Inequality Youthful vigor placed at God's disposal is viewed as functionally more valuable to God and society than the compromised weakness of old age (Ecclesiastes 11:10-12:7)
Created: Infinite Value Human beings (male and female) were created in and still bear (however marred by sin) the image of God, making them infinitely value to God regardless of their functional ability. (Genesis 1:26-2:17)	Functional Life: Realtive Value Age and gender were used in ancient Jewish agrarian culture to determine the relative functional worth of humans (Leviticus 27:1-8)

Biblical Valuation on the Eternal Worth of Persons Through the Metaphor of Investment

Jesus frequently compared God to a business executive who made investments with the expectation of return (Matthew 18:21-35, 20:1-6, 21:33-41, 25:14-13, *et al.*).

Since we are attempting to determine the Biblical view of the "value" of human life, it may prove helpful to follow Jesus' lead and compare four of God's great acts to "investments" made in the human race with the expectation of an eternal reward. The value of these investments (creation, redemption, sanctification and glorification) enable us to appreciate the infinite value placed on human beings by the God of the Bible.

I. Four theological concepts that determine the ultimate, priceless, spiritual worth of persons.

1.) The Initial Investment: Creation

Entrepreneurs create businesses that reflect their personalities and in this they resemble God who began the business of humanity by creating us (male and female together) in the image of God (Genesis 1:26-;27). While all of God's creation is called "good" (which implies "value"), what estimate of value can be placed on creatures in whom God invests (by analogy) His character and personality? This question can be best answered by understanding the value of subsequent investments God made (and will yet make) in the human race. All of these subsequent investments are arrestingly consistent with the foundational truth that humanity bears the image of God.

2.) Bankruptcy And Need for Redemption

However marred, even bankrupt, the image of God has become in humanity due to our willful disobedience of God's designs for us (sin), God has determined to yield an eternal return from the "business" of humanity. God first provided redemption from the ruin of spiritual bankruptcy by investing in humanity the life of Jesus Christ. Christians are described as "... bought with a price ...," the price being the infinitely valuable blood (life) of Jesus (I Cor. 6:19-20), I Peter 1:18-19, Psm. 49:7-8). In God's scheme of the eternal valuation of persons saved humanity is worth whatever the life of Jesus is worth!

3.) The Return of Solvency: Sanctification

This staggering investment of Jesus' life in humanity is expected by God to yield the short-term return of redeemed persons "... being transformed into the same image from [one degree of] of glory to [another degree of] glory ...," the "same image" being further defined as "... the glory of Christ, who is the image of God" (2 Cor. 3:18, 4:4). The business of humanity is to reflect God's image. Even in a fallen world, God intends to reap a partial return for the investment of Jesus' life by seeing Jesus' likeness being formed in those being restored to spiritual solvency.

4.) God's Ultimate Profit: Glorification

The ultimate value God places on humanity can be appreciated only when we understand the ultimate goal God has for the human business enterprise. That ultimate goal is the production of individuals who are completely and eternally conformed into the glorious image of Christ (Romans 8:28-30, I Cor. 15:45-49, I John 3:1-3, et al.). This return is so valuable that human intelligence alone is inadequate to appreciate this priceless commodity: thus, Paul prays for Christians to be supernaturally illuminated by God's Spirit so they may know " ... the riches of the glory of [God's] inheritance in the sanctified ones ... " (Ephesians 1:17-18). In the fullness of time, when God brings the entire business of humanity under the Headship of Christ, then the eternal purpose which God had in Christ since before time will be realized, to the eternal profit of both God and humanity (Ephesians 1:10, 3:10).

Balancing Two Biblical Truths: Persons Both Infinitely And Relatively Valuable

The four preceding theological concepts teach us that humans are infinitely valuable. However, at this juncture it is essential to note that other passages in the Bible place relative degrees of value on persons. Thus, we are suggesting that the God of the Bible distinguishes between a person's eternal, spiritual value and his/her functional worth in a time-space continuum. See Table 1 for a comparison of the temporal and eternal value of persons. If our observation is correct, how can we maintain the delicate balance of these two Biblical truths without compromising either one? Biblical writers not exposed to our technological expertise did not address issues such as artificial prolongation of life, or the financial and pragmatic realities attached to the cure v. care debate. Thus, no specific passages exist that speak to these issues.

The authors maintain that one method to bring the Scriptural truth to bear on these issues is by analogy. Are there analogies to the value of human life contained in the Bible that could enable moderns to balance the truths that human life is both infinite and relative in value? Such analogies (if valid) could help us resolve some of the complex tensions that exist between care and cure advocates.

The vocabulary and metaphor of business will be used to address ownership, stewardship and depreciation of our bodies during earthly existence. A Biblical, pragmatic valuation of our physical body will be contrasted to the eternal salvation discussed previously.

II. Three Analogies That Reflect The Functional Worth of Persons.

1.) The Analogy Between the Jubilee Year and Biological Life (Leviticus 25 and Psalm 90).

The Jubilee year was instituted by Yahweh in ancient Israel to reveal liberating truths to people about personal liberty, property and the provident grace of God (Leviticus 25). Every fiftieth year, all land granted originally to the individual tribes of Israel (which had been bartered or sold during previous years) was to revert to the original tribal stewards.

All Jews, both slave and free, returned to their original tribal families (Lev. 25:10). Jubilee was to be a general celebration of liberation, a formal recognition that God, as the Creator and the Redeemer, is the true owner of the land (Lev. 25:23) and lives (Lev. 25:55) of God's people.

Psalm 90 is a poetic rumination on the temporality of human life in light of God's eternity. The Psalmist reveals God as eternal, beyond the temporal continuum, to whom a thousand years are like a day, or a watch in the night, or sprouting and decaying grass (Psm. 90:1-6). Humans are seen as temporal, compared to "dust," who can generally expect their biological lives to span between seventy and eighty years, and those years filled with labor and sorrow (Psm. 90:3, 90:10).

This contrast leads the Psalmist to a cogent balancing of realism and hope, which terminates in the request, "teach us to number our days, that we may present to you [God] a heart of wisdom (Psm. 90:12). And what is "wisdom" in this context? Simply, that we ought to view our biological lives as a limited number of opportunities (which depreciate in value as our days increase) to work for the purpose of God and God's majesty (Psm. 90:96, 90:16-17).

As we studied Lev. 25 and Psm. 90, analogies emerged between the spiritual meaning of Jubilee and the relative value of human, biological life. While not exhaustive, the following analogies (if embraced) would enable us to achieve the Biblical balance of the infinite yet temporally relative value of human life.

a. Land is a "gift" from God, just as biological life is given to each of us as a "gift" (Lev. 25:2, Psm. 90:2, Psm. 100:3).

b. Thus, land belongs ultimately to God it's Creator. Humans are allowed to act as stewards of the land, but thoughts of permanent ownership are considered delusional (Lev. 25:23).

Biological life is analogous to land because biological life is created and owned ultimately by God. Humans are allowed to act as stewards (good or bad) of what is ultimately God's property (Psm. 90:3, 90:10, I Cor.

6:19-20, Mark 8:34-38).

c. The total time for land to yield a return to those working it was fixed by God at forty-nine (49) years, with the fiftieth being the liberating year of Jubilee in which land was returned to the original caretakers (Lev. 25:4, 25:10-12).

Likewise, the total time for a human life to yield a return to God and society is limited, being realistically (and in general terms) observed to terminate between seventy and eighty years (Psm. 90:10).

d. The functional value of land was determined relative to the number of crops it could be expected to yield until the terminal date of Jubilee (Lev. 25:14-16).

Similarly (though the Bible also views humans as infinitely valuable for the reasons stated earlier), the Psalmist implores God to teach us to view our biological life span as a limited time period granted to us in which we may yield service to God and others (Psm. 90:10-12, 90:16-17). This request makes sense only when we agree with the psalmist's realistic view that biological life has a functional value which depreciates as we progress toward its terminus (Psm. 90:10). Psalm 90 enlightens us because the inspired Word tells humans to embrace the concept that earthly existence is only one of the dimensions for which God created us. Our ultimate worth is more important and very different from our functional worth.

2.) Functional Worth and Age (Lev. 27:1-8)

Another demonstration of the Lord placing "relative" value on people based on their "functional worth" to society is found in Leviticus 27:1-8. In that agrarian and theocratic

PERSON AND AGES	Valuation in Shekels of Silver (1 Shekel = 224 Grains of Silver)[1]	Total Grains of Silver Required to Fulfill Vow For Each Person	Ancient Equivalent in Barley Seed (50 Shekels of Silver = 1 Homer 1 Homer = 11 Bushels; 1 Peck of Barley Seed)[2]
Male (20-60 yrs.)	50 Shekels	50 x 224 = 11, 120 Grains	11 Bushels 1 Peck (or 45 Pecks)
Female (20-60 yrs.)	30 Shekels	30 x 224 = 4,448 Grains	27 Pecks
Male (5-20 yrs.)	20 Shekels	20 x 224 = 3,336 Grains	18 Pecks
Male (60+ yrs.)	15 Shekels	15 x 224 = 3,336 Grains	13.5 Pecks
Female (60+ yrs.)	10 Shekels	10 x 224 = 2,224 Grains	9 Pecks
Female (5-20 yrs.)	10 Shekels	10 x 224 = 2,224 Grains	9 Pecks
Male (1 mo.-5 yrs.)	5 Shekels	5 x 224 = 1,112 Grains	4.5 Pecks
Female (1 mo.-5 yrs.)	3 Shekels	3 x 224 = 672 Grains	2.7 Pecks

1. The International Standard Bible Encyclopedia, v. 4, p. 2758.

2. The International Standard Bible Encyclopedia, v. 5, p. 3038.

society, persons' functional worth was determined by their ability to work the land. Thus, when persons were "dedicated" to the Lord, the "value" of persons being dedicated was determined relative to their ability to serve God and others. In such an agrarian society, age and gender were practical factors used to determine the relative value of a person's potential ability to work. Table 2 contains this relative valuation scheme.

We are not citing Lev. 27:1-8 to suggest its precise applicability to modern culture. Rather, we cite it analogically to suggest that the God of the Bible did (and still does) recognize that the functional worth of persons to God and others is determined in relative terms.

We recognize that the often superior knowledge, judgment, and wisdom of the elderly may be of more value in our non-agrarian society than strong bones and muscles, or quick reflexes and keen eyesight. Thus, functional worth relates to the needs of society.

3.) The Juxtaposition of Youth and Old Age. (Ecc. 12:1-8)

Further, Ecclesiastes 12:1-8 juxtaposes youth and old age so that the relative value of youth to the depreciating functional worth of old age is clearly revealed. While reading this Scripture we may inquire as to why the inspired writer exhorts us to remember the Creator in the "days of our youth." The writer answers this question in 12:1b - 8 with a poetic documentation of the decrease in bodily function during the aging process. This decrease is revealed to be an existential reality of human life. The writer expects that this exposition on aging and functional depreciation will lead the reader to the obvious conclusion: younger persons have the ability to accomplish more for God and society than elders with declining bodily functions.

Based on the passages cited, we observe that a distinction is made in the Bible between the relative value of a person's temporal biological life and the eternal value of the person whose existence transcends time and continues into eternity.

We therefore conclude that the attribution of ultimate worth to persons is an appraisal valid only for their eternal dimension. Thus, during earthly existence, the functional or pragmatic worth of persons varies with productivity and age.

The Biblical passages cited analogically provide us with a basis to formulate Biblical paradigms for some form of medical rationing or value based allotment of medical care for the elderly. These paradigms seem essential since the use of money for the medical care of the elderly potentially compromises the care of those in younger and more functional age groups. We would like to describe prudent models for rationing or allotment and apply them with some Scriptural paradigms useful in practice. These practical paradigms would require the same balance of truth and compassion (1 John 1:5, 1 John 4:7-8) that characterize the God we serve.

<u>Practice Paradigm 1</u>: "Going back to an earlier time in Medicine," emphasizing care (Matt. 25:31-46) and not just cure (Luke 10:25-37.)[20]

Early medicine was characterized by the sensitivity of care without the ability to cure. Conversely, the twentieth century with the rapid growth of technology and the use of certain saving drugs (e.g., Penicillin) is preoccupied with cure at the expense of care. Our Christian forefathers used the word "hospice" to precede the word "hospital" and in so doing reflected their attitude and the attitude of the early church to offer comfort care to the dying. We must return to a proper balance between care and cure which can be achieved with the juxtaposition of the following two Scriptures.

Many early pictures of Christ recognized Him as the great healer He was. Identification of Christian health care workers with Him in the model of curing (The Good Samaritan, Luke 10:25-37) must be juxtaposed with Matthew 25:31-46). Even though Christ is represented in the healer or caretaker, He is simultaneously represented in the one who is cared for or healed. That is why He tells the one who treats, " ... you did it to me."

Spiritual realization of this concept became much easier for us through the contemporary Christian song, "Distressing Disguise."[21]

"Every time a faithful servant serves a brother that's in need, what happens at that moment is a miracle indeed, as they look to one another in an instant it is clear ... only Jesus is visible for they both disappear."

If health care rationing decreases allotments during the next ten to twenty years and thus removes the elderly from "cure" situations, who will "care" for them in outpatient or hospice settings? The juxtaposition of the above Scriptures confronts the Christian with a paradigm shift for behavior. If this "care" is not remunerated by Medicare, it must be provided freely with the models that Scripture suggests. One such model is provided by Paul in 1 Timothy 5:3-10.

A First Century Model of Care

As cited earlier, the increase of medical sophistication has been accomplished by a staggering increase in financial costs. Unless some resolution of the cure v. care debate is achieved, we face the prospects of financial ruin[22] (with an accompanying decrease in medical services for all) or the rationing of medical services determined by a governmental (and thus most probably humanistic) world view ethic.

A possible way out of this dilemma could be achieved if we (especially Christians) followed the advice of Paul regarding the care of widows (1 Tim. 5:3-16) and saw an analogy between the church and modern government as providers of care.

The financial burdens for the care (not cure) of widows (and thus by implication family members with true needs) is to be borne primarily by the family unit to whom the widow or needy person belongs (1 Tim. 5:4, 5:16).

When there is no biological family to care for the widows or individuals in need, then the spiritual family (The Church, 1 Tim. 5:1-2) is to assume the financial cost involved in such care (1Tim. 5:3, 5:16).

Moreover, to prevent possible abuse of "unconditional" charity, criteria are provided to guide the church in the allocation of its limited (implied) resources (1Tim. 5:6, 5:9-15).

Thus, Christians (the "light of the world") who follow the model of assuming personal and corporate responsibility for the care of the needy could provide an illuminational example to others who have become increasingly (and disastrously) addicted to the expectation of unlimited and unconditional medical services, funded by equally decreasing government entitlement resources.

<u>Practice Paradigm 2</u>: "Front door allocation and compassionate care are more Biblical than rear door decisions motivated by the intent to cure."

To explain this concept, the authors interject the specialty insight of Nephrology. However, primary care practitioners and specialists can create their own examples for this particular care paradigm.

Many studies have shown empirically and repetitively that certain expensive medical technologies used in the elderly offer very little to no benefit in the postponement of death. On the other hand, the elderly do benefit from some treatments in ways comparable to younger patients. The former situation is evidenced very often in the ICU by acute dialysis, the latter in chronic dialysis.

In settings such as a renal failure complicating the course of ruptured abdominal aneurysm[23] or that of abdominal catastrophe, acute renal failure has mortalities in excess of 80% and in particular situations mortalities of 100% are determined. Despite the empiric proof of futility with dialysis in these "acute" situations in the elderly, treatment is often prolonged at high cost in both a monetary sense and in the sense of "burden" to patients and their families. However, the survival of elderly patients on chronic dialysis is better than was expected initially.[24] Chronic dialytic intervention may highlight the "care" side of treatment since the social milieu of a crowded dialysis unit often stimulates elderly patients who otherwise lead a solitary existence.

"Front door allocation" suggests that certain diseases in the elderly, e.g., acute dialysis after abdominal aortic aneurysm rupture, should receive a value allocation at the front door before expensive and burdensome technology is added in a futile way. However, if the elderly benefit and are not burdened by a therapy such as chronic dialysis, the front door can be opened and other allocation/rationing decisions made later as needed.

Practice Paradigm 3: "The Practice of Salt and Light" informed consent.

We are all called to witness the power of salvation through Christ as revealed in the Bible. True informed consent requires that the insights we gain from Scriptural revelation are shared with others. When families, confused by a world view dominated by scientism, demand "everything be done" at any stage of life, the futility of this attitude in lives saved, burdens added and poor stewardship of finances should be openly discussed. True informed consent should reveal to families the lack of success that underlies much of the technology applied to the elderly and medicine in general.

Concluding Discussion

The Bible reveals human life to us as "priceless" since it is invested with God's image through creation. That same life (though bankrupted by sin)

has the potential for redemption, sanctification and glorification valued at the infinite cost of Christ's blood. This is indeed an "ultimate" valuation of human life since the value transcends earthly existence and is elevated into the eternal realm (Eph. 2:6). However, the Bible (both inerrant and consistent) also teaches a depreciating value for these "sanctified" lives while they exist and age in the earth's time-space continuum.

The contemporary view, held by the majority, suggests that rationing medical care to the elderly is a gross miscarriage of justice. From the outset of study for this paper, the authors shared in this ethical struggle. However, though the conclusion of Scripture stands in contrast to prevailing thought, it presents no compromise in a consistent, Prolife stance. The rationing-allotment, cure v. care debate, framed in a Scriptural perspective, remains steadfastly pro-sanctity of life and anti-euthanasia. We sincerely believe that a decline in "cure" motivated money for medical care will demand greater sacrifices from the Christian medical community rather than their being the first step on a "slippery slope." One very temporally relevant example will highlight this fact since the example overlaps physician, nurse, and pastoral disciplines.

A controversial study[25] identified CPR as a futile undertaking in the elderly. In fact, CPR was unsuccessful in all 68 patients in this study older than age seventy (77 resuscitative efforts). Twenty-two of the 68 decedents who survived for 24 hr experienced "burdens"[26] without eventual survival. This is disturbing on so many levels that it must be discussed further. Anyone who has witnessed or participated in a code real-

izes that it can be a very painful and undignified process. Did the staff use valid informed consent which sensitively highlighted this futility prior to CPR? Did they promise these patients a "Quality of Mercy"[27] if they decided to forego CPR? Did they, if Christian, pray with the patients prior to the decision regarding CPR? Did the staff respect Biblical beliefs grounded in the "ultimate" eternal value of human life? All these unanswered questions demonstrate how rationing and value based allotment offer greater opportunity for witness and loving care without any compromise in a life affirming belief.

When this paper ends, the real challenges begin. These challenges will sorely test our obedience as disciples. They will require further reaffirmation from the Christian that, while Life is infinitely valuable, physical life is not the *summum bonum*. The early Christians, both in life and in death as martyrs, realized this with an intensity. We need to pray ceaselessly and at the same time diligently search Scripture to be reminded that we exist in both an eternal and physical perspective. We must combat the enlightenment and "scientific" world view which has elevated medicine and physical health to the position of idols. And finally, when the entitlement system collapses, we must volunteer as servants to provide "care" in Scriptural paradigms that will be removed from the financial excess of present day medicine. That's the Biblical practice of medicine anyway, isn't it?

ENDNOTES

1. Morganthore, T., with Hager, M., Cutting Through The Gobbledegook, *Newsweek*: 24-25 Feb. 3, 1992.

2. Binstock, R.H., Post, S.G., **Too Old for Health Care? Controversies in Medicine, Law, Economics, and Ethics**, Baltimore: Johns Hopkins Press, 1991.

3. Callahan, D., **Setting Limits: Medical Goals in an Aging Society**, New York: Simon & Schuster, 1987.

4. Mills, C., The Graying of America. *Rep. Inst., Philos. Public Policy*. Vol. 8(2): 1-5, 1988.

5. Webster, J.R., Berdes, C., Ethics and Economic Realities: Goals and Strategies For Care Toward the End of Life, *Arch. Intern. Med.*, Vol. 150, 1990, pp. 1775 - 1797.

6. Lubitz, J., Prihoda, R., The Use and Costs of Medicare Services in the Last Two Years of Life, *Health Care Financing*, Vol. 5(3), 1984, pp 117-131.

7. Eddy, D.M., Connecting Value and Costs. Whom Do We Ask, and What Do We Ask Them. *JAMA*, Vol. 264, 1990, pp. 1734-1740.

8. Daniels, N., Am I My Parents Keeper? **An Essay on Justice between the Young and Old**, New York: Oxford University Press, 1988.

9. What Did Governor Lamm Really Mean? *Hastings Center Report* (Editor's Comment), October, 1984, p. 26.

10. Veach, R.M., Justice and the Economics of Terminal Illness, *Hastings Center Report*, Vol. 18, (4), 1988, pp. 34 - 40.

11. Klein, R., On the Oregon Trail, *BMJ*, Vol. 302, 1991, pp. 1-2.

12. Silversides, A., Oregon Tackles the Health Care Rationing Issue, *Can. Med. Assoc. J.*, Vol. 143(6), 1990, pp. 545-546.

13. Steinbrook, R., Lo., B., The Oregon Medicaid Demonstration Project — Will it Provide Adequate Medical Care? *N. Engl. J. Med.*, Vol. 326, 1992, pp. 340-344.

14. Siegler, M., Should Age Be a Criterion in Health Care?, *Hastings Center Report*, October, 1984, pp. 24 - 27.

15. Jecker, N.S., Age Based Rationing and Women, *JAMA*, Vol. 266, 1991, pp. 3012 - 3015.

16. Jecker, N.S., Pearlman, R.A., Ethical Constraints on Rationing Medical Care by Age, *JAGS*, Vol. 37, 1989, pp. 1067 - 1075.

17. Levinsky, N.G., Age as a Criterion for Rationing Health Care, *N. Engl. J. Med.*, Vol. 322, 1990, pp. 1813 - 1816.

18. Binstock, R.H., Post, S.G., Rationing and Ethics in Health Care, *Christianity and Crisis*, Sept. 23, 1991, pp. 290 - 292.

19. Binstock, R.H., Post, S.G., **Too Old for Health Care? Controversies in Medicine, Law, Economics, and Ethics.** "Justice for Elderly People in Jewish and Christian Thought." Baltimore and London: Johns Hopkins Press, 1991, pp. 120 - 137.

20. Nelson, J.B., Rohricht-Smith, J.A., **Human Medicine**, "Caring for Human Health." Augsburg Publishing House, Mn. Mn., 1984, pp. 15 - 30.

21. Card, M., "Distressing Disguise" Album: Present Reality, The Sparrow Corp., P.O. 2120, Ca., 1988.

22. Burkett, L., **The Coming Economic Earthquake**, Chicago: Moody Press, 1991.

23. Gornick, C.C., Kjellstrand, C.M., Acute Renal Failure Complicating Aortic Aneurysm Surgery, *Nephron*, Vol. 35, 1983, pp. 145 - 157.

24. Husebye, D.G., Westlie, L., Styrvoky, T.J., Kjellstrand, C.M: Psychological, Social, and Somatic Prognostic Indicators in Old Patients Undergoing Long Term Dialysis. *Arch Intern. Med.*, Vol. 147, 1987, pp. 1921 -9 124.

25. Taffett, G.E., Teasdale, T.A., Luchi, R.J., In Hospital Cardiopulmonary Resuscitation, *JAMA*, Vol. 260, 1988, pp. 2069 - 2072.

26. Schiedermayer, D.L., The Decision to Forego CPR in the Elderly Patient, *JAMA*, Vol. 260, 1988, pp. 2096 - 2097.

27. Sulmasy, D.P., Geller, G., Faden, R., Levine, D.M., The Quality of Mercy: Caring for Patients with Do Not Resuscitate Orders, *JAMA*, Vol. 267, 1992, pp. 687 - 696.

ENDNOTES FOR COUNTERPOINT TO TEACH US TO NUMBER OUR DAYS
(Beginning on next page)

1. To avoid the cumbersome "individuals and family," I am simply going to use "family" to designate both.

2. I am using government in a generic sense to refer to federal, state, and local governments. Government, rightly understood, should also include individuals and families.

3. I do wonder about the "infinite value" of "humans" who will spend eternity in Hell, relative to 'humans" who will spend eternity in Heaven. Perhaps, this was just a careless statement by the authors.

Counterpoint to
Teach Us to Number Our Days (Psalm 90:12)

Franklin E. Payne, Jr., M.D.

*Dr. Payne is Associate Professor at the Medical College of Georgia. He is author of **Biblical/Medical Ethics, making Biblical Decisions,** and **What Every Christian Should Knowe About the AIDS Epidemic.***

My comments should be understood as disagreement within the family, i.e., the body of Christ. Dr. Rutecki is a valued supporter of the Journal. Both he and Mr. Geib are brothers in Christ. Further, theirs is a Biblical argument, the goal of this Journal being to apply the Bible to medicine and to medical ethics accurately and thoroughly. So, I am chagrined to disagree with their argument, but challenged to disagree on the same grounds, i.e., Biblically.

Also, there is much that I agree with in their paper. (See my concluding remarks.)

Rationing, the Family, and the Government

First, the authors accede that medical care has always been rationed. Families have always made decisions whether to take one of their own to the physician. Medical insurance companies have always had limits on what they would pay. Even Medicare and Medicaid have always had limits.

Rationing is talked about today because a crisis has developed between what is wanted (complete medical care for everyone and high salaries for physicians) and what can be paid. Everything in life is rationed: food, housing, clothing, transportation, recreation, etc. All families and every individual[1] decides on what they will spend their money. No one, not even the richest people, can afford anything and everything.

And, *we decide in different ways.* Some people spend more on recreation than others. Some families scrimp on virtually everything else to send their children to a private school. Some spend relatively more on clothes or cars or houses. The point is that *neither rationing, in general, nor rationing of medicine, in particular, is anything new.*

More importantly, *such rationing is made by families* according to their own values. *This shift of decision-making away from families is perhaps the greatest reason that rationing is such a prominent topic for medical economics.* Medical licensing (of physicians and medical schools) came first, then medical insurance, then Medicare, and then the "right" to medical care (everything for everyone). Increasingly, decision-making has been taken out of the hands of the family and into the hands of physicians and "third parties."

If these shifts had not taken place, there never would have been a crisis in medical economics, as there is no crisis in housing, clothing, food, or recreation. While the government[2] is exerting increasing control in these areas as well, most decisions are still made at the family level in a relatively free market.

My counterpoint is that the important issue is returning medical decision-making to the family. Wrestling with age-related or any other criteria of rationing is futile within the current government-controlled system. Modifying or structuring a cancer is not the solution — removing it is! The authors need to explore thoroughly the implications of the inevitability of rationing.

Thus, the major Biblical debate must be whether the government has any role in medical care. I will not present that argument here, as I have many times elsewhere. I simply point out where the real problem lies.

Age-Based Rationing Is Not Biblical

I fully agree with the authors' concept of the "ultimate, priceless, spiritual worth of persons," at least those who are eventually glorified.[3] However, a "person's eternal, spiritual value" is not easily separated from his "functional worth in a time-space continuum." Everyone's eternal destiny is precisely determined by his behavior (function) during his life on earth ("time-space continuum").

A person is relegated to Heaven or Hell according to his decision about Jesus Christ (Acts 4:12). Also, their every act in the time-space continuum is judged "good or bad" relative to eternity (I Corinthians 3:12-15). *These judgments are not based upon age at all, but their rightness or wrongness according to God's truth.* Thus, "ultimate, priceless, spiritual worth of persons" (the author's own higher values) continues to be determined in older ages as well as younger ages. The authors' separation of the aged from the younger is inconsistent with their own major premise of human value.

Further, a person's value cannot be relegated to his physical performance alone, even relative to work. The simple proverb, "Brains triumph over brawn," demonstrates this value. While an older person cannot do the physical work of a younger person physically, he may wisely direct the "brawn" of a younger person or of machinery to do far greater work than physical prowess alone could accomplish.

Age alone does not allow for one's wisdom and/or position of importance either. Age alone does not allow for the treatment of a corporation president who has more to offer his business in wisdom than anyone else in the firm. It does not allow for the treatment of elders who wisely govern their church. It does not allow for the treatment of the President of the United States who may be older than most, as Ronald Reagan was.

Same Conclusion, Other Criteria

The authors could have chosen to exclude medical care on the basis of efficacy and accomplished their goal of rationing without the criterion of age. They did touch on this aspect, but it was not their central argument. For example, recovery from acute renal failure is not determined by age alone. The younger person with diseased kidneys will fare little better than the elderly with their "aged" kidneys.

AIDS (acquired immunodeficiency syndrome) is another example of relatively futile treatments. Their annual cost of treatment is over $40,000 for patients who are primarily 20-40 years of age, compared with the authors' figures of $8,021 for "terminal" diseases in the "elderly."

Thus, they could have reached the same conclusion, basing their criterion on futility of treatment, rather than age and not have to face the inconsistency that age alone or "comorbid" requires.

Another View of Authors' Biblical Texts

Rutecki's and Geib's Biblical arguments should be interpreted differently. Their link of land to functional longevity (Leviticus 25) is an analogy that will not hold. While land does become depleted, with proper rotation of crops and/or fertilizer, it can once again become productive. No amount of medicine can ever restore some bodies. Further, the Jubilee was a cycle of years, but human life is a one-time event. Other reasons that make this analogy doubtful have been given above.

Their interpretation of Leviticus 27:1-8 comes close to being accurate. However, the functional worth of the different classes of persons related to *a specific task*, i.e., service in the tabernacle. Making a general principle of the value of life from *one specific task* is a great leap of logic, (i.e., reductive reasoning) that requires much more than one example to make it valid.

My arguments against Ecclesiastes 12:1-8 have already been presented. Spiritual worth to God has little to do with age, else the leaders of the church would be young people instead of "elders" (e.g., James 5:14).

Agreement on Conclusions

It is fascinating that I agree with Rutecki and Geib on the directives for medical care. Care should be emphasized over cure, a theme that I have championed for several years. Medical care should not be performed where it is almost certainly futile. The Church needs to consider its role in "caring," especially as we approach the failure of the "system." The family must again become the primary provider of the care of its members, including medical care.

While we agree on these practical directives, I do not agree that the authors have reasoned validly from Scripture. Their intent to do so is highly commendable, but not accurately executed. Finally, the mind of Christ which are our readers must decide. I offer them a counterpoint.

(Endnotes on page 102)

Letters to the Editor *(Continued from inside front cover)*

come, if not long overdue. I would, however, take issue with one of the articles in the particular issue I read, "Questions Surrounding the Withdrawal of Artificial Hydration and Nutrition from Patients in a Persistent Vegetative State, by Daniel E. Deaton.

My first problem with the piece is two terms in the article. One is "persistent vegetative state," abbreviated throughout as PVS. Chaplain Deaton himself asks, "How reliable is the diagnosis of PVS?" His own reply is, "I conclude that the diagnosis of the permanence of PVS is reliable, though not infallible."

What, then, is to be said of the article called "Vegetative State After Closed-Head Injury: A Traumatic Coma Data Bank Report, in *Archives of Neurology*, Vol. 48 (June 1991), pages 580 - 585? That report cites a scientific study that followed recovery rates of 84 patients with a firm diagnosis of PVS. Of those patients, "41% became conscious by six months, 52% regained consciousness by 1 year, and 58% recovered consciousness within the 3 year follow-up interval."

The other term used by Chaplain Deaton that is problematic, at best, is "artificial hydration and nutrition," abbreviated throughout as AHN. Nutrients and fluids supplied to a person through tubes are *real* nutrients and fluids; there is nothing "artificial" about them.

"PVS" and "AHN" are nonce expressions coined by proponents of euthanasia (hardly "advocates of the Lordship of Christ in medicine") to promote the goal of killing off "burdensome" people. If they can get

people thinking in their own language, they are half-way to their goal.

Re "AHN": A "Resource Paper" published by the U.S. National Conference of Catholic Bishops in April, 1992, called "Nutrition and Hydration: Moral and Pastoral Reflections," uses the expression "medically assisted feeding." If simple feeding (albeit "medically assisted) can be obfuscated by technical-sounding language, laymen will be deceived into thinking of it as "medical treatment." Indeed, Chaplain Deaton accepts the notion that tube feeding is "medical treatment" that may be removed from certain patients who are not dying from a particular pathology.

Removing a respirator from a patient whose lungs are not functioning allows that person to die from his condition. But stopping the feeding of someone who is unconscious — from whatever cause — does not "allow" the person to die; it kills him. The death does not result from the condition, but from starvation. The *intent* is to cause death. That is killing. And it is also playing into the game plan of the euthanasia promoters ...

Re "PVS": No human being is ever a vegetable. No matter how unconscious, comatose, or mentally incompetent a person becomes, he or she is in a "persistent *human* state." But when society begins to think in terms of "vegetables" rather than "humans," it is an easy thing to write these people off. That is exactly what happened in eighteenth and nineteenth-century Americans with the slaves, and in Nazi Germany with Jews: These victims-to-be were first

dehumanized in the language. Christians — especially those who are trying to be restore Christian principles to modern medicine — should not be misled into using the language of the anti-Christians. That's like speaking of abortion as "pregnancy termination"; it hides the truth.

I suggest that those who are going to engage in the debate about these issues begin by reading the materials of the enemies of "the Lordship of Christ in medicine," so they will not fall into the trap of accepting the deceptive language and ideas of the enemy.

For Life,
Thomas Longua, Vice President
Colorado Right to Life

Dear Dr. Terrell:

I wrote the enclosed comment of Daniel Deaton's article in the Summer 1992 issue of *JBEM*. Initially I wrote it just to be able to voice my concern and not really intending to mail it, [but] just to file it away in the computer floppy disc. But then, after reading the purposes of BEM I find Deaton's article so at variance with your avowed purpose that I had to send it, for two reasons. First, as a chastisement against the *Journal* for printing such a piece. And, second, as a direct response to Deaton and perhaps the other readers of *JBEM* that such a manner of solving ethical medical problems in the light of scripture should not be considered, or even read for that matter.

A CRITIQUE OF DEATON IN THE LIGHT OF II TIMOTHY 3:16

I would like to copy II Timothy 3:16-17:

16. *All scripture is given by inspiration of God, and is profitable for doctrine, for reproof, for correction, for instruction in righteousness;*
17. *That the man of God may be perfect, thoroughly furnished unto all good works.*

Paul wrote this to Timothy ... shortly prior to Paul's execution. There is little doubt Paul is speaking of all scripture but there is some discussion among Christian scholars concerning the extent of the writings to which Paul is referring, with some authorities stating he obviously means the Jewish scripture since they are the teachings by which Timothy was taught (see vs 15) and the New Testament had not been collected at this time. On the other hand, other scholars feel Paul is writing about the entire Bible since the vast majority of it had been written by this time and the books were already in the churches where there were men gifted with discernment of the spirits and able to distinguish between inspired writings and other types. Whichever school is correct, today we tend to consider all the Bible, new as well as old testaments, inspired and capable of Paul's instruction to Timothy concerning scripture's power for doctrine, reproof, correction, and instruction in righteousness. And, that the man of God may be perfect, that is something to which nothing need be added, thoroughly furnished, that is he should have all that is needed to insure success in his work whether a minister or a spiritual layman — or someone setting forth so-called ethics, ethics which impact fully, strongly, absolutely upon the patient, physicians, nurses, and family — in fact, anyone coming in contact with the particular medical situation in question. Ethics beyond a shadow of a doubt can only be answered by prayerfully being led through the Bible by The Holy Spirit.

And, indeed, I felt that is exactly what Deaton had in mind when he stated the aim of his paper was to bring the issue of ANH (artificial hydration and nutrition) under the scrutiny of Christian ethics — paragraph 5. And, of course, I knew he was on track when in paragraph 7 he mentioned human life as being made in the image of God and is a gift as a trust from Him. Paragraph 8 tells how God assigns value to human life, giving it and taking it away. And because sin, paragraph 9, is a word rarely used today except by the most fundamental Bible-waving, brimstone preaching, soul-saving redeemers of lost souls, I knew I was on to something big and eagerly read on.

But then the tone of things began to diverge. My first suspicion that things were beginning to run amuk was Deaton's reference to "Patients have the right ..." and there I questioned just where in scripture was the outline of a human's rights given. I know of the Bill of Rights, a nice and yet human writing. And with every new self-professed, abused, unrecognized minority group coming to the forefront, we have another list of rights: animal rights, right to medical care, right to profane God, right to do whatever, say whatever, and certainly write whatever. Deaton then launched into a rather pseudo-scholarly list of questions he felt he should answer and when he was successful, at least to his satisfaction, he then drew some conclusions. But there is where I feel the true heart of his paper came to light. He cited 36 references or Endnotes as they are referred to, and never once mentioned the Bible. Here is a man with three degrees in theology, serving as a chaplain in the Naval Hospital in San Diego, a member of a bioethics committee, writing a paper on ethics for a publication professing to be a Journal of Biblical Ethics in Medicine and he could not find, did not find, omitted, overlooked, forgot about, the Bible! Incredible, unbelievable, in this day when the world is polarizing in its views about God, Jesus, abortion, prayer, and on and on ... we have this sort of publication. I truly shudder when I think about the poor servicemen with shattered bodies and torn minds, spirits awash in a sea of confusion, being subject to the same type of counseling this paper represents. In formulating principles concerning care of human life, created by God, it is correct to rely upon the word of God, not some vain writings.

In closing, I can only think of I Corinthians 1:25-31: "Because the foolishness of God is wiser than men: and the weakness of God is stronger than men. For ye see your calling brethren, how that not many wise men after the flesh, not many mighty, not many noble, are called: but God hath chosen the foolish things of the world to confound the wise: and God hath chosen the weak things of the world to confound the things which are mighty; and base things of the world and things which are despised, hath God chosen yea, and things which are not, to bring to naught the things that are: that no flesh should glory in his presence."

Sincerely,
David G. Haney, M.D.
Rock Island, Illinois ·

LCDR DEATON RESPONDS.

The responses to my article, though largely adverse, are encouraging in that they show the need for further Biblical and theological reflection on the perplexing issue of the sustaining of organic life in persons who are exceedingly unlikely ever to recover their cognitive function. They also will provide an opportunity for me to clarify some of the points of contention.

I have no real quarrel with Dr. Orr's observations concerning the use of the term "quality of life." My caution in the use of the term stems from my objection to utilitarian and hedonistic judgments about "quality of life" being used as a basis for deciding whose life is worth living. So long as the inherent value of human life in the image of God is not diminished or rejected, "quality of life" may be a useful expression in decisions about which treatments or interventions are too burdensome or do not significantly contribute to the patient's well-being.

The comments of Mr. Longua of the Colorado Right to Life Committee require more lengthy analysis. First, the issue of the use of terms. Mr. Longua says that PVS and AHN are "nonce expressions coined by proponents of euthanasia" and as such are the "deceptive language and ideas of the enemy." In fact, the term "persistent vegetative state" first appeared in a 1972 article in *The Lancet* in which two doctors

described a "syndrome in search of a name."[1] The doctors offered the name PVS as a description of the absence of any clinical sign of cortical function combined with alternating periods of sleep and wakefulness. The word "vegetative" was taken from the Oxford English Dictionary meaning "an organic body capable of growth and development but devoid of sensation and thought." The origin of this term is not an intentional demeaning of human beings but rather an attempt to distinguish the condition from that of a coma, stupor, and other mental states. The doctors justified their term as follows: "It suggests even to the layman a limited and primitive responsiveness to external stimuli; to the doctor it is also a reminder that there is a relative preservation of autonomic regulation of the internal milieu."[2]

With Mr. Longua, I deplore euphemisms such as "pregnancy termination," etc. But for 20 years PVS has been used as the clinical description of a certain condition. I have no objection to other descriptions such as a "non-sentient state" or "decorticate state." However, to write a paper about the condition without using terminology that virtually everyone else is using would be foolish and reactionary.

Similarly, AHN is commonly used to refer to nutrition and hydration delivered by *artificial* means. This artificial delivery of nutrition and hydration requires the supervision of highly trained personnel and is highly invasive. Among the side-effects of AHN I have observed in the ICU where I work are infection, fluid overload, diarrhea, bleeding, electrolyte imbalances, and pneumonia caused by the aspiration of nutrients into the lungs. Is it not at least

arguable that these artificial feedings are more akin to medical treatment than to the provision of a glass of water or a bowl of soup to a hungry and thirsty patient?

It is difficult for me to follow the logic of those who accept the discontinuing of mechanical ventilation in patients who can no longer breathe naturally without accusing the doctors of suffocating the patient, and who accept the discontinuation of patients from renal dialysis in whom kidney function naturally has ceased without accusing the physicians of poisoning the patient, but who accuse those who would disconnect medically assisted feedings of killing the permanently unconscious patient who is no longer able to swallow. In all these situations, death would have occurred if treatment had not been begun in the first place. The intent of the withdrawal of treatment in each case is not to cause death but to cease treatments that offer no reasonable curative benefit. Each is an example of a life-sustaining intervention that can not reverse the patient's underlying condition.

Concerning the article by Levin, et al., noted by Mr. Longua,[3] I welcome the reference and hope that more studies like it will help physicians determine with greater accuracy the likelihood of recovery from PVS. In my article I cited American Medical Association and American Academy of Neurology reports to the effect that the odds of recovery from PVS after one year are very small, especially in older patients. I therefore recommended that AHN not be withdrawn before at least a period of a year has passed from the time of the original diagnosis. Indeed, the Levin article notes that : "severely head-injured patients rarely are capable of comprehending simple commands within one year if they have not done so by six months."[4] However, the article does report that 6% of the patients followed did improve between the first and second years. Beyond two years, the article concludes: "Improvement at such a late state must be regarded as a rare event."[5] Given the possibility that even this small number of patients may regain sentience between the first and second years, I would be wiling to advocate a two year waiting period before considering withdrawal of AHN until a more precise method for diagnosis of the permanence of PVS should become available. Of course, an accurate diagnosis may be obtained in some patients (i.e., those whose cerebral cortices have been severely damaged or atrophied) in a much shorter period of time. In these cases, AHN may be ethically withdrawn following the determination that recovery of consciousness is not naturally possible.

Finally, a word about Dr. Haney's comments. The *ad hominem* remarks about my ministry need not be answered. However, I am troubled by the assumption that since the Bible is not quoted throughout my paper, it is omitted, overlooked, or forgotten. Obviously, the issue of PVS/AHN is not directly addressed in Scripture. The primary Biblical issue is spelled out in my first affirmation -- namely, the sanctity of human life in the image of God (Genesis 1:26-27) and the prohibition of the taking of innocent human life (Genesis 9:6); Exodus 20:13). The central Biblical issue is whether the withdrawal of AHN from someone in a permanent PVS constitutes the wrongful killing of an image bearer of God.

As a Christian who seeks to live by the authority and guidance of the Word of God, I welcome correction from anyone who discovered in Scripture specific teaching or principles that can be applied to the complex ethical challenges brought about by the rapid advancement of medical technology. While I wholeheartedly affirm the truth of II Timothy 3:16-17 and I corinthians 1:25-31, simply stating these truths contributes nothing to the arduous task of actually applying the inspired and unchanging Scriptures to perplexing and ever-changing issues such as PVS/AHN.

1. Jennett and Plum, "Persistent Vegetative State After Brain Damage Name," *Lancet*, April 1, 1972, pp. 734-737.

2. *Ibid*, p. 736.

3. Levin, *et al.*, "Vegetative State After Closed Head Injury," *Archives of Neurology*, June 1991, pp. 580-585.

4. *Ibid*, p. 580.

5. *Ibid*, p. 585.

Letters to the Editor

(Continued from page 92:90

I am, however, disappointed that Mr. Duffee failed to note in my article how much weight I place on the inherent value of the fetus from the moment of conception. While it was not the purpose of my paper to give a full understanding of the nature of the image of God (see the title of my paper), I did try to define one aspect -- the nature of the image as corporeal -- and to show how that aspect would give the fetus inherent value from the moment of conception. I did not state or imply in my paper that the fetus has inherent value in his/her potential for procreation. Here Mr. Duffee is confusing my arguments regarding the *nature* of the image (where I do find clear evidence for the inherent value of the fetus) with my arguments for the *function* of the image (where I am not arguing for the inherent value of the fetus but do find clear evidence for God-like adult behavior in procreation). I attribute Mr. Duffee's oversight and confusion to my poor literary skills and will try to clarify my position now.

My main point in discussing the *nature* of the image of God is to include corporeality as an integral aspect of the image, not to exclude the other aspects, e.g., spirituality (although I do find far less support for this aspect in the Genesis passages themselves.). Unfortunately, many evangelical theologians have neglected the corporeal aspect of the image, and it is this neglect that I am addressing (see page 20 in my article). Corporeality as an integral aspect of man is seen to be integral to our understanding the nature of the image then human beings clearly have inherent value from the moment they become corporeal, i.e., conception. The zygote does not simply have the potential to develop God-like attributes. From the moment of conception it is the image of God and is worthy of the protection afforded the image in Genesis 9 (see pages 22 - 23 in my article).

My main point in discussing the *function* of the image of God is that procreation, as well as representative rule, is a way of acting that is God-like in some respects (see pages 20 - 22 in my paper). If procreation is recognized as an important function of the image, then abortion is an obvious rejection of our God-like role. Instead of filling the earth with divine likenesses through procreation we destroy the image of God through abortion and in so doing devalue the God in whose image we are created (see page 23 in my paper).

Sincerely yours in Christ,

Andrew A. White, M.D., M.A.T.S.

God Weeps For Anencephalics

Byron C. Calhoun, M.D.

Dr. Calhoun practices Ob/Gyn in Biloxi, Mississippi

Loma Linda University suspended its use of anencephalic infants for their transplantation program in 1988 but the use of fetal tissue remains a very active area for concern. The year 1992 saw the approval of a national tissue bank for aborted infants for research and possible medical use. What ought to be the response for the Christian physician to the use of anencephalics for tissue research?

The issue must be addressed in an organized, Biblical manner. The best way to discuss organ donation by anencephalics is to use a Biblical model for elucidation.[1,2] The framework we will use consists of a five part framework defined by the mnemonic of **THEOS**.

THEOS represents:

- **T** - Transcendance
- **H** - Hierarchy
- **E** - Ethics
- **O** - Oaths
- **S** - Succession

TRANSCENDENCE

We must deal first with the presupposition that the Lord is sovereign and speaks authoritatively on His earth. This article affirms the Reformed position of the absolute sovereignty of God with His transcendence over His creation. The Lord establishes His transcendence in Exodus 20:1-17. God clearly states in Exodus 20:3 that He is the sovereign on the earth and that there is no other God before Him. This is the key to the argument against organ donation of anencephalics. If we do not accept the sovereignty of the Lord, and, hence, His infallible Scripture, we cannot be expected to make the appropriate Biblical decisions. The reason we accept the Lord's authority concerning His sovereignty is simply because He is God. He has shown Himself faithful in truth throughout the Scriptures. Therefore, He is able to speak authoritatively to us today through His Word.

HIERARCHY

The hierarchy mentioned shows us that we are to be subordinate to God. God expects obedience through subordination to His revealed written will. God's hierarchy starts in the family through Exodus 20:12 and Deuteronomy 6:7. The development of the Lord's hierarchy extends to the nation of Israel as the priests are designated not only as spiritual leaders but physical healers as well (Lev. 13-15). The priests are God's designated representatives to initiate and substantiate "cure" through the power of God.

The New Testament carries the hierarchical concept even further to include all believers as "a chosen people, a royal priesthood, a Holy nation, a people belonging to God" (1 Peter 2:9). We Christian physicians inherit the hierarchical position of not only the royal priesthood of believers, but also meld with that of the New Testament gift of "healing." We are the New Testament "healer-priests." As such, we physicians have a tremendous responsibility to teach our patients not only proper physical but spiritual health as well. We must teach the correct, Biblical thoughts on the issue of anencephalics.

Because we hold such a position of trust, Christian physicians are expected to remain defenders of the helpless and weak. Nowhere do the Scriptures tell us that a specific set of physical or mental attributes make us human. It is in Genesis where we are "made in God's image" that we take on our humaness.

My frame was not hidden from you

when I was made in the secret place. When I was woven together in the depths of the earth, your eyes saw my unformed body. Psalm 139:15[3]

Therefore, just because a child has less brain than another it does not justify murdering him to obtain organs. God holds each child dear and Christ said, "suffer the children to come unto me" in Mark 10:14. Utility is never the coin of man's worth as deserving God's healing mercy.

ETHICS

How we ought to act lies in the ethics of the issue as revealed in Exodus 20:1 - 21:26. The Lord in Exodus 20:13 says, "You shall not commit murder." The Hebrew word here is *rashach* and signifies lying in wait and taking life. It is a premeditated murder. The idea is most like a vengeful murder. There is no intent here to include persons executed from crimes or killing in war. The distinction is quite precise. Perhaps the easiest way to explain the concept of killing-murder is to use C.S. Lewis' analogy that "all sex is not adultery any more than all killing is murder." Intention makes all the difference. Exodus 20:22-24 applies to a pregnant woman involved in a fight with a resulting premature birth. If there is a premature delivery with no serious injury there is a monetary fine for the assault. However, if there is serious injury or death,

... life for life, eye for eye, tooth for tooth, hand for hand, foot for foot, burn for burn, wound for wound, bruise for bruise. is required.

If the unborn infant is a person worthy of protection as the above implies, why should a live born anencephalic be different? The Jews never talked about children's rights because a live born Hebrew was assumed to be part of the covenant people with infanticide as unthinkable. That was something a Canaanite did. We need only look to the detestable practices of the followers of Molech, who heated up brass/metal statues with fires underneath outstretched arms and placed live infants on the white hot arms, to understand why the Hebrew children's regard of life and children was so high.

The intention of the present medical climate is to make it possible to use dead aborted fetuses and live anencephalics as organ donors and research tools. Dead fetal organs don't make good transplant tissue. There is a bit of squeamishness now but, as with abortion, once the initial horror is gone, it will be business as usual. The easiest route to the acceptance of this horrible practice is to make it "legal" as we did abortion. We merely legally define the anencephalic infant to be out of personhood and presto! Anencephalics no longer qualify for protection under the law because they are not legally "people" with the right of equal protection under the law.

The real crux is that, even if this horrendous law were to pass, what would be the medical utility of the organs harvested? A very articulate analysis is provided in the March, 1989, issue of JAMA.[4] It is noted that there are nationally 3.75 million births per year in the United States. The anencephalic rate is about 0.3 per 1000 total births. This would yield about 1125 anencephalics each year.

About 20% of pregnancies get alphafetoprotein screening for neural tube defects. Ninety-five percent of these anencephalics are aborted. This makes the number of births about 911. Two thirds are stillborn. This reduces the number to 304 live-born infants. About 50% of anencephalics are premature (less than 37 weeks) and some 50 - 80% have weights less than 2500 grams. If we assume 60% as being too small to use as donors, then we end up with 122 useful anencephalics. If about two thirds of families would donate, that would make the useable number 81.

Kidneys are generally not transplanted because of the higher success rate with older grafts and infants generally wait until 2 years for a graft. About 15% of the anencephalic hearts are unusable due to hypoplasia and 25% of the livers are unacceptable for similar reasons. This effectively brings the estimated number of useable organs to 0, 69, 61, respectively.

The actual number of transplantable organs is usually about 25% of the total number for various reasons due to compatability, transport of organs, or availability of recipients. So, the actual number of organs useful would be 0, 17, 9. The benefit at present is not really delineated. The long term survival of heart transplants is about 50% and liver transplants about 20%. This pushes the benefits to 0, 9,2 for kidneys, hearts and livers. The most optimistic benefits projected in the next 10 years at present rates of surgery and technology show 25 kidneys, 12 hearts, and 7 livers per year.

If we weigh what the Lord said in Exodus with even the most optimistic numbers, it doesn't justify disenfranchising a whole group of people. Even the utilitarian can see no benefit to using anencephalics for transplant. However, what if we become able to make our own anencephalics? If we can define away their "personhood" what is to stop a totally depraved individual from making an "organ farm?" If surrogacy is acceptable, we have the technology to create our own neural tube defects. We can pay mothers to have anencephalics and legally have no grounds to interfere. The organs could be sold to the highest bidder and the infants used in research. Methotrexate, valproic acid, or retinoic acid, all folate antagonists, could easily be used to "create" anencephalics at the critical time in neural tube closure. Vaginal ultrasound at 10-12 weeks could be used to confirm the skull defect and, if not present, just legally abort the infant and try again.

Lest we think this is too macabre, remember drug companies in Europe already use aborted infants' collagen in cosmetics. Aborted fetal pituitaries have already been implanted in Parkinson's patients for attempted cure. It is later than we think!

The final difficulty in dealing with anencephalics is to define what is consciousness and what is not. Anencephalics can range in type from total craniorrachischis to hydranencephaly. Human infants with intact brain stems can exhibit complex behaviors, distinguishing their mothers from others, consolability, conditioning and associative learning. Therefore, these infants do not differ in consciousness as much as in ability to accomplish further cognitive learning. If we use this standard, then we may destroy the retarded and senile humans as well.

The use of raw judicial fiat in the face of ethical considerations places no one safe from "legal murder." All we need do is make someone or some class of people "unhuman" under the law and all legal protections fall. It is only a short step, then, to euthanasia, i.e., Holland, infanticide (already done on Down's infants), and the gas chambers.

OATHS

To understand our position as physicians before the Lord, we need to understand that as people of God we took an oath before Him to serve and obey. Exodus 24:7-8 has the people, after receiving the law, confirming the covenant by swearing "We will do everything the Lord has said; we will *obey* (emphasis added). Moses then took the blood from the young bulls and said, "This is the blood of the covenant the Lord has made with you in accordance with all these words." The blood sealed the covenant for the Jews just as Christ's blood sealed our new covenant once and for all. We don't have the blood of animals any longer. The blood of Christ is the one and sufficient sacrifice.

"Sacrificing" our anencephalic children to the god of this age, the devil, only serves his purposes. We must obey the Godly convenants. They are operative today unless specifically addressed by Christ. Psalm 82: says,

Defend the cause of the weak and fatherless, maintain the rights of the poor oppressed.

SUCCESSION

The succession of the saints is addressed in Exodus 20:4 where God says that He will "punish unto the third and fourth generation" of those who hate Him and "showing love to a thousand generations of those who love me and keep my commandments." The ultimate hate of God is destroying those He made in His image. There can be no sin worse than the taking of innocent life. Murder is specifically prohibited and the Scripture says in Leviticus 24:17, "If anyone takes the life of a human being, he must be put to death." Christ does not invalidate this assertion in Matthew 5:38-42 when He says not to resist evil: He merely does away with personal vengeance. He says we are not to take "eye for an eye" in personal vengeance. The declaration of guilt for a murder applies to those who take innocent life in murder. Capital punishment for murder is not the issue, but breaking God's prohibition against murder is.

The punishment for the Jews for destroying infants by offering them to Molech (i.e., science) called for the penalty of death.

Any Israelite or any alien living in Israel who gives any of his children to Molech must be put to death ... If the people of the community close their eyes when that man gives one of his children to Molech and they fail to put him to death, I will set my face against that man and his family and will cut off from their people both him and all who follow him in prostituting themselves to Molech. Leviticus 20:1-5

The same lie by the god of this world is trotted out to us in the medical world. Sacrifice your children and for you it will be well. Just destroy these children so others benefit. After all, it is the "loving" thing to do since these children would just suffer anyway. God save us from such well-intentioned tripe, and the misguided minions of satan! If Sodom and Gomorrah were destroyed for their sins, we must soberly understand that any nation that sanctions infanticide is definitely under judgment. God will "set His face against us."

Succession for the Jew came as a result of bloodline. However, in Exodus 20:6 God makes clear that it is those who "love Him" and demonstrate their love by "obeying His commandments" who are the true successors in God's kingdom. We, as "grafted in/adopted children" in the family of God, become heirs with Christ. If we become disobedient, misuse our priestly role, and call to mercy, we become like Esau who traded his birthright for a "mess of pottage." We may not serve the flesh and God. The demonstration of our love toward God, and hence our legitimacy as heirs to Godly succession, is our obedience to God's commandments. Included is God's injunction to "not commit murder."

WHAT TO DO?

The most important action we take as Christian physicians is to know what the Word says about murdering. The Scriptures clearly forbids it. Infanticide is not directly addressed because it presented such a horrible crime the Jews could not imagine participating in it. We should not bow to popular pressure to allow anencephalics to be legally made into "nonpeople" as we allowed with unborn babies in the abortion mills.

Next, we need to be part of the solution and not the problem. We ought to be on the hospital ethics committees to insure the Biblical perspective is presented in a thoughtful, loving, and articulate manner. We must vote against candidates who support abortion, infanticide, and fetal research. We need to support those women pregnant with anencephalics not to abort them for organs. We need to deal sensitively with the impending death of the anencephalic child and work to support family involvement in the infant's life.

Finally , we ought to be involved directly and personally in taking these infants home with us to die peacefully in a loving, Godly atmosphere if the parents lack the strength to cope with the inevitable death of the severe anencephalic.

Anyone, then, who knows the good he ought to do and does not do it, sins. James 4:17

ENDNOTES

1. Kline, Meredith G., **The Structure of Biblical Authority**, Eerdmans: Grand Rapids, Michigan, 1972, pp. 131-153. Also, "Deuteronomy" **Wycliffe Bible Commentary**, Southwestern Co.: Nashville, Tennessee, 1962, pp. 155-204.

2. Sutton, Ray R., **That You May Prosper**, pp. 16 - 17.

3. All Scripture quotes are from the **New International Version**, Zondervan Publishers: Grand Rapids, Michigan, 1982.

4. Shewman, D.A., Capron, A.M., Peacock, W.J., Shulman, B.L., The Use of Anencephalic Infants as Organ Sources: A Critique. JAMA, Vol. 261, 1989, pp. 1773-1781.

Physician and Pastor - Co-Laborers

Part 1: A Truncated View of Man and Medicine

Hilton P. Terrell, M.D., Ph.D.

Dr. Terrell is Assistant Professor of Family Medicine at McLeod Regional Medical Center in Florence, South Carolina.

The scene is Vienna, in the Austro-Hungarian empire. The time is the 1840's. The chief character is the legendary Hungarian obstetrician Ignaz Semmelweis. He is self-perceived as an outsider. His German is poor; he does not write well in that language. Obstetrics is a field held in low esteem in medicine at that time. The moment is his "Eureka" experience, in which he has put together evidence that illuminates why so many women are dying from childbed fever in the Vienna General Hospital, where he heads one of the two divisions of obstetrics. Though he has never seen a germ, he has reasoned that some infectious principle is being transmitted from the autopsy rooms up to the delivery rooms, on the hands of the obstetricians. The student doctors are required to do autopsies on all of their patients who die. They do plenty of autopsies. The midwives who deliver in another division in the hospital do *not* do autopsies. The maternal mortality rate in the midwifery division is about 1%. In the division headed by Semmelweis the maternal mortality rate is 18%. Mothers who deliver at home or in an alleyway have a very low mortality rate.

Dr. Semmelweis institutes a rule: doctors in his division must wash their hands in chlorine water before delivering a baby. The mortality rate falls to about 1.5% or so. Dr. Semmelweis presents his findings verbally, perhaps clumsily. He is presenting the germ theory of disease to the bigwigs in the "ivory tower." His theory competes with other current theories including constitutional causes and seasonal miasmas. His theory is rejected and he ultimately leaves Vienna to return to Budapest where he dies a few years later.

Sherwin Nuland in his book, *Doctors*, in a chapter on the unfortunate story of Ignaz Semmelweis says, "Even had Semmelweis' explanation of seasonal variations [that is, how they fit into his theory] been generally available, however, it is doubtful that it would have been accepted. No matter the progress that had by then been made in pathologic anatomy and physical diagnosis, Western medicine still lived with various stunted vestiges of ancient theories of disease etiology, like miasmas and vague constitutional imbalances. Concepts of single causative agents, which would enter the arena with the advent of the germ theory less than two decades later, were only barely construed, if at all. There was little precedent for a doctrine that invoked the direct action of invisible particles of putrid organic matter. To many critics, it would take a leap of faith which they were unable or unwilling to make."[1]

Not long after his death Semmelweis was proven very substantially correct. The germ theory took root. It is a powerful concept. Great things have been accomplished in medicine by application of this theory. Ask today what the cause of pulmonary tuberculosis is, and nearly every physician will answer, "Mycobacterium TB" or one of the other Mycobacteriaceae. More than just for *infectious* disease, the germ theory is typical of a set of models which posit a *material* cause for each disease.

THE MEDICAL MODEL OF DISEASE

Common to these models is the idea that each disease is caused by an unbidden, alien, and usually unseen agent which invades a person against his will. The job of medicine is to find the alien and cut it out surgically or poison it out medically. Preventive medicine is supposed to lock *out* the alien substance or to lock it *up* harmlessly — be it cholesterol, elevated blood glucose, uric acid, or a developing nest of malignant cells. The patient's job is rather passive in all of this. The patient is basically to *hold still* while the doctor identifies and destroys the invader. The whole idea of prevention or therapy is to change as little of the *person* as possible. Only the *invader* needs to be destroyed. The person's attitudes, beliefs, motives, loyalties, or character are largely incidental to the process.

The germ theory has worked!

One and a half centuries later, we have become victims of our success in exploiting these models of disease which feature a "physical causative agent" that comes in willy-nilly on a gene or a germ. Thus planted and matured, this model of physical causation of disease has borne such fruit that people are trying to grow it well outside of its natural range.

HOW THE MEDICAL MODEL FAILS US

Physical causation for presenting complaints of patients has been transplanted to problems which do not have a physical cause, though they may have a physical *consequence* in the body. In addition, though multifactorial models for disease are now in ascendance, all of the multitude of factors examined are physical factors. The *spirit* of the suffering person is neglected as a factor, let alone as a key factor. The idea of physical agency for medical complaints has pushed the spirit of mankind out of its proper claim.

I wish to maintain that the *spirit* of mankind is actually the primary factor in determining health or sickness in the United States, and that the "basic science," as it were, of spiritual matters is Biblical theology. It follows then that Medicine should be functioning from a biblical framework that makes the natural science methodology *subsidiary* to theology.

Figure 1 attempts a simple illustration of a bifold conception of human beings. The overlap represents the difficulty we do have in ascertaining the relative contribution of body and spirit in many cases. The spiritual features of human beings cannot be apprehended by the method of natural science. Furthermore, while the Christian may not denigrate the body as do some pagan religions, the spirit is the more important of the two aspects. (1 Timothy 4:8; Matt. 10:28)

Asserting a primacy of the spirit in health may seem to be akin to the invocation of "miasmas" and "vague constitutional imbalances." However, it is normally "true" only *presuppositionally* that there exist "single causative agents" even for infectious diseases. Why have I never seen tinea corporis on my skin, despite having touched it on hundreds of patients? More properly, "single causative agent" should be rendered *sine qua non*. The germs for childbed

BODY

SPIRIT

Organs
Tissues
Physiological functions
Brain

Beliefs
Attitudes
Ideals
Thoughts
Mind

Figure 1

fever were necessary, but they were not sufficient. They required a steady source, which they found in the autopsy room. They required a portal of entry, which they found in the denuded uterine cavities, or

occasionally in accidental cuts on the hands of the doctors themselves. They required a vehicle for transport, which was the hands of the doctors. *They required, behind all these physical things, a belief system in what could be going on, and what could not be going on.*

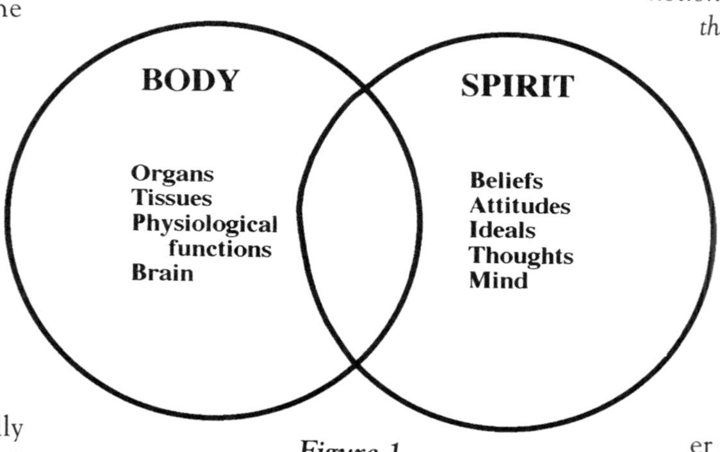

Dr. Semmelweis was not dealing here just with powerful, unseen germs. He was dealing with powerful, unseen attitudes in the Vienna medical establishment. His "solution," after all, was merely one of correcting an *iatrogenic* problem. Remember that the women who delivered at home or in alleyways in the city had almost zero maternal mortality. In his division of the General Hospital, before he instituted changes, the death rate was 18%. It is illuminating that Semmelweis is today remembered for reasoning out that an infectious agent was "the cause" of childbed fever. It is just as tenable to hold that the cause of childbed fever in Vienna was *wrong notions held by doctors*, or the *idea that babies should be delivered in hospitals* because something might go wrong if they did not. Indeed, the fact that something did regularly go very wrong was noted more by the lay community than by the medical community. The latter may well have considered the dangers of childbirth all the more reason to deliver under controlled conditions.

It seems likely that we today in medicine are not at all free of such reasoning.[2] For example, how do we know that it is necessary to treat all patients with acute myocardial infarction in a coronary care unit? Heresy! But, how do we really know? It has now become medical malpractice not to admit all acute MI patients to such places. The British published a series of investigations on this topic about 15 years ago. They presented some interesting evidence that for uncomplicated inferior infarctions patients with an adequate home situation fared as well or better at home than in an intensive unit, for patients over 60 years of age.[3]

Much has occurred in coronary care in the past 15 years, most notably clot lysis agents, the use of afterload reducers, and transluminal angioplasty. Yet, that is always the way it will be. By the time a therapy is really understood, and its true place understood, it will usually find a considerably reduced scope for application. Also by that time, there is a new therapy making the rounds. We are perpetually in a position in which some new *physical treatment* is in ascendance. One problem with this situation is that the *physical treatment* modality also gets ascendance over spiritual features in disease causation and control, and that is not by any proof, merely by presupposition.

Consider the similarity to our view that HIV is the "cause" of AIDS. Since medical science does not, most vehemently does not, deal with the law of God as it marks out sin for us, it thereby omits the whole aspect of sodomy, adultery, IV drug abuse, and fornication as causative of AIDS. The medical profession, in fact, is coming around *in support of* sodomy[4], fornication[5], and IV Drug abuse in very vocal and practical ways. We are caught in our own reductionism, whereby we reduce the matter to its simplest *physical* agency. Nationally, we even PAY for condoms for fornicators, "clean" IV needles for drug addicts[6], food and housing for the wilfully idle, Norplant for Baltimore schoolgirls, and "therapy"

for liars. We had a Christian Surgeon General recently who instructed the population in how to commit sexual sin more safely. He thought it was his job to do so, and that he could separate his job from his "personal" beliefs. The argument is that since sin is inevitable, and the consequences are so bad, we are best advised to counsel for safety. Note, though, that this argument implicitly places the *physical* consequences of sexual sin as more important than the *spiritual* consequences of sin. We must preserve the young people's physical bodies. We neglect their eternal souls.

What we are doing in medicine today — and in the Church and the rest of society — is very like what was going on in Vienna. We *do* wash our hands so as not to infect patients with *physical* germs. Yet we carry the germs of deadly spiritual ideas from a misbegotten medical orthodoxy — wrong ideas about the nature of people and their complaints — and bring those wrong ideas into our examination rooms. We are infecting our patients with these wrong notions. We are harming our patients both physically and spiritually by the infectious ideas we bring with us into the medical encounter. We are also harming them by keeping biblically correct beliefs *out* of the medical encounter.

Like Semmelweis, I would like to try to point out what some of these ideas are, why they are deadly, why they don't belong in our medical care, how we may proceed to wash our hands of them, and with what we may replace them.

As we begin to move from the problem to a solution, we will be moving toward an improvement in the relationship between physicians and pastors. The tale could be told

from either the medical side or the side of pastoral counseling ministry. Both sides have problems. The solution from the medical side prominently includes improved linkages with pastors.

We need to examine, though, a bit further, something of the nature of medicine beyond the Semmelweis story, to see that we do have a problem in medicine (and in the Church) and what its nature is.

NUMERATOR MEDICINE

Physicians deal with numerators. We see those who extract themselves from the general population and present their bodies a living sacrifice for our ministrations. We forget that we are seeing an extract. Even in primary care, we see people for not more than one out of three episodes of illness. Out of a thousand adults, in a month's time three-fourths will have at least one symptom for which they take some specific action. One out of three of those actions includes seeing a primary care physician. That physician will admit a small percentage of his/her patients to a general care hospital bed. Perhaps half or so of the patients admitted will have a consultation by a specialist. One out of the original one thousand will end up in "tertiary care."[7]

We draw our ideas about health largely from sick people. We do not as often draw our ideas about health from healthy people. Certainly, researchers do study the healthy sometimes, but the experiential basis upon which we function in medicine daily is based upon the sick and complaining. It is more biased even than that. Medicine is operated like a pyramid placed upon its apex. Figure 2 (see next page) illustrates the change from a time in which most physicians had a substantial experiential basis in general medicine and

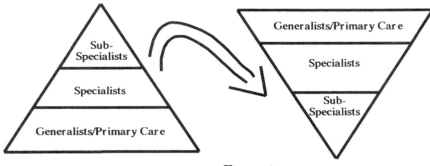

Figure 2

were thus in contact with the "denominators" of patient complaints. The pyramid of medical understanding stood upon its base, as physicians moved from the base toward the apex of their understanding in special areas.

Today, physicians initially *learn* about sickness from the sickest of the sick. The pyramid has been turned to stand upon its apex. "Tertiary care" hospitals collect the rarest of the rare. We have "zebra farms". It is in these holdovers from the time of Semmelweis, these large hospital systems, that we have maintained our fascination and fixation upon physical causation of disease. Hospitals are remarkably efficient for displaying diseases in several stages of development or varying manifestations as well as for studying their response to treatments. On one ward may be collected all manner of cancer or infection or genetic diseases. The benefits we have enjoyed in medical understanding from such collections is not to be underestimated. However, along the way, these collections have helped us to ignore the denominator populations from which they were drawn, as well as the possibility of taxonomies based upon other features than bodily diseases.

We collect and categorize physical ailments, using the medical model. Our field is differentiated largely by disease microorganisms (infectious disease), organs (cardiology), tissues (neurology), age groups (geriatrics), physiological events (obstetrics), and procedures (coronary artery bypass teams).

The whole of medicine is now categorized by reference to these physical features. Imagine a hospital in which the ill were categorized according to *spiritual* features. There might be a wing in which covetousness was the underlying spiritual feature by which a person came to illness, a ward for idol-worshippers, isolation rooms for those in whom stealing was the spiritual genesis of their problem, whole hospitals for the sexually immoral.

Figure 3 illustrates how important it is for every medical practitioner, generalist or specialist, to be aware of the denominator population from which his/her patients are drawn. The prior probabilities of disease profoundly influence the decisions of the practitioner in making diagnostic decisions. Generalists look at subspecialists and are tempted to conclude that they are always seeking zebras. Subspecialists are tempted to look back at generalists and conclude that they are always missing things. Our denominator populations are different. Our error *rates* are not necessarily different. Now, the status in medicine has been (and Semmelweis' experience of the pecking order is an example) for the narrow end of the funnel to tell the wide end how we ought to function. I could argue, from my wide end position as a generalist, against that very vehemently.

Rather than pursue medical internecine warfare, consider that we in medicine as a whole have been turning to the entire population and telling it how it ought to function for health. The estimates of patient self-selection prior to seeking medical attention is probably an *under*estimation of the self-selection that takes place before any of us in medicine see the patient. Other studies estimate that physicians see patients in only 6% of all episodes of illness.[8] Not only are we prone to be mechanistically disease-oriented, we see only a fraction of the whole picture!

GENOGRAM EXAMPLE

Perhaps the example of a hospital departmentalized by spiritual features

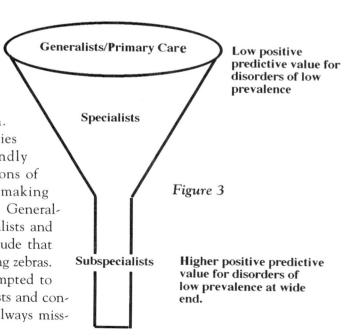

Figure 3

Low positive predictive value for disorders of low prevalence

Higher positive predictive value for disorders of low prevalence at wide end.

is far-fetched. Consider, however, a household I have encountered that is not all that unusual. A divorced woman in her forties heads the house, one of only two employed persons in the house. Her ex-husband contributes nothing to the support of his one surviving child, who is disabled. The other child died in infancy. The mother has three daughters by other men whom she never married. Two of these three already have illegitimate children of their own, out of numerous sexual liaisons, and the third adolescent is already quite sexually experienced. Educational and vocational aspirations find little encouragement or example in the house.

Out of this household has emanated sexually-transmitted diseases galore, depression, one murder, a person with a seizure disorder possibly related to childhood head injuries, severe visual impairment, numerous infections, premature childbirth, and so forth. Into this maelstrom of medical problems, our profession has hurled, modern obstetrics, Dilantin, antibiotics galore, surgery, tricyclic antidepressants, and vitamins. Not admitted to this arena of suffering, however, is any investigation, let alone challenge, of the erroneous *belief systems*. What is proper sexual behavior? What is a good basis for marriage? What is the right way to handle anger? Is it right not to work, when you are able to do so, and live off the means of others? These kinds of questions are begging to be asked and answered. Yet, with a vengeance, the medical profession is refusing even to consider them. All lifestyles are now being created equal. The Scriptures have answers to these questions. They are not rhetorical questions. Medicine, however, is halted well short of the eti-

ologies contained in values and beliefs. By means of working connections between physicians and pastoral counseling, we need to make these answers available to patients.

In a subsequent article, these physician-pastor connections will be explored.

FOOTNOTES

1. Nuland, Sherwin, **Doctors: The Biography of Medicine**, New York: Alfred A. Knopf, 1988, p. 253.

2. See as possible example, Guntheroth, Warren & Spiers, Philip, Sleeping Prone and the Risk of Sudden Infant Death Syndrome, JAMA, May 6, 1992, Vol. 267, pp. 2359-2362. "Before 1971, the Netherlands' SIDS incidence had been one of the lowest in the Western world, only 0.46 per 1000 live births. Following the public campaign [to teach parents to lay babies in the prone position beginning in 1972], the SIDS rate rose to 1.31 per 1000." Following publicity to avoid the prone position, once this alarming trend was noted, the SIDS rates in the Netherlands dropped 40% in 1988, in one year's time. Applying figures similar to these from other nations (Netherlands, New Zealand, Britain) to the United States, 2000 infants per year might be spared. Despite this evidence, local pediatricians are not yet making this recommendation.

3. Hill, J.D., Hampton, J.R., & Mitchell, J.R.A., "A Randomised Trial of Home-Versus-Hospital Management for patients with Suspected Myocardial Infarction," *The Lancet*, 22 Apr 78, pp. 837-841.

— Mather, H.G., et al., "Myocardial Infarction: A Comparison Between Home and Hospital Care for Patients," *Brit. Med. Jour.*, 17 Apr 76, pp. 925-929.

— Mather, H.G., et al., "Acute Myocardial Infarction: Home and Hospital Treatment," *Brit. Med. Jour.* 7 Aug 71, pp. 335-338.

— Eggerstein, Sam, & Berg, Alfred O., "Is It Good Practice to Treat Patients with Uncomplicated Myocardial Infarction at Home?" [editorial] JAMA, Vol. 251, No. 3., Jan 20, 1984, pp. 349-350.

4. Anstett, Richard, Kiernan, Martin, & Brown, Richard, The Gay-Lesbian Patient and the Family Physician, *The Journal of Family Practice*, Vol. 25, 1987, pp. 339-344..

— Caring for a Kid Who's Gay, *Emergency Medicine*, June 15, 1984, pp. 95-119.

— Terrell, Hilton, Should Doctors Judge? [letter] *Emergency Medicine*, November 15, 1984, pp. 10-11.

— Koop, C. Everett, Understanding AIDS: A Message from the Surgeon General, HHS Publication, 1988.

— Magallon, Dorothy, Counseling Patients with HIV Infections, *Medical Aspects of Human Sexuality*, Vol. 21, No. 6, pp. 129-147.

— Koop, C. Everett, The Surgeon General's Report on Acquired Immune Deficiency, U.S. Department of Health and Human Services, undated, p. 17.

5. *Medical Aspects of Human Sexuality*, October, 1989, p.62, "While surrogate partner sex therapy has proved to be highly effective in treating a wide range of sexual disorders and dysfunctions, this method is contraindicated in several situations … marriage,

depressed young men, adult male virgins who are lacking in social skills unless these skills are provided along with the 'surrogate' and in women who have a history of sexual abuse in childhood or who think it is wrong." A good translation for surrogate sexual partner as therapist would be "skilled prostitute" and for the physician who helps arrange the therapy, "pimp." In the name of "health," some of our profession are into pimping.

See also in this regard: Berkovita, Irving, Health Development of Sexuality in Adolescents: The School's Contribution, *Medical Aspects of Human Sexuality,* Vol. 19, October, 1985, pp. 34-49.

6. For Example, Des Jarlais, Don C. & Hopkins, William, "Free" Needles for Intravenous Drug Users at Risk for AIDS: Current Developments in New York City., [letter] *NEJM*, Vol. 313, No. 23, p. 1476.

7. McWhinney, Ian R., **An Introduction to Family Medicine,** New York: Oxford University Press, 1981. [The dean of family medicine in Canada. Quotes Karl Popper, "We are not students of some subject matter but students of problems. And problems may cut right across the borders of any subject matter or discipline." Valuable insights into the "denominator" populations of which we physicians are often ignorant and uncaring.]

8. *Ibid.*

Letters to the Editor

Dr. Douglas Heimburger writes in response to the article in this issue by Dr. Douglas Duffee:

Thank you for the opportunity to respond to "The Necessity for a Revelational Approach to Ethics." I appreciate the author's interacting with my previous writing, and applaud his desire to clarify further the approach that Christians should take to ethical dilemmas. The model I presented for ethical decision-making was developed from John Frame's ideas, published later in his *Medical Ethics: Principles, Persons and problems* (Presbyterian & Reformed, 1988). I think most of what the current paper's author proffers as a disagreement with Frame's model and my application of it to treatment decisions at the end of life may not be the difference it appears to be. Much of what the author described as being the role of the Holy Spirit through prayer is implied by what I, and I think Frame, had in mind in the existential "angle" on ethical issues. The existential concerns in ethical dilemmas are focused on the person, and imply freedom, which may be seen as granted by the agency of the Holy Spirit. To this extent the author may differ only semantically. A Christian ethic that does not incorporate these elements is not thoroughly Christian, and misunderstands the role of the Holy Spirit in applying propositional revelation to our hearts.

However, we may disagree more substantively on the nature of the revelation the Holy Spirit provides us. If by saying "revelational sources are understood as both personal and propositional," the author intends to imply that the Holy Spirit gives personal norms that stand alongside the propositional norms God has given to all persons, with similar authority, I disagree. The Holy Spirit reveals the character of our hearts, and gives us guidance. In doing so, He never guides contrary to His own written Word, for to do so would be to contradict His character. The Holy Spirit provides freedom, indeed, but always does so within the form circumscribed by propositional revelation.

Finally, perhaps the author also misunderstands that I (and Frame) was not suggesting that we can borrow from three of the world's philosophical systems (the normative, situational, and existential) in order to create a workable integrated ethical framework. Rather, the point is that the Word of God has sufficiently provided what the natural man, in devising these three ethical systems, is yearning for but unable to supply. To say so is to offer an apologetic for a thoroughly biblical ethic, and not syncretistically to merge worldly philosophy with Christian principles.

Douglas C. heimburger, M.D., M.S.
Associate Professor and Director,
Division of Clinical Nutrition
University of Alabama at Birmingham

To the Editor:

"The Case for Routine Neonatal Circumcision" [*JBEM*, Winter, 1992, James Fletcher, M.D.] provided welcome encouragement for a decision made with much hesitation some 13 years ago. In that case, the obstetrician who delivered our son at home also returned eight days later to perform the circumcision. Apparently, this biblical practice is also well grounded medically, for I have heard that the blood clotting factors are optimum at that time.

Dr. Fletcher would like to add something about the medical benefits of the "eighth day" circumcision; perhaps this practice might reduce even further the incidence of unhappy sequelae.

John K. Kippley

[Mr. Kippley is one of the Directors of the Couple to Couple League of Cincinnati, Ohio.]

Eternity In Our Hearts: Revelation Confronts Medicine

Douglas Duffee, M.D., M. Div.

Dr. Duffee is a fourth-year medical student at East Tennessee University in Johnson City, Tennessee, pursuing a residency training program in Internal Medicine. He received his Master of Divinity degree from Golden Gate Baptist Theological Seminary in California in 1989 and has served in various ministries.

THE NECESSITY FOR A REVELATIONAL APPROACH TO ETHICS

Setting the Scene

There is an attitude among medical students today which suggests that serious ethical discussion is peripheral and bothersome to the practice of medicine. As medical mercenaries waging war on disease, we are armed with the weaponry of exalted empiricism. This weaponry, best described as an application of the scientific method (with its reliance on repeatable and verifiable sensual phenomena) coupled with the emerging tools of molecular biology (unlocking the pathophysiologic principles of disease), allows the formulation of a diagnosis and treatment plan based on "the facts." Young physicians are well equpped in the advancing science of medicine. We are students of fact.

However, like mercenaries, young physicians often lack a moral impetus in waging this war. While the science and technology of medicine are increasingly able to fight disease in an empirical sphere, this same science and technology are unable to extend their answers to questions in a relational sphere.[1] This is illustrated most profoundly in the case of Mrs. Toivonen presented in a previ-

ous issue of this Journal.[2] This 83 year old woman, institutionalized with severe senile dementia, is hospitalized with pneumonia. "Why does Mrs. Toivonen have a fever?" is a question readily answerable by empiricism. A sputum gram stain and culture and sensitivity will demonstrate the causative pathogen in her pneumonia and allow the proper choice of an antibiotic for treatment. However, the questsion "Why should Mrs. Toivonen be allowed to die?", an option implied by the author of this case scenario (originally presented in the *New England Journal of Medicine*), is a question unanswerable by empiricism, extending beyond simple fact into an ethical sphere. For the field of medical ethics steps beyond the sensual when questions regarding the quality, value, or ending of life are added to the basic questions of physiology. These are questions whose answers lie beyond our senses, beyond our ability to objectively analyze and make reasonable our data. These are questions that deal with personality, family, relationships, and the soul. This is the point at which medical practice leaves the realm of the sensual situation and becomes a theological pursuit.

Thus, young physicians, trained

to manage the weapons of empiricism, are often unprepared when confronted by ethical questions. When presented with issues of an ethical sort the usual response is an apathetic "it is a matter of one's own opinion." In service to the god of empiricism (in spite of its strength in its proper sphere) and blinded to its limitation in an ethical sphere they respond, as characterized by Carl Henry, "granting to reason a pragmatic significance in this world of physical events [while cutting reason off] from any ontic relation to universal essences and absolutes and indeed denies the very reality of such."[3] This nihilism creates a moral bankruptcy, hampering the caring side of medicine, while producing a new generation of physician-scientists in search of their professional soul. In fact, it may be too optimistic to imply that there is even a search for a soul. Many, rather than seeking to understand the relational sphere and its application most notably seen in primary care medicine, opt for careers in procedurally-oriented subspecialties which operate within the comfortable environs of empiricism.[4]

THE LIMITATIONS OF MEDICINE

In theory, that empiricism alone can and/or should inform our actions in an ethical sphere exclusively is argued by relatively few. While non-revelational ethical approaches, characterized as "speculational" by Carl Henry, use varying degrees of human empirical and rational reasoning, very few (exceptions are pragmatism and logical positivism) argue that empiricism and the scientific method alone can be used to build these principles.[5] It is clear to most that the "tools" used to answer the question "Why does Mrs. Toivonen have a fever?" are different from the "tools" used to answer the question "Why should Mrs. Toivonen be allowed to die?"

In practice, however, modern physicians trained as biological scientists do not always realize the limitations of empiricism in an ethical sphere. Consider for a moment the family of Mrs. Toivonen. While the principle of patient autonomy is certainly the most important ethical principle in doctor-patient-family relationships, families (in the absence of advance directives and patient coherence and sometimes even competent patients themseles) often turn to physicians to inform their autonomy. While in this situation the empirical medical status and prognosis of the patient is crucial information, the family is also concerned about issues of life, death, loss, guilt, or even the hereafter. These are issues whose answers lie beyond a scientific capacity to inform them. Trained purely as biological scientists and informed only by opinion, conscience, or common sense, young physicians lack a moral authority to share relationally with their patients in these matters of the soul.

The limitations of empiricism were demonstrated early on in the philosophy of Descartes. In *Meditations on First Philosophy* he implies that while sense perception is adequate for "things near to us" (for example things in an empirical sphere), the senses are unable to inform reality in "things very far away" (for example things in an ethical sphere).[6] Scripture confirms this limitation of human reasoning by showing that while man is an empirically reasoning being and held responsible for what that reasoning deduces,[7] his reasoning ability is limited in its capacity to know God fully on its own.[8] Thus a dilemma is present. Human beings are built to function in an empirical sphere but are unable on their own to gain total insight into the ethical sphere. This is the source of frustration for empirical young physicians confronted with ethical questions. The result is an apathy toward ethical discussion so common in today's student-physician.

THE NECESSITY FOR REVELATION

What knowledge source should inform decision making in an ethical sphere? Descartes' rationalism confirms that sense perception alone has no foundational role in answering this question. These answers must come from beyond our sensory understanding of the situation. This source for Descartes was "first principles" or "objects of intuition."[9] Hume went even further in showing that not only was empirical reasoning inadequate for answering questions of an ethical sort but so was Descartes' rationalism. Others have offered alternative explanations for this knowledge source.[10] These alternatives fall short because they are fundamentally bound by the use of human deductive reasoning in a non-deductive sphere. When an empiricist or rationalist confronts an ethical situation, pragmatism, agnosticism, or subjective value systems are the only logical solutions.

However, a revelational knowledge source claims to provide insight from beyond the empirical sphere into the ethical sphere. This is the fundamental task of revelation.[11] This is not to imply that revelational truths are irrational, only that their source is not limited by empirical sense or rationally derived. John Baillie describes revelation as a revealing from divine subject to human subject truths that were previously a mystery (i.e., beyond our ability to deduce them). Further, he states, "the mystery described is nothing less than God's own will and purpose."[12] In fact, the application of revealed principles in ethical situations, their call on us to decision and response,[13] their reliance on faith rather than deductive reasoning for their reception and the hope this faith creates in a Revealer form the core of our relationship with God.[14] This is what fulfills the search for a soul. God in His infinite wisdom has gifted humankind with the ability to empirically reason and rationally deduce. But in His infinite wisdom He has also seen fit to limit the capacity of this reasoning ability so that a faith relationship can be fostered with Him through encounter with His revelation. It is through this relationship that revelation regarding Himself and the beyond can occur. It is through this relationship that our lives can attempt to imitate His revelation alone that provides answers for the relational question of life, death, family, and the hereafter. Thus "Revelational ethics" are necessary to inform the answers to questions such as "Why should Mrs. Toivonen be allowed to die?"

Difficult questions arise from this

approach to medical ethics when applied within the broad context of the whole of the medical profession as there are many and diverse belief systems within our profession. What constitutes a revelational principle? What individual or body of revelational norms are true and appropriate for use in the ethical sphere? How are these revelational truths applied to specific situations? The epistemological task of Revelational ethics is to evaluate and apply revelational principles through:

(1) A Phenomenologic theological method.[15]
(2) An appropriate hermeneutic.[16]

As the above tools are applied to this approach to ethics, we as Christians are convinced that the source of revelation will be seen as:
(1) The personal revelation of God in
  (a) General revelation[17]
  (b) The person and work of Christ[18]
  (c) The work of the Holy Spirit,[19] and
(2) The propositional revelation of God through the infallible and inerrant words of Scripture.[20]

THE APPLICATION OF A REVELATIONAL APPROACH TO ETHICS

— The imago Dei as a Point of Contact

How then is a revelational approach applied generally to the field of medical ethics and specifically to the doctor-patient relationship within which a diversity of people and belief systems will be encountered? Christian revelation states that human beings are created in the image of God (imago Dei).[21] Dr Franklin Payne offers a solid explanation as to the nature of this image of God in man from a survey of scriptural references and Reformed theology. He states "The image of God in man consists of man's righteousness, his mind (intellect and will), his assigned dominion over the animals and the earth, his 'in-created' (Kuyper's term) knowledge and possibly his ability to communicate and have fellowship with others and with God."[22]

However, the application of this revelational principle to medical ethics has historically been unclear. This lack of clarity is due in part to the question of the presence of the imago Dei in unregenerate man. If the image is not present in unregenerate man, the universality of a revelational approach to medical ethics is lost.

The classic debate as to the presence of the image in unregenerate man is seen in a dialogue which took place between two neo-orthodox theologians in the first half of the twentieth century. In his essay entitled "Nature and Grace,"[23] Emil Brunner states that part of the image remains in unregenerate man. He calls this the "formal" part consisting of man's "humanness" and dominion over creation. But he also claims that a "material" part of the image consisting of God's original image in man (justitia originalis) which formed the basis of fellowship with God before the fall is completely destroyed.

On the other hand, Karl Barth, initially in his commentary on Romans[24] and later in his reply "No!" to Brunner,[25] claims that the image of God is completely destroyed in unregenerate man. This "divine no" produces a barrier between man and God making man unable to understand anything of the divine nature or existence. He states that man's rational nature is only capable of bringing him into a "krisis," in which he comprehends this barrier and his need for revelation from God in breaking through it.

Dr. Payne suggests that the image of God is present in unregenerate man albeit in a markedly distorted form.[26] The extent of this distortion is the crucial question. Is unregenerate man capable of any spiritual longings or insights? Brunner, in his concept of responsibility implies he is. Barth in the "divine no" states he is not. Both Barth and Brunner cite Calvin in support of their positions.[27] Calvin himself seems to suggest a capacity for unregenerate man to have insight into spiritual matters while not denying that in his total depravity humankind's inability to relate to God without divine revelation and response.[28]

Two passages of Scripture seem to shed light on this question of the presence and nature of the imago Dei in unregenerate man. Ecclesiastes 3:11 supports that a spiritual dimension exists in all. In fact, it is possible that this "eternity in our hearts" is placed there by God in every person so that we can find His plan for our lives (or at least bring us into divine Krisis).[29] Further, Romans 1:18-23 shows that a rational nature capable of perceiving the uniqueness and existence of God by our senses through creation exists in all and which makes us responsible before God in our response to Him.[30] This seems to imply that a common aspect of the imago Dei exists in both the regenerate and unregenerate seen as spiritual longing and empirical rationality. There is a likeness of God, given from God, to and in every person. This is a core revelational principle.

The centrality of this principle to

revelational ethics is two-fold. As God's likeness is somehow present in every person, every person has an inherent worth and value. Brunner, citing Calvin, emphasizes this point.[31] It also provides for every person a point of contact with the revelational source. This allows a universal applicability of the revelational approach to medical ethics. At some level true revelation can speak to every person. As Christian physicians discuss options or even pray with patients for wisdom in ethical situations or as they inform a patient's autonomy in dealing with questions of life and death, revelation can speak to the "eternity in their hearts." The revelation may be rejected by patients in their autonomy, may simply satisfy the ethical question at hand or, by God's sovereign guidance and the power of the Holy Spirit in the situation, may lead them to the point where they "find out the work which God has done from beginning to end" (Eccles. 3:11) and enter a saving relationship with Jesus Christ. The phenomenological theological method introduced above safeguards the evaluation of other viewpoints in this revelational process. Thus young physicians in search of their professional identity and soul need not fear informing eternity in their own or their patient's hearts. We are not being academically dishonest as we utilize revelational principles and step beyond empiricism when justified. We have come back to our roots as spiritual image-bearing people when we can do so.

— *The trappings of casuistry versus the freedom of the Spirit*

In a prior issue of this Journal, Dr. Douglas Heimburger presents an integrated approach to ethical problem solving.[32] He incorporates the strengths of three historical approaches. He states that the normative approach provides "a firm standard of right and wrong"[33] "from a revelational source"[34] "adhered to out of the Lordship of Christ."[35] With respect to a consequentialist approach he incorporates the freedom it provides to make decisions in specific situations controlled by a sovereign God.[36] An existential approach also preserves freedom in a more personal sense.[37] He integrates the strength of these three approaches as equal factors in ethical decision making, illustrated as the three corners of an equilateral triangle.[38]

Dr. Heimburger importantly sees the necessity for biblical propositional revelational norms in informing ethical decisions. Furthermore, he senses a need for freedom of application of these norms personally and situationally because of God's involvement with us in every situation.

However, he chooses to integrate the normative approach with the situational and existential in an Hegelian fashion due to a limited application of the whole spectrum of Christian revelation. He implies, to the exclusion of God's personal revelation, that normative action in an ethical sphere is informed only by propositional truths.[39] While he does see a role for the Holy Spirit in "enabling us to be faithful to these [propositional] norms,"[40] he does not give the Holy Spirit a personal or corporate revelatory role in the life of an ethical decision maker. This eliminates the freedom the Holy Spirit provides in the choosing and applying of revelatory principles in specific situations.[41] Furthermore, if not accepting in total, he must now deal with the differing presuppositions that situational and existential approaches bring to ethical decision making, namely, the rejection of revelational absolutes and the elevation of empirical reasoning in informing the ethical sphere. A revelational approach as opposed to a normative or integrated approach preserves the strength of revelational absolutes in informing the ethical sphere while providing the freedom for individual families and physicians to apply these principles in difficult situations by the power of the Holy Spirit through discussion and prayer.

Dr. Heimburger also presents a powerful criticism of the classical normative approach to ethics (and in so doing incriminates the revelational approach) for its application of ethical principle irrespective of situational factors and in a "vacuum."[42] Ultimately this type of approach denies the freedom and break from the law provided by the ministry of Christ and the Holy Spirit.[43] This casuistry robs people of their freedom rather than leading them to be free in their Christianity. Helmut Thielicke further characterizes the danger of this application of revelational norms.[44] Heimburger states that strict application of normative laws to ethical situations actually runs counter to the sovereignty of God to act in ethical situations. Heimburger thus feels obliged to offer an integrated approach to ethical problem solving incorporating situationalism and existentialism.

Revelational ethics actually preserves the freedom of individuals to act in ethical situations. Through prayer and an expanded understanding of the ministry of the Holy Spirit, people can be guided by His supernatural power to apply revelational norms rightly in any ethical situation. This approach often is shunned due to the "perceived uncertainty" of what the Holy Spirit may be guiding us to do in any situation. Revelational principles are numerous and ethical situations are complex but God is faithful and will provide a genuinely seeking individual, asking for wisdom, the wisdom to choose appropriately in any given situation.[45] Our faith requires this confidence in us. Revelation provided by the Holy Spirit individually through Scripture study and prayer or corporately through correction by the church creates our freedom to choose in an ethical situation. It is prayer, study of the scriptures, and faith in light of situational factors and not situations informing our principles that create freedom to decide in ethical situations. This may be a matter of semantics, but the revelational approach guides one to prayer and scripture study in informing ethical decision whereas the other guides one to study the intricacies of the situation at hand. An integration of the normative and situational approaches with their differing presuppositions is not needed to preserve freedom in ethical decision making.

Dr. Theilicke refers to Matthew 10:19-20 in support of this ministry of the Holy Spirit in providing insight into ethical situations.[46] In emphasizing supernatural inspiration within the ethical situation, he preserves true Christian freedom. He also insists that true Christian freedom is done away with wherever the assistance of the Spirit is lacking.[47]

Thus an application of revelational principles to medical ethics is made possible by that part of the image of God present in every person. The freedom in applying revelational norms is seen in the ministry of the Holy Spirit. Prayer is the

vehicle by which the Holy Spirit, as "its object and acting subject"[48] empowers us to make ethical decisions and frees us from the trappings of casuistry.

CONCLUSIONS

1. Empirical ethical reasoning, as used by speculative approaches to ethics (e.g., situationalism, existentialism), is inadequate in informing decision making in an ethical sphere. The answers to ethical questions lie beyond our empirical rational capacity.

2. The source for informing ethical questions is thus by necessity revelation. Revelational sources are understood as both personal and propositional.

3. The pursuits of a phenomenological theological method, hermeneutics, and correction by the church are essential in determining the truth character of supposed revelational principles from numerous belief systems and the legitimacy of applying these principles to ethical situations.

4. The part of the *imago Dei* present in every person provides a point of contact for revelational principles. This part of the image seen as "eternity in our hearts" and our empirical rational capacity makes revelational principles potentially applicable to and understandable by all people.

5. The ministry of the Holy Spirit in all ethical situations preserves human freedom. We can trust the Holy Spirit to perceive the complexity of the situation and to inform our response to the situation. Even the unregenerate have the capacity to be informed by the Spirit in a limited way.

ENDNOTES

1. Thielicke, H., **Theological Ethics, Vol. 1: Foundations**, Grand Rapids, Eerdmans Publishing Co., 1979, p. 465. Here Thielicke emphasizes the necessity of human relationships as the sphere within which ethical decision making takes place.

2. Heimburger, D.C., "A Biblical Model for Medical Ethics, Part 2: Three Ethical Perspectives - A Biblical Integration," *Journal of Biblical Ethics in Medicine*, Vol. 1, No. 2, April, 1987, pp. 22-27.

3. Henry, C., **Christian Personal Ethics**, Grand Rapids, Eerdmans, 1957, p. 148.

4. Colwill, J., "Where Have All the Primary Care Applicants Gone? *New England Journal of Medicine*, Vol. 326, No. 6, 1992, pp. 387-393. Here Colwill suggests that a decreased interest amongst medical students of developing a meaningful philosophy of life is at least one factor in decline of interest in primary care.

5. Henry C., *op. cit.*, pp. 23ff and 97ff. Here Henry divides speculational ethical approaches into Naturalistic (similar to situationalism) and Idealistic (similar to existentialism).

6. Descartes, R., **Meditations on First Philosophy**, trans. by Laurence J. Lafleur, Indianapolis, Bobbs-Merrill Educational Publishing, 1980, p. 18.

7. Romans 1:20, "For since the creation of the world His invisible attributes, His eternal power and divine nature, have been clearly seen, being understood through what has been made, so that they are without excuse."

8. I Cor. 1:20-21, "Where is the wise man? Where is the Scribe? Where is the debater of this age? Has not God made foolish the wisdom of the world? For since in the wisdom of God the world through its wisdom did not come to know God, God was well-pleased through the foolishness of the message preached to save those who believe."

9. Schouls, P., **The Imposition of Method**, New York, Oxford University Press, 1980, pp. 33ff.

10. Henry, C., *op. cit.*, pp. 22-23.

11. Gal. 1:11-12, "For I would have you know, brethren, that the gospel which was preached by me is not according to man. For I neither received it from man, nor was I taught it, but I received it through a revelation of Jesus Christ."

12. Baillie, J., **The Idea of Revelation in Recent Thought**, New York, Columbia University Press, 1956, p. 28.

13. Henry, C., *op. cit.*, p. 132.

14. Rom. 8:24-25, "For in hope we have been saved, but hope that is seen is not hope; for why does one also hope for what he sees? But if we hope for what we do not see, with perseverance we wait eagerly for it."

15. This is my term for an apologetic theological method suggested by Carl Henry in Volume 1 of his systematic theology, **God, Revelation and Authority**, Waco, Word Books, 1976. In chapter 14 (pp. 225-244) he presents specific verifying principles for analyzing alternative revelatory claims. In chapter 3 (pp. 44-69) he presents principles for determining revelation from socio-religious myth. An interesting example of the application of this method is seen in the writings of Albert Schweitzer, **Christianity and the Religions of the World**, London, George Allen and Unwin, Ltd., 1923, and **Indian Thought and its Development**, New York, Henry Holt and Co., 1936.

16. Hermeneutics is the study of applying biblical principles from an original historical context appropriately into our modern day context through consistent methodology. For an Evangelical example, see Grant Osborne's text, **The Hermeneutical Spiral: a Comprehensive Introduction to Biblical Interpretation**, Downers Grove, Intervarsity Press, 1991.

17. see Rom. 1:18-23 and Acts 17:15-34.

18. Matt. 11:27, Luke 10:22, and John 12:38 show a role of Christ as revealing the Father.

19. John 16:13-15 and Gal. 5 show both the revelatory and "Helper" role of the Holy Spirit in the life of the believer. John 16:7-11 shows the revelatory role of the Holy Spirit in the life of the unbeliever.

20. II Tim. 3:16-17, "All Scripture is inspired by God and profitable for teaching, for reproof, for correction, for training in righteousness; that the man of God may be adequate, equipped for every good work."

21. Gen. 1:27, "And God created man in His own image, in the image of God He created him; male and female He created them."

22. Payne, F., **Making Biblical Decisions**, Escondido, Hosanna House Book Publishing Co., 1989, p. 114.

23. Brunner, E., and Barth, K., **Natural Theology**, London, The Centenary Press, 1946, pp. 22-23.

24. Barth, K., **The Epistle to the Romans**, trans. from 6th ed., by Edwyn C. Hoskyns, Oxford University Press, 1933, pp. 42-48.

25. Brunner, E., and Barth, K., *op. cit.*, p. 71.

26. Payne, F., *op. cit.*, p. 114.

27. Brunner, E., and Barth, K., *op. cit.*, pp. 94ff.

28. Calvin, J., **Institutes of the Christian Religion, I.**, Library of Christian Classics, Vol. XX, Philadelphia, The Westminster Press, 1960, pp. 56-57.

29. The Hebrew phrase *mibli asher* in Eccles. 3:11 may suggest a translation such as "without which" yielding a rendering as "God has given eternity in their heart **without which** man will not find out the work which God has done." This suggests a purpose relationship between eternity and plan. The **NASB** and **NIV** imply that in spite of eternity in our heart, man still can not find out God's work. In any case, these translations do not deny the fact that eternity is present in the heart of all. See Brown, Driver, and Briggs, **Hebrew and English Lexicon of the Old Testament**, Oxford, Clarendon Press, p. 115, for discussion of *bli* as an adverb of negation.

30. See Romans 1.

31. Brunner, E., and Barth, K., *op. cit.*, p. 42.

32. see footnote 2.

33. Heimburger, D., "A Biblical Integration," p. 23.

34. Heimburger, D., "A Biblical Model for Medical Ethics: Biblical Norms for Medical Ethics," *Journal of Biblical Ethics in Medicine*, Vol. 2, No. 1, Jan. 1988, p. 11.

35. Heimburger, D., "Biblical Norms for Medical Ethics, p. 11.

36. Heimburger, D., "A Biblical Integration," p. 24.

37. Heimburger, D., "A Biblical Integration," p. 25.

38. Heimburger, D., "A Biblical Integration," p. 22.

39. Heimburger, D., "Biblical Norms for Medical Ethics," pp. 10-11.

40. Heimburger, D., "Biblical Norms for Medical Ethics," p. 10.

41. In addition to the revelatory and "Helper" role the Holy Spirit provides as cited above, Romans 8:26 suggests that the Holy Spirit will help us even when we do not understand the situation we are in or what to pray for regarding its decisions and outcomes.

42. Heimburger, D, "A Biblical Integration," p. 25.

43. This is a central theme in the book of Galations.

44. Thielicke, H., *op. cit.*, pp. 456-457.

45. James 1:5-6, "But if any of you lacks wisdom, let him ask of God, who gives to all men generously and without reproach, and it will be given to him. But let him ask in faith without any doubting, for the one who doubts is like the surf of the sea driven and tossed by the wind."

46. Thielicke, H., *op. cit.*, p. 651.

47. *ibid.*, p. 652.

48. *ibid.*, p. 660.

Ethical Issues in Pharmacy: A Biblical Perspective

Therese I. Poirier, PharmD., M.P.H.

Dr. Poirier is Professor of Clinical Pharmacy at Duquesne University and Director of Clinical Pharmacy Services at St. Francis Medical Center in Pittsburgh, Pennsylvania. She received her pharmacy degree from the Albany College of Pharmacy in Albany, New York, and her Doctor of Pharmacy Degree from the University of Michigan. She is a member of Allegheny Center Alliance Church in Pittsburgh.

Pharmacy as a profession has evolved to a model of "pharmaceutical care." This is defined as the responsible provision of drug therapy for the purpose of achieving definite outcomes that improve a patient's quality of life.[1] Three major functions are involved: (1) identifying potential and actual drug-related problems, (2) resolving actual drug-related problems, and (3) preventing potential drug-related problems. The mission of pharmacy practice is no longer just to dispense the right drug upon the authorization by a physician prescriber but to render pharmaceutical care.[2] As the profession has evolved toward a more responsible role for outcomes of patient drug therapy, there are an increasing number of ethical issues faced by pharmacists.

The goal of this article is to present an overview of major ethical issues in pharmacy. This will be followed by a biblical perspective on these issues.

ETHICAL ISSUES

Five ethical principles are commonly encountered in pharmacy. These include autonomy, veracity, confidentiality, nonmaleficence, and justice. The ethical principle of autonomy versus interference with the physician-patient relationship is

an issue. Pharmacists are commonly in a position in which there is a conflict between patient's rights for informed consent and self-governance and the potential negative consequences to the patient of full disclosure of information regarding adverse effects of medications. For example, a physician may not desire that a patient be informed of the side effects from chemotherapy because of traditional paternalistic attitude that this information may harm the patient by his or her refusal to take a drug with certain side effects.

A second issue is veracity or truth telling versus social responsibility. This occurs when pharmacists are called to provide drug information to be used for questionable purposes. For example, a person may call for information before a pre-employment physical, *i.e.*, school bus driver, on the length of time marijuana remains detectable in the urine.

A third issue is confidentiality versus veracity. This occurs when a pharmacist is asked to identify drugs found in the possession of children or to reveal that a daughter is on birth control pills.

A fourth issue is nonmaleficence or "to do no harm." Pharmacists may be asked to dispense drugs used as abortifacients such as diethylstilbestrol, the "morning after pill." Can a

pharmacists conscientiously object to dispense these medications?

A fifth ethical issue that is becoming a major dilemma in the 1990's is justice. Pharmacists are being asked to ration the use of certain high cost drugs in an era of cost containment and limited resources. The question is how do we morally justify the use of new expensive biotechnologic ("biotech") drugs. An example would be an elderly person on Medicare with a clinical condition in which a high cost biotech drug may be indicated, but whose care is already a net revenue loss.

The final ethical dilemma is faced by pharmacists as a member of a Pharmacy and Therapeutics Committee. This committee is involved with making decisions on what drugs to include on a formulary and to set guidelines on what drugs are used in a hospital setting. Pharmacists have an active role in this clinical decision-making process. A potential conflict of interest could arise when a decision on a status of a drug must be made when there is personal vested interest, *e.g.*, owning stocks, research support, speaker's bureau, in the company who manufactures that drug.

BIBLICAL PERSPECTIVE

As Christians we are guided by the Scriptures which are our ultimate authority on what is right and wrong. The authority of God takes priority over any other authority. Thus there are times when other authorities must be disobeyed if there is a conflict with the Word of God. (Acts 5:29 -"We must obey God rather than men.") Christianity is also very person-oriented. Thus there is a focus on treating patients as persons.

The first ethical principle mentioned was autonomy. Frame believes that the word "autonomy" is contrary to the Word of God.[3] Autonomy implies lawlessness which is in contrast to man's responsibility to God. He prefers that any competent person has the right to make his own decisions about medical treatment and to be given informed consent. (Eph. 4:25 - "Each of you must put off falsehood and speak truthfully to his neighbor;" Exodus 20:16 - "You shall not give false testimony against your neighbor.") Competence according to the Bible is conformity to God's will.[3] If a person is incompetent then family and church family have the responsibility to determine the proper treatment for an incompetent person. The health care worker also has personal responsibility to refuse treatment or to give information that contradicts one's conscience or if one believes that this is in the patient's best interest.

In the first situation regarding revealing information about a drug to a patient, if full disclosure of information about adverse effects of medication is determined not to harm the patient, it is our responsibility to give the patient the information even though this may be contrary to the wishes of the physician. I would attempt to discuss the issue with the physician and inform him that it is my responsibility to inform the patient about the adverse effects of the chemotherapy. I would share with the physician that the patient's knowledge about adverse effects of the medications will not harm the patient and that patients do better when given the truth.[3]

The second principle is veracity. Again, we are commanded by Scripture to be truthful to one another. (Eph. 4:25, Exod. 20:16) However, the Scripture does not require us to tell the whole truth unless this omission is deceitful. There are situations in which nondisclosure is appropriate. Irrelevant or unhelpful information does not have to be given. Scripture also warrants nondisclosure, even deceit, to save life. (Exodus 1:15-22)

In the second situation when a person asks for drug information which will be used for questionable purposes, there are two approaches which are scripturally consistent. One approach is to inform the caller that this information will not be given because its intended use is contrary to the Word of God when there are risks to other lives involved. The second approach (the example of the marijuana question) is that of partial disclosure where the caller would be informed that the length of time the drug remains in the urine is highly variable and there is no way to deceive the system. It is imperative that pharmacists have the necessary background information in order to make a scripturally consistent decision.

The third issue is confidentiality. According to Scripture, confidentiality is not absolute. There are times when we must tell what we hear. (I Cor. 14:26; Eph. 4:29 - "Do not let any unwholesome talk come out of your mouths, but only what is helpful for building others up according to their needs, that it may benefit those who listen.") We can keep confidences only as far as our conscience permits. However, we are also instructed not to gossip. (Prov. 10:19 - "When words are many, sin is not absent, but he who holds his tongue is wise;" Eccl. 10:14 - "And the fool multiplies his words;" Prov. 11:13 - "A gossip betrays a confidence but a trustworthy man keeps a secret.")

In the third situation, revealing to parents that a child is on drugs or on birth control pills is reaffirmed by Scriptural principles. Parents have the responsibility to help their children to protect them from harmful behaviors such as promiscuity. We probably should also inform our patients that we will be following biblical principles of confidentiality. If they do not agree to allow us to do this, they should seek services elsewhere.

The fourth issue is nonmaleficence. The Scriptures forbid physical harm of the innocent. (Exod. 22:12-24) Thus any means to induce an abortion is morally wrong. We are commanded to disobey lower authorities when they conflict with higher ones. (Acts 5:29; Exod. 1:15-22) In the situation given, the pharmacist can conscientiously refuse to dispense the "morning after pill." The other guiding scriptures revolve around the motives. Scripture demands pure motives. (Deut 6:5 - "Love the Lord your God with all your strength;" Matt. 5:8 - "Blessed are the pure in heart, for they will see God.") It requires faith and love and condemns selfishness. When evaluating the act of abortion, it is obvious that this is not only the killing of a person but is also an act of selfishness.

The fifth principle is justice. The main criterion according to the scriptures in determining how to distribute medical care is need. The parable of the Good Samaritan illustrates this beautifully. (Luke 10:25-37) When scarce resources are involved, the priorities should be such that the help given is maximized. Thus factors such as geography, ability to contribute to the healing of others, and the prospect for success would be considerations. Factors such as age, ability to pay, social worth or part of the "group" should not be determinants of who gets care. All lives are precious in God's sight since each is made in the image of God. However, the scriptures do not command that physical life be prolonged as an absolute priority. (Phil 1:20-26)

Distribution of care should not be based on ability to pay. Human life is more important than economic prosperity. Neglect of the poor is a sin. (Exod. 22:25; Deut. 15:7-11; Prov. 19:17) The Scripture commands us

to be willing to share financial resources. (Acts 2:45 - "... selling their possessions and goods, they gave to anyone as he had need;" Also, 2 Cor. 8, Gal. 2:10, and Eph. 4:28.) However, the Scripture does not ask that we go bankrupt because of unreimbursed charity. A system of priorities should be used to determine who gets care.

In the situation give, the decision as to whether to use a high cost biotech drug should not be determined by the person's age or ability to pay. The determinant would be the likelihood that the drug's benefit would outweigh the risks involved.

The sixth ethical dilemma posed was a potential conflict of interest. Scripture guides us to act honestly and to base our decisions on the benefits to our patients and the avoidance of harm. We are guided not to act selfishly and for our own personal gains. Thus, a formulary decision

would be based on the objective scientific evidence of risks and benefits, and the availability of less costly but equally safe and effective alternatives. Basing a decision on one's personal vested interests such as stock ownership would be contrary to biblical principles.

ENDNOTES

1. Hepler, C., & Strand, L., Opportunities and responsibilities in pharmaceutical care, *Am. J. Hosp. Pharm.*, Vol. 47, 1990, pp. 533-543.

2. Commission to Implement Change in Pharmaceutical Education. Background Paper I, Nov. 1991.

3. Frame, J., **Medical Ethics: Principles, Persons, and Problems**, Presbyterian and Reformed Publishing Co., Phillipsburg, New Jersey, 1988.

The parliament of The Netherlands by an overwhelming majority has formally approved that physicians may end the lives of their patients in certain cases. Of course, the law has "safeguards," such as a requirement that a second doctor be consulted before administration of a lethal drug.

Should such a law ever be enacted in the United States, it seems likely that eventually such "physician services" would have their own CPT codes and be paid for through medical insurance. Thus, insurance policyholders would have the "privilege" of paying for murder, just as some do now for abortions. King Saul and his armorbearer should have lived in Holland. (I Samuel 31:3-5)

Michigan has a law against assisting someone in the commission of suicide, the only state with such a law. According to the *American Medical News*, the American Civil Liberties Union [ACLU] has challenged Michigan's new law as unconstitutional. The ACLU executive director in Michigan believes this area is one "in which the state must respect our personal freedom and autonomy."

No. Autonomy or "self-law" is not granted to individuals when it comes to the taking of human life. God has granted that power to the civil government, and allows even the civil government the power to take human life only when it is not innocent life. (Exod. 20:13; 21:12-27; Romans 13:1-6;

Gen. 9:6)

A woman in New York was awarded $125,000 in a malpractice judgment in which she claimed emotional distress, pain, and suffering from a botched abortion. Her abortionist knew from a pathology report that he had not succeeded and made inadequate efforts to let her know. She subsequently miscarried a dead fetus and "became hysterical" when she saw the four inch fetus, still attached to its umbilical cord.

Oh, that we were as distressed over our sin as we are over the temporal consequences of our sin. The plaintiff was only viewing what she herself had asked be done to her baby. If viewing the mere physical consequences of our sin is so abhorrent to us as sinners, how much more must be the sight of our sin in the eyes of a holy God. (Isaiah 59:1-3)

A recent issue of JAMA contained an article entitled, "Promoting the Healthy Development of Adolescents." Predictably, the article promotes both keeping information about dependent adolescents away from parental knowledge when the physician deems it helpful to do so, *and* promotes the provision of contraceptive services, STD treatment, and pregnancy services to them. The article also recommends that physician groups "help eliminate laws that restrict the availability of confidential care" for adolescents. In the same issue there is another editorial comment recommending more legislation to keep minors from purchasing cigarettes.

Which is more damaging, cigarette smoking or fornication, with its attendant erosion of moral barriers, STD's, illegitimate pregnancies, and abortions? By this reasoning the parents of a
minor should not be told of behaviors the minor is engaging in that are known to have severe potential health consequences, in order that they could "legislate" against it. This is because parental legislation is presumed not to work. The ultimate decisions about sexual intercourse must be left up to the adolescent. However, the state should legislate against tobacco use in minors, since they cannot make mature judgments about tobacco use. "But wisdom is justified by all her children." (Luke 7:35)*

A recent editorial in *Medical Tribune* dealt with HIV infection in cut-through-the-malarky tones. It was replete with statistics detailing the failure of education to stem the rising tide of infection. The villain? George Bush's bigotry, of course. Mr. Bush is said to stigmatize condoms and to be "obdurate" in calling for abstinence. Alas, the trail of responsibility for the spread of HIV is also traced by the savvy editor to its religious roots — "Calvinistic hogwash."

Where is that wall of separation between "science" and "religion" when you really need it? Permit a quaint editorial response — atheistic hogwash.

The drumbeat of testimonials favorable to "assisted suicide" continues, with a rising tempo. *Medical Economics* recently reported a family physician's story of sympathy for his parents' desire for assisted suicide. Or, was it euthanasia. The author was coy about his actions and even included a suggestion of telepathy near the time of his father's death. The author reasoned that "decisions made out of love and respect for our patients are the right ones."

Thus speaks a "love" devoid of biblical content. Scripture provides us with the needed boundaries. "You shall not murder." The increase of such stories is
reminiscent of the drip, drip of conscience tenderizer that preceded Roe v. Wade.*

Dr. J.H. Foegan, a business professor at Winona State University, reported briefly in *All About Issues*, Nov. - Dec., 1992, on the coming insolvency of Social Security. Abortion is a major factor. Twenty-five million potential taxpayers have been aborted in the United States in the last 20 years. Taxes on the incomes of the first persons aborted would just now be coming on line. If for no higher reason, Dr. Foegan hopes that the threat of a looming dependency ill-supplied with workers might persuade an aging America to outlaw abortion once again. The other major candidate for solving the dilemma is, of course, euthanasia for the elderly.

"All those who hate me love death." (Prov. 8:36b) It is interesting how God's commandment against murder is tracked by His ordination of economic principles; in such we can witness the ultimate example of integrity.

The Biblical Perspective on the Mind-Body Problem

Jay E. Adams, Ph.D., S.T.M.

Dr. Adams is the author of numerous books and articles on counseling and founder of the Christian Counseling and Educational Foundation. At present he is pastor of an Associate Reform Presbyterian Church near Greenville, South Carolina.

Adapted from a presentation to the Winter Institute on Counseling in Medicine given in San Diego, February, 1992, this essay is the first of a two part series.

The old ditty has it: "What is mind? No matter. Well, then, what is matter? Never mind." That's not very funny, but it's quite descriptive of our knowledge. That's about all that many Christians can say about the mind-body question, "Well, mind isn't body and body isn't mind." And, yet, there is much more we need to say and many things we need to think about very seriously.

My intention is to move us a bit farther along the road to understanding in this area — not to complete the job but to move us somewhere beyond total ignorance. The title contains five important items. The first is "biblical, *biblical* perspectives." That means that we're going to base our approach on Scripture. The Scriptures are the basis and ultimate authority for our conclusions. I shall presuppose the Scriptures as the inerrant Word of God, given as the *infallible* rule of faith and practice concerning everything of which the Scriptures wish to speak, not concerning everything, but *everything* that the Scriptures intend to teach.

The Bible doesn't authoritatively tell us whether we ought to buy an American or Japanese car, for example.

The second word is "Perspectives." The plural assumes that there are more than one and I take this to mean *ways* in which the Bible looks at the question. The third word is tough — "mind." It is a word *needing* Biblical definition, because there are so many views that people hold that compete with biblical concepts. For instance, Thomas Huxley once wrote, "Thought is as much a function of matter as motion is." Moreover, the vague notions that most Christians have when they use the word "mind" should be sharpened. The present view prevalent in our country today, and perhaps around the Western world at least, is very close to a complete somatizing of man — making him all body. Respac, for example, puts it this way: "Mind is nothing more than a term we employ to describe some of the functions of the brain." We'll have to examine that idea in some detail as we go along. The fourth important word is "body." We have to talk about body because, significantly, the Bible does not distinguish brain from the body. We must, therefore, understand as "body" everything that goes

into the ground and rots, including the brain.. (Some brains, perhaps, rot *before* they go into the ground). With physicians, the definition might need to be altered to state that everything that goes into a jar of formalin is body. Finally, there is the word "problem." The problem to be addressed is the relationship of mind to body. What *is* this relationship, the nature of it, and what are the implications of that?[1]

I. Body

The first point to discuss is how the Bible deals with the body. There are two principal terms for "body" in the Bible. One of these is *soma*. In the term "psycho*somatics* the word *psycho* means "soul" and somatics means "body." In the Old Testament the Hebrew word is *basar*, ("flesh") and its equivalent in the New Testament, *sarx*. "Sarcophagus," for example, means a "flesh eater". It is important to understand something of the use of these Scriptural words and something of the distinctions between them. "Body" speaks of this form that we know, that we see, that we touch, that we can feel. It often speaks of the form as a person. But, "flesh" means the *living material* of the body — the living material of this form and refers more to the composition of the body. "Flesh" also has the concept of weakness attached to it which goes along with the concept of sin affecting and weakening our bodies. Sin makes our bodies incapable of completely doing what they were originally designed to do.

The body is *respected* in the Scriptures. Scripture repudiates the Gnostic idea that matter is evil. Gnosticism taught that spirit is good and matter is evil. Many harmful ideas came from this basic Gnostic teaching which early got a grip upon non-biblical thinkers. Gnosticism was already a problem in New Testament times. Two whole books were written just to refute Gnosticism — the book of Colossians and the book of First John. Remember the passage in First John that says Jesus came not *only* "by water" but *also* "by blood." The Gnostics taught that Christ was not really the one who died on that cross — that some phantom or someone resembling Christ (there were various views of how it happened) died on the cross, but that the Christ who came upon the man Jesus was separable from Him and that this Christ left Him before the cross. It came upon Him at the baptism (the "water") and left before the cross (the "blood"). But John says, "No, He's the one who came not only by water but also by blood." He was arguing that Jesus Christ was a real man with a real body and that it was that body that died.

We see, therefore, that this problem already began in New Testament times, and that New Testament writers fought gnosticism even in its early stages. As it grew much larger many problems occurred in the Church. The Bible knows nothing of the body being evil. Matter was created by God and it was created good. When God finished creating matter He looked upon creation and He said, "It's good. It's all very good."

The idea that the body is evil, therefore, is not Christian. It is not a Biblical, concept. The body, however, becomes a *problem*, as we'll see later on, because of the way the soul programs it. Also, the body is affected by the results of sin, including God's curse upon this world, so that the body does not function as it ought. While it is not evil itself, the *effects* of evil are clearly seen in the body. In fact, the body is looked upon so reverently in the Bible that it has to be buried. Not to be buried, is considered a great insult. In Scripture, a dog eating an unburied body in Scripture is the epitome of temporal judgment. The dogs in the city were the city street cleaners. When a body was just cast aside and not buried and was eaten by dogs, that was a great disgrace. The ultimate insult to a living person was to call him a dog, because a dog was a scavenger.

The redeemed body is called the "temple of the Holy Spirit." I Corinthians 6:19, for example, contains a clear statement on that point. There God tells us how He looks upon the body of a redeemed saint. He says,

"Don't you know that your body is a temple of the Holy Spirit who is in you, whom you have from God. You are not your own since you were bought with a price, so glorify God in your body."

Not only is the body called the temple of the Holy Spirit, but it becomes a means by which a Christian is capable of glorifying God. Christ died not just for the Christian's soul, as some seem to think, but also for his body which was included in the price that He paid. Since the redemption of the body is part of redemption Paul says, "You're not your own." That means that the body, which God calls His, is now to be used for God to do good. The believer has become a slave of Christ in order to be free to do good. The will of the slave is the will of another. Christian — slave of Christ — God wants to be glorified through your body. All of this is basic to our consideration of the mind-body problem.

Romans 8:11 is an interesting passage because in this verse Paul is speaking about something that happens to the body right now that he calls a spiritual resurrection of the body:

"Moreover, if the spirit of the one who raised Jesus from the dead dwells in you, this one who raised Christ from the dead will give life to your mortal bodies through his spirit who dwells within you."

This is a resurrection of the body *to newness of life here.* Paul speaks of a new ability — the ability to live for Jesus Christ that body receives here and now. Romans 12 makes it clear how God has made it possible to present our bodies to God to honor Him.

But the body is also viewed as a problem in the Bible, and it is a problem. Remember the problem that Paul had with his body? Remember how he talks about it in Romans 6 and 7, in particular, how he says that he finds this body hindering him from doing the things that he wants? He finds his body going the wrong direction. All through the New Testament, we read in Paul, and Peter, and in others as well, that even this redeemed body has desires of its own, that are not always the same as the desires of the Spirit. The body wants to do things; it has its own agenda, you might even say. The body wants to go places and act in certain ways, and respond by certain forms of action. This body, though it has the potential to glorify God, doesn't always, and becomes a problem. Paul seems upset with his body. He calls it a "body of death," and, in near desperation, asks, "who will free me from this body of death?" He gladly affirms: Jesus Christ will do that. And in the 8th chapter he talks about how the Spirit of Christ does.

But, clearly, the body becomes a serious problem for the believer. And, if your body isn't a problem for you, then maybe you're not really a believer. Every believer struggles with this problem. Every person who has ever come to faith in Jesus Christ knows that there are things he wants to do for Christ and yet the body gets in the way. There are things he wants to stop doing that he knows are wrong, and yet the body wants to keep on doing them. That struggle is the whole point of Romans 6 and 7. What's behind the struggle?

The problem is that our bodies have been wrongly programmed by the nature with which we were born. We're born into this world sinners, with a sinful nature that will sin — a nature that was warped and twisted from the day of conception. No child could ever die, no child could ever have a defect, no child could ever be aborted if that child was not considered a sinner, because "the wages of sin is death." And that sin is what has also led to all the distortions and impairments of the body. Thus, from the very beginning you have a body condemned by God. Every person, body and soul, is con-

demned by God for his sin. The effects of sin begin to operate from the very earliest moment in a child's life. Because that child as a sinner has a corrupt nature he will go on sinning until such a time as Jesus Christ changes his nature, until the Holy Spirit comes in and regenerates him and gives him a new nature. The new, regenerate person desires and wants to do the things of God. But, during the whole time from the very earliest days on through the whole period before he is regenerated and, perhaps, even for a time afterwards that sinful nature programs his body. Because it's orientation is away from God it habituates the body, so that when adverse things happen (people say something critical, problematic situations develop, pressures come), the body is taught to respond habitually to those circumstances, in sinful ways. This nature programs the body to respond wrongly.

If I had a wand to wave over you, so that you would lose every habit pattern you ever had, so that tomorrow you'd wake up with no habits — none, I mean zilch, zero habits — now, just think what that would be like. You wake up, and there you are with your eyes closed, and you have to think consciously of everything you will comfortably or smoothly do. These are the four characteristics of habit. You can't do anything automatically, unconsciously, comfortably or smoothly. You're going to be awkward in everything that you do. You're going to feel conspicuous about it; you'll feel uncomfortable.

So, you have to think carefully, "What do I do next? I'd better open my eyes." So, you get them open. Then, you think, "Now, how do I get out of this bed?" You're awkward like a little child that tumbles over the

edge of his crib. You have to think, "Do I put the feet out, the hands out, or throw the whole body over at once?" You've got to make a conscious decision about such matters. Nothing is automatic. Nothing is unconscious. Nothing is comfortable. Nothing is smooth. You have no skills. That is, nothing is habitual. Then, you go through all the rituals of putting clothes on. For example, buttoning a shirt. You know now how to button a shirt, but remember when as a child you first learned how difficult it was to button something? You don't know whether to begin buttoning at the bottom and go to the top, the top and go to the bottom, or the middle and go both ways. Think about putting toothpaste on your toothbrush. First, you've got to unscrew a cap. You don't have those skills. You finally get it unscrewed and then you've got to aim it directly at a small, narrow toothbrush. That's hard to do when you have no skills. So, if you get half of it on the brush you're doing well; the other half will go up your arm and wrist. How about getting the brush in your mouth, instead of up a nostril? On and on and on this goes. Why, you would not get to breakfast by midnight!

Almost everything you do involves habit. You live by habit. God you a great blessing when he gave you the habit-capacity so you wouldn't have to think consciously about everything you do and go through with the awkwardness of learning to do it as if for the first time, every time. So, He gave you skills and ability to do things without thinking, comfortably.

You have the capacity to act by habit, a blessed and wonderful ability from God. This capability, however, may be used for a blessing or a curse. You have learned to respond to life wrongly as a sinner. When somebody says something nasty to you, what is your immediate, your learned, your habitual response? What kind of habitual responses have you built in as a sinner over the years? Do you figure, "I'll get him ten times over?" Do you do good or do evil to those who do evil to you?

Romans 12 says that all sinful habits must change and you've got to learn to overcome evil with good. That change is not easy, because as a sinner, a little sinner, born a sinner, manifesting yourself as a sinner, right away you began to program to respond sinfully to sinful things done to you. You learned those things so well you do them unconsciously, automatically, comfortably, and skillfully. Those are the characteristics of habit.

As a Christian, however, you've got to change, and that's the problem that you have with the body. That was the problem Paul had with his body. He wanted to do things God's way, but the body had been programmed to do something else. The lie slipped out before he even realized he'd told it. Then he had to go back and deal with that issue. The nasty word was spoken before he even realized that it was out there. He struggled to relearn and replace those sinful patterns with new biblical ones.

We haven't time to go into that whole dynamic of the "put off" and the "put on" of Ephesians 4 and elsewhere in the Scriptures that talks about replacing habit patterns, but we must at least be aware that this sin-affected body is not the wonderful body that was originally created for Adam. It has become distorted because your soul was passed down

corrupted and guilty and, so, it would program the body wrongly. The brain, *N.B.*, is part of the body, and it is the brain that is programmed to see to it that the rest of the body responds sinfully.

At death, you're going to receive a new body, if you are a believer. The new body is going to be like Christ's body. That's what we're told in Philippians 3:20,21:

"Our citizenship is in the heavens from which country we await the coming of a saviour, the Lord Jesus Christ, who will transform our degraded bodies, making them conform to His glorious body, by the power that enables Him to subject all things to Himself."

Though it was created perfect in Adam this body has been degraded. It was created to glorify God, and did, until the Fall. It was created to be used for His honor but, now the body is used for God's dishonor, as we know. Think of what people do with their bodies, all the horrible things that bodies get involved in, all the wretched things that bodies are achieving in this world against God, rather than for God. The body has been degraded by sin.

But, the body of the believer is going to be transformed. It is even being transformed gradually now, but someday that transformation will be perfect. It will possess all the powers, all the new properties that Christ's glorified body now possesses. His body could no longer be subject to pain; it was a body that had powers that we don't even understand. It could pass through the wall of a sepulchre! I'm looking forward to that kind of a body. And, I think every physician, in particular, ought to look forward to that kind of a body

after he or she sees how blighted bodies can become.

So, the body was made good, it became degraded, and it now, because of habits held over from his unsaved life, becomes a problem even to a believer. Someday, however, God is going to redeem the body fully, and Romans 8 talks about that hope in the latter part of the chapter.

I want to stop and consider *an implication* at this point. Begin to start asking yourself the question, "What is the Christian physician's goal in medicine?" The physician deals with the body. Is it your goal to heal? Is it your goal to ease pain? Is it your goal to make life more comfortable? We're not yet ready to answer the question but we can say this much now: In working with bodies you should certainly be more than a veterinarian. You should show respect for those bodies *because* those bodies have been made to glorify God. People are more than meat and bones. Any Christian physician who begins to look on bodies only as bones on which the meat hangs, has a very pagan view. What should be your goal in medicine and what should be your goal in treating the body? Serious questions arise, and we're going to look at some of them as we go along.

The redeemed body is an instrument for service by which a Christian may glorify and honor Christ. In Romans 6, the word "instrument" (also sometimes translated as a "weapon") frequently occurs. "Instrument" or "tool" is the proper translation of *hoplon* in the passage. The *hoplon* was the instrument or the weapon, with which the *hoplite* (Greek foot soldier) fought. It was his instrument, his tool for fighting. In Romans 6 and 7 the *hoplon* was probably some kind of *tool* that a slave would use, because all the way through this 6th chapter Paul has been talking about slaves and masters. He talks about sin as the master over us before we come to Christ, so that we are the very slaves of sin.

But, to those who have come to Christ, he says: "Don't present your bodily members to sin as *instruments*" — there it is — "of unrighteousness, but rather present yourselves to God as persons who have been resurrected from the dead and are living, and your members to God as *instruments* of righteousness (v. 13)." God wants the bodies of believers as instruments to perform righteousness in this world. Any physician who doesn't have that in the back of his mind as he is working on bodies misunderstands God's purpose for bodies. You must see the body as a tool that God wants used in His service.

Sin was your slave-master. You were born into that slavery to be used by sin. But, Christ redeemed and freed you from sin's dominion by the cross so that you could serve Him. Those very same members of your body — hands, feet, eyes, nose, brain — the members or organs of your body that once were instruments for sin, may now become instruments for righteousness. That is a critical point for you to keep in your mind as you think of bodies and what you as a physician do to them.

And yet, these are broken tools, abused tools, worn tools. The body isn't yet freed from the ravages of sin. It is a living-dying, warped tool, at best. That is what a body is. And, it interesting that God is willing to use even such tools for His purposes. This requires something of a partnership, an interaction between man and God. We're actually thinking here more of a partnership and interaction than the word "tool" (which speaks of almost of something that is inanimate) would imply. This body alone, apart from the spirit, does not constitute a competent person. The body alone is a *thing*. Yet the brain, which is part of that body, is more than a storage bin. It is an active filing and processing and controlling agent, that distorts, relates, molds, shapes data that are received according to its own biases, according to its points of view, according to its perspectives and dispositions, as well as according to its physical condition. And, it's that physical condition of the members of the body (which includes brain) with which you are concerned. As you think of the mind-body problem you should be concerned about the bodily aspect of this body-mind issue because that is your perspective and your focus.

You, the "you" that people call the "you" and the you that you call yourself, is identified very closely with that body. Your body is acted upon by your mind, and the body itself responds by acting according to its predispositions. There is an interaction within you that makes you, you. At death, the body will be lifeless and *mindless*. Yet, *you* will continue to exist consciously when your body is dissolved. You've lost your tool. That's what you can say about death. At death, *you* will become disassociated from your body: "The body without the Spirit is dead. (Jas. 2:26)

However, at the present time the courts rightly consider the body to be *you*. Right now, police take pictures of the bodily you and hang them on the post office wall. They take this body that they call "you" and put handcuffs on it. They throw it behind bars and lock the doors. And, then, when necessary, they take that body (which they call "you") and execute it in an electric chair. So, now, *you* are very closely and rightly identified with that body; it is an integral part of the "you" that you are.

But, let's now enlarge our previous implication, pausing once again. Your task as physician certainly brings you to the point where you must deal with sin's effects upon bodies. That is one thing that you are deeply involved in. Since bodies provide man with a means (tools, instrument) for expressing love for God and for one's neighbor, and thus for glorifying God, the highest goal of Christian medicine *is not comfort*, is *not ease*, is *not healing*. The highest goal of medicine is not being patient-centered at all. It is rather *to enable a man to use his body to honor God as an instrument of righteousness*. That's the goal that a Christian physician should have. But, what if he's an unbeliever, what if he doesn't honor God? That's his, not your problem. You make it possible for him to do so. And, if, at such a time as he should be saved, then because of your efforts he will be in better condition to do so.

Medical help may even speed *sanctification* (the process of growing out of sin into righteousness) in the sense that it may enable persons to do and think better than they might otherwise. It may even be part of an evangelistic tool so that the person may be enabled to hear and believe the gospel which he could not do prior to medical help. Therefore, the implication for physicians is that when they repair broken bodies, they are not mere appliance repair men; they are doing *spiritual* work. Muse on this point the next time you feel cynicism creeping over you.

I'm sure there are many physicians who get to the place where they see blood and guts enough that it's hard to keep this view of things in mind. I'm sure there are many physicians who begin to work on hunks of flesh and body and bones, sawing them apart, sewing them together, cutting them up — and doing all the things you do to them — who find it hard to remember. But the goal is to enable the patient to honor God in his body. If you are only thinking of healing people, however, and if you are patient-centered, you're going to get discouraged. If you can't see service to God behind what you're doing, and you can't see that you are potentially enabling people both better to hear and to receive the teaching the Word of God for salvation and for sanctification and to, therefore, fulfill the mandate that God has given to them, then you have missed the major purpose of medical work.

Truly, Christian medical workers see beyond that body to what it can do in the service of Jesus Christ. And, unless you can put Him first, unless your medicine is God-centered, then your work is going to become discouraging, defeating, and gruelling, worthless — nothing more.

II. Mind

Now, when the body, the brain, or some other organ is impaired, the mind is affected, and we'll get to what mind is in a little while. The body, we said, is like a damaged tool. That means it doesn't function properly. And so, the mind cannot use, or use to the full, that impaired part of that body. Wilder Penfield, the famous Canadian neurosurgeon, who worked for 30 years on brains, treat-

ing epilepsy, said that he observed mind acting independently of brain under controlled conditions that were reproducible at will. An interesting book called *The Self and Its Brain* (the title was changed from *The Self and* the *Brain*) by John Echols and Charles Popper, confirmed this view. Both authors are tremendously respected people, Echols being a Nobel prize winner as well as a renowned neurophysiologist. The body, what in you is acted on, by, and in concert with the mind — the body and that mind *together* — become an acting *soul* in the service of Jesus Christ. Your spirit uses your body to reach the world. The spirit doesn't directly reach the world. It uses the body to find out through the senses what's going on in this world, and having found out, uses the body as an *instrument* to do things to and in this world. We need a view of mind and body that begins to orient us in this direction.

In regard to mind and the body there are three principle biblical terms: (1) *nous*, the seat of consciousness or understanding, often contrasted with "flesh" as in Romans 7:23,25 and with *dianoia*, a compound word derived from *nous* meaning, "to think or be mindful of;" (2) *phren*, the second of those three words (and the *phren* family words: *phreneo* meaning "to think or be mindful of," and *phren*, meaning basically "midriff," as that was where the thought process was considered to take place by Greeks who invented this word;) (3) *leb*, an Old Testament word (which is also a big New Testament word) for "heart," which covers all the New Testament terms as well. It is the *only* word in the Old Testament used to refer to the mind, and its use is larger than the mind

itself.

The biblical word "heart" needs to be understood, and, maybe, we need to take a little while to understand it, because, in Western society "heart" has come to mean something quite different. When we look at a valentine, we see little cherry-cheeked cherubs with bows and arrows shooting little arrows into hearts. And, the meaning of heart in that context (one that comes out of the Roman background) in Western society is *emotion, feeling*. And, when we say, "I love you with all my heart," we are thinking of deep emotions that well up: oceans of emotions. That's not at all what the Bible is talking about when it uses the word "heart."

Whenever you read "heart" in the Bible, and think "emotion" or "feeling" you misread your Bible. You have poured a new content into the word that the Bible knows nothing about. When a preacher says, "Now, what we need is less *head* knowledge and more *heart* knowledge," he is making a totally non-biblical dysjunction. Nowhere in the Bible is the head (the intellect) put over against the heart: *Cf.* "...as a man *thinketh* in his heart", "The fool hath *said* in his heart, 'There is no God'" (You know why he's a fool, of course, because he's listening to one when he talks that way). This man is *deciding* things. Consequently, we read of the "*thoughts* and *intents* of the heart" in the Scriptures. So heart is not set over against the intellect, it *includes* the intellect.

"Heart" in the Bible, far from meaning emotion, is more often linked with the intellect than it is with the emotions. The word that is used for emotion in the Bible is "gut," "belly." Recall the passages that speak in the Bible about "bowels of compassion?" Think of the literal gut feeling you get in an old elevators. You don't feel it in your heart, you feel queasy down in the gut. Biblical writers understood that that's where the feelings, the emotions were principally experienced. "Heart," then, meant something else.

What does heart mean in the Bible? Well, if it isn't set over against the head, over against what is it set? It is set over against the lips: "This people honors me with their lips but their *heart* is far from me." It is set over against the mouth: Romans 10 says, "You must not only say with your mouth but you must believe in your *heart* that God has raised Him from the dead." So it is — *heart* and *mouth*, heart and lips. In the Psalms we read about the *hands* as over against the heart. In 1 Samuel 16:7 we read that man looks on *the outward appearance* but God looks on the *heart* — the outward appearance as contrasted with the heart. Lips, hands, mouth, outward appearance are set over against heart. What does "heart" mean? "Heart" means the *inner* you, the life you live *inside* of yourself that nobody knows anything else about except God and you. In Acts when the disciples pray they pray to God as the "Heart-knower."

When we think of "heart," there, we ought to be thinking about that inner life of the individual that motivates all that he does and all that he is and all that he thinks. Listen to what Jesus says about the heart in Matthew 15:18: "From the heart come evil thoughts, murders, adulteries, sexual sins, thefts, false testimonies, blasphemy." This is the source of evil and difficulty in our life. This word "heart," this *phren* — this *leb*, this *kardia* — is also used for "mind" in the Bible, but is bigger than "mind." And, the reason it is used for "mind" in the New Testament as well as these other words for "mind" is because it was the only term they had to use for "mind" in the *Old* Testament. Much Old Testament vocabulary and though comes over into the New, as well. Remember, Solomon wrote, "keep your heart with all diligence, for out of it are the issues of life." Out of it pour all the streams of your life — every aspect of your life begins, and is motivated by, is centered in, and is initiated by the heart. The heart is *critical* in Scripture. We must understand it.

What is the relationship between mind and spirit and soul? At this point I want to draw a distinction. The real problem is not mind - body. The problem, really, is a spirit - body problem. I don't want to talk so much about a mind-body problem after this but I want to talk about this spirit-body problem, because, mind is not the only aspect of the problem and it is part of the larger spirit/body problem.

In Matthew 22 is very interesting because of how Jesus quotes Deuteronomy 6:3. He says, "You must love the Lord your God with all your heart, with all your soul, and with all your mind." Jesus *added* the word "mind." "Mind" was not in the Hebrew passage, because, obviously, there was no separate word, as I said, in the Old Testament for mind. "Heart" covered it all. But, Jesus added the word "mind," so, that we understand clearly that mind was not excluded in loving God, but that with *all* that you are, and *all* that you have, you must love God. John Calvin says that "mind" was added here by Jesus so that "soul" and "heart" would be understood by this new word which had come on the scene in the meanwhile. Jesus didn't want people who had the word "mind" as part of their vocabulary to misunderstand Him. Well, that may be so, but He certainly wants you to know that with all you are and all you have you are to love God.

The truth is, there are quite a few terms used in the Bible that need to be understood and related to each other. These various terms get their meaning from this mind-body or spirit-body relationship. That's why we encounter various terms like "soul," "spirit," "heart," and "mind." The two terms, spirit and body, for example, stand on their own. The spirit is the immaterial entity that you are, thought of as *out of relationship with the body*. That is a most important point about its use. For example, in Luke 24:39, Jesus says, "A spirit has not flesh and bones as you see Me have." "Body" means that material entity you are that is not spirit. The interesting thing about "spirit" is that God is called a Spirit in John 4:24. He is never called a soul. And, the Holy Spirit is called the Holy Spirit, and never the Holy Soul. I don't know whether you ever thought of that or not. He is always called the Holy *Spirit*. The reason for that is because "soul" is the same immaterial "you" as "spirit" or "heart" but *in union with and animating the body*. The spirit in your body becomes soul. The spirit out of your body is called "spirit." God doesn't have a body so He can't be called "soul" but He can be called "spirit." The Holy Spirit doesn't have a body so He can't be called Holy Soul, but He can be called Holy Spirit. The spirit, then, is the same entity as the soul, but thought of as *out* of relationship to the body.

That the immaterial entity, when

in relationship with the body, is called "soul," is clear from the creation account. Remember, God breathed into Adam's body that He had shaped from clay the breath of life. And, as a result, man *became* a living *soul*. So, the spirit or breath is breathed in and man became an animated being, a living soul. But, then James says, when, at death, the soul is severed from the body, the body is dead. The immaterial you (now called spirit) departs from the body, the body is dead.

"Heart" is also the immaterial "you." It is one-and-the-same with spirit or soul. It is, however, viewed as within you — something that can't be seen or gotten to except by God and, to some extent, by you. Heart is your inner self contrasted with the lips, the hands, the outward appearance. It's the immaterial "you" thought of as inner "you," *not* outer "you," not the "you" that people can see. Not bodily "you," but immaterial "you" *in* that body. That's what "heart" means. And, "mind," once more is the same immaterial "you" or person *self-consciously thinking, willing, remembering, reasoning*.

The union of "mind" or spirit with the body forms a functioning unit oriented toward the material world. When the spirit, this immaterial me, is within this body that I also am, then I am oriented towards the material world, spirit and body. Not to say I don't believe that there is a God and an immaterial world, but I'm not really participating in what goes on in that immaterial world. I am participating almost 100% in what goes on in *this* world. Though I am in contact with that other world, my present orientation is towards the physical world. This union of body and spirit, rather than called

"dichotomy," as some people call it (meaning "to cut into two"), I would rather call "duplexity," (which means two things folded together, two things brought together). Dichotomy speaks of taking the two apart, and we might call that what happens at death (you are dichotomized), but what you are now is a duplex person. The spirit and the body are so united that should we under ordinary circumstances — and I'll explain that exception later — separate the one from the other, you would die, says James.

These two elements, then, are normally inseparable except at death. The only place where "mind" — *nous* — is set over against spirit that I can find is 1 Cor. 14:14-15, where it is talking about praying, not just with the spirit but also with the mind. Probably, he is here saying that the Corinthians thought the human spirit is under control of the spiritual gifts rather than the gifts under the control of the spirit. That is wrong. What he teaches is that there must be no mindless use of the gifts. That is forbidden in I Cor. 14:32. Yet, that is precisely today what many people applaud. "I put my mind in neutral and let things go." No. He says the mind ought always be under your control. "The spirits of the prophets are subject to the prophets."

It might be correct to say that the spirit has a mind as the body has a brain. I want to examine that statement a little further, but that's probably an accurate statement. At any rate, this duplexity, functioning in man, this body/spirit thing called "soul," has been scientifically observed, which is unnecessary for faith, but, nevertheless, very interesting. I want to close with some quotations from the work of Penfield, and

Echols, and some others just to add that dimension to what we are saying here. Remember, Penfield worked for thirty years cutting the skull cap off and prodding around with electrodes in people's brains observing what happens. In a now-famous paper he says,

"When the neurosurgeon applies an electrode to the motor area of the patient's cerebral cortex, causing the opposite hand to move, and when he asks the patient why he moved the hand, the response is, 'I didn't do it, you made me do it.' It may be said that the patient thinks of himself as having an existence separate from his body."

He explains: "I didn't do it, you made me do it by prodding my body."

"Once when I warned a patient of my intention to stimulate the motor area of the cortex, and challenged him to keep his hand from moving when the electrode was applied, he seized it with the other hand and struggled to hold it still. Thus, one hand, under the control of the right hemisphere, driven by an electrode and the other hand which is controlled through the left hemisphere were caused to struggle against each other. Behind the brain action of one hemisphere was the patient's mind. Behind the action of the other hemisphere was the electrode."

"So, we concluded, there are, as you see, many demonstrable mechanisms in the brain. They work for the purposes of the mind automatically when called upon, but, what agency is it that calls upon these mechanisms, choosing one rather than another? Is it another mechanism? Or, is there in the mind something of different essence. To declare that these two are one does not make them so, but it does block the progress of research."

That's part of what Penfield had to say. Let me give you one other comment of his, from another section of his paper that I think you will find interesting. He records one such occasion in which a young South African patient lying on the operating table exclaimed when he realized what was happening and it was astonishing to him to realize that he was laughing with his cousins on a farm in South Africa, while he was also fully conscious of being in the operating room in Montreal. Penfield observed the mind of the patient was as independent of the reflex action as was the mind of the surgeon who listened and strove to understand. "Thus," he says, "my argument favors independence of mind action." As Penfield put it, "if we liken the brain to a computer, man *has* a computer, not *is* a computer."

"This discovery was totally unexpected, but it was in no way singular. It was repeated again and again for hundreds of patients, each of whom could identify the scene recalled with ease, and virtually instantaneously. Patients could elaborate on what they saw and explain the circumstances, much as a TV viewer seeing a serial program might explain the circumstances to a watching companion who was ignorant of the previous events." He's sitting there eating popcorn

watching what is going on in his brain, in his mind's eye. "In such a situation there are clearly two elements — the viewer is not part of the TV program but an observer. Yet, he is more than an observer, insofar as the viewer can adjust the set, clarify the image, change the program, and, in recall situations, shut it off at will under normal circumstances by a shifting of attention, that is, tuning into another program."

"Here then, we have a dualism of object and subject, of brain and mind. It is no longer safe to view the mind as a computer, though the brain is indeed a computer of extraordinary refinement. But this computer has a programmer, and an operator who is using it as a tool of recall and of motor control. Epileptic subjects may sometimes experience times of total blackout as to consciousness, the mind apparently ceasing entirely to control the brain, providing that the brain has already been programmed, the subject becomes an automaton and completes the task in a state of total mindlessness. Patients may even complete a journey from work by car, provided that the journey is an habitual one, and that no unexpected interference occurs. Navigating the traffic and road turns is done by means of purely conditioned reflexes. Afterwards, nothing whatever of the journey will be recalled. The efficacy of the brain as a computer is, therefore, truly remarkable." Penfield observes that" the continual functions of the

normally active mind were apparent in such journeys," but, he emphasized, that" it is the mind that must first program the computer brain since the computer is only a thing, and on its own has no ability to make totally new decisions for which it is not programmed."

"Kornhuber discovered the existence of electrical potentials generated in the cerebral cortex following the exercise of will to action and prior to the actual performance of motor activity. Between the conscious act of will and the activity resulting from it, he consistently observed a measurable interval lasting a few seconds or less. During this brief but highly significant interval there is a flurry of electrical potentials over a wide area that gradually centers or concentrates the signals which then bring about the movement willed. This takes the form of a developing specificity of the pattern impulse discharges until the pyramidal cells in the relevant cortex area are activated to bring about the desired movement. The delay between willing and willed movement is quite measurable. The nature of the will and the resulting willed action correspond. The problem remains, however, as to how the neuronal impulses are set in orderly action by the will. One has to assume," Echols believes, "that there is a bridge of some sort across the interface between the mental world and the physical world. It seems to warn the will is about to act upon the mechanism. No such warning signal or attention-getter seems to be involved when action is involuntary, but consciously willed action takes time to be set in motion." Echols wrote, "I woke up in life, as it were, to find myself existing as an embodied self with this body and brain."" That's the way that he looked at it.

As Christians I think we need to do serious thinking about these matters.

This essay will be concluded in a subsequent issue.

END NOTE

1. I've reluctantly refrained from any discussion of the Holy Spirit at work in the believer, not because that isn't important -- I consider it *utterly* important -- but because it was not in my assignment. And, where I do allude to the Holy Spirit it is only to throw light on the issue at hand. This omission, you should realize, somewhat oversimplifies everything I say. But, I've attempted in spite of this not to falsify the facts.

Editor's Note

Like termites in an oak stump, articles on euthanasia continue to reduce to dry powder the humbled remnants of biblical precepts in medicine. The April, 1993, issue of *MD* magazine published a short story by Daly Walker, a general surgeon in Columbus, Indiana, in which he tells how he injected IV morphine into his friend suffering from terminal cancer. These renditions are a developing genre in medical literature. The story must be told with skilful sensitivity, since our culture now celebrates behavioral *style* above biblical substance. Dr. Walker is a sensitive writer, though he is selective as to what he will be sensitive. It is not the law of the Lord. Another necessity in the formula for telling tales of euthanasia-while-it-is-still-illegal is that the author be coy about his actions. Did he really *intend to kill his friend? What was the dose* of the morphine. Was he merely giving a dose sufficient to relieve pain and accepting the small risk that death would result, or was the dose one that was expected to be lethal? Dr. Walker doesn't tell us. He is more than usually vague. He doesn't even tell us that his patient died. When euthanasia falls into the hands of the crass, we can expect such artful reluctance to disappear. It will probably even be lamented by the sensitive ones. Euthanasia without sufficient premonitory agonizing is bad form, and bad form is as close to mortal sin as many humanists can get. Weighty matters such as killing a friend in the name of mercy must be done with feeling.

Dr. Walker's friend was reported to be a Presbyterian minister. He'd been in Selma, Alabama, with Martin Luther King, Jr., prized a piece of correspondence with Paul Tillich, and cherished his 'God Loves You' sermon above all his others. Clearly, ideas do have consequences. His wife doesn't "know what happens to people after they die." His friend apparently loved "witnessing." He asks Dr. Walker to kill him. His wife agrees to the request. Dr. Walker at first refused. Thoughts of loss of licensure or jail restrained him for a while as did the Hippocratic oath he says he once took. Quite honestly, he did consider that he might be a pagan. One wonders more about his minister-friend. He has "witnessed" to Dr. Walker, all right. All of our actions constitute our "witness" and our last actions have special weight. They are a kind of summative witness of our life. Dr. Walker took it in and took it to heart. He used his friend's "witness" in his decision-making. One features is, "... if it is wrong ... why has [he] asked me to do it?" What? Do ministers never make wrong decisions? Another "witness" that stuck with Dr. Walker is his friend's wresting of Philippians 1:22 so that Scripture is misused to suggest euthanasia as an option.

The solid oak of biblical precepts that once sheltered and nurtured our nation lies rotting on the ground. Termites infest the stump. What should a Christian physician's response be to articles that gnaw at the pitiful remnant? Do we boycott such physicians and the companies that pay for such publication? The article appeared close to ads for Cardizem by Marion Merrell Dow, for Prilosec by Merck, and Advil by Whitehall Laboratories. Surely, these companies would maintain that their advertisements are divorced from editorial policy -- that they cannot control magazine content. Just as surely, editorial policy would change if ads were withdrawn and the reasons cited to the publisher. Do we lobby for laws against euthanasia? The story contains evidence that the doctor was restrained at least for a time by legal considerations. Perhaps if they were enforced he would have desisted. It was only months ago that a similar tale provoked threat of legal action. Do we offer alternatives? The dying minister was already in hospice care. Once hospices become identified with euthanasia and "assisted suicide" their witness will be as clouded as was that of Dr. Walker's patient. Hospices that don't will be a different from those that do as crisis pregnancy centers are from abortuaries.

All these responses may be considered, but they aren't likely to set the matter straight. None of them alone will stimulate that stump to sprout a new tree. We must get at the wrong ideas, the wrong beliefs, that support such behavior. They must be challenged. We need to begin with ourselves before we turn to pagans. Do we have a theology of death and dying, a real one, not Bible verses poured over Kubler-Ross? Do we consider how to be as convincing to persons such as Dr. Walker as those who convinced him have been thus far? Do we care enough about physicians such as him to challenge him? Are we captured by the same dead elements in our culture that glorify tender sensitivities above biblical revelation?

Physician and Pastor - Co-Laborers
Part 2: Where the Power Is, and Applications of It

Hilton P. Terrell, M.D., Ph.D.

Dr. Terrell is Assistant Professor of Family Medicine at McLeod Regional Medical Center in Florence, South Carolina.

Part 1 appeared in Volume 7, Number 1.

In the previous section some of the limitations of the currently dominant medical model of disease were reviewed. Some of these limitations are: (1) reductionism — a proclivity to reduce our understanding toward the smallest component parts of causality, (2) materialism — consideration only of the *material* aspects of a human being when looking for etiology, (3) numerator medicine — failure of medicine to consider the denominator populations from which patients are drawn, skewing probabilities, and, (4) a pointed refusal to consider *spiritual* features in etiology, that patients suffer physically because of wrong belief systems. If we were to begin to correct these failures, what kind of issues would we consider?

THE POWER OF FAMILY GOVERNMENT FOR HEALTH

We would consider the power for health that intact families which have biblical authority structures possess. "Children in single-parent families are 20 percent to 40 percent more likely to suffer health problems."[1] Pastoral counselors who work to sustain marriages are also very powerfully engaged in the physical health of the household. You are strengthening a locus of government which is far more powerful to maintain health than is medical care. Would we in medicine not dream to be able to reduce health problems by 20% to 40%? Physicians who prescribe for a family member need to consider the "side effects" of our prescription on the family structure and authority. If what we prescribe weakens that structure, then that prescription would have to be very powerful indeed to be more important for health than what it weakens.

THE CHALLENGES TO FAMILY GOVERNMENT

Pastoral counseling which points out the family's primary responsibility to care for its own has health power. As one example, the widespread use of group day care facilities needs to be challenged. While it seems reasonable that a family may delegate at times portions of its child care duties to others, the family retains the responsibility for what occurs. Day care just cannot be as healthy as a biblical family. A toddler enrolled in day care can expect to be bitten by another child within an average of 73 days.[2] While siblings within homes also bite one another, the toddler at home is not going to be surrounded by 20 other toddlers who are in the prime "biting age." One mother just cannot give birth to that many children in a short period of time. It requires collecting them from many households.

The risk of infectious disease in day care is two to four times greater than for children cared for at home.[3] This includes gastrointestinal infections, which are also carried to other family members at home.[4] Otitis media also is increased in day care children.[5]

You would expect such information would impel reasonable people toward a view that small children, if possible, are better cared for in homes than in group day care, and that policies to support that end would be the best ones. Instead, as example of the narrow way medicine has of conceiving of problems and their solutions, listen to the "answer" of the researchers of a major review of illness and day care, persons at the Bush Institute for Child and Family Policy at the University of North Carolina at Chapel Hill. "... government intervention is justified when a market fails to measure adequately the true costs or benefits of a given market transaction. ... It seems reasonable ... to recommend specific regulatory provisions ... regulations requiring parents to demonstrate that they have been following a schedule of health visits for their child, (such as that recommended by the American Academy of Pediatrics.)"[6]

That government policies encouraging two-parent wage earner families built into the tax structure and otherwise is the problem is not even *considered*. That changing policies to reduce the demand for group day care is a better approach is ignored.

I witnessed recently a clear instance of chasing your tail on this issue. A young Christian family, young in Christ also, with two small girls who had many visits to their pediatrician because of otitis media. There were numerous prescriptions of very expensive antibiotics. Finally, both of the girls were sent to an ENT doctor to have myringotomy tubes placed. One of the girls had a complication from the procedure. Actually, she didn't have a complication. In routine blood work done after the procedure, it appeared that she was having a rare, dangerous reaction to some medicine or other that she had received, possibly an anesthetic, it was thought. A worrisome hospitalization ensued, with consultation from other specialists. Finally, it was decided that there never had been a problem and the child went home. The medical bills were very substantial.

Both parents worked. The mother had a medical insurance policy which covered the family. The father did not, though he made more money. Both girls were in group day care. No one mentioned to the mother the connection between day care and otitis media. When the topic finally came up incidentally, her notion was that she couldn't afford to keep the children herself at home because she would lose their health insurance. In fact, she said,

her medical insurance for the children was the main reason she was still working. She would otherwise much prefer to be at home.

Thus, you work in order to have medical insurance for the children, whom you place in day care in order that you may work, where they contract otitis media, making you glad to have medical insurance. You work to have the medical insurance for the children, whom you place in day care in order that you may work, where .... and around the circuit goes this family and many others. How narrow our medical view can be! Our presupposition that things that matter most in health are physical things — microbes in the middle ear space — is diverting us sometimes from more powerful actions. Counseling the mother to stay home with the children while they are small, while not "medical" on its face, could be powerful for health and not so damaging for the pocketbook.

As Semmelweis in the case of the infectious agent in childbed fever was thwarted by the presuppositions which framed the issue, so also are we being thwarted by a framing of medical issues by a false presupposition that mankind is a material entity only, and that only material entities may be practically considered in illness and injury.

A TYRANNY OF EXPERTS

From early medical training on, the message to the physician results in a kind of tyranny of the experts. These experts consider only the material, the *soma*, the physical *sine qua non* of disease. These are experts who know more and more about less and less until they know everything about nothing. I wish to be a bit more like the philosopher who knows

less and less about more and more until I know nothing about everything. Actually, we need experts, we just need each expert to recognize his or her area of expertise and to stay within it. To know all about one *sine qua non* of disease is a far cry from knowing about other features of the disease, including other *sine qua non*, some of which might well be spiritual.

EXAMPLE OF THE SUPERIORITY OF PASTORAL COUNSELING FOR PEDIATRIC LIFE EXPECTANCY

Here is part of the opportunity for the pastor. What may have been behind a particular episode of illness? We have been overly impressed by the fact that not every episode of illness has a particular sin that caused it. Jesus did teach us that not *all* illnesses are due to particular sins in the person or his family. [John 9:3] In John 5:14, Jesus met again a man whom he had healed of 38 years of lameness, and told him, "See, you have been made well. Sin no more, lest a worse thing come upon you." In the United States, it is definite that, while most *deaths* may not relate that much to lifestyle choice, most years of potential life lost *is* due to "lifestyle" choices.

The famous "leading causes of death" in the United States are heart disease and cancer. However, since these two causes tend to strike near the end of the life span, conquest of them would lead to a surprisingly small increment in average life expectancy, maybe three to four years. We would only have two new leading causes of death. Accidents, homicide, and suicide, on the other hand, tend to kill the young, subtracting a much larger portion of potential life. These events tend to be associated with "lifestyle," which is an expression of what people believe. Abortion by definition takes life at its youngest and removes the most years of potential life, about thirty times more than all the other causes of pediatric deaths under one year of age. *Pastors, physicians, or pro-life counselors who try to impart reverence for life, even if they succeed only 3% of the time, will save as many years of potential life as would the total eradication of all deaths during the first year of life!*

Pastors and teachers who teach God's law are promoting preventive medicine when they teach what are now called "parenting" skills from Scripture. The number of medical contacts resulting from unbiblical parent-child relationships is large, including: preventable accidents, drug abuse, venereal disease, functional abdominal pain, tension headaches, illegitimate pregnancy and more. Small children whose parents, for example, tolerate "sass" or disobedience, as in a church nursery, can be provided with inexpensive, powerful health maintenance without any physician involvement whatsoever. Nouthetic counselors can admonish the parents on the fifth commandment and its applicability in the present life and in the life to come.

Bernard Cohen produced what he calls a "catalog of risks" in which he tries to put the various risks life has to offer into order according to their "riskiness."[7] He uses the method of years of potential life lost which he terms "lost life expectancy." The results of his work are eye-opening, revealing the narrow mindset medicine has developed. For example, a person who lives an alcoholic lifestyle on the average lops 4 thousand days (about 11 years) off of his life. If a counselor were successful only 5% of the time in seeing an alcoholic changed, he would save as many years of life as would the medical profession if the medical profession were able to save all burn victims, or all poisoning victims. If the counseling were an effective instrument in getting people out of poverty by means of getting them back to work, and was effective only 3% of the time, the counseling would save as many years of potential life as would be saved by eliminating *all* deaths by motor vehicle accidents if the relationship that poverty has with mortality is causal.

MORE CHALLENGES TO FAMILY GOVERNMENT

At this and many other points, nouthetic counselors will necessarily run headlong into medical dictums. For example, the medical profession is building pressure rapidly to do away with corporal punishment of children. Listen to this from the American Family Physician: "We believe that corporal punishment should not be used in children. It does not usually have a lasting effect, and it may impair the child's confidence and trust in the individuals to whom he or she looks for love and guidance. Moreover, if administered in anger, it may lead to child abuse."[8] "No lasting effect!?" Prov. 23:13-14 states, "Do not withhold correction from a child. For if you beat him with a rod, he will not die. You shall beat him with a rod, and deliver his soul from hell [Sheol]." In plain revelatory words, then, correctly administered corporal punishment actually withholds children from death. How long-term can you be? The "studies" upon which the anti-corporal punishment dictum are based are doing very well if they have 5 year follow-up. The vast majority of them are retrospective studies, in which older children or adults who are judged to be doing very well are compared with those who are in some kind of financial, legal, vocational, or health trouble. Typically, they will be asked to recollect how they were disciplined. Some difference is found in corporal punishment patterns and that difference is pegged as the one which caused the later problem in life. There is a cause and effect issue here. There is also a problem with the probability of selective recall. Even if the studies are splendid, does one assume that clear revelation is somehow overturned by empiricism?

BACKING DOWN SOME CHALLENGERS

Let's imagine a scenario between a physician and nouthetic counselor over this issue. You have a family in your church in which a child is misbehaving. The child has already been to a pediatrician or family physician and has received some counsel and, perhaps, even some medication. The parents relate to you that they have been advised against the use of corporal punishment on the misbegotten theory that behind every crooked behavior there lies a crooked molecule. You see spanking as one of the appropriate options in this given case. One option you may *not* have utilized is to "rattle the physician's cage." Kindly. Firmly. To this date, the majority of pediatricians and family physicians still support corporal punishment.[9]

While trying not to catch the parents in the middle between conflicting advice (that may not always be possible), you may call or write the physician, with the family's permission, stating your advice and your reasons for it in brief. Hopefully, a conversation might ensue. The physician's cage can be rattled in several ways, but one would to engage the physician at a metaphysical level.

Counselor: "I was wondering on what basis you recommended to the family that they not use corporal punishment for their child. As I have indicated, I am advising differently."

Physician: "I don't believe that spanking works."

Counselor: "Doesn't work *to accomplish what end* ?"

Physician: "You know, to see that the behavior changes."

Counselor: "Which behaviors did you have in mind?" Physician, now a little irritated perhaps: "Pinching his sister, cursing, and flinging paint on the walls at home. Things like that. Didn't they tell you? (Lapsing now into the lecture-of-ignoramuses mode) Violence begets violence. If you use violent means to combat violence, the child learns that violence is an appropriate way to solve problems."

Counselor: "Well, we certainly have some major differences on this. It seems to me that all 'violence' is being lumped together. Be that as it may, how do you know that violence is *wrong* ?"

Physician: "Well, don't *you* believe that it is wrong?"

Counselor: "My question was how *you* know that it is wrong. If your answer is to consult my opinion for your own, I am first of all flattered. Secondly, you'll have to change *your* views, because I *don't* believe that all 'violence' is wrong. If corporal punishment is violence, it is mandated in

the Bible."

Physician: "Well, I am not a theologian. (Intonation indicates that the physician holds theologians only a half-notch above mass murderers in esteem.) I just practice medicine. I don't drag the Bible into everything."

Counselor: "How do you know that the Bible does *not* belong in everything?"

Physician: "Well, research shows that children do better if they are not spanked, if other methods of discipline are used. If the Bible says otherwise, somebody must be interpreting it wrong."

Counselor: "Then you assume that research is the guide to how we *ought* to live and how we ought *not* to live. That its answers are sort of self-authenticating."

Physician: "Yes, I believe that."

Counselor: "You have faith in the ability of research to answer questions of that sort?"

Physician: "Yes, I believe it does answer questions."

Counselor: "Well, then, since I don't believe you *really* meant for me to determine for *you* that violence is wrong, explain to me how *research* shows that violence is wrong."

Physician: "It *hurts* people! I'm here to *help* people."

Counselor: "That only removes the question one step. How is it that you *know* that hurting people is always wrong?"

Physician: "This is crazy. *Everybody* knows that is wrong. Everybody, maybe, but you."

Counselor: "I really doubt you want to maintain that you know what is right and wrong based upon what 'everybody knows.' There are times and places in which 'everybody' knew that blacks were inferior, that Jews were scum, that cannibalism

was okay, and that stealing from enemies was acceptable. (Lapsing into *his* lecture mode) What I believe you are doing is using information from research about the state things are in — what *is*, — to try to answer questions about the way things *ought to be*. That is logically inadmissable. You cannot legitimately use a statement about what *is*, to answer a question about what *ought to be*. For questions about what ought to be, we need a self-authenticating standard. That is why I use the *Bible* to advise people. You are using *research* as your self-authenticating standard. I don't share your faith that research can answer questions of that sort. You believe it does. We are both moving from a *faith* position, though I recognize you probably don't like the religious connotations of that word, and I am not trying to foist my religion off on you. I am, rather, trying to *convince* you of the value of mine, and to convince you that you *are* foisting your moral beliefs off on your patient, who is my church member. My faith position is up front. Yours is surreptitious. I'd rather work *with* you, but if we cannot resolve this issue, I am going to have to advise the family to find another physician."

Now that is all a confrontational type of encounter. You aren't likely to convert a physician with that approach. However, you will probably introduce some much-needed caution into that doctor before he spews his error quite so casually in the future. You will hurt him a little bit economically, if you can convince the family. You will have the further advantage that his "methods" don't work, whereas God's methods *do* work. Instead of *being* on the defensive, you may occasionally put the medical professional legitimately on the defensive. The *majority* of physicians who deal with children still believe in corporal punishment and will have far different conversations with you. They can be strengthened in their witness by you, if only you will risk it. Many of them are cowed by the vocal minority who despise the teachings of the Bible.

LIMITATIONS OF THE DISEASE MODEL: HOW TO MISS THE POINT WHILE BEING VERY SCIENTIFIC

The medical profession's perception has become so limited to the theoretical constructs known as "disease entities," by which is meant only the physical causes and manifestations of disease, that it is unable and unwilling to see that mankind is a living, breathing spirit folded into a body. Pastoral counseling offers one major avenue to instruct the medical profession and other onlookers, as it instructs the direct recipients.

Of the many possible examples, one of my favorites is a two-page ad for the anti-viral drug Zovirax appearing in many medical journals. Page one of the ad shows a downcast young woman seated alone in a sidewalk cafe lamenting that genital herpes has put her into "solitary confinement." Page two shows the same girl smiling and in the convivial company of another young woman and two very nice-looking young men. The girl was in "solitary confinement" *only* in that she could not fornicate. Better living through chemistry "solves" the problem by enabling her to fornicate somewhat more freely. The ad treats of the issue of genital herpes as though it is merely a matter of viruses, their DNA structure, and chemically substituting a different

base in the thymine, guanine, etc., pairs. The acceleration of this kind of narrow thinking is traceable to about 1960. Since that time, all of our venereal diseases have increased in frequency, greatly, with the addition of new diseases such as AIDS.

How far afield we have gotten in medicine, off on zebra hunts! The world's most prestigious medical journal may be the *New England Journal of Medicine*. In a recent index we find titles such as "Controlled trial comparing foscarnet with vidarabine for acyclovir-resistant mucocutaneous herpes simplex in the acquired immune deficiency syndrome."

Imagine these article titles of obscure issues being superimposed on a TV screen of some current events of health significance — a sort of MTV for medicine. That one, for example, could go on an image of the doorway to a sodomite liaison center masquerading as a bath house. With a little musical accompaniment we have articles addressing "rare bird" medical issues overlying views of much more potent causes of disease .

"Inhalation of a coin and a capsule from metered dose inhalers." Dancers in a bar heavy with cigarette smoke.

"Ratio of low-density lipoprotein cholesterol to ubiquinone as a coronary risk factor." An argument begins in the bar.

"Outbreak of herpes gladiatorum at a high-school wrestling camp." Fists fly; a woman is struck. A gunshot. The bar clears, leaving only the smoke, a trail of blood, and a prostitute too drunk to leave.

"Inability to attribute susceptibility to primary sclerosing cholangitis to specific amino acid positions of the HLA-DRw52a allele." Cut to the legendary fiddling of Nero while

Rome burns, then fade out.

No cheap shot at basic research is intended. The point is *not* that we don't benefit from the sort of information addressed by researchers examining a material *sine qua non* of obscure diseases. The point is that that kind of information has ceased to be nearly as relevant to the health and safety of people in the United States as are the issues of the *heart* of mankind. Our priorities in medicine are badly skewed. The heart is the neglected *sine qua non* of health in the U.S. today. Jesus said, "For from within, out of the heart of men, proceed evil thoughts, adulteries, fornications, murders, thefts, covetousness, wickedness, deceit, licentiousness, an evil eye, blasphemy, pride, and foolishness. All of these things come from within and defile a man." Mark 7:21-23] We need this kind of "kardiology" for our spiritual and physical health.

NUMERATORS OVER DENOMINATORS

Physicians deal mainly with sick *numerators*, persons who have presented their bodies a living sacrifice for us — our community is the sick. There have been efforts within medicine to deal with the whole community, and public health medicine is its best expression, but for most practicing physicians, the community is more or less out of reach. As far as sickness is concerned churches deal with *denominators* — both the sick and the well within the community of faith. The Church also deals with the "fields white unto harvest," the pagans, both sick and the well in those fields. While medicine has incorrectly restricted itself to empirical, evidential data[10] it has also drawn its data too often from numerators only. The Church has the opportunity to see these sick numerators in the illuminating context of their spiritual denominators — how sickness relates to spiritual condition. Furthermore, medicine has cut off revelational data - input from the Bible. Pastoral counseling can restore this missing feature of revelation to its powerful role in maintaining and regaining health.

EVIDENCE FROM SOCIAL SCIENCE (If You Aren't Used to Standing on Revelational Evidence)

House, *et al.*, in a community-based study, examined some features relating to health as they related to the crude measure of mortality.[11] They found suggestions of relationships for a number of activities which, in themselves, don't look at all like "health care:" pleasure drives and picnics, visiting friends and relatives, attending church, attending meetings, attending spectator events, classes or lectures. At moderate levels of involvement these appear to reduce your likelihood of death, with the effect more pronounced for men in most cases. While these were correlations and not causations, they are interesting. As has long been known, being married is a healthy estate.

Can doctors in today's regime encourage this? Not without strident criticism. Can the Church? Yes. On the grounds of evidence such as these researchers accumulated? No, rather because the Bible commends it as the norm for most people. Yet the general consistency with what biblical counseling might at times recommend is illustrative. In his "catalog of risks," Bernard Cohen, mentioned earlier, found that poor social con-

nections — living a relatively isolated life — ranked fourth among the causes of loss of life expectancy, after smoking, alcoholism, and poverty.[7] He estimated a loss of about 3 years of life expectancy for such persons, exceeding suicide, murder, AIDS, drowning, electrocution, natural hazards such as floods and earthquakes, and many other things that we get all worked up about.

WORK FOR HEALTH

For another example, consider work. To be employed is health-promoting. Counseling from Eph. 4:28 ("He who has been stealing must steal no longer, but must work, doing something useful with his own hands, that he may have something to share with those in need.") will have healing and preventive qualities. We have too much, "I can't work because I'm too sick." We have too little, "You're sick so much because you are not employed."

Christian teaching for the denominator population is a powerful force for health. If Churches were more obedient, it would be an even more powerful force. The medical profession needs the input from the Church to clean up its act, to put its powerful tools into the right perspective, to make sure that our methods are harnessed to the right questions.

While science pretends to abhor the method of authority, and tells tales about the bad old days in which medicine kow-towed to authorities who did not do experiments, we still live in an authoritarian system. The authorities tell us not only that the only method of any real use is the "scientific method," they also insist on casting the questions in materialistic terms only, throwing *revelational* epistemology off the playing field.

They are applying *their* epistemology where it does not legitimately apply, to *normative* issues. We have a "tyranny of the expert," who knows much more than we do, yet who does not see that the depth of vision has been gained at the substantial cost of a breadth of vision. The Church can restore the breadth of view to illness and health, can reclaim the validity of the method of revelation, and pitch out the method of natural science from its stolen territory.

Medicine has become somewhat like the man who knows the cost of everything and the value of nothing. There is a need for a generalist — not speaking here of a medical generalist, which I am, though that is true, — but of someone who has the whole person in view, in the context of the family, church and society, as well as a time span that extends beyond a six year follow-up study. We need someone to have a view all the way to the deathbed and to eternity beyond. Medicine demands now an illegitimate thing of its practitioners — that we give up our general office of believer and priest in order to become a body mechanic. *The body mechanic image is a very dangerous one for medicine.*

While it is generally believed that the day of the Renaissance man — the one who could by dint of intelligence and hard effort still encompass all the branches of knowledge adequately — is gone due to the explosion in knowledge, there needs to be at least a collusion between physician and pastors over the matter of the spirit and body in health and illness. If no one can encompass it individually, then the Church with its gifts should try to do it corporately.

Christianity is the only key to full health and the *best* key to health even in a limited, physical sense. Medicine needs help of the gospel ministry in accomplishing this. Medicine is *under* the Gospel. It functions too often as though it were apart or *parallel*. The pastor and physician are ideally co-laborers, not adversaries. We exist in a hierarchical relationship. The pastor represents to us the overarching Word of God. The physician is under the gospel - both the natural science aspect and the spiritual aspect. The gospel applies to all of life. Medicine is not excluded. The special problems of the relationship of spirit and body, their sometimes unfathomable blend, require that we work together, both under the Word of God.

PRACTICAL MODELS FOR CONSIDERATION

How might we accomplish this co-labor? Let's look at it from two perspectives. One, where the ailing person presents him/herself first to a physician (Figure 1). In Figure 1 the percentages given at the first decision node reflect conservative estimates of the frequency of organic causes versus non-organic causes in new problems presenting in primary care medicine. The other perspective is that in which the person presents first to a pastoral counselor (Figures 2 and 3). In this instance, two outcomes can follow depending upon the orientation of the physician with whom the counselor may communicate.

One of the problems is that the physician who is not willing to be a co-laborer will divert the patient from a spiritual problem represented in Figure 2. I believe this to be unfortunately the norm within medicine, including with Christian

physicians. Figures 1 and 3 represent the preferred flow of cooperation between physician and counselor.

From the physician's end, I find that real pastoral counseling is difficult to locate. It seems that the pastors are all too willing to leave such problems to the medical model. One thing I have tried with limited success is to define for the patient that I believe the problem is spiritual (after having gone to that point in an evaluation). I then offer to *go with* the patient to see his pastor. This offer serves several functions. It sorts out the serious patients from the trifling patients. The latter won't let it happen. I won't treat it medically, and they are left to wallow in their pit of despair. When I *can* go with them, my major function is to keep the issue from being "medicalized." In a sense, it keeps the pastor's feet to the fire, to uncover and manage the spiritual issues involved. The counselee

terminology and deviate toward the psychological or medical models. With both the pastor and the counselee so prone, a physician present can prevent them both from avoiding their responsibilities by medicalizing what is not biomedical.

A CAVEAT ON COUNSELING MERELY TO CHANGE FEELING STATES

Again, from the physician's end of this collusion between medicine and pastoral counseling, consider briefly the matter of counseling for bad feelings. While many bad feelings stem directly or indirectly from sinful behavior, many do not, but stem from poorly understood bodily problems. Once a nouthetic counselor has reviewed a situation sufficiently to see that there is no reasonable connection between a person's beliefs and his feelings, and has established as well as possible that

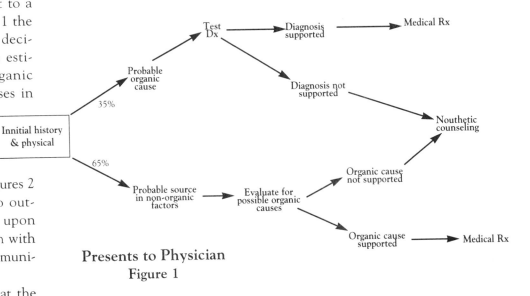

Presents to Physician
Figure 1

often continues to use the psychological or medical terms in which they have cast the problem up to that point. Due to their training or reading, pastors are often prone to such

there is no sinful behavior pattern ongoing, we don't need to resist medical efforts to relieve bad feelings. We in medicine, too, may have no idea what it is that is making the person feel bad. However, we may have a tool to relieve the bad feeling at least to some extent. As long as it is safe to do so, and not idolatrously expensive, what is the harm in doing it?

We don't understand all that much about many of our medicines — how they work. A handy example is that of aspirin. It has been known for over a century, but not really understood in its mechanism until the last couple of decades. If would not be wrong to use aspirin for chronic headaches in a person whose body has been combed through for

health care should not be left to the medical profession alone. Homosexuality may have exited the closet in the 1970's, but death and dying entered the closet beginning in the 1950's, as the new social taboo. Until the 1950's, the majority of deaths in the U.S. occurred in the home. Since that time dying has largely been an institutional phenomenon. Why should dying be inevitably medicalized? (It is clearly a metaphysical event. The enfolded spirit leaves the body. [James 2:26] Inasmuch as the spir-

ment?

(f) how much does it cost?

(g) what kind of treatments are available to maintain function as long as possible?

(h) what kind of treatments are available to relieve suffering?

(i) why do I have to go into a hospital? what can be done there that can't be done somewhere else?

(j) will the family and close friends be allowed access if the patient wants it?

(k) bring up the issue of "CPR" or "Code status."[12]

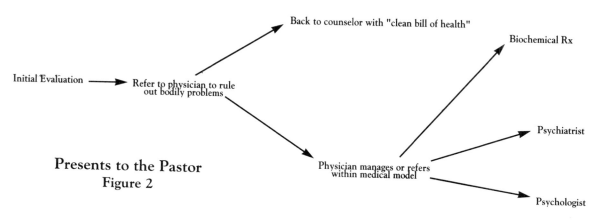

Presents to the Pastor
Figure 2

known physical causes, with none found, and whose life has been combed through by nouthetic counseling for causes rooted in sin, with none found. Pastoral counseling need not be exclusivist in its approach to bad *feelings*. Bad *behavior*, yes. Despite the incursions of psychology, it is Biblical turf. Defend it. Bad *feelings*, no. That is not the exclusive turf of pastoral counseling.

SOME AREAS IN WHICH PASTORAL COUNSELING IS DESIRABLE:

1. Approaching death. The issues of "living wills" or (the preferred) durable power of attorney for

it is by definition beyond the method of natural science to measure, we depend only upon indirect measures.) Pastoral counselors, prepare your church members for the inevitability of death. Prepare them in detail. Prepare in grisly detail. The techno-wonders of medicine so capture families that the hard, needful questions never get asked:

(a) what are the prospects for recovery *without* treatment?

(b) what are the prospects for treatment *with* treatment?

(c) what is the treatment like?

(d) what is life like *with* treatment?

(e) What is life like *without* treat-

2. Pastors and elders may want to lead the diaconate into practical counseling with regard to the choices being made in medical care by members, including costs and alternative choices available in therapy. Someone needs to help some patients and families to ask these same hard questions in many situations, not just dying. Especially carefully should hospitalization be considered. Few things isolate us from our family and friends the way a hospital does. The routine of the hospital takes precedence over the conversation of visitors. Family members often are fearful even of touching a patient for fear of dislodging a

tube or interfering with some other device in the room. Even in battles to restore physical health which we are very likely to lose, the physical ministrations displace approaches to spiritual matters.

3. Reproductive issues. Do you have physician church members counseling *against* fornication with their mouths and counseling *for* it with their hands as they write prescriptions for birth control pills for the unmarried, or install Norplant?[13] Do you have a resource you can call on, and some background knowledge of your own, regarding the new technologies for married couples to achieve conception? Have you thought about the implications of artificial insemination by donor? Are you aware of the common practice for all forms of artificial insemination to fertilize large numbers of eggs, but to freeze or throw away some? There are some excellent references available to you for these kinds of questions. There is no need for every pastor to plow through these issues without help.

4. Addictionism.[14] Are you relieved to be able to refer your counseless (or your patients, if you are a physician) to addiction specialists? They are so hard to deal with. Nothing much seems to work. They take up so much time. They pull whole families down with them. Surely, they need "expert" help. Study the issue from a biblical perspective. If II Tim. 3:15-17 is true, where is the foundation for your answer in Scripture? Again, there are excellent resources now for you to read. Do not be deceived by claims that addictionologists are all that successful. They are using the classic ploys:

(a) expanded definitions of "addiction" capture persons who are less afflicted than the "classic" skid-row drunk. With less afflicted persons to begin with, your outcomes will look better,

(b) early diagnosis is supposed to yield a better outcome. Not only does early diagnosis inevitably include a number of people who are not afflicted, it also may identify them earlier in the progression of the problem. As is the case in the early diagnosis of incurable cancers, to find someone early gives the false impression of effective therapy just because they were found early.

(c) sobriety cannot be the sole criterion for success for Christians. Those who say, "I'd do *anything* in order to be sober," need to be shown that that is a careless statement. We are *not* free to use any and all means to achieve even a good end. If a person stays sober by exercising some New Age technique, for example, the accomplishment for their eternal "health" is most unimpressive, however impressive it may be temporally.

(d) redefining the problem as a relapsing disease, thus permitting exoneration of bad results which might otherwise cast doubt on the disease theory of alcoholism and its methodology. We are often told that Christian religious dogmas of blame don't work for alcoholics, only serving to drive them further from help, with the evidence being those for whom it obviously didn't

work. Then, while our attention is diverted by quasi-medical talk, we are told that the disease theory includes prominently that the disease is chronic and relapsing. That's why you cannot use failures of that model against the model itself.

5. "Parenting." Habits for life may be established early, for good or for bad. Are your church's parents abandoning their responsibility? Don't trust the schools to do the parents' job. "A paternalistic state has no room for fathers." (David Chilton) Neither leave part of it up to physicians. The orthodox practice in medicine now, including, of all things family medicine, is to hold what dependent young people say to their doctors *confidential* from their parents! This tenet has it that the value of that confidentiality with a doctor *exceeds* in health value the value of having informed parents. Explain not that parents often do not care. Of course, many do not. For those outside the church, the physician will not be able to make much of a parent. For those inside the church, the chore for such children begins with holding the parents accountable for their responsibilities.

6. Family involvement in illness. Often an ill person will need some sort of assistance that is not strictly medical — financial, nutritional, transportation, information, etc. I have noted a reflex has developed within medicine to turn *first* to civil governmental agencies of a social service nature. While not necessarily implying that the family or church should duplicate services needlessly, I

Presents to Pastor
Figure 3

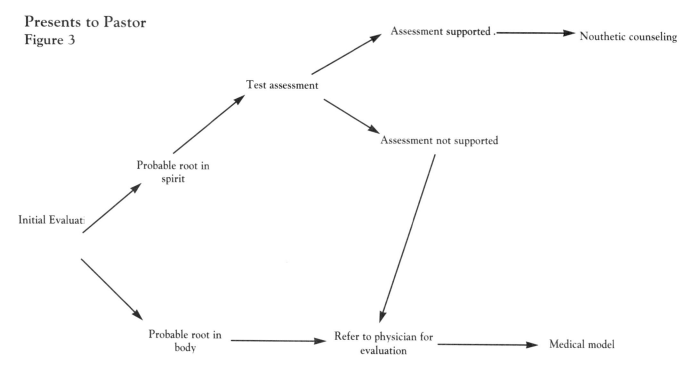

have found it illuminating to ask a patient who expresses such a need, "Does your *family* know about this need?" Most commonly, the answer is, "No." If I ask why not, a common response is, "They have their own lives to live. I don't want to bother them." I restrain myself, usually, from saying, "You don't seem to mind bothering anonymous taxpayers with your request that they underwrite what God gave families the privilege and duty of providing." Sometimes I discover that the reason the patient is reluctant to let their family know is some unresolved family conflict. What an opportunity! I recommend that the family be notified of the need and offer to be the one to do so. In almost every case, when I have notified a family, they have responded — either out of love, duty, or perhaps merely because they would be embarassed to say 'no' to a doctor.

Not only is the need met, the family is strengthened by doing what it is designed to do. The family has been instructed by the very asking of the question. We physicians are so consequentialist in our practice. If we know it won't "work" to accomplish a given end, we economize by not bothering. The problem comes when our focus is sometimes on too narrow a set of consequences. Both pastors and physicians can teach by maneuvers of this sort. We need to see if there is some way to diaconally institute it.

7. At the risk of sounding like Jim and Tammy Faye Bakker, churches need to talk about money. Not only the kind that members give, but how the portion that members retain is spent. Church members give something on the order of 2% or so of income. Medical care is consuming 13% of the gross national product. There is an idolatrous disproportion here. The gospel message has competition in the world, and it is measurable at a pocketbook level. Where a man's treasure is, there will his heart be also. Some of the *other* places in which money can be spent than on services labeled "medical care" may have as much or more actual productivity for health.

SUMMARY

How may overarching supervision of the medical care by Christians be recaptured by the Church?[15]

1. Church discipline of physicians who are practicing gross sins. So you have no abortionists in your congregation? Do you have those who refer for abortion?

2. Church discipline of members who are practicing gross sins. It is neither kind nor healthy to overlook gross sin.

3. Preaching the Word to the

Church, with applications to health where they are present. This is not the same as locating biblical "support" for current medical practice.

4. Teaching the word to the Church, with applications to health where they are present.

5. For # 3 & 4 above, the issues which relate to health taught in Scripture include: "parenting," marital relations, indebtedness, work habits, Sabbath-keeping, addictionism, education, etc.

6. A diaconal ministry instructed and involved in helping Church members ask the right questions of physicians during illnesses, politely but persistently.

7. Visitation of the sick. For the hospitalized ill, seeing to it that appropriate visitation is taken seriously by the hospital staff.

8. Anointing with oil and prayer for the sick.

9. Developing a working relationship between physicians and pastors in which the pastor is not the junior partner, for the identification of the source(s) or patients problems.

10. Nouthetic counseling for Church members. De-medicalize the management of problems-in-living through the use of cooperation with a physician who appreciates the proper position of medicine in the health equation. Not everything felt *in* the body is originating *from* the body.

11. Escape the straightjacket. The medical profession's viewpoint on health and disease is very narrowly conceived.

12. Physicians at every level of the system need to have an appreciation of the prior probabilities of disease, and to use it in helping patients prioritize their health

issues among the other issues of life.

ENDNOTES

1. Christensen, Bryce J., In Sickness and in Health, *Policy Review*, Spring, 1992, p.72.

2. Smith, Garrard, Epidemiology of Human Bites to Children in a Day Care Center, *AJDC*, Vol. 142, June, 1988, pp. 643-650.

3. Thacker, Stephen, *et al.*, Infectious Diseases and Injuries in Child Day Care: Opportunities for Healthier Children, *JAMA*, Vol. 268, October 7, 1992, pp. 1720-1726.

4. Haskins, Ron, and Kotch, Jonathan, Day Care and Illness: Evidence, Costs, and Public Policy, *Pediatrics*, Vol. 77, Supplement, June, 1986.

5. Froom, Jack, & Culpepper, L., Otitis Media in Day Care Children: A Report From the International Primary Care Network, *The Journal of Family Practice*, Vol. 32, 1991, pp. 289-293.

6. Haskins, R., *op cit.*, p. 974.

7. Cohen, Bernard, Catalog of Risks Extended and Updated, *Health Physics*, Vol. 61, September, 1991, pp. 317-335.

8. Leung, Alexander, Robson, Wm, & Lim, Stephen, Counseling Parents About Childhood Discipline, *American Family Physician*, Vol. 45, March 1992, p. 1188.

9. McCormick, Kenelm, Attitudes of Primary Care Physicians Toward Corporal Punishment, *JAMA*, Vol. 267, June 17, 1992, pp. 3161-3165.

10. Even Christians have fallen into the error that God's revelation is secondary to empiricism. As example, take the comment of Douglas Culver, who wrote: "We

are unable to accept a profound, *empirically-verified* fact: Man cannot live by bread alone, though every loaf is guaranteed by a seemingly omnipotent state." (emphasis added) [The Moral of a Great Failure, *World*, October 17, 1992, p. 21.] Verification is the establishment of the truth or accuracy of something. How is it that a Christian could believe that anything could establish the truth of what Jesus has spoken? The greater confirms the lesser. If empiricism verifies Christ, then our observations are the greater, and His words the lesser. Revelation is thus subjugated to science.

11. House, James, Robbins, Cynthia, & Metzner, Helen, The Association of Social Relationships and Activities with Mortality: Prospective Evidence from the Tecumseh Community Health Study, *American Journal of Epidemiology*, Vol. 116, 1982, pp. 123-140. See also in this regard, Berkman, Lisa & Syme, S. Leonard, Social Networks, Host Resistance, and Mortality: A Nine-Year Follow-Up Study of Alameda County Residents, *American Journal of Epidemiology*, Vol. 109, 1979, pp. 186-204.

12. When a person knows that he is near death, there may be some final business to transact, such as those seeking reconciliation or a final word of encouragement or instruction. When nothing else *physically* speaking can be retrieved in a case of someone dying, sometimes something *spiritual* can. Teaching at the end can be potent. Thomas Hooker, a formerly well-known Puritan pastor of Connecticut, on his

deathbed was asked, "Sir, you are going to receive the reward of all your labours." He answered, "Brother, I am going to receive mercy." (Mather, Cotton, **Magnalia Christi Americana,** 2 vols., Edinburgh: Banner of Truth Trust, (1852), 1979, as quoted by Steve Wilkins, in lecture #5, *America: The First 350 Years*, p. 22.) At his death last year, my father's last words were, "My cup runneth over." A summary for the entire family, who knows it to be true, to reflect on for ourselves. For the likes of that, in pursuit sometimes of the last full *second* of life, we have notably *unmemorable* deathbed scenes from the ICU: "Is that a flat line?" "Set it at 300 joules." "Another amp ᴄᶠ bicarb." "Let's check the ET tube placement."

13. Is this practice an example of "speaking lies in hypocrisy" (I Tim. 4:2)? What about the practice of prescribing birth control pills to a young unmarried woman and then warning her to see that her consort(s) also use a condom so that she won't get AIDS, etc? Is the condom not good enough for both? What is the lie? Not merely that condoms aren't sure enough in the prevention of pregnancy, but more fundamentally the lie is that fornication can be made safe through the chemistry of norethindrone or the physical properties of latex. The narrow conception here is that pregnancy is "caused by" spermatozoa meeting ovum and that STD's are "caused by" infectious agents such as viruses, protozoa, or bacteria. The broader biblical teaching is that illegitimacy is caused by fornication. The choice to abide by the narrower conception is not one mandated by the natural science data, it is a moral choice. Pregnancy is not evil. Yet the medical profession treats it as if it were *the* evil to be avoided.

14. Addictionism teaching is rampant and enjoys almost unchallenged hegemony in medicine. For example, the *Journal of the Medical Association, JAMA*, in its January 13, 1993, issue (p. 213) printed an exchange of letters. A Minnesota physician wrote in criticizing an article which, he said, failed to seriously consider the virtues of health insurance with premiums adjusted to lifestyle choices such as smoking and drinking alcohol. The challenged author's answer as to why such a type of insurance is *not* a good idea included the following: ".... what class and ethnic biases are manifest or latent in these strategies [of making people pay premiums adjusted to health risks.]? Smoking and drinking in certain subcultures and income groups are the norm. Not to join in would be bizarre. The people in these cultures usually have grueling lives and little money. Are we upper-middle-class professionals going to punish them for their habits of relief and pleasure? Moreover, most of their occupations are higher risk, but how much choice did they have?" The public is listening to the medical profession's teaching. We need to counter this sort of lying illogic. The first thing we need to do to counter it is to abandon equivalent teaching ourselves. A key in nouthetic counseling is the idea of responsibility. The whole addictionism lie undercuts responsibility. We cannot have it both ways.

15. Not much has been said here about the civil smoothness of communication between pastors and physicians. My observation has been that things on the surface proceed rather smoothly. I am more concerned that the functioning relationship implicitly and powerfully excludes practical use of spiritual features. Change which incorporates practically the spiritual nature of man as it relates to health, can be expected to make things, in some cases, proceed *less* smoothly. There will be no gain without some pain.

"Some Biblical passages of note as they relate to health, obedient living, and God's superintendence of our health:

Exodus 4:11 [God answers Moses' plea of physical disability] "So the Lord said to him, "Who has made man's mouth? Or who makes the mute, the deaf, the seeing, or the blind? Have not I, the Lord?"
Leviticus 26:16ff "I also will do this to you: I will even appoint terror over you, wasting disease and fever which shall consume the eyes and cause sorrow of heart..."
Deut. 11:18-21, "Therefore you shall lay up these words of mine in your heart and in your soul, and bind them as a sign on your hand, and they shall be as frontlets between your eyes. You shall teach them to your children, speaking of them when you sit in your house, when you walk by the way, when you lie down, and when you rise up. And you shall write them on the doorposts of your house and on your gates, that your days and the days of your children may be multiplied in the land of which the Lord swore to your fathers to give them, like the days of the heavens above the earth." ["Parenting" is crucial to health.]
Deut. 28:21ff "The Lord will make the plague cling to you until He has consumed you from the land which you are going to possess. The Lord will strike you with consumption, with fever, with inflammation, with severe burning fever, with the sword, with scorching, and with mildew; they shall pursue you until you perish. ... The Lord will strike you with the boils of Egypt, with tumors, with

the scab, and with the itch, from which you cannot be healed. The Lord will strike you with madness and blindness and confusion of heart. ... The Lord will strike you in the knees and on the legs with severe boils which cannot be healed, and from the sole of your foot to the top of your head."
I Chronicles 10:13, 14 — the reasons for King Saul's violent death
Psalm 41:1-3 "Blessed is he who considers the poor; The Lord will deliver him in time of trouble. The Lord will preserve him and keep him alive, and he will be blessed on the earth. You will not deliver him to the will of his enemies. The Lord will strengthen him on his bed of illness; You will sustain him on his sickbed." [Mercy as an HMO?]
Psalm 91:9,10 "Because you have made the Lord, who is my refuge, Even the Most High, your habitation, No evil shall befall you, Nor shall any plague come near your dwelling;" [Do we overly spiritualize passages of this sort?]
Psalm 107:17 "Fools, because of their transgression, And because of their iniquities, were afflicted, Their soul abhorred all manner of food, And they drew near to the gates of death."
Psalm 119:71 "It was good for me to be afflicted so that I might learn your decrees." [After recovery from serious illness, might there be a church counseling ministry to investigate what might be learned of God's Word from the experience? This investigation would not necessarily or even usually be of the sort to find a particular sin which caused the illness, but rather to relate providence to Scripture.]
Prov. 3:1,2 "My son, do not forget my law, But let your heart keep my

commands; For length of days and long life And peace they will add to you." [Why has catechising and memorization fallen onto such hard times? When we do memorize, do we choose those passages that are more of a "pick-me-up" for momentary use and discard than deeper study?]
Prov. 4:20 - 22 "My son, give attention to my words; Incline your ear to my sayings. Do not let them depart from your eyes; Keep them in the midst of your heart; For they are life to those who find them, And health to all their flesh."
Prov. 5:7-13 "Therefore hear me now, my children, And do not depart from the words of my mouth. Remove your way far from her, And do not go near the door of her house, Lest you give your honor to others, And your years to the cruel one; Lest aliens be filled with your wealth, And your labors go to the house of a foreigner; And you mourn at last, When your flesh and your body are consumed, And say; 'How I have hated instruction, And my heart despised reproof! I have not obeyed the voice of my teachers, Nor inclined my ear to those who instructed me!'" [It is a mark of our departure from the authority of Scripture that we think we need "evidence" such as that provided by "medical research" to tell people to be sexually pure.]
Prov. 9:10 - 11 "The fear of the Lord is the beginning of wisdom, And the knowledge of the Holy One is understanding. For by me your days will be multiplied, And years of life will be added to you." [Do not send young people off to college to pursue a degree if they do not have the beginning of wisdom. Is a fool in possession of a degree and much data more useful than one without?]

Prov. 14:30 " A sound heart is life to the body, But envy is rottenness to the bones."

Prov. 16:31 "The silver-haired head is a crown of glory, If it is found in a way of righteousness." [Longevity is related to righteousness.]

Isaiah 5:8-25 - Greed, drunkenness, falsehood, those who call evil good and good evil are in line for illness and death.

Matthew 4:4 "...It is written, 'Man shall not live by bread alone, but by every word that proceeds from the mouth of God." [Medicine is sustenance of the same sort (though of lesser necessity) as is bread. To try to live by medicine without the Word of God is destined for frustration and failure.]

John 12:27: "Now My soul is troubled and what shall I say? Father, save me from this hour? But for this purpose I came to this hour? Father, glorify Your name." [The preservation of life is *not* the highest value.]

I Cor. 11:30 "For this reason many are weak and sick among you, and many sleep."

Eph. 6:1-3 "Children, obey your parents in the Lord, for this is right. 'Honor your father and mother,' which is the first commandment with promise: 'that it may be well with you and you may live long on the earth.'"

I Corinthians 6:15-18 "Do you not know that your bodies are members of Christ? Shall I then take the members of Christ and make them members of a harlot? Certainly not! Or do you not know that he who is joined to a harlot is one body with her? For, 'the two,' He says, 'shall become one flesh.' But he who is joined to the Lord is one spirit with Him. Flee sexual immorality. Every sin that a man does is outside the body, but he who commits sexual immorality sins against his own body." [The anemic Church of Common Morality feebly recommends fleeing sexual immorality, then counsels that you approach it with a condom in hand, tacitly teaching that flight from that immorality is not possible.]

1 Tim. 4:8 "For bodily exercise profits a little, but godliness is profitable for all things, having promise of the life that now is and of that which is to come." [My message in a Scriptural nutshell. Physical elements have a place. Godliness has a greater place, not only for the here and now, but for the hereafter, also.]

Too Many Rights Make Wrong

Rev. David Hall

Mr. Hall is pastor of Covenant Presbyterian Church in Oak Ridge, Tennessee.

"If I am sick unto death, and the only thing that will save my life is the touch of Henry Fonda's cool hand on my fevered brow, then all the same, I have no right to be given the touch of Henry Fonda's cool hand on my fevered brow. It would be frightfully nice of him to fly in from the West Coast to provide it. It would be less nice, though no doubt well meant, if my friends flew out to the West Coast and carried Henry Fonda back with them. But I have no right at all against anybody that he should do this for me."[1]

Recent communications have begun to notice the ubiquity of rights-claims. Rights are claimed for privacy, even if another life must be expended. The rights mantra is changed whenever one demands that the state provide everything, from disaster relief to health-care to the right to 12 weeks of family leave. While some of these problems may deserve attention, it is highly debatable that one agency or another *owes* solutions to every citizen in all areas. At present we hear rights claimantswhining that they have rights to live and die, rights to privacy and the right to invade one of the most private of sectors via condom distribution, the right to conceive and the right to abort, the right to a job for college graduates, the right to have the government subsidize one's art, the "right to be born physically and mentally sound."[2], and the "right of personal dignity and autonomy" (in *Roe v. Wade*). Could it be that we have too many rights? Could it be that the present rights-o-mania is harmful to individuals and society?

Recently, a *Wall Street Journal* (5/20/93) editorial featured an expose of the claims by poorer nations to have a phantom "right to development." This editorial spoke to the pervasive claim for rights in general, and in particular how infested various U.N. bills and charters had become with "rights." It seems that everyone and every nation is claiming a right to this and a right to that. One group claims a right to work, while another claims a right to leisure. One lobby pleads for the right to day care, while the rival pleads for the right to have tax shelters. And, in the past decade, the United Nations has been saturated with third-world countries claiming a "right to development." This clamor led the editorialist to ask, "Do all nations have a real right to material prosperity through development? And, if they do, who's stopping them from developing?" What these people are really claiming with the "right to development" is for someone else to pay billions of dollars for their development. Sure, they may have a right to develop, but that hardly transfers responsibility to fund their development. Most asserted rights today nearly always involve someone else's payment or loss.

For example, one person wants his right to full and unhindered access to all public sectors, but — due to his own choices — he has a fatal and possibly contagious disease. Do we grant him "rights" at the possible expense of others' lives? Or, does he have some responsibility as well? Do we all have some imagined universal "right" to health care, or does the responsibility to care for the health of our families reside with ourselves? Many of the most hotly debated subjects in modern society involve the tension between rights and responsibilities.

As an experiment in personal sinfulness a few years back, I monitored my vocabulary and raised a mental flag every time I said I had a right. Do we really have rights to so much? And, says who? A funny thing to claims to rights: These seem to quickly turn into demands. Especially where God is concerned, we don't have rights to demand anything from Him. What can you *demand* from God? What do you have a right to receive from Him — long life? ... health? ... great kids? ... good job? Even eternal life is not something we can demand, or have a right to. I wish to propose that the Christian ethic disavow any basis or claim to rights, except insofar as explicity revealed and limited by God's revelation. Those which are legitimately derived from Scripture may become known as "derived," "acquired," or "negative" rights. However, the ever-multiplying specie of affirmative rights being claimed in our day are not rooted in the Scripture.

Isn't it really the case that we all receive only what God mercifully chooses to grant? I am finding that it is better to lay aside "rights" vocabulary altogether, and instead use the vocabulary that is used throughout Scripture. Instead of rights/responsibilities, a return to talking about "obligation/privilege" might assist us in ethical formulation. Terminology of obligation or privilege us places at the outset more in harmony with God's ways than as rights-squawkers, who nag, "But, God, it's my right ... " A more humble and thankful posture is to see God's gifts as privileges.

In the ongoing welfare reform debate, for example, the policy is frequently based on a rights claim, which fantasizes that there is some universal obligation on the part of the state to care for each of its citizens, even to the provision of economic subsistence. If asked why so many citizens should receive cash payments, the bottom-line answer in many cases is an appeal to "rights." Do we really have a right to "welfare?" Based upon what?

One of the causes which stultifies welfare reform according to William Willimon is a rights-centered approach to life. Says Willimon, "One of the greatest detriments to the Christian view of charity is the notion of human rights. The notion of "rights" is not a biblical idea. It is a legacy of the European Enlightenment. The notion of rights has been helpful in forming liberal societies, that is, societies formed without reference to God. No one need feel grateful or say "thank you" in a society of rights."[3]

Several recent books have documented this trend. One such interesting book is Charles J. Sykes' *A Nation of Victims* (St. Martin's, 1992) which chronicles how our nation in its aversion to responsibility has turned to the doctrines of fulfillment and the "triumph of the therapeutic." Sykes criticizes the "happiness-as-entitlement" ethic which is pervasive in our culture of victimization.

Another book, *Rights Talk: The Impoverishment of Political Discourse* by Mary Ann Glendon, is a superb treatment of the growth of "rights dialects" in political discourse. Glendon, formerly a Law Professor at Harvard University, supposes that while many other countries are just beginning their steps of democracy, the United States seems to be at the crossroads in which the uncompromising language insisting on rights impedes discourse and throws up numerous shibboleths. She claims that as the catalog of rights grows at an accelerating rate, we risk collision over and the trivialization of essential democratic values. When all rights are valued to the level of absoluteness, then each right inherently counteracts any common good.

Commenting on "dialect of rights as being uniquely American," Glendon decries the fact that we are so consistently silent about our duties and obligations, while always shrill about our rights. She says, "The American rights dialect is distinguished not only by what we say and how we say it, but also by what we leave unsaid. Each day's newspapers, radio broadcast and television programs attest to our tendency to speak of whatever is most important to us in terms of rights, and to our predilection for overstating the absoluteness of the rights we claim. Habitual silences concerning responsibilities are more apt to remain unnoticed. People for the American Way expressed surprise when research revealed that our nation's young people are aware of their rights, but "fail to grasp the other half of the democratic equation" which the researchers defined as meeting personal responsibilities, serving the community, and participating in the nation's political life. Yet, it is hardly astonishing that the survey reflects the relative proportions of attention accorded in public discourse to rights and general responsibilities."[4] Later, in "Refining the Rhetoric of Rights" Glendon says, "The strident rights rhetoric that currently dominates American political discourse poorly serves the strong tradition of protection for individual freedom for which the United States is justly renowned. Our stark simple rights dialect puts a damper on the processes of public justification, communication, and deliberation upon which the continuing vitality of the democratic regime depends. It contributes to the erosion of the habits, practices, and attitudes of respect for others that are the ultimate and surest guarantors of human rights. It impedes long-range thinking about our most pressing social problems. Our rights-laden public discourse easily accomodates the economic, the immediate, and the personal dimensions of a problem while it regularly neglects the moral, the long-term, and the social implications."[5]

In the 1948 UN Universal Declaration of Human Rights, one may be amazed to be informed of rights never before imagined. Article 22 postulates that "everyone, as a member of society, has the right to social security." Even more utopian in scope, Article 25 of the same charter alleges that everyone has a right "to a standard of living adequate for health and well-being of himself and his family, including food, clothing, and housing."[6] Another encyclopedia lists the following supposed "rights": right to confidentiality, right to die, right to fertility control, right to food, right to health, right to health care, right to information, right to life, right to privacy[7], and others.

The same refrain is now being heard in one of the latest variations on this central theme, health-care reform. Our population is repeatedly informed that over 35 million Americans do not have health care *insurance* (not health care, mind you), and that moreover, they have a *right* to health care, despite the fact that millions of these who have been deprived of the right to health care spend their income on TVs, food, cigarettes, cars, entertainment, and other products. In short, they have purchasing power, and wilfully choose to purchase certain products, leaving the government to provide health care, and then plead that their rights have been impaired, in

that they have not received health care.

Interestingly, if the above number were true, that would mean that only about 85% of Americans have health care, while 98% have TV sets! Is there a right to have a TV set?

Rights claims are proliferating with the effectiveness of breeder-reactor technology. Such a mindset has also caught the evangelical church unaware, and even evangelical groups are adopting this rights-vocabulary. (Liberal groups did this over a generation ago, and helped themselves into decline.) To the student of Scripture who is also a critic of humanistic society, the claims to rights are beginning to sound like shibboleths, which clue us to an underlying poverty in theology.

Not too long ago, the Youth Director in our church came into my office wearing thick chagrin. He had been trying to work with an ecumenical youth organization, and had been almost stretched to the breaking. The doctrinal anything goes-ism, the pursuit of diversity (albeit evangelical), and the toleration of therapeutic-oriented evangelical-ese had come too close to the pursuit of multiculturalism and political correctness he'd seen on campus. He was dismayed (and rightfully .. er, understandably so) when he saw this part of the organization's credo stated in terms of the idolatry of rights. In one of its publications, the organization stated that it was a sin to bore teenagers with the gospel. Instead, kids had the following *rights:*

— They have a right to know who He is (Cf. Mt. 16:16; Rom. 11:33)
— They have a right to know what He has done for them. (Cf. Eph. 2:1,8)
— They have a right to know how

they relate to that. (Cf. Rom. 6:23, Eph. 2:12)
— They have a right to know Him personally. (Cf. Jn. 6:44)
— They have a right to make their own choice about Him. (Cf. Rom. 9:11,16,18)

If the source were to remain unknown, most evangelicals would see little underlying difference between this and the 1948 UN Charter above. Has the church capitulated to this latest version of humanism? This budding theologian did not have to be told that these rights were incompatible with Scripture. Unfortunately, however, thousands of others associated with this organization did not comprehend how damning such a theology was to true conversion and ministry. In an earlier age, such heterodoxy would have been ruled a heresy. Imagine, influencing our youth with this. We should inquire about the origin of this modern rights-ism, and consider it in light of Scripture.

Ask of the Scripture: Do we really have a *right* to know who God is, and what He has done for us? (Mt. 13:10-17; Mk. 4:10-12; Lk. 8:9-10; Rom. 9:6-22; 11:7-10) Do we really have a *right* to hear the gospel, or know Christ personally? Or, isn't it scriptural that all we have a right to is condemnation apart from Jesus Christ? Do we really have a *right* not to be offended by the gospel presentation, especially in light of I Cor. 1? Do we have a *right* to make our own choice about Him (Rom. 9:11)?

It might be advisable not to translate these as "right."

The second word which is occasionally (*ca.* 5%) translated "right" is the strong Hebrew word *mishpat*, predominantly translated elsewhere as justice. The first (of 15) instances of this word is in Gen. 18:25, where Abraham pleads, "Shall not the Judge of the earth do what is right?" This word really means to do justice. Psalm 9:4, Prov. 12:5, Prov. 16:8, Is. 10:2, and Dan. 3:35 are examples of how "right" in this sense is founded squarely on justice. It is not too much to claim that the underlying notion behind *mishpat* is equitable justice; hence "right" when translated from this cannot refer to a redistributional seizure of one's property to be given to another. Such "right" would contravene Old Testament *mishpat* and must be seen as a contradiction in terms. It is highly questionable if these should even be rendered "right." Justice, if not so politically incorrect a notion as at present, would be a better translation in most of these cases.

Also sometimes translated "right" is the term which is derived from the custom of the firstborn son inheriting the father's estate. In Dt. 21:17 the legislation is clear that, by law, not by arrogation, the firstborn is the heir of the estate. Jeremiah 32:7-8 also refers to this custom of inheritance "rights," which clearly are derived or acquired from God's unfolded will. The solitary reference in Ruth 4:6 to the practice of kinsman redeemers claiming first right to care for a relative, is not the same as a positive right, either. These cases may be understood as rights only as derived from divine revelation, a source that the modern rights-mania seems uneager to acknowledge.

Hence, out of some 300 instances, very few if any of the phrases translated "right" are even vaguely equivalent to our modern notion of rights. About the only possible Old Testament references to the modern concept of rights are II Sam. 19:28 and Ps. 140:12. Psalm 140:12 speaks of the "rights of the poor" (KJV), while the New International Verstion (NIV) translates with the more consistent "I know the Lord secures *justice* for the poor," and this certainly means justice, not inequity. In II Sam. 19, Mephibosheth rhetorically asks, "So what right do I have to make any more appeals to the king?" In this verse he disavows that such a right to continue to exercise appeals is warranted.

The development of human thought shows that the vocabulary of rights did not even begin to develop until post-Old Testament times, under the influence of Greco-Roman law. Even then, the concepts are severely limited (when compared with today's rights-explostion), and circumspectly defined. It is questionable whether the Latin language even has a word which is truly synonymous with the modern notion of rights. For example, sometimes *rectus* (rectitude), *aequus* (equal), *aptus* (apt), or normally *ius* (justice, law) will be translated "right." Or, on another occasion, *vindicare* (to vindicate) or *restitutere* (to effect restitution) may be translated into English as "right." In all these cases, such linguistic concepts are parallel to the Old Testament notion of rights *only* as prescribed by law and justice, or as negative rights. Some historians even contend that "rights" (as we know them) were not developed until the second millenium A.D., which issue we'll leave for below. One is tempted to wonder, if "rights" have always been so inherent in nature, why parents closer to nature in antiquity did not leave linguistic relics to a greater degree than their vocabulary allows.

Nonetheless, it is important to note that when a character in the Old Testament felt wronged, he did not instinctively appeal to his "rights." One searches the Scripture in vain to see Noah assert his rights, or Joseph plead for a right to sexual expression when approached by Mrs. Potiphar. Nor does Moses exercise his rights, nor David (except, insofar as his monarchy allowed). Old Testament characters rarely, if ever, resorted to a rights-claim, if canonical Scripture is our infallible source. One begins to sense that rights-ism indeed has its origin in sources other than Scripture.

It is not too much to say that Old Testament characters did not even think in such modern categories as positive rights. Perhaps they were wiser than we. What "rights" these did have were primarily of two sorts: (1) as divinely revealed and legislated by God, *e.g.*, inheritance customs for the first-born, or the kinsman-redeemer, etc., or (2) property rights codified by the eighth and tenth commandments, and the subsequent clarifications. The first of these is derived, while the second is acquired or negative, *i.e.*, protection from confiscation.

One might even review the Ten Commandments to see if these guaranteed rights. Strictly speaking, even the pinnacle of revealed ethics, the Decalogue, did not serve as such. The first three commandments, far from giving rights, revealed restrictions. The fourth commandment is a restriction (from work), as well as a mandate (to rest and worship). While God grants the Sabbath as a gracious gift for His people, it is hardly a right, nor even a proper possession apart from God's gracious provision.

The second table of the law hardly enshrines rights either. While it does prescribe *duties*, it is difficult (if not impossible) to stretch these duties into reciprocal rights. For example, while one had a duty to honor one's parents and superiors, it is not biblically asserted that they have a right to such honor. Only God does. It is futile to seek a "right to honor" in the Scripture, although the "duty to honor" is manifest. This may be one area of biblical ethics which is not symmetrical.

Similarly, we have duty to refrain from killing innocent life, adultery, stealing, and false speech. However, it is questionable whether one has a right to truth, or a right to sexual purity. It may be debatable that we have a "right" to life (although even ardent pro-lifers have recently sensed this and begun to speak more in terms of "sanctity of human life"), or a right to property. Even at the height of law, God's law is not so much employed to support individual rights, as to regulate society and prevent abuses.

It may even be that the Old Testament doctrine of rights is best translated as the New Testament Golden Rule: "Do unto others as you would have others do unto you." Beyond this, we may not have any rights, and even the ones afforded by the Golden Rule can be classified as acquired or negative rights. E. Calvin Beisner, in a book review of Peter Berger's 1990 *The Capitalist Spirit*, cites the work of Walter Block, who suggests the superiority of negative rights. They are superior in that they are: (1) timeless, *i.e.*, not as fluid as affirmative rights; (2) realistic and realizable, while all positive-rights obligations could never be met; (3) better capable of allowing for a natural disaster, without imply-

ing that those affected by natural disaster have a claim on forced restitution; (4) acknowledge that changing socio-economic conditions are legitimate, without implying that some increase in estate assumes the dimunition of another's; (5) more adroit at permitting true charity, thus avoiding a positive-rights view which deems that "the recipient may legitimately claim that any excess in the giver's wealth over his own violates his positive right"; and (6) Negative rights can be equal, while "positive rights cannot, since there are differences of condition not susceptible of equalization."[9] Indeed, more emphasis on negative rights, while not as expansive and glamorous as the modernistic positive rights view, would place us in firmer biblical territory.

In sum, from our Old Testament foray, it becomes clear that:
(1) "Right" in its modern connotation is seldom used, if at all.
(2) Even in these exceptional instances, "right" is based exclusively on divine legislation, and not open to unlimited expansion.
(3) The basic meaning is tied into notions of morality and justice, not so much personal provision, gratification, nor positive blessing.
(4) Right is subservient to divine law.

Rights are never autonomous in the Old Testament, never rooted in humanity; always in God's plans. The Old Testament view of things acknowledged very few rights, and those were negative or acquired. In contrast with our modern age, rights were derived, and at that, few in number, usually tied to physical property, or divinely legislated family/inheritance provisions. In sum, the modern connotation of "rights"

could be totally eliminated from the Old Testament, and the root words (except as spatial locators) adquately translated by other terms. Indeed, none of the positive rights enunciated at the head of this article were evident in the Old Testament, which got along fine without them.

II. New Testament

In light of the previous Old Testament findings, a lack of plentiful examples of "rights" in the New Testament indicates that the modern Christian who appeals often to these is admittedly depending on a non-biblical construct, or perhaps an unbiblical one. Some versions do at least use the word, although it may be questioned whether those are possibly by-products of 20th century rights-ism reflected in more recent translations, particularly if the older versions (e.g., KJV) did not employ rights vocabulary.

One may legitimately query, "Should the word 'right' even occur in the New Testament?" On one occasion the NIV presents us with 'right' in Scripture, and the translation may be misleading. Consider John 1:12, which speaks of those who believe as having "the right to become the children of God." The word used here (*exousia*) is normally translated "authority," and in the context would be better understood as believers having been authorized by a sovereign act of God to be adopted as His children. The very next verse proceeds to deny that any of us have any right to do that autonomously; in fact, such adoption is "not by natural descent, nor of human decision, or of a husband's will, but born of God" (John 1:13). So it is doubtful that this verse supports rights-ism. Authority is different from right, and perhaps this word should be consistently rendered "authority." One wonders why "right" would even be used in John 1:12 apart from certain theological intrusions.

The major New Testament term which is sometimes rendered "right" is *exousia*. This word has the primary meaning of "power to effect, or liberty to choose," and is commonly used with wills, contracts, and legal documents to denote a claim. It is associated with the right given by law for a superior to use all the influence of his position, and can also refer to persons of high office, authority, or the power of rule. It is a governmental term, which connotes the power of a greater over a lesser, as in Rom. 9:12 (the Potter over the clay). This word may also mean to have power over someone or something, and can at times be translated as absolute power for the monarch, or derivatively as "warrant" if under a constitution. *Exousia*, in its New Testament instances, is not the same as, nor does it lend support to, a modern notion of rights. Again, Hastings is clear in his summation: "In early Roman law itself, which did so much to develop the idea of personality, the idea of duty ... is far more prominent than rights ... these seeds of the idea of the rights of man had to await a soil congenial to them, ..."[10]

Another instance is Rom. 9:21. While at first it is undeniable that God does, if anyone, possess rights to do as He wishes with His creation, even in this case a better translation may be found than "right." As Paul argues that God the Creator, based on the analogy of Potter to clay, has the right (*exousia*) to do as He wishes with His creations, even in this case

the sense is a reference to the sovereignty or power of God to do so. It is not based so much on a rights-system outside of Himself (*ab extra*), as on His own (*ad intra*) sovereignty or power. Even in this case, "right" may be misleading, albeit totally correct in application to God alone.

Hebrews 13:10 and I Cor. 9:4 also are translated with this concept of right (Today's English Version uses "right" no less than six times in I Cor. 9). The former verse speaks of the unlawfulness of defiling God's altar (a definite prohibition, even if in rights vocabulary!), while I Cor. 9 represents Paul claiming a right to food, drink, and marriage. Yet, twice the apostle avers, "But we did not use this right" (12,15), and the real issue is over who is or is not authorized by God to make a living from the Gospel ministry, not an intrinsic claim to the Office itself. Again, an attempt to support any aggressive rights claims from the New Testament is not sustainable.

The rest of the usages of "right" in the New Testament are equivalent to either "correct" (Rom. 3:4; Rom. 12:17; II Cor. 8:21; Eph. 6:1; Phil. 4:8; II Thess. 3:13; Jas. 2:8; I Pet. 3:14, I Jn. 2:29), or the directional locator "right" as in right hand (Matt. 6:3, 22:44 and 25:33; Acts 2:35, etc.) or right side. More graphically, according to *Strong's Exhaustive Concordance* (p. 846), of the 33 translations of "right" in the KJV Gospels, 27 refer to direction, with six referring to correctness (Matt. 20:4,7; Mk. 5:15; Lk. 8:35, 1028, and 12:57), and *none* to the modern notion of rights. If one performs a red-letter search, or restricts their study to the Gospels, in vain can one find Jesus' support or endorsement for rights proliferation. So the

rights-crusade develops after, or contrary to, Jesus' own words.

Thus, of the 24 references in the NIV to "right," only a few bear any semblance to the modern notion of "rights." As mentioned, of those, one is mistranslated (Jn. 1:12), another refers not to human rights, but actually to the subservience of human rights to God's prerogatives (Rom. 9:21), one to an apostolic mocking of first century right-ists (I Cor. 9:4), and two final instances in Revelation. Out of a total KJV New Testament corpus of 66 instances, 53 are to direction, with 11 to correctness, and only two (Heb. 13:10 and Rev. 22:14) to rights as we know them. If terminology tells us anything, "right" is translated as a claim less than 4% of the time it is used in the New Testament. The NIV (a modern version) increases "rights" instances over the KJV in the following verses: Jn. 1:12; Rom. 9:21; I Cor. 9:4; Rev. 2:27 and 3:21.

In actuality, it may be that if the rights-infection is subtracted from this otherwise excellent modern translation, the case may be made that there are only two genuine occurrences of "right" as we know it (as with the KJV), and both of those are either a denial of rights (Heb. 13:10) or a granting of privilege only by God (Rev. 22:14). In fact, there are more denials of "rights" in the New Testament than affirmations of enumerated rights.

In the apocalyptic epistles to the seven churches the apostle John records "right" in perhaps the only cases which are truly compatible with modern claimants, however with the understanding that such rights are bestowed by God. Revelation 2:7 speaks of believers having a right to eat from the tree of life in paradise, but this is surely a derived right, and likely better translated as "authority." The same is true for Rev. 3:21 which mentions a right to sit with God on the throne. These are assuredly gifts by the grace of God, and not claims which can be demanded, based on anything outside of God.

What about Paul's appeals in the latter part of Acts? It is certainly the case that the apostle lodged legal appeals, and did not forfeit his civic rights. In response to this, it must be noted that this was an aspect of law, not a claim to provision. In addition, it can be noted that such appeals were in reference to certain judicial processes or to secure non-property loss. Again, these were more negative than positive, *i.e.*, to prevent loss or to enforce justice and preservation of equity.

Classical literature does not support a modern notion of rights, rarely even employing terminology close to the contemporary meaning. As earlier argued, the Hebrew Testament does not even have an exact word for "right" in the sense of a proper claim apart from God and His revealed will. Earlier commentators even remarked at how elementary it was for "student[s] of Greek ethics ... [to] know that in its classical exponents there is as yet no word corresponding to either 'rights' or 'duties' in the modern sense. We have to wait another generation ...."[11] The earliest Greek literature uses the term *diakaios* (normally translated "righteousness") as early as in Homer, but even there in its most original locus it carries the sense of adhering to rule or custom as sign of civility, in contrast to the absence of manners. It has been noted that while classical cultures recognized *doing right*, there

was a vast difference between doing and *having rights*. In early Greek, the only existing notion was one of the following acceptable rules, and the good of the whole was elevated over the good of the few — a conceptual stumblingblook which for centuries held the right-ists at bay. The eradication of the subservience of the individual to the greater community was an essential shift for the modern world.

Later, the Stoic philosophers would rally around the term *katheko*, the verb meaning "belonging to, or is fit for" an individual. But here again rights as a concept is circumscribed by law, custom, or property. This word is best translated for many of the Hebrew words which are sometimes translated 'rights.' It occurs in Rom. 1:28 of those who "do what ought not to be done," and is in this sense clearly an ethical concept, bounded by ethical norms, not by the subject's own claim or whims. Elsewhere in I Clement 3:4 this phrase is even used — so far from demanding autonomous rights — for the admonition to conduct oneself in accord with one's duty toward Christ. So even the Greek term *katheko* is not the same as our modern rights claims.

III. Progression throughout History

In history, a definite trend line of rights frequency is observable. In the Old Testament the widesprad admission of rights were few and far between, and those were strictly tied to material concepts and protection from interference. In essence both the Old and New Testaments were pre-rights. Despite the fact that the English word "right" is given for a few Old and New Testament phrases,

nevertheless, it is questionable that the Bible in any occasion recognizes the legitimacy of "rights" in the modern sense. Going behind the superficial appearance of the term alone, one sees that the concept of rights as we know it is foreign to the canonical Scriptures.

One might naturally inquire, therefore, as to the origin of the modern idea of rights. If this notion did not arise during the two millennia of scriptural history, if rights is a post-scriptural phenomena, then where and when did it originate? A quick scan of the first thousand years of theology after Christ does not evidence any significant frequency of rights claims. While it is true that Greek philosophy and Roman law introduced modern precursors to concepts of autonomy still, in the main, these earlier humanisms did not seem to spawn a proliferation of rights.

Not until the obliteration of feudal economies and the rise of early market economics did rights begin to grow. James Hastings summarizes that, "while ancient theories of the nature of justice ... are susceptible of translation into terms of rights, the problem of the ground of rights in explicit form is essentially a modern one. It was not till the question of the rights of the subject was definitely raised in 16th century England"[12] that the modern notion of rights began to reproduce.

Even up to the time of the Reformation, there is not a great amount of rights dialect, the phenomenon beginning to show its first real surge in the 17th century. It is the age of "social contract" in which we begin to notice growth in rights. Hastings alleges that Grotius was "the first clearly to assign them [rights] a ground in man's social nature," if not the actual "discoverer of natural rights."[13] Hastings locates the paradigm shift as first evident "when English tradition and temperament led to a revolt against social and political despotism in the time of Wyclif. By the middle of the 17th century, and still more by the 18th, the claims of rights in both Old and New England were already deeply tinged with individualistic theory ..."[14]

John Locke was one of the apostles of modern rights. In dealing with the question of the foundation of social thought and public polity, Robert N. Bellah has noted: "If there is one philosopher behind the American experiment it is Locke. Locke, as we know, begins with a state of nature in which individuals who have worked and gained a little property by the sweat of their brow, decide voluntarily to enter a social contract through which they will set up a limited government...."[15]

Locke's teaching is "one of the most powerful, if not the most powerful ideology ever invented. Indeed, it is proving to be more enduring and influential, which is not to say truer, than Marxism."[16] As Bellah correctly surmises government is created for the protection of property. Then individuals "freely consent" by social contract with their sole basis lying in voluntary agreement. One natural consequence is rights *apriori-ism*. Bellah says, "In many respects this vision has turned out to be as utopian as Marx's realm of freedom. The Lockean myth conflicts with biblical religion in essential ways. It conflicts fundamentally with the Hebrew notion of covenant ... And, the covenant is not a limited relation based on self interest, but an unlimit-

ed commitment based on loyalty and trust."[17]

Further, Bellah notes, "The Lockean myth conflicts profoundly with the Pauline understanding of the church as the body of Christ."[18] In addition he says, "The problem is that the Lockean notion of contract does not exist only in the economic and political spheres; it influences our understanding of all human relations, including both family and church."[19] Locke added fuel to the rights flame, and with his social contract theory aided and abetted in the imperialism of rights, even though under his constructions one of the factors which delimited this first rights expansionism was that this usage of rights was normally tied to physical property or business regulation.

Others have recognized a post-17th century fault-point, as rights have more and more consumed the attention of guild philsophers.[20] Medieval philosophers concerned themselves more with duties which men owed their lord, church, or God, while during the 17th and 18th centuries such legitimate questions gave way to a more person-centered preoccupation with natural rights and liberties. The shift was too significant to miss, especially as its fruit seems to have ripened in our own time. What was at first a freedom from interference has now been transubstantiated into an open list of positive benefits which are claimed. Such transubstantiation is deadening.

Cresting at the time of the French Revolution, the dawn of modern rights infatuation was codified in the motto of the revolutionaries' rally cry: Liberty, Equality, and Fraternity. The newest member of that triumvi-

rate was equality, a definite rights-claim.

More than one critic has identified the French Revolution as a paradigm shift in viewing rights. Guillaume Groen Van Prinsterer, for example, analyzed culture in terms of being either Reformation-oriented or Revolution-oriented. A tell-tale sign of Revolution-orientation is its location of rights within the nature of man.

One of the most dangerous expressions of revolutionary ideas is the preferred status awarded to individual rights. As we view our society looking for a rights-centered ethic to guarantee homosexual service in the military, health-insurance as a right, and the explosion of rights claims for nearly everything, we can marvel at the foresight of Van Prinsterer (1801-1876), who predicted the errors of this approach a century and a half ago.[21] Van Prinsterer was most perceptive to isolate the totalitarian expansionism of Rights-ism. If the rights premise is allowed to flourish in a body politic, it will further the unraveling of societal fabric. The claimants to rights-for-everything are the genetic offspring of revolutionary ideas, not biblical ethos. A first step to recovering a Christian polity is the critique and expose of Rights-ism. In our own time, when justice has become hostage to individual rights, the Christian may often return to this theme.

Reminding that one of the associated causes was that "rights" became more important than justice,[22] Groen says, "Justice, in a philosophical sense essential and historical par excellence, was placed above History. It was this dominion of Right over fact that gave rise to a whole series of acquired rights."[23] Thus, Van Prinsterer notes that formerly respect, "for acquired rights meant ... respect for the highest principles of justice,"[24] but not so after the French Revolution. Subsequent to the French Revolution a dangerous dogma was created in which men used rights "to demand passivity for subordination, to mistake autonomy for independence, to regard free activity as rebellion, in every respect to subject everything found within the state's territory to the arbitrary will of the state, to oppose on principle any self-government of private persons or corporations."[25]

In sum, Van Prinsterer, who sounds hauntingly familiar, alleges that in the revolutionary reconstruction, "Too much attention was paid to questionable historic rights, to the detriment of general principles of justice.[26] At the heart of Van Prinsterer's criticism is the extension of rights and privileges into nearly every domain. Van Prinsterer decried that "'Rights have been represented as limitless when in fact they did have limits."[27]

Others also saw this error as well. Early on, Jeremy Bentham was astute enought to diagnose the social compact view of rights as nothing more than the "anarchical fallacy," applying a tough-minded critique of this "metaphysic on stilts." Bentham analyzed: "Rights are the fruits of the law, and of the law alone. There are no rights without law — no rights contrary to the law — no rights anterior to the law."[28]

A little over a century ago, Robert L. Dabney made some salient observations in his 1888 "Anti-Biblical Theories of Rights."[29] Although his essay spends about half its space defending slavery, he was prescient at the time to identify "Another hostile

banner"[30] which was already unfurled and ready to attack millions. This assault, which proceeded from "professed social science" was derived from the "atheistic French radicals,"[31] and was in process of being unwittingly adopted by thousands of American Protestants. At its heart, this new anti-biblical theory of rights posited an absolute mechanical equality,[32] in contrast to the earlier-held and historically orthodox moral equality.

This new radical theory asserted that "all men are born free and equal" in the beginning and logically led to the following:

"Consequently the theory teaches that exactly the same surrender must be enacted of each one under this social contract, whence each individual is inalienably entitled to all the same franchises and functions in society as well as to his moral equality; so it is a natural iniquity to withhold from any adult person by law any prerogative which is legally conferred on any other member in society. The equality must be mechanical as well as moral or else the society is charged with natural injustice."[33]

That is to aver that, if we do not treat people absolutely the same (mechanical equality), then we have somehow violated their rights. Indeed, the mechanical has now superseded the moral, with the spectacle of homosexuals demanding state-sanctioned "marriages" and medical care without regard to the substantial contributions to illness achieved by sodomy. Dabney lamented that this new nomenclature had so confused the issues, as

well as the lack of discernment by Christians.

"So widespread and profound is this confusion of thought, that the majority of the American people and of their teachers practically know and hold no other theory than the Jacobin one ... history and science show that it is a fatal heresy of thought, which uproots every possible foundation of just freedom, and grounds only the most ruthless of despotism. But none the less is this the passionate belief of millions, for the sake of which they are willing to assail the Bible itself."[34]

Sadly, many Christians did not heed these early words of warning, which so clearly foresaw the inherent contradictions between the social compact view of rights and the biblical view. As Dabney stated his goal, his sole object was "to examine the scriptural question, whether or not the integrity of the Bible can be made to consist with the Jacobin theory and its necessary corollaries."[35] Thus Dabney's warning of the "coming contest"[36] went largely unheeded, as few entertained the question as raised by Dabney, "Will you surrender the inspiration of scriptures to these assaults of a social science — so-called?"[37] Indeed, that is what is at stake.

To Dabney, this view of rights was one reason for the decline of erstwhile stalwart evangelical bodies,[38] as they "piously borrowed even from French atheism."[39] To him, it was clear that a student of Scripture should detect that "this radical theory of human rights and equality, born of atheism, but masquerading in the garb of true Biblical republicanism"[40] had numerous and definite corollaries. Despite being "passionately held by millions of nominal Christians,"[41] Dabney dared to warn of the "collision between the popular political theory, so flattering to the self-will and pride of the human heart, and so clad in the raiment of pretended philanthropy,"[42] and asserted that this anti-biblical theory of rights had "become the occasion of tens of thousands making themselves blatant infidels, and of millions becoming virtual unbelievers."[43] The rights-ists, said Dabney, "Those who wish to hold both the contradictories have indeed been busy for two generations weaving veils of special pleadings and deceitful expositions of Scripture wherewith to conceal the inevitable contradiction. But these veils are continually wearing too thin to hide it, and the bolder minds rend them one after another and cast them away."[44]

Predicting that "the struggle cannot but be long and arduous,"[45] Dabney gave some beginning advice for those who contend against rightsism. His caveat was:

"Since the opinions and practices hostile to the Scriptures are so protean, so subtile, and so widely diffused, there is no chance for a successful defense of the truth except in uncompromising resistance to the beginnings of error; to parley is to be defeated. The steps in the 'down-grade' progress are gentle, and slide easily one into the other, but the sure end of the descent is none the less fatal. He who yields the first step so complicates his subsequent resistance as to insure his defeat. There is but one safe

position for the sacramental host: to stand on the whole Scripture, and refuse to concede a single point."[46]

Dabney is wise to title this essay "Anti-Biblical theories, for these are truly at odds with biblical teaching. A more modern writer might call these "alternative" biblical theories. However, as Dabney put it: "Every fair mind sees that this is not only a different but an opposite social theory."[47]

What if we were to totally purge "right" from our vocabulary? Could the Christian do that? Might we not be better off to radically excise this phrase from our discourse? The Old and New Testaments and the first 1500 years A.D. managed to get along without these notions. We might do better as well. It may even be time to revive the old notion of duty.

IV. Application to Medical Care

Although I am particularly concerned that medical personnel make these needed distinctions, all Christians need to be informed by biblical studies such as the above. That is the first step — to realize and to resist initiatives, be they governmental, psychological, or ecclesiastical, which are based on a view of rights that is contrary to Scripture's own. Christians must heed the earlier warnings, and be better students of Scripture to contend in the arena of health care, but in many others such as education, welfare reform, economics, and foreign aid.

We have grossly misunderstood our country's constitutional documents and principles of freedom if we think that all people are absolutely equal in all areas, and deserve identi-

cal, mechanical treatment. That version of equal rights myth is based on one of our century's grandest errors, that people are entitled to certain things. When you come down to it, as far as absolutes are concerned, in reality the Christian physician needs to know and apply the fact that actually each of us is entitled to ... 000. We are not owed a thing, not favorable treatment, not societal care, nor office, nor place in life, not even welfare or health care. God not only doesn't promise a rose garden, He doesn't guarantee a garden at all ... except Eden. Since the fall, we have no legs to stand on if we hope to press our claim that the state or the church or the hospital is obligated, or owes us something. That is a legend in our times, an idea although in our minds but not in Scripture nor reality.

We need to teach men and women that, according to the Bible, all are not equal. To be sure, in Christ, there is neither Jew nor Greek, slave nor free, male nor female. But, that applies to our standing before God, our salvation, not our callings in life. A slave might remain a slave, or a Jew would remain a Jew after salvation. Similarly, after coming to Christ, a woman or a man does not cease to be the gender each was created. We are a saved person of gender, but we are not somehow neutered in the process. Salvation does not cancel creation; it only saves it. We are not all equal in all areas. We are not equal in physical health, in mental abilities, in geographic opportunity, or in parental legacy.

Christians are all equal in terms of our standing before God, as sinners saved by grace, but we are not all equal in terms of our subsequent callings or duties. Those are assigned by God. So we must remove from our heads the notion that we are all to do the same thing, or that we are all entitled to receive the same thing. That is a legend to dismiss. Most other centuries dismissed it with more ease than we seem to possess. We must learn that even if our society religiously chants this over and over, even if every media outlet evangelizes this dogma, and even if the majority believe that each person has rights in all areas, that neither makes it right, nor does it overturn what the Bible says on the subject. And, without this central footing of egalitarianism, rights-ism tumbles.

Let me conclude by urging action by three parties: physicians, pastors, and parishioners.

First, I would urge every Christian doctor to have as many conversations with patients about rights and health as possible. Just 30 seconds to raise the question might not only help them to be better off, but could also lead to sharing the gospel. For example, have a biblical article on rights, or the role of the state, or personal responsibility available to give to every patient. The physician should seek to raise this question with as many patients as possible, as part of his world-and-life view witness: "According to God's revelation, is health care a God-ordained duty of the state, and on what (if any) basis should the state be involved in your health?" While you're providing health care for your patients, seek to educate them as well.

In addition, each physician could take one issue or area where rights-ism is rampant in their own specialty, and develop some expertise. Most communities have plenty of forums for physicians to be guest speakers.

Hundreds can be reached in these not only about your primary topic, but also about the secondary matter of "Who has the responsibility for health care?" Work it into your presentation, and take these opportunities; those of the other faith will. In addition, nearly every evangelical church has a faulty view of responsibility in this area, so use some of your resources (or some back issues of this Journal) to teach a 3-4 week Sunday School class. Attendance will be large (as will resistance), because people are most interested in their bodies and health: "After all, no one ever hated his own body, but feeds and cares for it." (Eph. 5:29)

Christian doctors could also be leaders in local (county) medical associations to disseminate more responsible approaches to health reform. And, if you want to catch the eyes of even your critics, find a way (while there may be time) to provide genuinely charitable indigent care. If not a tithe, what about 5%? Perhaps some real Christian charity will go a long way, and while you're at it, you'll also have to surrender your right to comfort. On the supposition that there are, e.g., 36 million citizens without care, if one-fourth of the country is evangelical, and one-fourth of the physicians also, then in theory one-fourth of the problem could be dismissed by voluntarily taking on the poor for medical charity. Surely, another one-fourth is statistical hyperbole; thus, one-half of the problem could be cured without draconian socialist measures. Evangelical doctors can take the lead in this. They once did.

Pastors must increase their vigilance as well. They must address these subjects from the pulpit and classromm as part of the Lordship of

Christ. We have been too reticent to stress personal responsibility, and our churches and culture are suffering for that. Pastors should lead in recommending classes, articles, and other resources to help the average church member. They need to teach preventatively on these subjects, and by their counsel support personal responsibility and financial sanity in medical decisions, seeking the "whole counsel of God." (Acts 20:28)

Parishioners must lend a hand as well. The average Christian must be ready to assume a non-delegated responsibility for the health care of himself and his family. This responsibility cannot be sinfully foisted off on some other agency. Chrisitans (especially aging baby-boomers) also need to do a better job at accepting the realities of illness, pain, suffering, death, and physical imperfection. The medical industry is not a *deus ex machina* that can produce perfection. We must not displace our faith and look for medicine to provide protection. And, Christians, especially heads of households, must familiarize themselves with the true costs of medical care, as well as the amount of employer payments. If those costs are carefully investigated and seen as God's possessions, many of us may seek change. As a rule of thumb, anytime an expense exceeds the tithe (with present average spending on health care at around 13%) stewards must seek their Lord's wisdom and honor.

Christian doctors seem, at present, to be on the front lines in these battles. They need to learn to be leaders in these areas, especially in situations where the clergy and others who should know better, do not take the lead. At a minimum, every

Christian doctor should have access to biblical studies on this subject, and be able to rebut the underlying philosophical error contained in most health-care proposals. Maybe it's time to resurrect the "Just Say No" slogan, with physicians being unalterably opposed to right-ist approaches to medicine. We might do well to remember: If its right-ist, it's probably wrong.

Endnotes

1. Taken from Judith Jarvis Thomson's **Rights, Restitution, and Risk,** Cambridge, Massachusetts: Harvard University Press, 1986, p. 8. This quote is amidst an article and a set of essays which is frequently contrary to the thrust of this essay.

2. As reported in **Exploding the Gene Myth** by Ruth Hubbard and Elijah Wald, Boston: Beacon Press, 1993, p. 26.

3. Willimon, William H., "The Effusiveness of Christian Charity," *Theology Today*, April, 1992, pp. 79-80.

4. Glendon, Mary Ann, **Rights Talk: The Impoverishment of Political**, New York: The Free Press, 1991, p.76.

5. *Ibid.*, p. 171.

6. **The Encyclopedia of Philosophy**, New York: MacMillan, 1967, p. 195.

7. **The Encyclopedia of Bioethics, Vol. 4**, New York: MacMillan, 1976, p. 1498.

8. *Young Life Relationships*, Spring 1993, p. 4.

9. Cf. *Contra Mundum*, No. 4, Summer, 1992, p. 68. While I am indebted to Prof. Beisner for this helpful information, we do have a slight disagreement over my contention that even the Decalogue does not provide rights. Beisner argues that, e.g., I have a duty not to murder you; therefore you have a right not to be murdered. While in essence we agree (and Beisner is clear that he only intends to assert that the commandments provide negative rights, not positive provision), I'm still unsure that all duties translate into reciprocal rights. I hope he is correct, and perhaps my hesitancy is merely a reaction to the abuse of rights-claims. In any event, his work and comments on Block are most insightful.

10. Hastings, James, **Encyclopedia of Religion and Ethics, Vol. X**, New York: Scribners, 1928, p. 771.

11. *Ibid.*, p. 771.

12. *Ibid.*, p. 772.

13. *Ibid.*, p. 774.

14. *Ibid.*, p. 771.

15. For example, in "Cultural Barriers to the Understanding of the Church and its Public Role" in *Missiology*, October 1991, Vol. XIX, No. 4, p. 461.

16. *Ibid.*, p. 462.

17. *Ibid.*, p. 462.

18. *Ibid.*, p. 463.

I9. *Ibid.*, p. 463.

20. Cf **The Encyclopedia of Philosophy**, *op. cit.*, p, 195.

21. Cf. the recent new translations of **Lectures on Unbelief and Revolution** by Harry van Dyke, Ontario: Wedge, 1989.

22. *Ibid.*, p. 45.

23. *Ibid.*, p. 46.

24. *Ibid.*, p. 47.

25. *Ibid.*, p. 47.

26. *Ibid.*, p. 44.

27. *Ibid.*, p. 98.

28. **Encyclopedia of Religion and Ethics, Vol. X**, *op. cit.*, p. 773.

29. **Discussions of Robert Lewis Dabney, Vol. III**, Edinburgh: Banner of Truth, 1982, pp. 21-46.

30. *Ibid.*, p. 21.

31. *Ibid.*, p. 22.

32. *Ibid.*, p. 23.

33. *Ibid.*, p. 24.

34. *Ibid.*, p. 24.

35. *Ibid.*, p. 26.

36. *Ibid.*, p. 27.

37. *Ibid.*, p. 27.

38. *Ibid.*, p. 39.

39. *Ibid.*, p. 39.

40. *Ibid.*, p. 38.

41. *Ibid.*, p. 38.

42. *Ibid.*, p. 38.

43. *Ibid.*, p. 38.

44. *Ibid.*, p. 38.

45. *Ibid.*, p. 43.

46. *Ibid.*, p. 44.

47. *Ibid.*, p. 47.

The Biblical Perspective on the Mind-Body Problem Part 2

Jay E. Adams, Ph.D., S.T.M.

Dr. Adams is the author of numerous books and articles on counseling and founder of the Christian Counseling and Educational Foundation. At present he is pastor of an Associate Reform Presbyterian Church near Greenville, South Carolina.

Adapted from a presentation to the Winter Institute on Counseling in Medicine given in San Diego, February, 1992. Part I appeared in the Spring, 1993, issue.

We come now to the question which is the heart of it all — what is the relationship of spirit to body? Remember, I said that I want to talk about *spirit* more than about *mind* because that is where the real issue is. And, we'll see why, I hope, as we observe the relationship of spirit to body in normal activities.

In Gen. 2:7, we read about the creation of man. God first shaped man's body. It was a lifeless lump until He breathed into its nostrils, and man became a living *nephesh* (soul). The spirit that He breathed into man constituted him a living soul. Before that time the body was mindless. Don't miss that point. Mind was not originally part of the body, but when the body was given life, it began to operate rationally. Mind began functioning; this was man in the fullness of what man is. Man was not truly man prior to that time. *Mind entered when life entered, and mind leaves when life leaves.*

When I look at a corpse lying in a casket as I did two nights ago, I was not looking at something that possessed mind, because it had no life in it. It was a lump of tissue that once lived but now had lost that dimension. Remember this as we discuss mind (or spirit): that it is not *body* that is the foundation or source of mind, but the *spirit*. That activity began only when spirit entered the body and man became a living soul.

These words each have a special meaning. The word "spirit" means the inanimate, non-material part of man viewed as *out of* relationship to the body; separated from it. That same non-material part of man viewed *in union with* the body is called "soul." This same immaterial part of man viewed as the inner you, over against what you and I see and hear — one's outward appearance — is called "heart." The spirit within is called "heart" as over against the body, the lips, the hands, the voice — the outward appearance. That is the way the Bible uses those terms, and it will help to get these straight as you begin to think about them.

The word "mind," then, means a human being *functioning* in such a way as to remember, think, decide. At the present time, during the duplex period when body and soul are folded together so that to remove one or the other from that union would bring about death in most instances (and I'll tell you why I'm making that exception later on), you cannot know yourself as pure spirit. Neither can you cannot know yourself as pure body. This fact occasions most of the problems that we have in thinking about the mind-body problem.

There is such a close union between body and spirit that we cannot imagine what it will be like to be "unclothed," as Paul called it (II Cor. 5), when our bodies are laid aside temporarily and we become something less than what man was intended to be (but, this time, in the opposite way). Even though the soul is perfected at death, man is incomplete until a glorified body is someday united to it. But, at this present time, we just can't imagine what that separation will be like. We can only talk about it, understand certain facts about it, but we cannot experience it or even imagine what that experience will be like. Therefore, many of the problems we shall consider can be solved only partially. Some questions must be left hanging. I am not able to answer them because I am neither pure spirit nor pure body.

The members of the body, the *hoploi* as we saw previously (the instruments or tools that God uses to work through us to understand and affect this material world) include the brain. The brain is to be *used by the spirit* to serve God, by affecting and being affected by the world. The one exception to which I referred is a most interesting one. It is recorded in the twelfth chapter of II Corinthians. Paul here speaks about something that happened to him 14 years before. He describes himself in the third person to avoid boasting. Indeed, the experience was so exceptional that God gave him a thorn in the flesh to keep him from such boasting.

He says, "I shall come next to visions and revelations from the Lord. I know a person in Christ, who fourteen years ago was snatched away to the third heaven." (Incidentally, the Bible doesn't say anything about a *seventh* heaven. That has to do with movies.) The first heaven is the atmosphere around the earth, as when Scripture speaks of "The birds of the heavens" (or "sky.") The second way in which the word "heaven" is used is of the place where the universe is — the stars, the moon, the sun, the galaxies. The third heaven is where God is. Paul says that he was snatched up to the third heaven. Then he says, "Whether in his body or outside of his body, I don't know, but God does, and, I know this person, whether in his body or outside of his body, I don't know, God knows, was snatched away to Paradise and heard ineffable words that it is not permissible for a human to speak."

This event raises interesting questions. Paul was postulating the possibility of an OBE (out of body experience). He did not say that *was* how he had experienced these revelations, but he said that was a conceivable way in which it *might* have happened. He didn't rule it out. He thought one genuine possibility was that, out of the body, he as pure spirit, could, while still living in this world, have had an experience in the third heaven. We'll come back to this later but that's the exception I have mentioned when I've said that a person cannot be alive when you rip the spirit from the body. James 2:26 says that "the body without the spirit is dead", except, in Paul's very unusual circumstance, we see, such a possibility existed. We'll come back to that in a few moments as we look at some possible implications of Paul's having visited the third heaven without a body in spirit alone. For that matter, the other possibility he mentions, visiting *with* the body, raises enough interesting issues to keep you busy for the next twenty-five years.

Spirit, or mind, now functions (with this exception) only in the duplex relationship of the body and brain. Duplexity exists to the very end: death. Stephen standing there, being stoned and about to die, says, "Lord Jesus, receive *my spirit*." He doesn't say, " ... receive *me*," because he is still in that duplex relationship. Yet, he knows that duplexity is about to end. So, he says, "Receive my spirt," knowing that duplexity will soon become dichotomy. He's going to leave that body, and he's going to be received by the Lord Jesus Christ. But, to the very end he still talks about his spirit in his body, because it

has yet to be released. It is interesting how one talks about himself. The language used to describe duplexity is informative, especially as the apostle Paul uses it in the sixth and seventh chapters of Romans, where he writes, "I do what I don't want to do, and I don't do what I want to do." Think about the "I" in that sentence!

In II Corinthians 4:4 we read that man's mind is "blinded" until such time as regeneration occurs. It's blinded by the sin with which each one comes into this world. Man's corrupt nature keeps him from finding God. Reason cannot take you to God, in spite of some people who think, Thomistically, that it can. The mind, itself, is defective. There have been noetic effects of sin upon the capacity to think: that's why we have erasers on pencils. That's why word-processing is so valuable — you don't have to retype everything because of one error. The world's history would have been different had we had computers from the Garden of Eden.

1 Corinthians 2, is a significant passage. Failure to understand 1 Cor. 2 means inability to understand anything at all about the mind-body problem. Without interpreting the passage in depth, notice, Paul teaches that regeneration is absolutely essential for understanding God's truth. First Corinthians 2:14 says that "a natural person does not welcome the teachings of God's Spirit." That means he does not welcome Scriptural teachings. "And, they are foolishness to him, and he is not able to know about them, because they must be investigated spiritually."

Anywhere you are there are sounds and sights that you neither hear nor see. But, if you had a television set you *could* hear those sounds and see those pictures. The reason that you don't see and hear is because you do not have a receiving set. God says that the unregenerate person (one without the Spirit of God) *cannot* receive the things of the Spirit of God, because he doesn't have the capacity — the receiving set— to pick them up. Verse 9 says, "As it is written, the eye has not seen and the ear hasn't heard, and what hasn't been conceived by the human heart is what God has prepared for those who love Him." So, the unregenerate human being does not have that capacity, as verse 14 says, to investigate Spirit-given truths, and doesn't welcome them. God has supplied these things only for those who desire them, whose ears have been unplugged, whose eyes have been opened and whose hearts have been made ready to receive them. In verse 10 Paul writes, "To those who believe in Him God has revealed these things by His Spirit. The Spirit searches into everything, even the deep thoughts of God." The Holy Spirit is the One who knows the deepest thinking that goes on in God. "Who knows," verse 11 asks, "the thoughts of a person except the spirit of the person in him." Notice, it is the spirit *in* the person. "So, too, no one knows God's thoughts except God's Spirit." And, then, he says, "Christians have not received the world's spirit, but the Spirit who is from God so that we may know that which God has freely given to us."

In a sense, Paul is saying, when the Holy Spirit enters a believer's life it is almost like a brain transplant.

That's something we can't even fathom or begin to conceive of. We can talk about it with laughter, but the complexities of such a thought far outstrip anything we can ever dream of. But, God thought about it. It's like sawing off the top of your skull, removing your brain and putting God's brain in instead. When the Spirit comes in the Spirit becomes the receiving set for the things of God. And, so, in verse 16 he says, "we have the mind of Christ" because dwelling within us we have the Spirit who knows the mind of God.

All of the foregoing is to say that the relationship of spirit to body is *often* thought of in the Scriptures. This question *does* arise, and the matter *does* become significant in Scripture; it's not avoided. It's something about which the Bible has a number of things to say from which we may learn.

Now, we have viewed God's description of the body in *normal* activity. But, what about bodily injury? What about impairments and incapacities of the body — brain tumors, fevers, comas, drugs, alcohol, various things affect the body significantly? The question: is the spirit so tied to the body in this duplex form in which we now live that it loses ability to relate to this world as the body becomes impaired? The answer is, obviously, "yes." Though the spirit has an interest in doing things in this world, both learning from it by gathering data from it through the senses, and acting toward this world through the members of the body, it becomes difficult for the spirit, when the body is impaired, to do what it wants to do. It has a broken tool that it's

trying to use and finds that this becomes a hindrance. The spirit is hindered from working properly by this damaged tool, and the mind, therefore, does not always function even in full capacity, because, even internally, when a man thinks within himself, as he carries on a dialogue inside, this too depends on the interaction of spirit and body. Even within the mind then, let alone in the outward gathering of data and affecting of the world, bodily impairment causes a problem.

When the body becomes impaired, the spirit does not function with reference to this world as it was intended to. That failure, of course, results from Adam's sin, not necessarily from the individual's sin. The mind functions poorly when it uses inaccurate or inadequate data. If your senses do not work well, then you gather inadequate data. I'm beginning to learn more and more about that. I have a bit of a hearing problem, and people always mumble, it seems. So, through the years they mumble more and more. It's amazing how they've gotten worse and worse!

If I'm hearing one word and somebody is saying a different word that sounds like it I could get a very wrong concept of what he is talking about. My spirit has to operate with the data that it receives through my senses. If it receives inadequate data then it's going to act in an inadequate or inaccurate way. The reaction may do harm rather than good. Thus the body *does* affect the spirit in that way. Senility — physical brain deterioration — really is accurately described as losing one's mind, because the mind loses more and more contact with the world when it recedes into the background as brain cells die. The person is not capable of doing things that he once did and is unable to communicate and relate to other people and his world as he previously could. The mind does not function as it should because the spirit is unable to get out there to gather data.

Yet, of course, we know this is not absolute. Even in deep comas, or under anesthesia, the mind may function in spite of the failure of some bodily organ to function. We've all heard of experiences such as, for example, the nurse who was sued because of a comment she made when she thought a patient was unable to hear because of anesthesia. When a fat woman lay on the table before surgery, she said to another nurse, "What is this, another beached whale?" The woman who was anesthetized heard her and sued her afterwards. How much gets through and and how much doesn't is extremely interesting.

Then comes the question of death — and the relationship of spirit to body in death. It's from death that we learn a lot about life. It's from this separation of the two that we learn many of the things that we know. That the two aspects of man can be separated and are separated is very plain from the words of Christ Himself. In Matthew 10:28 He says, "Do not be afraid of those who kill the body but cannot kill the soul. Rather, be afraid of the One who can destroy *both* soul and body, in Gehenna." When He talks about "both" He's making it clear that there are two items, two aspects of man.

Many today will tell you there is no way you can ever separate, even

at death, the body from the soul. They simply do not agree with our Lord Jesus Christ. They keep telling us that the Hebrew concept of man did not allow for the separation of one from another. And, yet, here is Jesus Christ, with all His Hebrew background, making it *explicit* that there are two separable elements. Reject that kind of teaching; it will only confuse. This view has been prevalent, not only in liberal circles where it began, but in the last twenty years has gained great acceptance among conservatives who think that man is a unified being, *period*. On this view, at death, nothing remains. Yet, the opposite is precisely what Jesus was talking about — that the body and the soul can be thought of as separate units, and that they can be treated differently at death as separate units. So, He says "both." Christ viewed man as composed of two elements.

Do I need to turn to Philippians 1:23, for further proof? There Paul says that it is "far better to depart and be with Christ" than to remain in this world. And, yet, it was necessary for the Philippians that Paul remain, so that he could be a blessing to them. "Far better" for *what?* It is certainly not far better for Paul's *body* for him to depart because the body dies. The body disintegrates. The body rots in the grave. So, he must mean that it is far better for the *spirit* which continues after death and is with Christ. He talks about that spirit "departing" and being "with Christ" — literally, "setting sail," as though it were to leave the port behind and set sail for a new adventure. In second Corinthians 5:8, Paul describes death as being "absent from the body." Words could not be clearer. To be absent from

the body is for the spirit to be "at home with the Lord." *What* is absent from the body? What is at home with Christ? Certainly not anything material. The spirit is what he refers to. To die, therefore, is "gain," because the spirit leaves this world of sin, sorrow, heartache and sickness and death behind. It is gain for your spirit to be with the Lord.

The fact that the spirit departs at death raises questions. Stephen can say, "Lord, receive my spirit." Jesus could say in similar language: "Father into Thy hands I commend my spirit." The fact is that he *did* go into the unseen world. Peter and Acts 2 quote the Psalm that says, "I will not leave his soul in Hades." Don't get the idea that Hades means the place of punishment; it is simply the word that means the "unseen world." The unseen world is composed both of the place of torment and the place of blessing, Paradise. Jesus told the thief on the cross, "Today, you will be with me in Paradise." That's where His spirit went when He died. Nevertheless, it says in the second chapter of Acts that God did not abandon Christ to the grave (Peter is quoting the passage from the Psalm) but He raised that body on the third day. That's the point that he's making.

Now one of the problems related to this concept is that the storage capacity for memory seems to be in the brain. Storage, as Penfield's experiments seems to indicate, is located in various areas of the brain. Stimulate one area and you smell baked goods that you smelled when you were a kid, just as if you were back in the kitchen with mom. Stimulate another chunk of brain and something now appears on the

TV screen of your imagination. When people talk about wracking their brains for something they are trying to remember they express the idea that it is in the brain that memory is stored.

The problem is, then, how does the spirit retain memory after the brain is left behind? That is an interesting question. Does the spirit gain new ways of knowing and remembering? Or, is the brain itself only one way of storing and remembering material? Or, is memory not a capacity that is needed by the spirit in the new world? Does God wipe away all memories of the sinful world from a believer?

But, that doesn't solve the problem because in Luke 16 we have the unbeliever remembering his brothers back on earth. And, yet, are we trying to cull too much from that example? Lots of questions arise. I don't have all the answers to them. Note well, however, that mental capacity entered the body as the spirit came in at creation. And, it seems like the mental capacity that the body possesses leaves when the spirit departs at death. So, in some way, the mental capacity goes with the spirit. I don't understand how it happens, but that is what the Scriptures teach. The spirit is self-conscious (as Philippians above says) when it has departed from the body. As pure spirit, it has been made perfect according to Hebrews 12:23, "... the spirits of justified men made perfect." That, also, is important to understand. The spirit is not perfect in this world and needs to be made perfect at death.

If we were to chart this whole process you could say that at creation a body and a spirit come together. The spirit brings the mental capacity into being, which becomes a nousomatic (mind-body) being. At death, however, when these two separate and the spirit goes to be with God and the body goes into the ground, mental capacity does not go into the ground but goes with the spirit. The spirit which *was* oriented toward this world to work from it and toward it through the body, *now* is oriented toward the unseen world to work in and toward that world. The laws of working as a pure spirit, in an unseen world, where there is no need for the senses that we depend on today, may require entirely different ways of knowing, remembering, and deciding, which we don't now know about.

Both the spirit and the mind need to be changed in conversion. In Ezekiel 36:26 we read that the Holy Spirit gives a new heart. This heart is this inner you, thinking, willing, remembering. It's the place from which the issues of life flow like streams. That heart, at birth, is a heart of stone, according to Ezekiel, dead as far as the things of God are concerned. It is lifeless, cold, unreceptive to the things of God. At regeneration the heart (or spirit) is transformed. It is, says Ezekiel, like ripping out the heart of stone and replacing it with a heart of flesh, that is, a heart that's alive, warm, receptive, malleable, rather than hard, firm, and unmoved. At regeneration God changes the spirit so that now it seeks, and is able to do those things that please God. He enables the spirit to so orient and utilize the body that its members are yielded to righteousness leading to further righteousness, rather than yielded to sin leading to unrighteousness. The body, then, is freed from the tyranny of sin and it is day by day being renewed in its patterns of life. It's being *rehabituated* just as the spirit within. The Holy Spirit, working through the spirit within, begins to transform one's way of life. These things are all taught in a number of places in Scripture that I haven't time to go into here. But, if you want to read further about them, I have considered the question in depth in my book, *The War Within*.

In I Peter 1:18 there is a very interesting passage, I want to translate quite closely to the original: "Knowing that you were not set free from the useless behavior patterns that were passed down from your forefathers by the payment of a corruptible ransom like silver or gold, but with Christ's valuable blood." Christ's blood has set us free from useless behavior patterns that have been passed down through the generations. We are bound no longer by what posterity has said and done and the models they have provided. One tires of hearing people say that you can't love others unless somebody loves you first. They say that you have a wrong view of God unless your father was the right kind of a father and that models that came out of childhood are so *determinative* of what we are or what we will become that we are stuck with them for the rest of our lives. That strange dogma is taught even by Christians, though it comes straight out of pagan views of Abraham Maslow. Peter, in contrast, teaches that change is possible. One may break from the influence of the third, fourth, fifth — or hundredth — generation. I don't care how many generations have promulgated a way of life, through Christ a person can break out of that, *fully*. He is *not* bound by what his ancestry has done. He is not stuck!

Moreover, it's time to get rid of that Freudianism, which seems to permeate everybody's thinking, and return to the Bible. If the Bible teaches that Christianity does *anything* it teaches us that it frees us to serve God — no matter *what* has happened in the past. It's so tiresome to hear people saying, "I was abused as a child. I've been abused as a teenager." Well, I don't want to minimize the tragedy of true abuse or the sin that was behind it. But, then, psychologists teach people to build a *lifestyle* around the abuse: "I am an abused person." Not "I'm a farmer, a mother, a child," or anything else. I'm an "abused person." A whole present lifestyle is built around the past.

Do you believe that in Thessalonica and Corinth — where a thousand prostitutes from the temple legally plied their trade on the streets — that in pagan cities of the Greek and Roman world where infanticide was the rule (if the father didn't like the child he just exposed it), do you believe with the kind of background that paganism provided that there was no abuse? Do you believe that nothing wrong was ever done to children, that they all grew up under wonderful, favorable, optimal conditions? Of course not! If anything, things were worse than they are in this country today (as bad as it is here). But, do you ever read — even once — that the apostles Paul or Peter or John or James said, "Oh, I know you were abused. I know that you have this terrible background. I know all these things have happened to you. You come out of a culture where you've been

trained for generations in this way. I don't expect much change from you. I certainly understand and I realize how hard it is to make change. I'm not expecting much, or, at least, not much for a long while, until we love you lots so you can learn to love others." Not once do you read that kind of nonsense. What you read is, "You turned from idols to serve the living and the true God." Get with it! That's what you read in your New Testament. You have all the resources in the Word of God and the Spirit of God dwelling within you to do everything that God ever asked you to do. Now, use them! Stop wallowing in the past. The more tragic it may be, the less reason to wallow in it. Romans 5:20 is still in my Bible!

So, then, at conversion, the human being is freed to serve God. That body, which had been held captive, and whose members had become slaves of sin, are now freed to become the slaves of Jesus Christ. Rehabituation enables the spirit to function properly toward the world. As one is rehabituated, sanctified more and more, learning to live according to the biblical alternatives and the ways of God, he becomes more efficient in the use of this body not only to evaluate things properly and to store the right kinds of memories — that he can call upon in making decisions in days to come — but also in making decisions right now to do the things that ought to be done. But, the effects of sin on the body — a body that was injured before conversion — if they can be repaired by a physician will more fully allow for rehabituation and sanctification.

Seize that fact brothers! Your job is not merely repairing bodies; it is enabling the spirit to work with and through a body so that God's will can be done, so that the things of God can be accomplished by that body. You, therefore, are involved in a very *spiritual* activity. I hope you'll remember that when you're just playing around week after week after week with colds and snotty noses and that kind of thing because, even in this, more than a snotty nose is involved.

Now we come to that time toward which everything has been moving in these lectures — some observations, some questions, some answers, and a few conjectures. If my spirit uses my body to gain access to and affect the physical world, through the senses and other bodily members, does physical injury or incapacity (short of death) impair or stop the spirit's learning and functioning? The answer is that it would seem that the body *may* frustrate the spirit in this as well as in other ways. When the spirit is willing but the flesh (material side) is weak, Paul indicates, problems do arise. Here is a sick person. Here is an old, worn-out body. These people just don't (and are not able to) learn the Word of God well when it is taught to them, or when they study it. Pain may get in the way of study. Dizziness that accompanies atrial fibrillation would certainly does so.

Various kinds of physical problems hinder growth. That means hindering learning as well as functioning in this world. Preachers have to remember this. They can't expect the same results from every person when they teach. But, physicians also have to know that they can cooperate with those who are preaching the Word to help wherever they can. You can't make an old body new, and you can't do a lot of things for a body that is incapable of ever going back to an earlier stage, but, where you can, by healing him, you may enable someone to better learn the Word of God, and live more adequately for Christ. Bodily parts, impaired, worn, dulled, broken are ineffective tools of the spirit. Therefore, medical efforts that enhance bodily function make greater spiritual activity possible.

Medicine, moreover, may serve an evangelistic dimension making it possible for some unbeliever to understand the proclamation of the gospel more clearly. The doctor-patient relationship, as a result, is inevitably *religious*. It is not neutral. It is inevitably a religious relationship, because if your goal is not merely to heal, comfort, or remove pain, but, first and foremost, to honor God by helping that person to come to faith in Christ. You, as a physician have a *religious* relationship to every patient.

It is also true that Christians are *obligated* to seek medical help. It is true that there is no biblical command to go to a doctor, but the conclusion is inevitable. If we want to be fully capable of doing what God wants us to do, we must do everything we can to bring this body up to snuff so that through it we can serve Jesus Christ as well as possible. That means James 5 must be taken seriously. People have wrong ideas about what is taught in James 5. When James says, if you're sick you must call the elders of the church, the first thing that implies is that there is an important relationship

between Christianity and sickness. It is not that you first necessarily call the doctor, but you certainly do call the elders *along with* the doctor. In those days, especially in the Roman period, when almost everybody did his own doctoring because there were so few physicians around (and many of them were held in very low repute) the elders did three things: the elders prayed over the patient. (Literally, in the Greek it says "prayed *over* him.") That pictures somebody in a pretty serious condition so that they must bend over him as he lies on the bed.

The second thing is, if he has committed any sin they probe about it and help him to confess it so that, if this is a judgment of God upon him like those people who were judged for their sin and were sick in Corinth, (I Cor. 11) he would be healed.

But, the third thing which the elders did in a day in which everybody did his own doctoring, was to anoint him with oil. People today have made a ceremony out of what was medicine. That passage is not talking about ceremonial anointing at all. The King James did us in again, as it did so many places, by translating two different Greek words by one English word.

There are two words in the Greek that are translated in the King James Version by the English word "anoint." The word which means a *ceremonial* anointing — *chreo* — is related to *Christos* or Christ (the Greek equivalent of the Hebrew *Meshiach*, or "messiah,") meaning the "anointed one." This is *not* the word used in James 5. Kings and priests were anointed to set them apart for

their work. But that's *chreo*, to pour some kind of oil or water, whatever was used in a given case, upon someone to anoint him, set him aside, to that task. That's *not* the word that's used in James 5. James' "anointing" is not ceremonial. People go around holding little services in which they take flasks of oil and anoint people. This is totally out to lunch as far as James is concerned.

The word he used is *aleipho*. *Aleipho* is a word used by Hippocrates and all the old Greek physicians. It meant "to rub or smear." It depicts anything but a *ceremonial* anointing! It was used of rubbing down Greek athletes. Oil and wine, of course, were the two mediums that were used to rub medicinal herbs into a person's body. That's what James is talking about. Greeks even took oil baths. The elders would administer medicine, just as they would pray and they would seek to elicit a confession *if* there was sin involved in this problem. Sin wasn't always involved, but if it was, confession should accompany prayer and medicine. So, at an early date then medicine had a relationship to the person, and he was obligated to do whatever he could do to bring his body into shape where he could serve Jesus Christ more fully. He was supposed to use medicine, prayer, confess sin — all the possibilities were laid out in James 5.

Now, for a second question or conjecture on the foregoing relationship of spirit and body. If the disembodied human spirit has a mind, that is, it has the capacity to think, reason, and so on (remember mind is not some little organ or a black box; it's a capacity of a human spirit) then this mind must function differently when in a duplex union with the body than when it is not. But, that is to be expected since, in the disembodied state it relates to the *unseen* world rather than the material world. God is pure Spirit with mental capacity. Mental capacity, therefore, is not therefore tied to brain. God remembers. In fact, He knows all things from the beginning and all things all the way to the very end. God has total mental capacity, and yet has no physical body. Angels are spirits. They took upon themselves human form now and then and appeared to human beings. But Hebrews says they are *spirits* sent forth to serve the heirs of salvation. So, here are ministering spirits, angels, who have mental capacity, capability to reason, think, remember, and so on, and yet they don't have bodies, except as they take upon themselves a body to appear in this world to a human being on rare occasions.

When Paul was caught up into the third heaven he did not know whether this happened in the body or out of the body. The implications of that are several: First, evidently, Paul thought that it was possible to hear, or to see things, and understand things, whatever was revealed to him, *as a pure spirit* when he was having an out of body experience, if indeed that is how it happened. At any rate, he conceived of that as possible. If he didn't conceive of that as possible, he would not have said "whether in the body or out of the body, I don't know." He'd have said, "Well, it had to be in the body because that couldn't happen out of the body." But, as it is, he assumed it could happen out of the body. That

is, as a spirit he could have engaged in mental activity that did not require the use of his body. Certainly, Paul thought it possible under extraordinary circumstances for a body to continue to survive without the spirit. Seemingly contrary to James 2:26, which must have been the general rule, Paul contemplated an extraordinary circumstance. Here was a body still surviving on earth while the spirit had left it. Then, the spirit returned and the body's soul continued in duplexity. Now, was Paul's body dead — that's the only other possibility — in some sense during that period, or, was there some kind of a coma, some kind of a circumstance, where the spirit left and the body became mindless? Did the spirit enter heaven for a time while out of that body, and yet that body survived?

If so, some very interesting things are possible. Can it be that a body sustained on life supporting systems, may be kept alive as a corpse full of tissue that's alive (like tissue can be kept alive in a petri dish) while the spirit has already left and gone to be with God. Is that possible? Was that little baby in that condition this past week when her doctor, after six codes, still was trying to keep the baby alive, and I was gritting my teeth more and more and more. He was giving her family false hope. I don't know the answer to that, but I can conceive of that as a possibility that perhaps, in some situations where "heroic" measures are used, we have already had death, that is, the separation of the spirit from the body, and all you're doing is retaining some tissue. Now, I know there are tremendous implications if that could ever be proven true, implications about harvesting organs, etc. But,

I'm just asking the question, and it does pose itself, if you think about this situation.

In Revelation 1:10 and 4:1,2, we read that John was "in the spirit" on the Lord's day. And, as such, he *went* and *saw* revelations of various sorts and *heard* various things. All throughout the book of Revelation it said, "Then I saw ..." "Then I heard ..." "Then I saw ... " "Then I heard ...." It seems to be that John had the same sort of experience as Paul (or at least Paul contemplated). John seems definitely to have had an O.B.E. The spirit alone was hearing and seeing, conducting activity, mental activity. Paul considered that spirit alone might engage in mental activity, even though it was brainless activity, toward the non-material, unseen world. And, the body was probably not dead. In these unusual circumstances that means the spirit can act toward the unseen world now. If Paul went to Paradise *in the body*, then other problems arise. Was he somehow enabled to see and hear that which a physical being cannot ordinarily see or hear in the invisible world? An interesting question! The question arises in the Old Testament passage, II Kings 6:16, 17, where he says, "Those who are with us are greater than those who are against us" and suddenly all heaven was full of chariots and armies that could not be seen normally were seen in that extraordinary circumstance. So there are many things about this invisible world, and the visible world in which we live, that we don't know much about.

But, the problems with the spirit are the same as those we have with heaven and hell, and with the unseen world in other respects. We have to use language and images from this world to describe something very different. Therefore our descriptions are neither detailed nor final. They only give us some indications of what these things are like. And, often, language can be no better than negative when we talk about the invisible world, i.e., the *not*-visible world. We don't use a positive word to tell us what invisibility means. When we talk about God being "infinite," we mean He is *not* finite, but we don't know what we really are talking about beyond that. And, if we talk about heaven being paved with streets of gold, these are the best images we can find for something that is far more wonderful. We talk about hell being like a lake of fire, where the smoke of their torment ascends up forever and ever. Probably hell is far worse. Yet, that is the best human description we can get of it. We're limited considerably when we talk about these things.

Even in this world some sort of distinction may normally be recognized. For instance, the biblical outer-inner distinction is continually made about people who are here now *as though we can recognize that distinction*. We read about the hands, the lips, the mouth, the outward appearance over against the "heart." In II Cor. 4:16 Paul thinks that way about himself. He says, "As a result, we don't give up even though our *outer person* is decaying because on the other hand, our *inner person* is being renewed daily." Paul is saying, "I'm coming apart at the seams physically. The outer man, the physical being, the body that I have is decaying. It's going to pieces. Yet, this inner person that I am, this non-physical part, is being renewed daily."

Now, Paul couldn't have spoken of a physical renewal because it was the body that was physically decaying. Physical strength is precisely what he was losing. So, this renewal must involve strength of purpose, resolve, etc., that came from the Scriptures, as the Spirit of God ministered those things to him.

In I Cor. 2: 10,11 Paul says that the Holy Spirit knows the deep things of God, and that He knows them just as a person's spirit knows his own thoughts. Notice, he doesn't say *brain*, or just that the *person* knows, but that the *spirit* knows. He locates knowledge in the spirit. He is using the relationship of man's spirit and body to show the relationship of the Holy Spirit to God. The spirit is identified in that passage with mind. When we receive the Holy Spirit, we receive the *mind* of Christ. That is to say, we can think as God does, think His thoughts after Him. Remember Isaiah 55:8 that says, "Your ways are not My thoughts, your thoughts are not My thoughts." What does God do? Change His ways and change His thoughts? No. God demands that we change our ways and thoughts so that we begin to think His thoughts and walk His ways after Him. In Hebrews 5:12 we read that God's Word judges the desires and the thoughts of the heart. It gets down to the very innermost part of our being.

Now consider the question of demon control, which I am not going to get into in any depth. Demonic control of men seems to indicate something about the body being *used by a spirit*. In this case, it is a spirit other than the spirit of the individual. The spirit of the demon is in control of his body, using it to

do things — destructive things, evil things. The demon used that body as a means of getting at the world. In this case the control and thinking comes from a person other than one's self. How does the spirit enter? Does the demon control cut off the person's spirit entirely? Partially? Does it get in between, so to speak, the spirit of the individual and the body, interposing itself in some way? Does it take the human spirit captive and use it in some way to control the body? We don't know. But, in some way it stands in the position of that human spirit. Possessed persons are *used*, just as our bodies are "possessed" by our spirits to be *used* for God's honor.

When one is "absent from the body," at rest, and "present with the Lord," selfhood or "I-ness" passes exclusively to the spirit. We don't read that I am in the grave *and* I am in a place where I am with the Lord. There is no split in the personality. *I* am with the Lord. Selfhood goes along with the spirit and the body is no longer the self. It is no longer "I." People may become preoccupied with a body but the body is no longer that person. That person has gone, set sail, left the harbor behind. It's possible to amputate large sections of the body and/or replace large portions by transplants or prostheses. Yet, the individual remains the same person.

I suppose it's theoretically possible over the years to come, to replace almost every part of one's body, so that, a person is only 10% of whatever he was when he first came on the scene. Now, he is all plastic and tubes, or contains pieces (transplants) from other individuals, or a combination thereof, or whatever, and yet he is still the same person; he has the same social security number, you might say. And, he would be the same "social security number" before God, even if he were not, before men. I won't even try to think about what a brain transplant might mean should that ever be possible; we can't even conceive of it now. But, I would think that, if it were possible, a transplanted brain relating to a spirit in a body into which it was placed could not be another person if the spirit remained, because the spirit/mind continues when the body is buried at death, and that new brain would be buried at death as well. Of course, the spirit would have to deal with a whole new set of stored data, habituations, etc. It is almost unthinkable. But, thinking of it gives you the concept that the continuation of the person, of the selfhood, of the "I-ness," is with the spirit, not fundamentally with the body. Does duplexity make the possibility of such transplants always, forever impossible? I would think, probably, so.

Last of all, among these observations, weird thoughts, and so on, consider truth-telling by physicians. Patients have a right to know what the doctor knows about their condition. Under many circumstances to withhold this is pure theft. However, the issue in many cases may not be *whether* to tell someone, but *when*. The doctor may have to wait until the spirit has full enough bodily access to the data to understand and make intelligent decisions. When a person is feverish, when a person is only half with-it physically, and his spirit is not operating through that body efficiently, a person may misunderstand a great deal of what you say. Thus, there are times, I would think, when it isn't wise to tell the whole truth and nothing but the truth because the person can't receive the whole truth.

All in all, the mind (spirit)/body problem is both perplexing and fascinating. I have only scratched the surface today. Go on thinking and contributing to this issue. After all, only Christians can think properly about the matter because only they begin from a foundation of God's Revelation.

Rationing Medical Care to the Elderly Revisited: Futility as a Just Criterion

Gregory W. Rutecki, M.D.

Dr. Rutecki is Clinical Associate Professor of Medicine at Northeastern Ohio University College of Medicine.

"The prolongation of life is ultimately an impossible or rather an unobtainable goal for medicine. For we are all born with those twin and inescapable diseases — aging and mortality." Kass[1]

On August 3, 1993, in preparation for house debate of his economic package, President Bill Clinton observed that his plan would, "cut health care costs without hurting the elderly." His statement, at least for now, ended ten years of debate concerning the rationing of medical care to the elderly. The debate began in 1983 ostensibly with economist and later Federal Reserve Board chairman, Alan Greenspan, responding to the statistic that people over 65 comprised 12% of the population but consumed 1/3 of our nation's health resources. He addressed this disparity with the rhetorical question, "Whether it is worth it?"[2] This is the crux of the elderly-rationing question — is the allotment of extensive Medicare monies to the elderly associated with a verifiable reduction of morbidity/mortality in the later stages of life? Is a continued disparity worth it? This is the subject and question that will engage our discussion.

The debate concerning the elderly and rationing should begin with an outline of the project at hand. First, I will review the definition and description of the "rationing" enterprise. This description will include discussion of *de facto* and *de jure* medical rationing, with the Oregon state Medicaid program serving as the latter example. Second, I will develop a rationale in an attempt to answer why rationing appears attractive, especially if it is specifically applied to the elderly. Third, I will review three different attempts to justify rationing to the elderly — what is now the minority view — which include Daniel Callahan's *Setting Limits*[3], a paper I co-authored, "Teach Us To Number Our Days,(Ps. 90:12): Age and Rationing of Medical Care: Use of Biblical Valuation of Personhood,"[4] and a counterpoint to the co-authored paper which was written by Dr. Ed Payne.[5] Finally, a review of these three sources will culminate in a synthesis extracted from the pro-rationing arguments and consideration of their impact on the elderly.

Rationing: Definitions, Descriptions, and Experiments

No free society in the contemporary technologic era of medicine can provide everyone with every medical intervention and survive. This is the basis for any discussion which considers the rationing of medical care. This by necessity leads to some initial definitions. Rationing may be defined as the *de facto* or *de jure* allotment or limitation of medical care necessitated by a shortage of money available. Inherent in such an allotment or limitation of medical care expenditures is that it will be based on a just, nondiscriminatory standard. The debate, pro and con, which confronts rationing encounters a biased citizenry in the United States of America. Any such dialogue implies the pejoratives of scapegoating, shortage, unequal access and opportunity — all very un-American concepts. Though most Americans withhold approbation for medical rationing, the realism interjected recently by its inception in the Oregon Medicaid program makes further discussion a contemporary imperative.

The State of Oregon confronted Medicaid shortages with a rationing plan that engages a "just standard" through a program based on the "what" and not the "who" that gets covered.[6] To accomplish the "what" led at first to a cumbersome list of 709 disease entities, reduced later to a still unwieldy 587. The "list" is a hierarchy which includes for example valuation of "prenatal care" over the less favored and less successful expensive technologies (*i.e.*, heart transplant). I would like to digress slightly in the context of the Oregon rationing experiment and study certain essential ingredients of this particular form of rationing, and, in so doing, increase rationing vocabulary through application of the concepts of futility and justice. The definition and expansion of these concepts will be crucial to our later synthesis of medical rationing. Since the Oregon rationing project uses both as criteria for "what" is covered, they will be discussed at this juncture.

Hepato-renal syndrome is defined as end-stage liver dysfunction with functional but irreversible kidney failure.[7] No medical or technologic intervention short of immediate liver transplantation is known to reverse an inexorable, fatal course. Usually, this course is so acute and the patient so critical that transplant is not feasible. Hepato-renal syndrome is one of the "whats" not covered in the Oregon rationing plan.[8] The rationale for non-coverage is as follows: further treatment does not benefit the hepato-renal patient who is, for all intents and purposes, terminal. Hepato-renal syndrome will serve as a paradigm for the concept of futility. This concept may be defined as any medical treatment which secures mere biologic survival but not meaningful recovery or reversibility. Futility may also be defined as any medical treatment that prolongs the dying process but does not result in meaningful survival. For example, from the dialysis patient's perspective, when dialysis is applied to most forms of kidney failure it secures a reasonable quality of life. However, dialysis does not lead to survival in hepato-renal syndrome and thus should be considered a futile intervention. Futility should be utilized more frequently during ethical decision making in medicine — especially as it pertains to rationing. This digression provides a preliminary overview of the concept.

The second decision as to "what" is covered in Oregon attempts to engage the concept of justice. For example, the Oregon program does not reimburse liver transplants in people who suffer from alcoholic cirrhosis.[9] However, cirrhosis from other or "nonbehavioral" causes, i.e., primary biliary cirrhosis, is reimbursable. The designers of the Oregon protocol perceived that the transplantation of people who did not "cause" their own liver disease was just. A more detailed discussion of justice in the context of rationing will be delayed until our final synthesis, but implementation in a contemporary rationing plan such as Oregon's is a valid starting point.

Rationale for Medical Rationing: Two Questions

Rationing on state and local levels may evolve into a more comprehensive federal program. An approach to two questions re: rationale for such and targeting of plans toward the elderly should be addressed now.

A relevant previous observation, "no society, especially in the age of expensive technology, can provide everyone with every medical intervention and survive," will be substantiated. Statistics in 1992 documented that 738 billion dollars per year were spent on health care in the United States — a full 13% of the gross national product.[10] Future projection of these figures, without change in present growth rates, would create policy trends expending 26% of the gross national product by the year 2030. Such medical costs stand in stark contrast to medical spending in the United Kingdom and Canada, in that the United States is 74% and 27% higher than either of these two countries, respectively. With contemporary medicine modeled as autonomy and consumerism, costs will continue to escalate as the public concomitantly demands immediate access to medical service, state of the art technology, and limited price.

One logical method to halt this escalation in medical expenditures would begin with identification of a group which receives disproportionate monies for health care. This might also be a group increasing both in size and health care costs, and most importantly with a group that does not appear to get maximum value for the dollar spent. For many, such a group is the American elderly.

By 2005, thirty-five million Americans will be older than 65 years of age and 50% of those older than 75 years of age.[11] Trends suggest that 100,000 people will celebrate their 100th birthday the same year. Within the group of elderly, hospital costs increase for the same diagnosis as the elderly age further. For example, costs are 50% higher for the same diagnosis in someone age 85 compared to ages 66-71.[12] Translated into dollars and cents, in 1987, 28% of the total Medicare allotment (22.7) billion dollars) was reimbursed on 6% of Medicare recipients, all of whom died that same year.[13] Statistics such as these serve to highlight not only the vast sums of money expended, but they may also raise a question of value for such dollars spent.

Review of these figures should substantiate both the rationale of rationing as well as the use of age as a potential criterion. In this context, I would like to review the pro-rationing arguments of Callahan, Rutecki-Geib, and Payne prior to an attempted synthesis and prescription for the issues discussed.

Daniel Callhan and His "Setting Limits"[3]

We begin with a Callhan quote which may serve as a substantive ethical statement in his attempt to place boundaries on any rationing proposals. "There is an imporant difference between taking age into account in order to provide the most appropriate treatment and the use of age as a standard for the discriminatory denial or modification of treatment."[14] The essence of this quote is its stress on approrpriate criteria for rationing — which do not include age discrimination — as the *sine qua non* for justice in medical allotment decisions.

Though Mr. Callahan reasons and writes from a secular-pluralistic world view perspective, there is much in his book with which I agree as a Christian. He articulates a necessary differentiation between care and cure, a key in any discussion of the elderly and rationing.[15] Further development in his concept of care-cure espouses a philosophy which realizes that a significant part of the elderly identity problem is ontologic and expressed in the question, what does it really mean to grow old? Though this question cannot be answered by a pluralistic society, Callahan does decry medical futility in its endeavor for a fountain of youth. He further attempts to juxtapose aging with appropriate meaning, and finally concludes that the heart of the problem is a society which does not have a *telos* for aging.[16] All of these observations accurately portray contemporary medical intervention adrift without consensus.

Following this background material, he provides a test for potential rationing as follows, "individual human life is respected for its own sake, not for social and economic benefits and the individuals may not be deprived of life to serve the welfare, alleged or real, of others."[17] He then attempts to posit some pragmatic tenets of his rationing enterprise. The one he offers is an age-based standard for the termination of life extending treatment perceived as a legitimate beginning.[18]

I would argue his age-based termination of life support as follows: If we were to choose dialysis as an example of such life-extending therapy and arrive at an age-based

standard, I would have great difficulty with the justice of that choice. The incorrect assumption that life support is homogenous when it is based on age may lead to unjust practices. For example, Kjellstrand has studied two groups within the confines of the elderly who are dialyzed with different outcomes.[19] In the elderly, chronic hemodialysis leads to a reasonable quality of life and not a particularly disturbing mortality. However, acute dialysis with specific diseases (ruptured abdominal aortic aneurysm with renal failure) may be associated with 100% immediate mortality. This will be discussed in more detail later. For now, Callahan's use of an age-based standard is faulty in this regard and one must arrive at more just criteria in the application of medically rationed dollars.

The other shortcoming in his proposal emanates, not from himself or his argument, but from the very nature of the society which he inhabits. He states, "a community that did not care for its elderly would not be a moral community."[20] Also, "because of pluralism we lack any common coherent vision of the wellsprings of moral obligation towards the elderly in general."[21] This assertion is a disturbing parallel to William May's quotation about the dying, "death is not only a crisis of the flesh, it is ... a crisis of community. Death will also reveal starkly and unmistakably something about the communities in which a dying person lives."[22] The aspect of Callahan's "setting limits" scenario that is most unnerving is the one that would set limits on the medical care of the elderly in a community that lacks a vision of moral obligation to the eldlerly. This may suggest euthanasia as *de rigeur* and a substitute for moral obligations that remain yet undefined.

Rutecki-Geib: A Biblical Approach to Rationing[4]

In this paper, the ultimate valuation or sanctity of human life was substantiated through God's four investments in mankind:[23] 1. Creation (Gen. 1:26-27); 2. Bankruptcy by sin necessitating redemption (Pet. 1:18-19); 3. Return to solvency: sanctification (2 Cor. 3:18; 4:4); 4. Ultimate profits: glorification (Rom. 8:28-30; 1 Cor. 15:45-49). In this context, life — elderly or otherwise — has an infinite value (1 Pet. 1:18-19). However, the authors note that other passages in the Bible seem to place relative degrees of value on persons and do take age into account during this valuation (esp. Lev. 27:1-8; Ps. 90:1-12). The authors attempt to bring scriptural truth to bear on this discrepancy of spiritual *vis a vis* existential valuation — through analogy. Scriptures cited for the application of analogy include: Lev. 25; Ps. 90 — both noting that biologic life depreciates in a fallen world, that biologic life ultimately belongs to God, not to individuals themselves, and that life is limited in length; Lev. 27:1-8 — age and functional worth seem to vary; Ecc. 12:1-8 — youth juxtaposed with old age reveals declining bodily function as expected with aging.

The authors' application of the scriptural analogies leads to the following conclusion: paradigms for rationing medical care to the elderly "seem essential since the use of money for the medical care of the elderly potentially compromises the care of those in younger and more functional age groups."[24] In retrospect, I think that the Bible intended these verses to furnish a perspective on the inevitability of aging and death in a fallen world. I no longer believe that they, by analogy or otherwise, are an indication for the rationing of medical care to the elderly. I would like to proceed to substantiate this later observation through the use of selected contemporary and corroborating statistics.

The average life span in this century has increased from 47 to 73 years. It is critical in this context, however, to note that maximum life span has not increased.[25] The change in the 47 to 73 year span represents rather progress in the elimination of early death, particularly in the neonate.

Minor, recent increases in longevity from age 75 to the early ninth decade are consistent with an asymptotic curve; further indefinite increases in survival and age are thus unrealistic. In aggregate, the scriptures used by Rutecki and Geib illustrate just such an asymptote of the inevitability of aging and death, not an indication in itself for rationing. The only way a leap may be made from the finite life expectancy remaining in the elderly to rationing is through further development of the concept of futility. Otherwise, age-based rationing would be discriminatory and inconsistent with justice. This last point will lead to Dr. Payne's counterpoint to the above biblical study.

Dr. Payne's Counterpoint to "Teach Us to Number Our Days" (Ps. 90:12)[5]

Dr. Payne's contention is straightforward and may be summarized: though age-based rationing itself is not biblical, rationing may be considered when it is based on the criteria of efficacy — futility.[26] This is a critical distinction and requires further discussion.

The concept of medical futility has been defined earlier. The value of this concept in ethical medical decision making is not only of recent vintage. A short but trenchant review of the application of futility in a Judeo-Christian world view perspective is essential to the further development of Dr. Payne's observations.

The Hippocratic tradition is comprised of both Hippocratic oath and other writings called the Hippocratic corpus. Ludwig Edelstein noted in his translation and commentary on the Hippocratic corpus that "prudent Greek physicians had an obligation not to treat incurable diseases" (futility).[27] The Hippocratic tradition is consistent with the Christian practice of medicine and as a starting point for our discussion should not be minimized, especially as it is applied to futility.[28]

In Jewish tradition, a stringently and explicityly pro-life tradition, the physician was told that he had no duty to treat *gesisah* (someone terminal who would die in less than 72 hours). Any attempt to cure such a person would be construed as an artificial impediment to death.[29]

Modern Christian traditions (Catholic: no extraordinary care, Protestant: do not prolong the dying process) are consistent with a philosophy to forego attempts at cure in futile situations.[30]

Finally, the President's Commission (1983) states that a physician is legally and ethically justified not to use futile care.[31]

Though Dr. Payne agrees that limitations in medical spending are a necessity, his conclusions drawn from this fact are different. He believes that care should be emphasized over cure; he suggests increased involvement of the church and family in providing scriptural approaches to terminal care. Finally, he would agree with conclusions of Rutecki and Geib on rationing if they were based on considerations of efficacy and futility. This conclusion offers us an insight into a scriptural and nondiscriminatory approach to rationing.

Synthesis: Rationing Medical Care

My revisit to rationing now reaches a conclusion similar to Payne's, *i.e.*, rationing is necessary and just but for reasons different than I first believed. In order for a rationing program directed towards the elderly to be just, it must have a sole foundation, *i.e.*, futility. Since the elderly have more futile care applied to them than almost any other group,[32] they will be affected by medical rationing more than others. However, limits to medical care will not be based on the discriminator of age but rather on a technology which does not provide meaningful survival. Major obstacles

to implementing a program such as this (rationing by futility) are two: pluralism in the contemporary consumer model of medicine and the ever-present danger of euthanasia.

Pluralism impacts a definition of futility more than any other contemporary impediment.[33] Since Callahan is correct in that there is no agreed upon *telos* for the aging process, the individual autonomy which leads to this conclusion also results in the impossibility of defining futility. What kind of care would be considered futile if 100 different people have 100 different conclusions as to what is acceptable life expectancy, quality of life, and access to an ever expanding array of unproven technology? Despite this lack of meaningful consensus, I would like to attempt an initial definition of futility in the elderly by looking at the application of three different medical interventions. This will include: the use of cardiopulmonary resuscitation in the elderly, dialysis intervention both acute and chronic, and finally the application of ICU outcome measures (*i.e.*, APACHE criteria).

Cardiopulmonary Resuscitation in the Elderly[34]

A recent controversial study identified cardiopulmonary resuscitation in the elderly as a futile undertaking. In fact, CPR was unsuccessful in all 68 patients in this study who were greater than age 70. These elderly patients underwent a total of 77 unsuccessful resuscitative efforts. Twenty-two of the 68 decedents who survived for 24 hours after the first attempt at CPR experienced burdens without

meaningful survival. Further studies such as these, particularly those that identify diseases which are associated with futile CPR[35] might identify the application of expensive interventions not associated with efficacy. This also brings us to the contemporary care in lieu of cure debate in medicine. In this study, did the staff attempting CPR discuss it as a futile endeavor prior to application? Did the staff allay significant fears and promise patients who did not want CPR that they would receive significant "quality of mercy" after a refusal? Did Christian staff pray with patients prior to and after a decision regarding CPR? These unanswered questions help us understand not only why futility has been so difficult to specifically define, but also that care is provided after cure is foregone demands substantial commitment.

The impact of just such an approach to CPR futility and DNR (do not resuscitate) orders may be empirically studied. Dr. Kanoti and associates at The Cleveland Clinic [36] implemented a well-defined" DNR policy January 1, 1988. The impact of this "ethically and legally responsibile policy change" decreased length of stay a median of 21 days. In 1989, this policy led to a total reduction in length of stay for Medicare patients of 1,911 days. The authors concluded that "appropriate use of a DNR policy not only provides quality care but also conserves medical resources."[37] In essence, the writing of DNR orders shifts terminal patients from cure to care treatment, decreases end of life futile and expensive interventions and is a just attempt at rationing.

Dialysis in the Elderly — Chronic and Acute

We have alluded previously to Daniel Callahan's limitation of elderly health care spending through the use of age-based criteria in the application of life support. I would like to expand that concept further with dialysis serving as one example of life support.

One construct for futility in the elderly has been postulated in the setting of acute renal failure complicating the course of a ruptured abdominal aortic aneurysm.[38] Age over 70 years in this specific setting was associated with 100% mortality. Further, no patient who developed positive blood cultures or had coma during their course survived. Finally, patients in this study who were not completely alert after three weeks of treatment all died. When Dr. Kjellstrand used these criteria in his patients, approximately 300 unnecessary treatment days were avoided without a change in mortal outcome. This provides another model in an attempt to define futility for the elderly.

However, Dr. Kjellstrand observed in other studies[39] that chronic dialysis in the elderly does not have such a dismal outcome. As mentioned previously life support application *per se* cannot be used as a criterion for rationing; rather the outcome or efficacy of that life support when used is critical.

The Use of the Acute Physiology and Chronic Health Evaluation (APACHE) in the Determination of Futility in the Subspecialty Practice of Nephrology

The APACHE II classification is based on 12 physiologic variables which are weighted according to deviation from normal ranges. These variants help define ICU accompaniments which predict a mortal outcome. A final score is calculated for each patient and then combined with a weighted score which takes into account the patient's age and other chronic diseases. The method has been developed in extensive multicenter studies which initially involved 13 hospitals and more than 5,800 patients.[40] The accuracy of the APACHE system in predicting death is remarkable. However, it is better at predicting those who will die than those who will live (low sensitivity and low negative predictive value).[41] For our purposes, however, the definition of futility requires greater accuracy in predicting death than in predicting life.

In one study, APACHE II criteria were used to evaluate the outcome of patients who required hemodialysis in an intensive care unit.[42] A "risk of death" was calculated for each patient in the study (n=100). The APACHE system correctly predicted the demise of patients who eventually died with 100% specificity regardless of what interventions were carried out.

Even though we may each have an aversion to predicting patient

survival through use of a computer data base, one cannot ignore the accuracy of the APACHE index in the context of the ICU nor the APACHE specificity in predicting mortality in high risk groups. These include the patients in whom cure oriented interventions are futile and increasingly expensive. Pluralism and autonomy may often lead to the application of just such expensive technology in these patients anyway, but this is exactly the reason why futility becomes the only just way to implement rationing. The APACHE II criteria may be applied to the elderly in the ICU and obviate the need for expensive life-prolonging therapy that provides no benefit by such an empirically documented system.

It is my intention that these three examples initiate a dialogue about the necessity for an accepted definition of futility. I have tried to be more specific, pragmatic, and empirically grounded than Callahan. At a minimum, I believe that a definition of futility is possible if American society can reach a just consensus.

Concluding Comments

A definition of futility in terminal patients will lead to one of two disparate attitudes in the community in which such patients die. These attitudes will either resemble on of two possible responses already practied in the European community. Those dying in Great Britain access a hospice system which cares for them and does not in any way accelerate the dying process.[43] However, the dying in Holland access a system of voluntary euthanasia which offers acceleration of dying rather than care. Even if rationing is applied justly based on futility, I still fear that the community response to the terminal in American will tend towards voluntary euthanasia in lieu of care. This tendency is a concern Callahan shares as he describes the lack of consensus in America with regard to the aging and dying only through an increase in hospice presence. The debate must address when it is appropriate to change from cure to care. This is the only viable alternative to euthanasia. Christians must illuminate a theology of medicine which realizes ultimate cure comes only through Jesus Christ and is only realized at the resurrection of the body. Until then, medicine cannot indefinitely prolong life. Christians should understand that a belief in futility is consistent with Biblical constructs. Lastly, Christians must do all they can to combat the practice of medicine as technique modeled on autonomy and consumerism. These models lead to a misapplication of medical technologies and makes medicine an idol and a religion in and of itself.

Endnotes

1. Callahan, D., **Setting Limits: Medical Goals in an Aging Society**. Simon and Schuster, Inc., 1987, p.61.
2. Binstock, R.H and Post, S.G., (ed.), **Too Old for Health Care? Controversies in Medicine, Law, Economics, and Ethics**. Johns Hopkins University Press, 1991, p. 5.
3. *op. cit.*, Callahan, D., 1987.

4. Rutecki, GW, and Geib, J.D., "Teach Us to Number Our Days" (Ps. 90:12): Age and the Rationing of Medical Care. Use of a Biblical Valuation of Personhood." *Journal of Biblical Ethics in Medicine*, 1992, Vol. 6, pp. 95-102.
5. Payne, F.E., Jr., Counterpoint to Teach Us to Number Our Days (Ps. 90:12), *Journal of Biblical Ethics in Medicine*, 1992, Vol. 6, pp. 102-104.
6. Silversides, A., Oregon Tackles the Health Care Rationing Issue, *Can. Med. Assoc. J.*, 1990, Vol. 143. p. 545.
7. Schelling, J.R., and Linas, S.L., Hepato-renal Syndrome, *Sem. in Nephrol.*, 1990, pp. 565-570.
8. Steinbrook, R., and Lo, B., The Oregon Medicaid Demonstration Project — Will It Provide Adequate Medical Care?, *N Engl. J. Med.*, 1992, Vol. 326, p. 341.
9. *ibid.*, Steinbrook, R., Lo, B., 1992, p. 341.
10. Morganshore, T., with Hager, M., Cutting Through the Gobbledegook, *Newsweek*, Feb. 3, 1992, pp. 24-25.
11. Mills, C., The Graying of America, *Rep. Inst. Philos. Public Policy*, 1988, Vol. 8., pp. 1-5.
12. Lubitz, J., and Priboda, R., The Use and Costs of Medicare Services in the Last Two Years of Life, *Health Care Financing*, 1984, Vol. 5, pp. 117-131.
13. *op. cit.*, Rutecki, G.W. and Geib, J.D., 1992, p. 95.
14. *op. cit.*, Callahan, D., 1987, p. 54.
15. *op. cit.*, Callahan., D., 1987, p. 15.
16. *op. cit.*, Callahan, D., 1987, pp. 32, 53, 59.
17. *op. cit.*, Callahan, D., 1987, p. 116.
18. *op. cit.*, Callahan, D., 1987, p. 116.
19. Gornick, C.C. and Kjellstrand, C.M., Acute Renal Failure

Complicating Aortic Aneurysm Surgery, *Nephron*, 1983, Vol. 35, pp. 145-157. Also, Husebye, D.G., Westlie, L., and Styrvoky, T.V., and Kjellstrand, C.M., Psychological, Social and Somatic Prognostic Indicators in Old Patients Undergoing Long Term Dialysis, *Arch. Int. Med.*, 1987, Vol. 146, pp. 1921-1924.
20. *op.cit.*, Callahan, D., 1987, p. 86.
21. *op.cit.*, Callahan, D., 1987, p. 97.
22. May, W.F. in **Theological Voices in Medical Ethics**, Wm. B. Eerdmans, 1993, p. 254.
23. *op.cit.*, Rutecki, G.W. and Geib, J.D., 1992, p. 97.
24. *op.cit.*, Rutecki, G.W., and Geib, J.D., 1992, p. 99.
25. Fries, J.F. Aging, Natural Death and the Compression of Morbidity, *N. Engl. J. Med.*, 1980, Vol. 303, pp. 130-135.
26. *op.cit.*, Payne, F.E., 1992, p. 104.
27. Temkin, O., Temking C.L. (eds.), **Ancient Medicine: Selected Papers of Ludwig Edelstein**, Johns Hopkins Press, 1967, pp. 96-98.
28. Cameron, N.M., deS., **The New Medicine**, Crossway Books, 1991.
29. Feldman, D.M., Rosner F. (eds.) in **Compendium on Jewish Medical Ethics: Jewish Moral, Ethical and Religious Principles in Medical Practice**, 6th ed., Fed. of Jewish Philanth. of NY, Inc., p. 101.
30. Lantos, J.D., Singer, P.A., and Walker, R.M., *et al.*, The Illusion of Futility in Clinical Practice, *Am. J. Med.*, 1989, Vol. 87, p. 82.
31. **President's Commision for the Study of Ethical Problems in Medicine and Biomedical and Behavioral Research: Deciding to Forego Life Sustaining Treatment**, Washington, U.S. Printing Office, March, 1983, p. 219.
32. Some may juxtapose AIDS with the elderly in regards to futile

interventions. The volume of elderly still exceeds those with end-stage HIV infection.

33. The majority of contemporary medical ethicists believe that futility is impossible to define. I provide a sample: Lantos, J.D., Singer, P.A., Walker, R.M., *et al.*, *op. cit.*, pp. 81-84, Youngerner, S.J., Who Defines Futility? *JAMA,* 1988, Vol. 260, pp. 2094-2095, Truoy, R.D., Brett, A.S., and Frader, J., The Problem with Futility. *N. Engl. J. Med.*, 1992, Vol. 326, pp. 1560-1564.

34. Taffett, G.E., Teasdale, T.A., and Luchi, R.J., in Hospital Cardiopulmonary Resuscitation, *JAMA,* 1988, Vol. 260, pp. 2069-2072.

35. George, A.L., Folk, B.P., Crecelius, P.L., *et al.*, Pre-arrest Morbidity and Other Correlates of Survival After In-Hospital cardiopulmonary Arrest, *Am.J. Med,* 1989, Vol. 87, pp. 28-34.

36. Kanoti, G.A., Gombeski, W.R., and Gulledge, A.D., *et al.*, The effect of do not resuscitate orders on length of stay. *Cleveland Clinic Journal of Medicine,* 1992, Vol. 59, pp. 591-594.

37. *Ibid.* Kanoti, G.A., Gombeski, W.R., Gulledge, A.D., *et al.*, 1992, p. 594.

38. *Op.cit.*, Gornick, C.C., Kjellstrand, C.M., 1983, pp. 145-157.

39. *Op.cit.*, Husebye, D.G., Westlie, L., Styvoky, T.J., Kjellstrand, C.M., 1987, pp. 1921-1924.

40. Knaus, W.A., Draper, E.A., Wagner, D.P., *et al.*, APACHE II: A Severity of Disease Classification System, *Crit Care Med.*. 1985, Vol. 13, pp. 818-829.

41. Dobkin, J.E., Cutler, R.E., Use of APACHE II Classification to Evaluate Outcome of Patients Receiving Hemodialysis in an Intensive Care Unit, *The Eastern Journal of Medicine,* 1988, Vol. 149, p. 542.

42. *Ibid.*, Dobkin, J.E., et al., 1988, pp. 547-550.

43. Twycross, R.G., Hospice Care -- Redressing the Balance in Medicine, *The Royal Soc. of Med.*, 1980, Vol. 73, pp. 475-481.

Editor's Note

Several months ago I attended a two day seminar on the diagnosis and treatment of alcoholism and drug addictions. I looked forward to it about as much as to extraction of impacted wisdom teeth. Nevertheless, it is supposed to be helpful to expose yourself periodically to opposing points of view. If you are not changed, you at least know your opponent better. One of the speakers was relating her method of teaching those troglodytes who do not believe that alcoholism is a disease, despite decades of propaganda to establish it as a fact. She tells her charges, "For the next six weeks, *act* as though you believe it is a disease." You "kind of con them," she says, into the "proper" belief by having them first act as if they believe it.

Alas! Her advice exposes an ailing epistemology that also afflicts the Church. It assumes that the pathway to a true understanding is *experiential*. The position that experience is ultimately the best teacher is certainly a *possible* one, but it is not a *necessary* one. But, is it right to "con" someone at the level of epistemology? While experience is crucial to our understanding, experience must begin with some presuppositions, some axioms, a place from which to begin. A Christian would assert that the Bible is, by faith [i.e., presuppositionally], true. Our experience is thereafter *interpreted by* the Scripture. It is not the other way around. We do not interpret the Bible in the "light" of our experience. Experience may exemplify Scripture's truth, but it cannot "prove" or buttress it. If our individual experience *proves* Scripture, then we are implicitly presupposing that our experience is superior to Scripture in validity.

A Christian should be "up front" with the confession of a presupposition that the Scripture is true and is the objective measuring device for experience. Such a confession allows other persons to opt out of further conversation on the basis of non-agreement with the Bible. Some Christians see that option exercised by others so often that they want to conceal their foundation. It doesn't seem to "work" in evangelism. "You don't have to hit them [unbelievers] in the face with Scripture," they say. What, however, is gained by "soul-winning" which cons unbelievers into repeating word formulas without a clear grasp of the elements of salvation? Is this one reason that the Church in American today, despite decades of reports of marvelously successful evangelistic campaigns, has produced but a minor effect on the nation's course away from God?

The ubiquitous lapel pin which reads "Try Jesus" suggests an experiential approach to the Gospel. Certainly, the gospel can and needs to be experienced in the individual life. Yet, making the objective truth of the gospel submit to a subjective test of experience -- an experience not interpreted by Scripture -- is wrong. A person who does that remains presuppositionally committed to the veracity of his own experience; he is actually encouraged to canonize his experience. A person who is confronted with the gospel truth proclaimed as ultimate truth has to make the decision about axioms at the beginning of any relationship to the Word made flesh. That is where the decision needs to be made, since it is a watershed issue. A Church composed of "believers" who unwittingly canonize their own experiences should not be surprised at members who do not accept parts of the Scripture, or who "interpret" it in bizarre, erroneous ways.

Returning briefly to alcoholism, it is the same issue. Chronic drunkenness has been first determined to be a disease. Following upon that determination, all the studies, "evidence," and teaching is organized around the faith position that it is a true disease. To try to discuss the concept itself that alcoholism is a disease is to find oneself quickly ruled off the playing field. Needless to say, I was quickly relegated to the seminar sidelines for introducing the quaint believe that morality played the significant role. The seminar proceeded on smoothly with diagnostic and treatment methodology, process blithely preempting propriety. If you are not conned, then you are not convenient to the further purposes of the group of believers.

The Case Against the Use of Oral Contraceptives

Richard O. Schamp, M.D., Alan L. McGaughran, M.D., Stanley Lang, M.D., and Paul F. Doughty, D.O.

The authors practice together in the Agape Family Health Center in DuBois, Pennsylvania. The article comprises the text of a patient information brochure used in the Center. Following is a postscript giving a sketch of the practitioners' pathway to this position.

The Birth Control Pill

After study and prayer, the physicians of Agape Family Health Center have concluded that we will stop the routine prescription of oral contraceptives (birth control pills) effective July 1, 1993.

Introduction

The use of the birth control pill gained rapid and widespread acceptance in the 1960's and 1970's. This acceptance marked (and promoted) a major change in our culture, which few persons have realized. For the first time in human history, it became much more possible to separate the act of sex and the process of reproduction. Pleasure, even among the married, has become the main (and in many cases the only) reason for sex. The fundamental relationship of sex to reproduction has often become only an unwanted side effect.

Physicians, and the public at large were won over to the use of the Pill by a variety of reasons. One reason was the "lesser of two evils" idea. That idea reasoned that prevention of an unwanted pregnancy was better than abortion. However, the rate of abortion has closely paralled the use of oral contraceptives. Now we know that contraception and abortions are closely linked philosophically, psychologically and in biological ways. The widespread cultural acceptance of the Pill mentally denies the great and unchanging truth that children are a blessing from God.

The "good" that was hoped for has become overwhelmed by the negative aspects of the Pill and the related anti-child philosophy. Few plausible reasons remain for its use.

Basic Physiology: Definitions

Ovulation — the release of an egg (ovum) by a woman's ovary, normally in her reproductive cycle.

Fallopian tube — the part of the uterus that reaches around the ovary and through which the egg must travel to reach the uterine cavity. Most pregnancies are conceived while the egg is in the tube.

Fertilization — when an egg is joined with a single sperm and an embryo results. This is considered by scientists and the courts as the beginning of life.

Implantation — when an embryo implants within the lining of the uterus and develops a sac, placenta and blood supply.

Breakthrough Ovulation — when egg production is not inhibited by the Pill

Endometrium — the lining of the uterus.

A normal woman produces an egg in the middle of her reproductive cycle, about two weeks after her menstrual period starts. Her bodily changes allow only a few days during which fertilization of this egg can occur. The birth control pill changes this normal pattern in several ways: by stopping ovulation, reducing transport through the Fallopian tube, creating an unfavorable endometrial lining and by changing the cervical mucus. We discuss each of these changes below.

Inhibiting Ovulation

The original intention for the birth control pill was to inhibit ovulation, or the release of an egg (ovum) by a woman in her reproductive cycle. The original Pill contained high doses of hormones and prevented ovulation rather well. During the

1960's, a medium dose (now considered a high dose) was used widely because the higher doses had too many side-effects. Most birth control pills today are a combination of two hormones with varying strengths and potencies.

If ovulation is not completely prevented, then fertilization (thus, pregnancy) is possible. Over the last 30 years, studies have shown that "breakthrough" ovulation rates are 2 - 10%. This assumes that no pills are forgotten or skipped. If a pill is missed, then chances of breakthrough ovulation are higher. Many common medications, such as antibiotics, can further decrease the Pill's effectiveness in preventing ovulation.

Ovulation can be detected both by direct and indiret methods. The most obvious way to detect breakthrough ovulation is when someone gets pregnant while "on the Pill." This rate is commonly accepted to be 1-2 pregnancies per 100 woman-years (100 women taking the Pill continuously for one year).

Another way to detect breakthrough ovulation is the direct observation of an empty egg sac on an ovary of someone taking the pill. This has been observed on many occasions. Using ultrasound (sonograms), researchers can demonstrate the developing follicle (sac that holds an egg before release) and concluded that up to 4% of these release their eggs in spite of taking (low dose) birth control pills.

The "mini-pill" was popular for a while, but has been mostly abandoned. It had breakthrough ovulation rates of about 14%. This pill contained only a single type of hormone, much like the newer method, the implantable hormone called Norplant. Depo-Provera is a once-a-month shot of a similar hormone, with similar effects.

The original goal of the birth control pill was to prevent pregnancy by stopping egg production. However, in some cases, it may also prevent pregnancy by one of the following methods.

Tubal Transport Effects

Hormonal contraceptives slow down the transport of an embryo or egg in the fallopian tube. This can cause the egg or embryo to "dry out" and die.

Endometrial Effects

The Pill has several other known effects, even in the more recent "low dose" forms. One effect is the prevention of implantation. The Pill affects the lining of the uterus in such a way that makes it unfavorable for a fertilized egg to implant and continue its normal development.

These two effects (tubal effect and endometrial changes) mean that an egg is produced and fertilized but is then not allowed to develop normally. This is the same as a very early abortion.

Cervical Mucus Changes

The mucus that is normally present in a woman's cervix goes through predictable changes in a normal cycle. The mucus normally becomes thin and stretchy at the time of ovulation. This allows the passage of sperm at the time of intercourse. This natural effect inreases the chance of becoming pregnant. The birth control pill causes this mucus to remain sticky and thick, being somewhat of a barrier to sperm. However, it is clear that sperm can get through anyway in some cases.

Side Effects

The list of side effects for the birth control pill is very long. Some side-effects are not dangerous at all, and some are life-threatening. Nearly all of the physical side-effects are related to the change from the natural function of a woman's body. Very often, the false assurance gained by the pill leads to sexually transmitted diseases.

Emotional side effects occur in some women with the change in hormone balance. This can be very disturbing to her or her family. We have observed many women seem relieved when they stop taking the pill. They convey a sense of guilt often, even if they have not "felt" guilty before then. Many have an uneasy feeling about the unnatural things that occur when taking the pill.

The Pill is often associated with promiscuity. When this is true, spiritual side effects also happen. Shame, poor self image and rebellion can poison a woman's spiritual life.

Conclusions

Outside of real medical uses, the birth control pill plays a big role in an anti-child philosophy. It is closely related to the abortion philosophy and does actually cause early abortions in some cases. The Pill promotes sexual activity for pleasure alone. It often encourages irresponsible or promiscuous sexual activity. The Pill is very unnatural and has many side-effects.

These values represented by the birth control pill are unbiblical and mostly immoral.

Recommendations

Contraception should not be a medical issue. It is a family issue, decided by mutual family values. Rare is the medical need for the birth control pill.

Some other forms of birth control (besides the Pill) are also not recommended. These forms are likewise considered to cause abortion. They include the intra-uterine deviceds (IUD), the new French pill (RU-486) and the so-called "morning after" pill.

We can recommend certain methods of birth control. We will give you specific information about these methods if you desire. In general, these options can be divided into barrier methods and abstinence methods.

Barrier methods use a condom, sponge, diaphragm or some other barrier to prevent passage of sperm into the uterus. These barriers are much more effective if used with a spermicide jelly or cream.

The recommended abstinence method is Natural Family Planning. This is a scientific way for a woman to determine when her egg is produced. Then she can avoid intercourse for a few days to prevent pregnancy. This requires an informed and willing husband. This method produces a lot of satisfaction for couples who use it. It should not be confused with the "rhythm" or "calendar" methods. We are fortunate to have excellent certified instructors available locally who can teach you the Natural Family Planning method. Please ask us for more information if you are interested.

We hope you understand our reasons for not prescribing the birth control pill and we invite your questions if you need further explanation.

A postscript re: "The Case Against the Use of Oral Contraceptives"

Our journey to our present position, which proscribes the use of birth control pills for non-medical purposes, has been a long and prayerful expedition. We do not judge any patient or physician who disagrees with our conclusions. Yet silence on the subject, once concluded, serves no one. We emphasize the following points:

* Our initial goal was to achieve a unity in our practice about this issue, believing such would be a watershed issue, and set the stage for future growth in understanding bioethics applied to medicine in general and our practice in particular.

* Some of us have been struggling with this for over ten years.

* One of us (Alan) made his decision first, upon joining the practice. This, in effect, gave the rest of us permission (encouragement) to reconsider the issue which had been ignored by reason of "busyness," ignorance, convenience, or fear.

* The published data are clear. See especially NEJM, 5/27/93.

* If we are right, then Christian or pro-life physicians everywhere should reconsider this issue and pray for wisdom about what to do and then pray for courage to do it.

Pastor's Column

Aging

The Reverend Byron Snapp

Rev. Snapp holds a B.A. from King College and an M. Div. from Reformed Theological Seminary. He is assistant pastor of Covenant Presbyterian Church and principal of Covenant Christian School in Cedar Bluff, Virgina.

The inspired Paul was exactly right. "The last enemy that will be destroyed is death." (I Cor. 15:26) Unless one is alive when the Lord returns, the individual can be assured that his physical body will one day face death and lose.

However, we live in a culture that does not want to face the thought of death. There are several reasons for this avoidance. First, many are not prepared to face God. Hebrews 10:27 teaches us that men die once and then face judgment. If men can avoid thinking about death then they can better avoid the thought of facing a holy God. I believe this is one reason that our culture demands extraordinary means to preserve life (except for the unborn humans). Respirators, tubes, expensive surgery, monitors, etc., all seemingly postpone the inevitable death and life on death's other side.

Secondly, death is often hidden from the living. In previous generations people generally died in a home of family members. Death was hard to avoid as relatives had to tend to the needs of the dying. The pain and effects of approaching death upon the physical body were clearly evident. Even children could not escape seeing death's advance upon its prey.

Today our culture is quite different. The dying are often in a hospital room. They are nursed by their closest family members and the hospital's nursing staff. As death makes its final advance often family and friends are ushered out of the room so they are not confronted with death's victory over one's physical life. Thus, one can go through life without seeing death firsthand.

Thirdly, the thought of death is often suppressed because death is abnormal. Man was created to live and bring glory to God. Adam's sin which was in God's eternal plan, resulted in death, physical and spiritual, coming on all of Adam's descendants. Thus, that which is abnormal to the body became a normal part of life. Man is conceived in sin and thereby spiritually separated from God. Man also faces physical death — the separation of the body from the soul.

Fourthly, man takes little thought of death because he lives in the present. He is alive now. Tomorrow often does not matter today. To keep the present longer, man will go to great expense to look youthful. In and of itself looking youthful is not wrong. At the same time "youthful" man will often continue to be involved in unhealthy lifestyles at work and at meals that lead to stress and overweight. These along with immoral lifestyles can lead to medical problems and, humanly speaking, hasten death's approach.

For these and other reasons man is often unprepared for debilitating illnesses that result in life's slow ebb. Therefore it is important for those in and out of the medical profession to give some thought to preparing for this time in life.

First, one must realize that spiritual death is worse than physical death. To prepare for one's physical death it is important that the individual confront spiritual realities. Without God-given repentance and faith, man will end up in hell on death's other side. The inspired writer's words need to be taken to heart, "Remember now your Creator in the days of your youth before the difficult days come." (Eccl. 12:10a) If one does not make peace with God in youth, hearts often become hardened as the years go by.

Christian medical personnel can often minister spiritually when giving a patient a diagnosis of a terminal illness. If the doctor is unsure of the patient's salvation, it is a good time to ask, "Are you ready to meet God?"

I know such a question goes against the grain of cultural thinking. Sadly, relatives often want to keep the thought of approaching death away from the terminally ill. Death must be faced however. God may use this pointed question and your accompanying ministry in a saving way.

In ministering to younger patients, doctors are also to minister to the whole person. You may see signs of a lifestyle or bad habits that can hasten debilitating illness. You have a duty not only to treat the person physically but also to minister spiritually by pointing out the effects of the lifestyle on one's body. Offer the preventative medicine set forth in Scripture — that of the importance of turning away from sin and turning to God. This involves replacing sinful habits with godly practice.

At the report of a terminal illness to a Christian, the Christian needs to be assured of God's promises such as Rom. 8:28, "And we know that all things work together for good to those who love God, to those who are the called according to His purpose." Second Corinthians 4:16-18 is also important, "Therefore we do not lose heart; even though our outward man is perishing, the inward man is being renewed day by day. For our light affliction, which is but for a moment, is working for us a far more exceeding and eternal weight of glory; while we do not look at things which are seen, for the things which are seen are temporal, but the things which are not seen are eternal."

Another approach may well be to remind the patient of God's tender mercies. When deadly illness comes as a sudden onslaught an unprepared individual may have no time to take care of important business in life — reconciliation with God and/or with relatives, the disposal of possessions, and reflecting on one's life. Although fatal illnesses are no fun, their slow work provides time for any necessary decisions to be made.

Spiritual matters can also be approached by having a tract or booklet that Biblically explains the Gospel to hand out to the patient along with literature on the deadly disease. The patient may well read the spiritual material and reflect on it when he/she will not readily talk to you about it. Why not include some good Christian booklets on worry, anxiety, salvation, etc., in your waiting room reading material? You may be surprised how often this material has to be replaced because they are taken for further study by the sick who are suddenly open to spiritual matters.

Your spouse can have a part in this ministry by seeing that the tracts and booklets are replaced when needed. Also, wives may need to needlework of appropriate Scripture verses to be displayed in the rooms where patients wait for you to enter.

This waiting can be agonizing whether or not one is deathly ill. God may well use these verses to get the patient's attention regarding spiritual matters. You may well call attention to these verses in your conversations with patients.

This ministry cannot be had if word of debilitating illness is left for a nurse to deliver by phone to a patient. From a layman's viewpoint I cannot stress enough the importance of a doctor's delivering a displeasing test result to the ill. This is particularly true for those who have no family members with them at the time the report is given.

I have spent much time on the first step one needs to take when confronting a debilitating illness. The importance of this first step cannot be overly stressed. It has eternal consequences. Christian doctors can often be on the front lines of ministry in these situations. Never forget that one's ministry is to the whole man, not just the physical aspect.

Other preparations that need to be made for the possible approach of wasting diseases will be covered in a future article.

Editor's Note

In this issue is an editorial by Dr. Jane Orient, who is editor of the newsletter of the Association of American Physicians and Surgeons. She is vitally interested in the ethics of contracting for medical care, and her concern and action are not abstract, but real and risky. the ability of adults to enter into contracts with other adults is a basic requisite to fulfilling our obligations before God. [Prov. 6:1; 17:18; 22:26; Acts 5:4; Matt: 26:9; etc.] There are certain forms to which the civil magistrate may require contracts to adhere since it is often the magistrate who will be called to adjudicate disputes arising out of contracts. The contracts need to be clear. Also, the civil magistrate may not assist in the enforcement of contracts to perform otherwise illegal acts, such as prostitution (except in Nevada) since it is the magistrate's duty to sanction such actions. Beyond limitations of this sort, however, people need to be free to contract with each other, to their mutual improvement, as adjudged by each for himself. It is frequently necessary for us to enter into contracts in order to fulfill our duties toward God and our fellow man. [Matt. 20:3]

Keeping the temple of the Holy Spirit is one duty Christians have before God. From time to time, there may arise problems with the body which the person lacks either the ability or the knowledge to perform. It may range from looking into the ear canal, which is very difficult to do on one's self, to performing abdominal surgery, which is nearly impossible to do on one's self, even if one knows how to do it. The individual must then seek out help. We need to contract with a physician.

The fact that human beings are a folding together of body and spirit makes it important to consider the influence of the spirit upon illness and treatment. Medical care is intrinsically a spiritual activity. What one believes in one's spirit -- about what is true, about the nature of the physical world, about how and why illness comes, and so on -- will influence the choice of an approach to healing. [Amos 3:3] The ill person, then, will want to select a practitioner whose spiritual orientation and beliefs are most in accord with his own, if possible. What has happened with Medicare is a preview of what is impending for all Americans. Medicare "beneficiaries" are no longer legally able to choose a practitioner who is free. The civil government now implicitly but powerfully inserts into every contract between a Medicare patient and physician a lengthy, obtuse set of contractual provisions which neither party to the contract may escape. It is misleading for patients to be told that they are free to choose their own doctor, if the doctor is not free to practice as he believes is best.

In the Medicare system, the *price* is set, meaning that the physician is not free to offer for sale to the patient any service for which the government is unwilling to pay the cost of. It is glib to think that a physician may just charitably give away the service *ad infinitum*. Unless the physician has some other source of income, that will not be long possible. About half of the cost of physician services are actually covering direct costs that the physician must pay. The *services* are set, meaning that they may not contract to provide services in a way which the government has decided is not proper. It doesn't matter if the patient and physician think otherwise. The *privacy* of the patient is violated. If patients were but aware of all the people who get to know their medical business as a result of the government entry into their medical care, they'd be appalled. The *definition* of medical care is dictated. If a patient and physician are agreed that there is a significant spiritual aspect to either the illness or its management, the government has determined such discussions to be outside of the purview of medicine, and will impede free contracting between the patient and physician in pursuing the benefits of their common understanding. There is no CPT code for biblical counseling known to me.

Dr. Orient has decided that the freedom of contract is so important that she is willing to risk the sanctions of the civil government. Her agreement with her patients is a tool by which they may be taught that their freedom to contract has been surreptitiously taken away from them. The handwriting on the wall is clear enough for her to read aloud. Will her patients heed the warning?

On Private Contracting

Jane Orient, M.D.

This editorial is reprinted by permission from the AAPS News, Vol. 49, October, 1993, the newsletter of the Association of American Physicians and Surgeons (AAPS), of which Dr. Orient is the editor. Dr. Orient is in the private practice of internal medicine in Tucson, Arizona.

Many questions come to the AAPS office regarding the issue of contracting privately with Medicare-eligible patients, especially after recent articles concerning Stewart v. Sullivan. In addition, there is escalating intimidation. Here is one letter a physician received from a carrier:

This letter is in regards [sic] to beneficiary agreements not to use Medicare coverage.

"Some physicians are requiring Medicare Part B beneficiaries, as a condition of acceptance for or continuation of treatment, to enter into agreements with the physician not to use their Medicare coverage.

The Medicare law does not exclude services from coverage or physicians from Medicare requirements on basis [sic] of such agreements. In enacting the provisions for Medicare coverage of physician services and the Limiting Charge, Claims Submission, and other requirements that apply to physicians, Congress clearly intended that Medicare beneficiaries should be able to use their Medicare coverage and physicians who treat beneficiaries should comply with the specified statutory requirements. We view agreements of the kind described as contrary to the public policy of the United States as reflected in those provisions, and as therefore invalid. All Medicare requirements with respect to physician services continue to apply, and Medicare payment may be made to beneficiaries for covered services, not withstanding [sic] these agreements.

Violations of these requirements are generally subject to sanctions, including civil monetary penalties and/or exclusion from the Medicare program.

Thus, if a Medicare beneficiary disregards his agreement and complains to the Medicare carrier about the failure of the physician to submit claims, or submits his own claims, the physician may be subject to possible civil penalties for such failure.

If you have any questions, regarding this correspondence, please call us at (number given)."

(signed), Senior Supervisor, Program Monitoring

Editorial

I do have some questions:

Is it the "public policy of the United States" to encourage citizens to violate contracts and to rupture the patient-physician relationship?

Does the "public policy of the United States" as enunciated by this Senior Supervisor have the force of law? Can such statements by any public official be used as the basis for depriving persons of their liberty and property?

Has the Medicare program become an involuntary one for physicians and patients, rather than a voluntary one, despite assertions by Congress and the Courts?

Does "should be able to use" their coverage mean *must* use their coverage?

Your editor has not asked these questions of [this Senior Supervisor]. To paraphrase George Bernard Shaw, "to ask the question is to answer it." Furthermore, it is the editor's opinion that all public agencies should use the disclaimer cited by employees of the Arizona Revenue Service every time they answer a question, to the effect that the agency is not bound by the answer.

Your editor, along with other physicians and patients, has declared independence from the Medicare program. Contracts are based on consideration; we accept no consideration from the Medicare program. In our opinion, one becomes subject to the requirements of Medicare upon submitting a claim. One must submit a claim if one provides a covered service to a Medicare beneficiary. We provide noncovered services to non-Medicare beneficiaries.

As [the Senior Supervisor] correctly declares, a piece of paper does not exempt a person from compliance with the law. However, an assertion by a public official does not constitute law. There is no law that *requires* a Medicare-eligible patient to take advantage of his entitlement and thus become a beneficiary, and no law that *forces* a physician to accept a patient who wishes to take advantage of that entitlement. Patients are by law free to decide whether or not to accept their benefits and to consult any willing physician. (HHS encourages them to see a "participating provider;" nearly 60% of physicians "participate.")

The Health Care Financing Administration has declared physicians to be second-class citizens in refusing to recognize our legal right to enforce a contract. Likewise, Medicare-eligible persons, in the eyes of HCFA, are like minors — they are not able to enter a legally-binding contract. If a Medicare-eligible patient asks for our services and agrees to pay for them, and then renounces his agreement, we probably have no legal recourse.

In fact, we may be well advised to refund any payment in an effort to avoid administrative penalties. Our only protection is the patients' morals. If is always possible that our government will choose to make an example of us, attempting to defame or bankrupt us, even if the law is on our side.

I have drafted the following statement for my patients:

I, _____, do solemnly affirm upon my sacred word of honor that I am consulting Dr. Orient as a patient and not as a government informer. The medical history that I give is true and is presented for the sole purpose of obtaining medical counsel and treatment. Specifically, my history is not contrived for the purpose of entrapping Dr. Orient into prescribing a drug, treatment, or diagnostic test that is unnecessary, not indicated, or in possible violation of a government regulation.

Furthermore, I affirm that I am of sound mind and capable of making decisions for myself regarding my medical, financial, and general well-being. I promise that I will not enter any agreement, written or oral, with Dr. Orient if I consider that agreement to be to my disadvantage. I will not pay her any amount that I believe to be unreasonable or unjust. If I later regret a decision for any reason, I will speak directly to Dr. Orient herself.

If I keep my word faithfully, may I enjoy my life and prosper, respected by all men and in all times; but if I swerve from it or violate it, may the reverse be my lot.

I do hereby enjoin any person purporting to represent me to refrain from any action that, if undertaken by me personally, would dishonor my word.

Signed _____ this _____ day of _____, 19__. Witnessed by God and _____.

I recognize that I am at risk. My colleagues and this Association might or might not be willing or able to come to my aid if the government attacks me. I have become particularly wary of any patient who lists a government agency as his employer. Distrust works both ways, and it is possible I will offend some patients. But the purpose of the above agreement is not so much to protect myself (today, there are no guaranteed legal protections) as to educate patients about how far we have moved in the direction of tyranny.

Those interested in knowing more about the Association of American Physicians and Surgeons may write: AAPS, 1601 N. Tucson Blvd., Suite 9, Tucson, AZ, 85716, or phone (800) 635-1196.

Big Brother with a Black Bag:
Four Non-Superficial Flaws of TennCare and the Nationalized Health Care Plan
Rev. David W. Hall

Mr. Hall is pastor of Covenant Presbyterian Church in Oak Ridge, Tennessee.

On November 19, 1993, the state of Tennessee, not always identified with the vanguard of medical science, made headlines in the *Washington Post* for its leading role in health care reform. Along with the states of California and Vermont, Tennessee (hereafter TN) is on the leading edge of health care reform even ahead of the national plans recently introduced by the President. As most are aware, health care reform will be one of the larger and most discussed items in 1994, and possibly the most far-reaching if approved. If, as reported, some 37 million Americans are damaged in their health because of legislative negligence then indeed many will support a plan for improved health. However, if that estimate proves dramatically lower,[1] or if non-surface flaws of such health care proposals come to light, then the American people may genuinely desire to avoid the lemming lurch to socialized medicine, even in the face of unrivalled hype about a fabricated "crisis."

It is possible that the estimates are as exaggerated as other recent epidemics,[2] and also that there are clear defects in the plans, which flaws cannot be cured by ever so much adjustment, amendment, or fine-tuning. If the health care proposals before us in the coming year are warmed over socialisms of the 60's, or more of the type of plans attempted but even now being jettisoned in Sweden, or if they are fundamentally, philosophically, and irrevocably flawed, then they could realistically violate the first part of the Hippocratic Oath: First do no harm. If such plans are more harmful than helpful, then indeed we can argue that we would be better off doing nothing, rather than creating more harm, be it ever so well-intentioned.

It may even be that we would be far better simply leaving health care alone, since it has worked quite well when arranged between non-governmental parties, instead of creating a new super-bureaucracy to manage our health. It might be better to identify and subsidize the truly needy (likely about 5 million) and provide them a Cadillac policy for $5,000 a year. According to such a direct approach at remediating a single issue, a mere $25 billion expenditure would suffice, helping to cure our national debt, since health care expense is purportedly the real barrier to budget balancing. Such $25 billion annual expenditure would cost less than 10% of the Defense budget, or we could cancel some foreign grants, or eliminate a few outdated expenditures, allowing us to then care for the disadvantaged, as well as be on the way to curing the deficit, if those were all we really wanted to accomplish. Yet, as such simple solutions are eschewed, it becomes apparent that larger political goals are the real driving forces behind present health care reform, not the actual amelioration of those in need; for all the while, numerous other economical and sensible plans to genuinely remedy the uninsured are rejected.

> "This plan is in all probability a pioneer for the version of nationalized health care..."

Tennessee has become one of the leaders in health care reform, winning modified approval from Health and Human Services (HHS) to begin TennCare in January of 1994 to replace its state medicare. This plan is in all probability a pioneer for the version of nationalized health care that eventually will be put forth for legislation. One of the difficulties in analyzing the national plan, supposedly clear in the minds of the 500-plus secret planners, is that no clear plan is ever presented long enough to weather criticism. As soon as a plan is announced it is criticized and the administration denies that the plan is really the health care plan it will present. It is indeed difficult to assess or tarnish phantom plans, which factor, of course, some crafty administration would exploit.

In an effort to assist some who wish to go beyond phantom-cum-incorrigible plans, emotion, horror stories, scare tactics, or crises by exaggeration, I would like to put forward a critique of TennCare, in that it is one of the few plans which is now a matter of public record, and also in that it is likely a portent of things to come, a pilot program, if you will, of what can be expected on the national level. I will first describe briefly the TennCare proposal and then highlight some flaws.

As with most of the present plans, the goal of TennCare is to provide universal coverage at the highest possible level of benefit. These present plans - with regional rates, regardless of health or lifestyle[3] - will employ regional collectives (euphemistically called "regional health alliances," but collectives nonetheless) supervised by either regional health boards, or in the case of the Clinton plan, a National Health Board - consisting of seven Clinton appointees (otherwise known as apparatchiks). These mammoth bureaucracies will then promise universal care to all members of the state's party, purportedly for a lower aggregate sum than at present. Euphemisms aside, this will result in rationing with the state (through its politburo) controlling the centralized plan.

Furthermore, physicians will be required[4] (upon threat of criminal penalty) to provide services through Managed Care Organizations (MCO's), and will be reimbursed at per capita rates. Supposedly, the benefit package to recipients will be comparable to or better than present plans, and will include abortion services and most psychological services (although recently the Clinton plan has reduced those out of economic necessity). In sum, the populace has been told that it will receive better care at lower cost, and without the possibility of future revocation. In light of such promises, one can see why so many people are clamoring for such promises. If only they were true.

As a prime example of the utopian promises, consider the stated Goals of TennCare, as proposed by the Governor of Tennessee in April of 1993.[5]

- *Comprehensive health insurance for virtually every Tennessean:*
    - *Resolves the "Medicaid problem ..."*
    - Eliminates the Hospital Services Tax (March 31, 1994);
    - *No other new tax or tax increase is required;*
    - Eliminates most "cost shifting" from the uninsured to the paying patient and the business community;
    - Encourages the market to limit total health care spending in Tennessee which would save, if limited to the growth of our economy, an estimated $6.5 billion by the year 2000;
    - Creates a competitive environment by encouraging the creation of competitive provider networks at the community level;
    - Encourages welfare independence by eliminating the link

between welfare and health benefits by providing health benefits to the working poor;
    - *No health care reductions;*
    - Maintains the current Mental Health System;
    - Maintains the current Public Health System;
    - Preserves and enhances the Children's Plan'
    - Nursing Home Services and services to the Mentally Retarded are maintained under the traditional Medicaid program.

Thus, in sum, TennCare will, according to its own inventors, care for children, welfare recipients, mental health recipients, all other public health needs, "virtually every Tennessean," while at the same time resolving the "Medicaid problem," and saving both the state and federal government over 8 billion by the end of the decade. It also is supposed to eliminate some taxes, and create "No other new tax or tax increase" *and* all with "No health care reductions"!! Smoke and mirrors take over health care.

The impossibilities are manifold. Even if we admit some enthusiastic hyperbole and admire the benefits of competition in reducing health care costs, there is no possible way that all of the above can be provided at a cost of less than the present. The math is spurious and the economics impossible. Yet, the TennCare plan reasons as follows:

According to the original TennCare proposal, we are in a "crisis" that demands we take action in a short time. Our choices, if we do not reform health care are to "have a major tax increase or make major reductions in health care for almost one million Tennesseans who are covered by the Medicaid program."[6] It is presently estimated that Tennessee expends approximately the national average on health care, 13.65% of the gross domestic product (GDP). It is noted that this is "more than double the share of the GDP which health care consumed in 1965."[7] But watch this: the TennCare plan assumes a *constant* percentage of increase in medical costs, a large and unsubstantiated assumption, and projects that if there is no health care reform, citizens will spend ca. 18% of GDP on health care by 2000. Further, it assumes that total state costs will double from $13 billion to $27 billion by the year 2000. This extrapolation at a 1965-1993 constant rate is without warrant, especially when it is noted that the trend line for health care increase in costs has actually declined the last several years.

Moreover, the TennCare proposal has the lack of insight to base its model on state government employee's plan (similar to that chosen by Congress for their own families), which in fiscal year 1992 expended an average of only $1463 per person. But two things must be noted. First, that the per capita price was as low as it is because of genuine market forces (these state employee plans, similar to the Fedeal Employee Benefit Health Plan, being among the most competitive and efficient), and secondly, for a family of four or more, that annual cost is still nearly

$6000 ($5852 for four). So, even for the best of plans and on the most efficient of assumptions, such cost basis is not a real reduction at all, yet it is represented to potentially save nearly half of the $13 billion cost, supposedly able to reduce costs from $13 billion to $7.2 billion if used by all citizens.

The goal of TennCare is to cover all medicaid recipients and uninsured citizens (estimated at 1,000,000) and still care for a net increase of 14 - 16%[8] of population with no explained financial revenue. The only winners appear to be hospitals and a few of the larger insurance agencies. In order to gain their support, hospitals were promised that the Hospital tax would be eliminated in the first year.[9] A few insurance agencies will have the inside track on MCO's.

Of course, as in the nationalized schemes, all health care providers will be coerced to participate. Yet the chronic categories such as the mentally ill, children in state custody, nursing homes, and public health costs will still have to be covered by Medicare, indicating that Medicare will not be entirely phased out. These categories are perhaps the most severely underfunded on a per capita basis. Those remaining massive costs must be funded somehow, too. In addition, the single largest hypothesized source of revenue for TennCare will be "Charity Care" ($595 million) amounting to nearly half of the proposed budget.[10] That proportion may be as unintentional as accurate, as indeed it would likely require half of all medical practice to be chalked up on a charitable basis to make this program economically feasible. Health care providers may be

charitable, but it strains the credulity of such plans for budgets to anticipate that nearly half of their revenue will come from "charity care," an amount of philanthropy by physicians that is 12 times that of revenue expected from local government funds according to the TennCare proposal.[11]

Consider the fact that few physicians or hospitals have a very substantial source of income outside of their practice. Therefore, true charity from physicians and hospitals can mean only one of two things: (1) that they will accept *much* less profit, or, (2) that they will cost-shift to their paying patients. If TennCare is effective in stopping cost-shifting it is assuming an unrealistic notion of the degree of profit in health care and the willingness of providers to see it drop. Would the state planners propose to fund public education through the teachers?

The challenge is for the state of Tennessee to come up with a plan that covers those who pay little or nothing, at a cost of nearly $6,000 per year for a family of four, based on one of the lowest and most competitive (perhaps even privileged) rates per capita. In order for this rosy scenario to come about the rest of Tennesseans will have to fund about $1.5 billion per year, at the lowest present rates. Few have found a way to effect that without a recurrence of the original dilemma, either a huge tax increase (even if hidden), or a vast reduction of services for all citizens. The other four million Tennesseans will each have to bear a real economic burden of $1.5 billion in addition to their own $6,000 per family of four per year. That shared portion will amount to nearly 400 extra dollars per person per year, or about $1,500 per year for a family of four. This is socialism alright, but hardly an approach to commend even when compared to the present "crisis."

Although the plan insists that there will be no new taxes, Commissioner David Manning refuses to rule out a tax on physicians, and may at a later date reduce payments to providers of health care.[12] In addition, to provide a glimpse into big Brother Medicine (or medicine according to the Veterinarian model as opposed to the human model), this plan will impose "monitoring standards" for appointment scheduling and waiting room times: "Appointment scheduling targets are three weeks from the date of a patient's request for regular appointments and 48 hours for urgent care. Waiting room times should not exceed 45 minutes."[13] This Big-Brotherization of medicine will certainly appeal to those who complain about long lines to see physicians, but will assuredly create whole new levels of regulatory bureaucracy to maintain compliance.

Under such, one Chief of Staff of a TN hospital said that if TennCare is enforced it will mean the immediate reduction of the nursing force by at least 15%. This hardly inspires confidence that health care will improve as economic strictures are put in place. Hospitals are governed by laws of economics, even if politicians hope not to be. Further, hospitals and physicians will assuredly take measures to stay in business, even if it means rationed treatment or diminished staff.

Despite the promises of no long waits, the lines in Canada for certain procedures are probably predictive for

Tennesseans. Tennesseans will not like waiting six months (as in Ontario) for a CT scan, or up to a year for eye or orthopedic surgery, or four months for an MRI, or two years for lithotripsy on a kidney stone.[14] Before signing on to TennCare, Tennesseans will first want to be informed that "In Canada today, the average wait is 10 weeks for a mammogram and five months for a Pap smear. Canadian heart surgeons estimate that the statistical risk of dying on the waiting list for heart surgery now exceeds the risk of dying on the operating table."[15]

While these opiate promises appeal to frustrated patients, to be sure, and to the envy among people who think physicians are little more than travelling witch-doctors, sly and only in search of profit, there are real and profound flaws in this plan. Those who examine it either in light of the teachings of Scripture or prudence will find it wanting. In what follows, four non-trivial flaws at the deepest levels will be discussed. Regardless of superficial changes in some of the details of TennCare, or any of these present socialist plans, these areas will still present fundamental challenge to the schemes proposed: (1) the nature of man *qua* consumer, (2) basic economics, (3) the proper role of the state, (4) the object of dependence, and (5) faith in and dependence on the state.

1. Expectations of Altruism

The TennCare plan might work in utopia, or could be conceived as workable in an idealistic compound like a high-school Governor's Honor program. Then again, perhaps its

authors have a greater sensitivity to the presence of a millenium than I do. However, in any level above Economics 101, this model simply cannot be financed. The only possible premise upon which this could be financed would be if citizens dramatically and immediately changed their health care consumption and became health care minimalists, which of course the TennCare plan denies to be the intent or effect.

The only possible way to prevent bankruptcy (I'm told by some physicians that this could occur within 6 months, based on the eonomic assumptions versus the economic realities) is if consumers covered by the plan cut their health care consumption by at least half. Now that might be a worthwhile objective. We might even want to state that as a prudent goal. However, how do we get citizens to do that? Or, if they are guaranteed health care, is there any empirical basis to expect that they will voluntarily reduce their own family's health care by 50% apart from economic necessity?

Our government planners may cling to a wish that humanity were that altruistic, but there is no reason to assume that to be man's normal character. To the contrary, it is proven that apart from either external constraints (law) or internal gain (profit) there is no reason to expect citizens to do the right thing automatically, consistently, and altruistically. In addition (see below), there are several documentations that when total care is subsidized people do not restrict themselves from consumption. Such abuse lies at the heart of the inflation in health care costs. These costs will only decline when that behavior is changed, as may be the case now in the process of correction under our present partly-free market forces.

Theologians call this propensity "depravity," or the expectation that even the best of human beings will not act righteously apart from some mechanisms of constraint. If human beings are indeed self-interested, then these plans will not encourage them to limit their choices. On the contrary, citizens can be counted on to "Get what's coming to them," and to use the system to its fullest. Yes, Virginia, there is a human nature.

Creators of health care plans should factor in that users will avail themselves and their families to the ceiling of health care, not voluntarily opt for floor-level health care. The only people who will consistently opt for floor-level health care are those who have other external incentives (again largely dependent on self-interest) to do so. That is why plans such as those by Stuart Butler at the Heritage Foundation, or the plans conceived by Phil Gramm, Don Nickles, or Richard Armey, combine economic savvy with realism about human nature. The TennCare plan (and others) fail to admit the reality about human nature, that we are indeed selfish and self-centered. We will routinely take all that we can, and give as little as we can. This behavior will lead to bankruptcy in these related plans. The failure to admit this human nature is a non-superficial flaw of this plan which will not be cured by superficial adjustments.

As Ronald Nash coments, "No economic or political system that assumes the essential goodness of human nature or holds out the dream of a perfect earthly society can possibly be consistent with the Biblical world view."[16] Realism about depravity must be included in any succeessful health care reform. In addition, with a Fallen universe as a constant in our formulations, resulting health care reform will be delimited from seeking either utopian or totalitarian means and ends.

The various socialist experiments

> **Theologians call this propensity "depravity,"...the expectation that even the best of human beings will not act righteously apart from some mechanisms of constraint.**

of the twentieth century have demonstrated this depravity write large. It should be part of the body of social truisms by now that if some other agency will automatically make a provision for individuals, invariably the individuals will rely on that agency to provide for it continually. That is to say, if the state guarantees welfare, unemployment, disaster insurance, agricultural subsidies, or health care, then citizens will allow it to, and abuse the guarantees in the meantime. Such is the effect of depravity applied to public policy. Informed public policy will take this anthropological given into account.

Such abuses of provision will not take a long time to be felt in effect. The reason lies in the very nature of man (theological or philosophical anthropology). Not only is this the case theoretically, i.e., that sinful people look for their own advantage, and not altruistically to the concerns of fairness or justice, but it is also abundantly demonstrable from the last generation of social experimentation.

It is now as well-proven as it is lamentable that when a society subsidizes immorality, the recipients of that MCO will take the government up on immorality or non-efficiency. As the illegitimacy rates have risen dramatically and steadily since the creation of the "Great Society," who, other than partisan ideologues, can dispute the deleterious effect on the rate of illegitimacy of welfare payments to mothers of out-of-wedlock children? Health care reform plans like TennCare share this non-superficial deficiency on the level of principle.

When one asks whether all this expenditure-oriented approach has helped, it can be noted that in 1965 there were less than a quarter of a million illegitimate births to blacks and yet after some 20 years of social engineering (a generation to those bearing children) it was reported that "In 1980 48% of live births among blacks were to single women compared to 17% in 1950."[17] Further escalating, by 1988 "63.5% of all black babies were born out of wedlock."[18]

Steven Moore has noted that, "Welfare rolls have skyrocketed from two million families in 1970 to 3.5 million in 1980 to 4.6 million in 1990. The child of a parent on welfare is three times more likely to be on welfare as an adult."[19] It is still more shocking to note that,

"Despite a great society effort now well into its third decade — the cost of more than 2.5 trillion dollars — the life of many inner city residents has never been worse, for blacks especially. Today blacks comprise almost half of the prison population. The homicide rate for black males age 15-24 has increased by 40% since the mid-1980's, and is now the leading cause of death for that age group. Forty percent of those murdered in the U.S. are black men killed by other black men. Sixty-five percent of all black babies are born to unwed mothers; the number is as high as 80% in many inner cities."[20]

The centralized planners of the coming health care reforms could learn the anthropological lesson from a cousin to medical care, welfare. If human beings have responded to welfare provision as they have, then what reason is there to believe that they will respond any differently to health provision? Based on the nature of man, there is no reason.

The same kinds of graphs will no doubt be forthcoming (although it will not take 30 years to show) for pandemic health care abuse. Because of our self-interestedness, if an insured is guaranteed health care, without restriction, in the present philosophical soil he will overuse and wrongfully use the syustem which is without cost to him. Not only that, but also those who abuse themselves with immoral lifestyles will continue to reap health repercussions which will also be as fully treatable (not to mention, subsidized) as those who live healthy lifestyles. In the present proposals there is an ignorance of this basic anthropology, and such ignorance cannot give a good reason

for "Why be healthy, if unhealth is equally subsidized?" While in the past we could depend on moral or religious codes to persuade in favor of health, in our present climate about all we have to convince a self-interested population is economics. It is precisely those economic disincentives which, having been stripped from present proposals, will no longer help limit self-interest in the consumption of health provision.

Consequently, if access and guarantees are given apart from economics, the true costs will soon skyrocket and continue to increase exponentially as welfare payments have over the past 30 years. The flaw is the same in both attempts: no one ever calculated that recipients are truly sinful, and even in the best of scenarios they take from the system more than they give. They are in it for themselves, and until precautions are taken to limit that, no system will endure.

2. Economics

Many people show an abysmal lack of grasp on economic consequence. Economic ideas do have consequences. TennCare is faulty on the economic front in several regards.

(a) **The Budget projections are unrealistic**. From the outset, it may not be the case that health care costs rise at a constant rate. Nowhere is it considered that perhaps we've seen the most inflationary period of health care costs in western history. It has not been proven that the costs of health care will continue at the same exponential upward trend as the past decade. To the contrary, in 1992, health care costs only increased

5.7%, the lowest rate since 1973,[21] and also the basic inflation rate is significantly lower than this time 10 years ago (ca. 13% then, as opposed to 4% now). The decline in rate of increase is from:
9.6% in 1990 to
7.9% in 1991 to
5.7% in 1992 to
5.4% in 1993 to
4.4% in the second half of 1993.

Neither is it certain that the projections of revenue from the federal government, nor from "Charity Care" will actually materialize, leaving contracted providers responsible to care indefinitely for a bankrupt system out of the goodness of their hearts (even if they had no objections to socialized medicine), or else leaving genuinely sick people out in the cold. Do any dare imagine that a state (or national plan) would actually recognize a problem of economic short-fall and care for its citizens?

Of course, it has not been definitely proven that health care costs will either decline or that the rate of annual increase will fall. But the market force correction begun in the past few years should encourage us at least to wait before making such drastic attempts.

Yet, perhaps the chief error in extrapolation is the fabricated number of Americans without health care. It would be a titanic challenge actually to locate 37 million Americans without health insurance, as even the Urban Institute admits that 70% of these are only without insurance for nine months or less,[22] likely only between jobs — which may be a legitimate concern, remedied by other means. Matthew

Glavin has even more conservatively estimated that of the purported 37 million without health insurance "half are without insurance for four months or less, and only 15% are uninsured for more than two years."[23] Burkett and others have also demonstrated how the purchase of health insurance is a choice, in that over 16% of those supposedly without insurance could certainly afford it, having incomes in excess of $40,000 annually, and that nearly "half of the uninsured had incomes greater than $20,000."[24]

Another matter of economics altogether, which is seldom mentioned is the reported fact that perhaps as much as 40% of people will pay more under the Clinton plan (even with its rosy suppositions), and that as many as 7 - 18 millions of jobs could be lost by this plan, according to the National Federation for Independent Business.[25]

(b) **The capitation rate is spuriously low.** The annual capitation rate (the amount of money the state will allow a provider to collect; thus indicating how much can be spent on health care) for TennCare as announced by the state on September 3, 1993, to be effective on January 1, 1994, is:

-$179.28 for ages 1-13 (Presently that would not cover a case of ear infection and strep throat per year, much less any serious illness.)

- $685.68 for males 14-44 (an amount less than a single inpatient surgical procedure);

- $1505.52 for ages 45-64 per year;

- $378.36 for 65 and over (This figure certainly does not plan to spend much on senior citizens, in their most expensive health care years, or else severely limits the number of services to this sector.)[26]

If the capitation rate is the amount of revenue for a medical business to continue, it will not be able to provide the superior care promised by the benefits above for these rates, which include severe overstatements of charity care. It may well cover inexpensive care, such as immunizations, a lot of "two aspirins," and pharmaceutical prescriptions. However, it will not cover *major* medical procedures.

(c) **Cadillac plan for Chevrolet costs?** Another economic aspect of TennCare that is dubious is the claim that costs can be lowered, while simultaneously providing a universal and comprehensive range of medical benefits. According to TennCare, the deductible would be only $200 per individual, capped at $500 per family. Superior corporate plans presently have higher deductibles on the average. TennCare would pay 90% of medical costs (most corporate plans are 80%, with only the very best co-paying at 90%), with an out of pocket maximum per family at $2,000 per year in an MCO. Mental illness costs are reimbursed at 90% for hospitalization, with 75% of first 15 outpatient sessions (which can include any kind of counseling) covered. Even substance abuse is covered up to 90%, with full psychiatric costs (up to 45 days per year). There is no limit to TennCare's benefit for outpatient service (present Medicaid limits to 30 visits per year), physician serivces whether inpatient or outpatient (presently limited to 20 and 24 visits per year respectively), psychiatric inpatient care, lab and X-ray procedures (presently limited to 30 occasions per year), hospice (presently limited to 210 days, although admittedly this is terminal care), pharmacy (presently limited to 7 prescriptions per month), medical supplies and ambulance services.[27] The only things not fully covered are dental work (non-surgical) and eye care.

This is a Cadillac plan that would cost many Tennesseans more than the present $6,000 per year per family of four. If services are not reduced somewhere, it is simple economics to admit that costs and revenues must increase. Yet, TennCare and other, national, plans deny this fundamental economic truism.

(d) **No worst case scenario.** None of the above plans calculate any reserve of the magnitude necessary to stay afloat is there is any downturn, or economic depression. Furthermore, until late January, the plan stated that physicians would not be reimbursed should funds be depleted. They would, however, be compelled to continue to provide treatment.

All in all, it never reckons with the fact that users will take more than they give, unless there are economic disincentives to the contrary. Related to the anthropology above, no system of economics can truly provide a fiscally sound basis for the above TennCare plan. These and other economic uncertainties caused even HHS to issue a conditional approval (although that has not been publicized in the major media, even within the state) for the TennCare plan on November 18, 1993, with the state required to meet 35 additional waivers *within 30 days* to gain final approval. These 35 waivers not only reveal the economic inadequacy of the plan, but further show how intrusive the governmental medical approach really is.

Since these waivers have not been widely publicized, one might be interested in a few of them. Among the waivers which help effect even more of Big Brother's encroachment into medicine are the following: In order to qualify for federal funds, the state must have all MCO contracts approved at the federal level by the Health Care Financing Administration (HCFA).[28] Furthermore, the state must develop extensive auditing procedures and, "Within 45 days of awareness, the State must submit a workplan to the HCFA project officer that includes detailed criteria for monitoring the financial stability and quality assurance controls of each plan."[29] Imagine the novel levels of bureaucracy that will be needed to accomplish this. Out the door goes privacy and the right of individuals to secure their own health care. Nor should it be overlooked that no later than "30 days after the end of each quarter, the State must submit the Form HCFA-64 quarterly Medicaid expenditure report, showing actual Medicaid and matchable TennCare expenditures made in the quarter just ended."[30] These waivers grant broad review powers to the federal level, while requiring virtual surrender of determination from the serfs below.

To further insure exact inspection (and to make sure that no one shines the light on failures until administrative rationalizations have been well-secured), "The HCFA project officer shall be notified prior to formal presentation of any report

of statistical or analytical material based on information obtained through this project. Formal presentation includes papers, articles, professional publications, speeches, and testimony. In the course of this research, whenever the principal investigator determines that a significant new finding has been developed, he or she will immediately communicate it to the HCFA project officer before formal dissemination to the general public."[31] Freedom of information, academic inquiry, non-partisan analysis, and unhindered scientific research will also have to be subordinated to the whim of the state, through its project officer. We could end up having a lot of big brothers.

> "...abstinence-based medical programs will not satisfy Big Sister."

Moreover, "At any phase of the project, including the project's conclusion, the awardee, if so requested by the project officer, must submit to HCFA analytic data files, with appropriate documentation, representing the date developed/used in the end-product analyses generated under the award ... [including] primary data collected, acquired, or generated under the award and/or data furnished by HCFA."[32]

The morality of TennCare is thinly veiled as it contains this prerequisite for funding: "Within 60 days of the date of approval, the State must submit a written plan that describes how family planning services will be made available to TennCare enrollees ... The plan must

delineate how the confidentiality of enrollees (particularly adolescents) who receive family planning services through such health plans will be maintained."[33] Hence special care is taken to provide for groups like Planned Parenthood and other condom-distributors, while requiring secretiveness and impunity for immoral lifestyles. These and only these moral options will gain approved funding. It is clear that abstinence-based medical programs will not satisfy Big Sister.

What is to be gained from all this surrender of personal liberty? The answer to that question helps explain the economics. As argued above, the income is at best half of what is needed to finance such a program. The state of TN must magically secure a large revenue source, or depend on unprecedented and uneconomical levels of charity. However, tucked away in waiver #12 is the solution: The federal government, as much as admitting that the plan cannot balance its own books, in order to prop up such demonstration will allow taxpayers from the whole nation to help finance its socialist experimentation. According to waiver #12 HCFA will match funds to pay for "the actual cash capitation payments ... made by the State to MCOs for each TennCare enrollee."[34] In addition, this clause explicitly commits the federal government to match expenditures for "unreimbursed TennCare costs (including medical education costs) borne by participating TennCare providers," "services provided to TennCare enrollee and eligibles in private hospitals in Knox and Davidson counties," "services to a TennCare enrollee residing in an institution for Mental Diseases," and "actual ongoing non-TennCare costs ... of the Medicaid program."[35] Thus, TennCare will not really pay for itself, nor will Medicaid truly be phased out. We will merely have national taxpayers cover those bills. But, the costs must be paid for by someone. The laws of economics cannot be ignored.

Under this plan, Big Brother will gain a lot of turf, health care will not be improved, and the costs for services will not truly be reduced at all. The true costs will simply be hidden, elusively passed on to the next level of central government, and the people misled. Yet, someday, these bills will come home to roost, while in the meantime we are capable of irreparably destroying an adequate medical delivery system. One legitimately wonders also how the federal government will try to pass on its cost when it seeks approval for its medical plan?

3. Distorted view of the role of the state

There is absolutely no rational or empirical basis to support the idea that the state should or can do a better or more efficient job of managing health care than individuals and private groups. Nor is there any constitutional basis for government agencies to assume this role.

Individuals and families are responsible for health care. It cannot be delegated to some other agency, and the particular agency of the modern state is one of the least likely to succeed, if charged with individual responsibility. It is a misplaced faith to rely on the state to take care of individual needs. It cannot, nor will

it, although it may enhance its own goals in the process, leading to more dependency. The state has no warrant to move into this realm. This fact has led columnist William Rusher to query if the next liberal cause may be to propose a "right to eat."

"Do you realize that 40 million Americans go to bed hungry every night? ... Can the world's wealthiest society allow this disgrace to continue? So, down the road some smiling demagogue will wave a small card in the face of a joint session of Congress and tell the applauding lawmakers that this piece of plastic will guarantee every American a basic diet of three square meals a day (duly modified for variations in ages, size, and gender) from cradle to grave."[36]

It is also the case that thousands of individuals in the USA will die in the next year. Can the state step in and stop, or take over, that area, too? Can the state provide Managed Care Longevity? It is not a *deus ex machina*, even if its citizens click their heels together, close their eyes with ever so much concentration, and wish it to be. It is high time to realize that the state is limited in its warrant and ability. Only individuals can do certain things, and we must be healed of the modern delusion that all problems find their cures in state intervention. They certainly do not, and some things can only be executed by individuals. After all, the state is invisible if stripped from its individuals. It is the sum total of individuals writ large.

The state can produce nothing. It can only raise money from its taxes, thus paying for health care (or any

plan), only with our money. Already that is what happens. We are already the payers, and should wisely seek to find out if we're getting a better deal for our money. Health care will always be funded from our own money — either directly by individuals, or indirectly and less efficiently by the state. It is still our money; the state has none of its own.

Then again, the state is all too prone to be expansive and take over by default whole areas which truly belong to individuals. Others have warned us against the creation of totalitarian states, along with their correlative tendencies. Helmut Thielicke warned against the totalitarian state because it "necessarily seeks to penetrate every sphere of life and hence to take over the care of children, the chronically ill, the sick, and the aged ..." and cautioned, "The totalitarian state plays the role of the 'universal father,' attending men with its claims and services from the cradle to the grave, it forces on them the same kind of dependence as is evident in all spheres of life."[37] This totalitarian or maximal state, "is always a threat to the very foundation of the doctrine of the two kingdoms. The state as universal father, the state which intervenes in all things, exploiting even the inner powers of man ... and registering everything and laying claim to everything, transgresses its allotted sphere ... and — whether latently or deliberately — assumes the role of a pseudo church."[38]

According to Thielicke, this has institutional ill effects. Even though other systems may not be free from error, the error or the maximalist state in Thielicke's analysis is more severe than the others. Of the inhibition which can be foisted on health care by the maximalist state, Thielicke comments, "It is conceivable that the modern threat to human society, to put it bluntly, arises less from chaos than from an overabundance of state order, a political superorganization which acts as an institutional buffer to isolate men from one another, depersonalize them, ... and turn love of neighbor into a welfare machine."[39]

Later Thielicke argues, "once the state establishes a monopoly in [a field], once it is forced to render 'complete care for its citizens in body and soul,' it not only reduces individual initiative but also kindles suspicion of ... other groups."[40] One of the ill effects is the turning over to the maximal state the arena of health care. Thielicke diagnoses the two-step process as: "The first phase is the development of the state monopoly. The second is the exclusion of all independent outside actions which seem to dissipate the centrally directed effort and introduce ideologies of their own."[41] Moreover, "How far all this can get from any direct person-to-person care of a fellow human being finally becomes clear in the fact that the burden of the material requirements ... must be borne by general taxation." It is most amazing to note that these things were written much earlier, about truths which we now see played out.

His recommendation toward the end of this section should be heard in full.

"In thus warning against the utopia of a humanly inaugurated

perfect state of affairs at the end of history, Christianity has to draw attention to three points. The first is that external perfection unaccompanied by the buttressing of inner substance gives rise to new forms of sickness in society. The second is that if the state would be true to itself, avoid totalitarian perversion, and remain in the kingdom of the left hand, it cannot create these inner equivalents. And, the third is that for this reason the state cannot claim a monopoly in [health care], but so far as possible must delegate the tasks ... to agencies which have a message and can devote themselves to more than merely external welfare. At any rate, the state must in principle not exclude but allow for such institutions ..."[42]

Thus in a properly related posture, the minimalist state embraces private responsibility, "always standing ready to give up tasks as other non-state agents become available ... Negatively, this means that the state should oppose the trend toward a total and direct assumption of all ... tasks, and recognize that in this area, too, it ought ideally to be a minimal state. Obviously, this ideal arrangement has to be fought for, and the church ought to take the lead in fighting for it."[43]

In conclusion, Thielicke stresses,

" ... that the principle of the minimal state derives ultimately from the theological character of the state as an emergency order. This concept

contains within itself the postulate that we should commit to the state, not everything we can, but only what we must. It is in keeping with the provisional and interim character of the state that its claims are possible only with the caveat of an ultimate 'Nevertheless.' Where this caveat is omitted, there arises the totalitarian tendency which we have discussed in detail. ... This tendency is accompanied by a similar tendency to level down all distinction, to ignore personal maturity and dignity and to degrade persons to the position of mere objects, and to establish the dominion of the perfected machinery. It was up against this background that we insisted that the state should give up as many tasks as possible and commit them to other agencies ... This means that the movement towards totalitarianism will be stemmed only to the degree that non-state agencies actively assume responsibility. The movement will be arrested not by the insight — even the theological insight — of responsible men and groups in government but only by the power of these non-state interceptors, only by men who are prepared to act."[44]

It is indeed scary to hear that the requirements for TennCare eligibility depends on "primary care physicians [to serve] as gate-keepers for all health care services provided to enrollees as the case managers for all cases warranting intensive case management."[45] One analysis of the Blue Cross Blue Shield contract for TennCare[46] points out that physicians will be required "to allow on-site inspections and audits, including copying at no charge, of all TennCare related records." This is excessive state domination.

> "The state as universal father...assumes the role of a pseudo church."

The state neither has these roles by natural law, by constitutional authority, nor by common interest. It is unwise at best to delegate to the state such roles. It would even be preferable to simply preserve the present "crisis." As Cal Thomas observes, the only drive to move to such a socialist system is if "a flawed philosophy about humanity and government — that it is and should be our redeemer — permeates all of their policies and rules their proposed health care reform package. ... When the trade is made, there will be no stopping government from self-deification, especially in matters involving life and death. ..."[47] He further cites a recent British assessment from *The Economist*: "Not since Franklin Roosevelt's War Production Board has it been suggested that so large a part of the American economy should suddenly be brought under government control."[48]

Moreover, what should give one confidence in a governmental approach when the President's health care proposal is 1,342 pages in length after federal spending on Medicare is up 526% in past 14 years. Larry Burkett has reminded us that in 1965 when Medicaid was invented its budget was 1 billion dollars, while in 1992 it actually cost $72 billion. And "in 1965 the government estimated that by 1990 Medicare would cost $12 billion in inflation-adjusted dollars. The actual cost was $107 billion."[49]

However, many — even thoughtful Christians who should know better — do not critically assess these alternatives. Due to the fact that many have forgotten the proper role for the state, people are willing to surrender the world's best

medical care (even though not perfect) for one which is characterized by governmental control, regional surrogates, the abolition of private health insurance, a one-size-fits-all approach through employee mandates, price controls, MCOs for all, fewer specialists and new research, and rationed waiting lists. To exchange such, it would seem that some state would necessarily have proven its competency in these areas beyond a shadow of doubt. Or else, citizens may be looking for the state to do something that is entirely impractical, and not even within its properly defined jurisdiction.

If citizens wish to have sound health care, they'd best get their view of the state right, before it takes over important parts of their life. It is utopian and unfounded to look to the state for health care. It is wrong for the state to expand its role outside of its jurisdiction as well. TennCare and other plans all assume an inflated and ill-conceived role for the state, which becomes Big Brother with a black bag.

4. Faith in & Dependence on the State

Implicitly, those who look to the state to care for our health are violating the first commandment, and worshipping another god. To do so is to attempt to create a deified state which provides health. The state simply cannot do this, and we do wrong to search for it from the state. Only God can truly provide for our health. Sure we can take some preventative steps and should. But even the best of those only yield slight improvement on any scale.

Dependence for health must be

placed only on the One who can truly provide. These various health care proposals are cases of misplaced providence, the attempt to find suitable provision from a source which cannot deliver.

As a people, we have come dangerously close to deifying the state. We look to the state for cradle to the grave employement, education, welfare, subsidies, and now health. These commodities — work, wisdom, relief, income, health, and even safety — were once the domain of providence. It seems that we now have produced a generation (or three) who rely on the secular state to provide these things. Our faith and dependence may have been gradually and unwittingly transferred to a non-deity. It may be the case that we actually have come to trust the governmental agencies instead of God to provide for our most basic needs. Such substitution surely leaves us impoverished and unhealthy.

The health that we do worship may, in the end, only be guaranteed by God. It is likely that the plethora of health plans — knowingly or not — are but imitating the provisions that only God can bring. Substitution of a lesser agency — the state — will only result in frustration of those goals, if they can never be furnished by any other than our Creator. In the meantime to depend on some other is to perpetuate a non-superficial and substantive error.

There are other flaws in this plan, and will be in every plan. I have barely mentioned the inconvenience that more than 37 million will feel as they wait like our Canadian friends for long periods before certain procedures. We have not even addressed the loss of personal relationship with a caring physician in the transition to the newer Veterinary model. Nor have we begun to calculate the burden placed on physicians,[50] the vast majority of whom are very caring, ethical, professional, and no more greedy than any other class of workers.

Still one of the most fundamental flaws in these plans is the concession that human beings have rights to medical care. Philosophically that contention is as questionable as it is novel. Neither the history of philosophy nor ethics supports the expansive rights claims today.[51] According to William Willimon, "The notion of 'rights' is not a biblical idea. It is a legacy of the European Enlightenment. The notion of rights has been helpful in forming liberal societies, that is, societies formed without reference to God. No one need feel grateful or to say 'thank you' in a society of rights."[52]

Commenting on the "dialect of rights as being uniquely American" Mary Ann Glendon decries the fact that we are so consistently silent about our duties and obligations, while always shrill about our rights. She says, "The American rights dialect is distinguished not only by what we say and how we say it, but also by what we leave unsaid. Each day's newspapers, radio broadcasts, and television programs attest to our tendency to speak of whatever is most important to us in terms of rights, and to our predilection for overstating the absoluteness of the rights we claim."[53] Later, in "Refining the Rhetoric of Rights" Glendon says, "The strident rights rhetoric that currently dominates American political discourse poorly serves the strong tradition of protection for individual freedom for which the United States is justly renowned. Our stark simple rights dialect puts a damper on the processes of public justification, communication, and deliberation upon which the continuing vitality of the democratic regime depends. It contributes to the erosion of the habits, practices, and attitudes of respect for others that are the ultimate and surest guarantors of human rights. It impedes long-range thinking about our most pressing social problems. Our rights-laden discourse easily accomodates the economic, the immediate, and the personal dimensions of a problem while it regularly neglects the moral, the long-term, and the social implications."[54]

Perhaps our post WWII invention of rights shares the perspective of the U.N. In the1948 U.N. Universal Declaration of Human Rights one may be amazed to be informed of rights never before imagined. Article 22 postulates that "everyone, as a member of society, has the right to social security." Even more utopian in scope, Article 25 of the same charter alleges that everyone has a right "to a standard of living adequate for the health and well-being of himself and his family, including food, clothing, housing."[55] Another encyclopedia lists the following supposed "rights:" right to confidentiality, right to die, right to fertility control, right to food, right to health, right to health care, right to information, right to life, right to privacy,[56] and others.

The same refrain is now being heard in one of the latest variations on this central theme, health care reform. Our population is repeatedly informed that over 37 million Americans do not have health care insurance (not health care, mind you), and that moreover, they have a right to health care, despite the fact that millions of these who have been deprived of the right to health care do spend their income on TVs, food, cigarettes, cars, entertainment, and other products. In short, they have purchasing power, and wilfully choose to purchase certain products, leaving the government to provide health care, and then plead that their rights have been stultified, in that they have not received health care.

To base health care reform (or any other reform) on such a tenuous foundation is most unwise. We could only wish for those who will be affected to enter into such radical change with their eyes open. It is hard to justify another socialist experiment after the twentieth century, even if those in leadership insist. The people may just say no.

Recently historian Paul Johnson commented with clarity:

"The question future historians will ask is not why politicians and public opinion turned against the welfare state, but why it took them so long. Indeed, if ever a theory has been tested and disproved, it is that of the all-powerful, all-benevolent state — a theory that has led in practice to wars, to the death of millions of people, and to the scorching of entire economies and environments. Never before has mankind created such an all-consuming monster. In both its totalitarian and social-democratic versions, it has proved efficient in nothing except a capacity to squander resources and lives."[57]

Socialized medicine, if it is imposed, won't be the end of the world, although it will surely create a lot more problems than it will solve. It can easily do harm, and once created will leave its participants pining for these days when they had real health care. But, it won't be the end of the world. It would just be highly stupid. These and other non-superficial flaws may lead us to simply oppose on grounds of principle. We may just say, "No" to socialized medicine, and not even be required to offer alternatives, so manifestly flawed are thse present plans. If one person proposes an action that is manifestly imprudent (say mass jumping off the Golden Gate Bridge without bungee cords), another person is justified in simply refusing to participate, rather than first proposing an alternative prior to rejection of such an imprudent idea.

The same may be true if we adopt plans like TennCare. If TennCare is an aberration from the forthcoming nationalized schemes of health care, then this has been a mere exercise in critiquing one flawed plan. If that is the case, then we could even see a disjointed patchwork of flawed plans, underscoring the need for citizens to be involved in their own states, not only being fixated on the federal level, as if Washington could genuinely heal an illness. However, if TennCare is a sibling of the other plans now being considered, if it is organically related to the Clinton plan, then these non-superficial criticisms will apply to that plan as well, even before the administration puts something forward in writing and sticks to it. Any one of these could sink such a plan, even

independently of one another, much less in concert as is the case with the present prescription. To ever persuade, all four of these must be healed.

Matthew Glavin may have it right: "Health care reform is one of the most complex public policy issues to face this nation since the creation of the social welfare programs of the 1960's. And, like the welfare programs of the sixties, the decisions currently being discussed in Washington will affect not only health care for millions of individual Americans, but the very foundations upon which our free society was built."[58]

Endnotes

1. Say, as much as 80% lower, as in the recent study by the Cato Institute which estimates only 5 million truly without adequate health care.

2. For example, when homelessness was - without evidence - estimated at 3 million, while it was only about 10% of that, or Lord Kinsey's estimate of homosexuality at 10%, again being subsequently proven to be too high by a factor of ten.

3. In a recent experiment in the state of New York, as this regional averaging was imposed, actual costs increased 170% in the first year.

4. The proposal by President Clinton, being the most extreme in this aspect, will even abolish non-participating private insurers, and make it illegal to purchase medical procedures or care outside of the system. Even the more socialistic single-payer plan proposed by Rep. James McDermott (D-WA) allows for purchase of non-covered procedures.

5. Taken from, *TennCare: A Proposal for Health Care Reform* by Governor

Ned McWherter. Emphasis added.

6. *Ibid.*, p. 1.

7. *Ibid.*.

8. Note that one million actually exceeds 20% of TN's slightly less than 5 million population, thereby skewing projections based on this by about 30%.

9. Yet, by Dec. 3, 1993, Commissioner Manning admitted that in order to satisfy HHS waivers, this promise could be annulled. *The Oak Ridger*, Dec. 3, 1993, p. 2.

10. *TennCare: A Proposal, Ibid.*, p. 4.

11. *Ibid.*

12. "HCFA Provides TMA with TennCare Assessment," *The Oak Ridger*, Nov. 29, 1993, p. 1.

13. *Ibid.*

14. Goodman, John, "Lessons from Abroad" in *National Review*, Dec. 13, 1993, Health Care Supplement, p. 4.

15. *Ibid.*, p. 11.

16. Nash, Ronald, **Poverty and Wealth**, Westchester, IL: Crossway, 1986, p. 62.

17. Doner, Colonel, **The Samaritan Strategy**, Westchester, IL: Crossway, 1988, p. 142.

18. Rubenstein, Ed., *National Review*, May 11, 1992, p. 35.

19. Moore, Steven, Reform Afoot, *National Review*, May 11, 1992, p. 36.

20. *Ibid.*

21. Larry Burkett, *Money Matters*, Nov. 15, 1993, p. 5., As further confirmation of this inchoate trend, participation in HMO's increased nearly 10% in 1993, further deescalating health care costs. With more participants in HMO's double-digit increases were fading. According to the Group Health Association of America, "the increase in HMO premiums moderated for the fifth year in a row. Premiums rose 8.1% in 1993, compared with a 10.6% increase in 1992. They will rise an estimated 5.6% in 1994, the report said." (Source: *Wall Street*

Journal, 12/10/93, p.B5) With a trend line like this, and a 5.6% increase (only slightly above inflation), the crises may be solved already.

22. *Ibid.*, p. 2.

23. Glavin, Matthew J., Health Care and a Free Society, *Imprimis*, Nov, 1993, Vol. 22, No. 11, p. 3.

24. Burkett, *op cit.*

25. *Ibid.*

26. Memo to MMC Physicians from Becky Lew, 9/10/93. It is worth noting that these rates, when compared to the present rates, allow for as little repayment as 30 cents on the dollar, with capitation rates respectively of 179.28 (compared to present 607.20), 685.68 (compared to present 113.60), 1505.51 (compared to 1933.44), and 378.36 (less than half the present 806.28).

27. See *TennCare: A Proposal*, Attachment E-3.

38. "Health Care Financing Administration Special Terms and Conditions" for Tennessee TennCare Demonstration, #11-C-99638/4-03, (Nov. 18, 1993), p. 1.

29. *Ibid.*, p. 3.

30. *Ibid.*, p.4.

31. *Ibid.*, p. 8.

32. *Ibid.*, p. 8.

33. *Ibid.*, p. 2.

34. *Ibid.*, p. 3.

35. *Ibid.*, pp. 3-4.

36. Rusher, William A., Next Liberal Cause: The Right to Eat, *Newspaper Enterprise Association*, Nov. 11, 1993.

37. **Theological Ethics: Politics**, Vol. 2, Grand Rapids, Eerdmans, 1979, p. 289.

38. *Ibid.*, p. 290.

39. *Ibid.*, pp. 291-292.

40. *Ibid.*, p. 302.

41. *Ibid.*, p. 303.

42. *Ibid.*, p. 311.

43. *Ibid.*, p. 312.

44. *Ibid.*, p. 316.

45. See *TennCare: A Proposal, op cit.*, p. 7, Attachment D.

46. Issued by the Tennessee Medical Association, 9/13/93, p.7.

47. Thomas, Cal, Clintoncare: A Question of Trust, *Los Angeles Times Syndicate*, Nov. 4, 1993.

48. *Ibid.*

49. *National Review*, Dec. 13, 1993, p. 8.

50. In one analysis of the contract with Blue Cross Blue Shield of TN as provider under TennCare, the following were noted as unfairly burdensome: (1) the requirement of on-site audits at physician expense and with no prior notice, (2) withholding of up to 20% by MCOs until revenues are sufficient, (3) a "cram-down" provision by which a physician is presumed to be participating and contractually obligated, unless he withdraws from the BCBS Tennessee Provider Network, and (4) a clause in the contract which guarantees reimbursement only upon condition of state solvency, to wit, "To the extent and only to the extent that BCBST is provided with funds by the State for the payment of TennCare claims, BCBST shall make payments to PHYSICIAN for Medical Services rendered to TennCare Enrollees pursuant to the provisions set forth in this Amendment and the TennCare Schedule of Payments." (p. 3).

51. Cf. the author's Too Many Rights Make Wrong, *Journal of Biblical Ethics in Medicine*, Spring, 1993, Vol. 7, No. 2.

52. Willimon, William H., The Effusiveness of Christian Charity, *Theology Today*, April, 1992, pp. 79-80.

53. Glendon, Mary Ann, **Rights Talk: The Impoverishment of Political Discourse**, New York: The Free Press, 1991, p. 76.

54. *Ibid.*, p. 171.

55. **The Encyclopedia of Philosophy**, Vol. 7, New York: Macmillan, p. 195.

56. **The Encyclopedia of Bioethics**, Vol. 4, New York: Macmillan, p. 1498.

17. Johnson, Paul, Whatever Happened to Socialism, *Reader's Digest*, Oct., 1991, p. 112.

18. *Imprimis, op cit.* p. 1.

Addiction as Besetting Sin

Franklin E. Payne, Jr., M.D.

Dr. Payne, *author of several books, is Associate Professor of Family Medicine at the Medical College of Georgia, in Augusta, Georgia.*

Addictive disorders and alcoholism cost $165 billion a year in the United States alone![1] The addict screams, "I can't help myself! I'm addicted." In response, "experts"[2] and society feel compassion with ever increasing programs for them.

However, I want to substitute "besetting sin" for "addiction." The primary problem is moral and spiritual,[3] not medical, and cannot be addressed without that perspective.

What is Addiction?

"Addiction" is a slippery term (as are most psychological labels). From my own observation, a definition of addiction should be divided at three levels. First, there are the strict and detailed definitions that careful professionals use.[4] Second, there is the careless use among professionals. Third, there is the use of the word in popular literature and less formal discourse.

The first level is the *Diagnostic and Statistical Manual of Mental Disorders (Third Edition — Revised)* (DSM-III-R). While "addiction" is not named as a

diagnosis there, Psychoactive Substance Use Disorder (PSUD) and related terms are. An introductory sentence from that section of the DSM-III-R serves as a definition of PSUD at this first level.

"This diagnostic class deals with symptoms and maladaptive behavioral changes associated with more or less regular use of psychoactive substances that affect the central nervous system. ... Almost invariably, people who have a PSUD will also have ... Intoxication or Withdrawal."[5]

The second level involves the careless use of addiction among professionals. Likely, most readers have never seen such a classification. However, it is quite real among physicians and psychologists,[6] and most other professions as well. This practice is a failure to use any formal definition in exchanges among professionals.

For example, I have yet to see any patient's chart with the diagnosis of "depression" with reference to criteria that would fit any formal definition, such as the DSM-III-R. Yet, millions of patients carry this label and receive potent

medications based upon this slipshod approach. Both the label and the medications have great potential for harm, as well as good. Further, such imprecision applies to virtually every area of medicine, not just psychiatric diagnoses. (A discussion of this "mal-practice," however, would require another paper in itself.)

An example, relative to addiction, is "sexual addiction." What is meant is a repetitive, compulsive sexual activity, such as nymphomania or the viewing of pornographic materials. If the DSM-III-R is any standard at all, the application of "addiction" to sexual activities is careless and certainly not "scientific."

The third level is the "popular use" of addiction and only reflects the careless use among "professionals." However, as would be expected, any connection to a precise definition is even more distant. Gambling, shoplifting, overeating, excessive TV viewing, and other habitual behaviors become "addictions."

Curiously, this careless professional and popular distortion of addiction finds its way into Christian literature. One example is found in a text on "Biblical and Christian ethics."

"An addiction is an exaggerated and pathological dependency of one human being upon another person, institution, substance, activity, or even series or pattern of interior mood states or thought patterns. ... Potential addiction agents include food (compulsive overeating and other eating disorders); activity, achievement (workaholism), rigid performance standards (perfectionism), the emphasis on form rather than substance in spiritual matters (religiosity, religious legalism), or spiritual addiction; erotic fantasy and arousal (sexual addiction); money (compulsive spending, hoarding, or shopping); and interpersonal relationships (codependent relationship roles of victim, victimizer, and/or rescuer)."[7]

From such broad generalizations by this psychologist, the blurring between the careless use of addiction by professionals and its popular use is complete.

Using these liberal criteria, in the United States there are estimates of 20 million alcoholics, 80 million coalcoholics, 20 million addicted gamblers, 50 million addicted to eating too much (overweight) and 30 million to eating too little (anorexics and bulimics), 75 million addicted to tobacco, and 25 million addicted to "love and/or sex."[8] The matter of definition and treatment is no small matter!

Pleasure as a Dimension of Addiction

Curiously, any reference to pleasure in addiction is not found in the DSM-III-R or in the Christian Textbook's definition (above) either. However, I want to add that element, because it is an important dimension of addiction. For simplicity, I will use pleasure quite broadly to include a range of emotions, such as enjoyment, excitement, euphoria, elation, contentment, and satisfaction.

Pleasure may become accompanied by feelings that have more to do with comfort or security over time. Because an addict is agitated when he is separated from his addiction, the addiction becomes a relief from this agitation. In many instances, this relief (comfort or security) becomes the primary driving force of his addiction.

For example, a workaholic may initially get a great deal of pleasure from his work, but over time it becomes a burden. However, he is far more comfortable (or finds his security) in his familiar work patterns. With the drug "addict," there is no doubt that pleasure is the primary motivation for beginning that behavior. Over time, the "addiction" becomes a heavy, destructive burden. However, even here, pleasure remains a strong motivating influence, not just the compulsion and physical need for the drug(s).

Addiction as Primarily Involving Sin

There has been a great deal of debate among American evangelicals concerning whether addiction is disease or sin. Perhaps the debate could be divided into two categories according to the presence or absence of drugs. There is little or no debate that cocaine abuse or even cigarette smoking create a physical dependency. By contrast, a compulsive gambler has no physical dependency, only a mental craving.

However, in spite of this distinction, I want to keep all addicts in one category. First, many "professionals" (as documented above) do so. Second, the mental drive (as pleasure and/or comfort — see below) to an addiction far exceeds the physical drive. Thus, *such compulsive behavior is better labeled "besetting sin," rather than addiction.*

Besetting Sin

"Besetting sin" was common parlance in evangelical circles for several centuries until the last few decades. The concept derives from Hebrews 12:1 where this word makes its only appearance in the New Testament. "Therefore let us also, seeing we are compassed about with so great a cloud of witnesses, lay aside every weight, and the sin which doth so easily beset us, and let us run with patience the race that is set before us ..." (KJV).

Thomas Hewitt argues for besetting sin as one that "clings so closely ... to some ... who, failing to break from it, were still at the starting-post of the Christian life."[9] E.K. Simpson writes that besetting can "be used in a pejorative acceptation of a state of beleaguerment, or exigencies and straits ... like ... a 'squeeze.'"[10]

John Calvin writes of besetting sin.

"This is the heaviest burden that impedes us. ... He (the writer of Hebrews) speaks not of outward, or, as they say, of actual sins, but of the very fountain, even concupiescence or lust, which so possesses every part of us, that we feel that we are on every side held by its snares."[11]

John Owen devotes three paragraphs to "besetting" in his Annotations to Calvin's commentary on Hebrews."[12] He concludes in this way:

"The (Greek) word *euperistaton* means literally, 'well-standing-around' ... or 'the readily surrounding sin,' that is the sin which easily surrounds us, and thereby entangles us, so as to prevent us, like long garments, to run our courses. ... If the word be taken in an active sense, then what is meant is the deceptive power of sin...."

Noah Webster in his 1828 dictionary defines "beset" as "1) to surround; to inclose; to hem in; to besiege ...; 2) to press on all sides, so as to perplex; to entangle, so as to render escape difficult or impossible."[13] As an adjective, he defines "besetting" as "*habitually* attending."

In this way, Webster links "beset" to "addict" which is "to apply oneself *habitually*, to devote time and attention by customary practice ... more usually in a bad sense, to follow customarily, or devote, by habitually practising that which is ill, as a man addicted to intemperance."[14]

What Difference Does a Label (Diagnosis) Make?

The cause of a problem virtually determines its solution. In medicine, the diagnosis determines the treatment. A physician does not give a heart medicine to a patient with a bacterial pneumonia who needs an antibiotic. In engineering, the cause of a bridge's collapse determines what is needed to prevent another collapse. Increased strength of materials will not give greater durability to a bridge with a foundation in soft earth.

The problem with addictions is primarily their mental component. By "mental," I mean moral or spiritual. My brief argument for this position is three-fold. First, physical dependence cannot be the primary determinant of addiction. Simply, some people addicted to the same drugs at the same dosage are able to quit while others cannot. The explanation cannot be physical, that is, purely biochemical since the biochemical situations (including genetic factors[15]) are virtually the same.

Second, addiction has been applied far beyond physical dependence on drugs, as we have seen. As described above, this extension has been almost careless.[16]

Third, the Bible clearly labels one form of addiction, drunkenness, as a sin (Proverbs 20:1; 23:29-35; Ephesians 5:18; I Peter 4:4). In certain passages, e.g., I Corinthians 6-9-10, drunkenness is listed among other grievous sins that can be conquered ("and such *were* some of you," v. 11). This passage argues strongly that God does not consider the physical dependence of one sin (drunkenness) an excuse for one's indulgence.[17] The passage argues, but much less strongly, for such passages being lists of addictions, especially in the common parlance of today.

A Definition and a Wrap-Up

In light of the above, I want to suggest a new definition for addiction.

"Addiction is a repetitive, pleasure-seeking behavior that is habitual in spite of moral or physical reasons (i.e., harm) that should rationally preclude its practice and that displaces spiritual obligations."

Further, I want to suggest that "besetting sin" be a synonym for addiction. Jay Adams uses the term "life-dominating"[18] which is a good, descriptive synonym also. Besetting sin, however, links the modern craze to label so many behaviors as addiction with a biblical text and with past centuries. This link prevents modern psychological labels from overshadowning the reality that these repetitive patterns are sin.

First, besetting sin reveals that these sins are not new. While some particulars may be new or more prevalent (drug abuse, anorexia, etc.), their life-dominating, irresponsible patterns are not.

Second, solutions to the problems of addictions as besetting sins point to regeneration and obedience to biblical teaching rather than a psychological and/or medical approach. As a physician, I realize that physical dependence on alcohol and drugs is a real phenomenon. Further, withdrawal from some of these substances can be severe, even deadly. However, apart from the immediate withdrawal period, the mental (spiritual) craving far exceeds the physical craving.

My purpose here is not to outline a plan to manage these life-dominating problems. In changing the label of "addictions" to "besetting sins" both the counselor and physician would focus on the primary dimension of the problem. What is needed is a whole-lfie, comprehensive approach to the "addict's" spiritual life, as Dr. Jay Adams has directed (above). The medical and psychological models of such besetting sins are designed for failure because they do not deal with the great spiritual need in these people. Perhaps this paper will generate further discussion and implementation of a more thoroughly biblical approach.

Endnotes

1. Sykes, Charles, J., **A Nation of Victims: The Decay of the American Character**, New York: St. Martin's Press, 1992, p. 13.

2. In my writings, I am increasingly putting such people as "experts," "officials," and "professionals" within quotation marks. While they have such status by academic degree, peer recognition, or rank of government office, such standing is dubious at best, because they are unable and/or unwilling to speak the moral element of problems (which is often the most important element). Almost exclusively, these people are humanists, anti-Christian, and anti-God. God says that they are "fools" (Psalm 14:1).

3. I often use "moral," "spiritual," "ethical," and "biblical" as synonyms. I am aware of the nuances of these words, but their primary meaning is often the same.

4. I am not endorsing these diagnoses as accurate or true. I am merely pointing out here that any claim that modern psychiatry is "scientific" can be countered simply by professionals' failure to use their own recognized standards!

5. **Diagnostic and Statistical Manual of Mental Disorder (Third Edition, Revised)**, Washington, D.C.: American Psychiatric Association, 1987, p. 165.

6. I use the general label "psychologist" to include psychiatrists. While there are some particulars to each, their general approach to diagnosis and treatment of patients (clients) is similarly unbiblical. Using both labels, psychology and psychiatry, makes for awkward writing and reading.

7. Harrison, R.K., Ed., **Encyclopedia of Biblical and Christian Ethics (Revised Edition)**, Nashville: Thomas Nelson Publishers, 1992, pp. 6-7.

8. Bobgan, Martin & Deidre, "Behavior or Disease," *Journal of Biblical Ethics in Medicine*, Vol. 4, 1990, pp. 67-69, quoting Stanley Peale, **Diseasing of America: Addiction Treatment Out of Control**, Lexington, MA: Stanley Heath & Company, 1989, p. 68.

9. Hewitt, Thomas, **Tyndale New Testament Commentaries: Hebrews**, Grand Rapids: Wm. B. Eerdmans Publishing Company, 1960, pp. 189-190.

10. Quoted by F.F. Bruce in **The International Commentary on the New Testament: Hebrews**, Grand Rapids: Wm. B. Eerdmans, 1964, pp. 349-350.

11. Calvin, John, **Commentaries on the Epistle of Paul the Apostle to the Hebrews**, translated by the Rev. John Owen, Grand Rapids, Baker Book House, 1979, pp. 394-395.

12. *Ibid.*, pp. 311-313.

13. Webster, Noah, **American Dictionary of the English Language**, 1828 edition, San Francisco, Foundation for American Christian Education, 1967.

14. *Ibid.*

15. Genes that have been thought to predispose or cause addictions have little or no correlation as to whether an addict is able to quit or not.

16. There is some evidence that opiate-like endorphins and enkephlins in human brains may provide something like a drug dependence in addictive behaviors. If further research gives greater substance to this relationship, then many, possibly all, addictions could also have a physical basis. However, such findings would not negate my position here.

17. Ephesians 5:18 argues for moral/spiritual control, rather than the lack of control of a chemically-induced state, drunkenness.

18. Adams, Jay E., **The Christian Counselor's Manual**, Grand Rapids, Baker Book House, 1973, pp. 206ff.

Beisner's Bites

Excerpts from an address by E. Calvin Beisner to the
Conference on Christians in a Pluralistic Society, Covenant
College, (Tennessee) June 27 - July 1, 1993.

Per capita health expense compared with selected other expenses, 1990

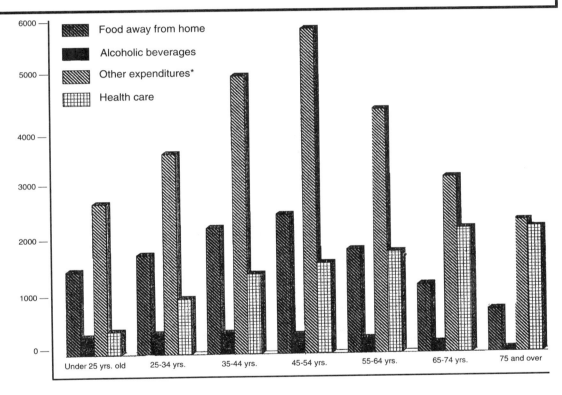

Cal Beisner has researched carefully a number of the economic features of health care in recent decades. Among the fascinating relationships he has uncovered is the following: "Most families spend several times more on such largely discretionary items as food eaten away from home, and a group of other combined expenses (including entertainment, "personal care," reading, education, tobacco and smoking supplies, cash contributions, and miscellaneous expenditures) than they do per capita on health costs, and almost as much on alcoholic beverages as on per capita health costs. Relatively non-painful shifting of spending priorities would enable most families to handle their health costs without assistance."

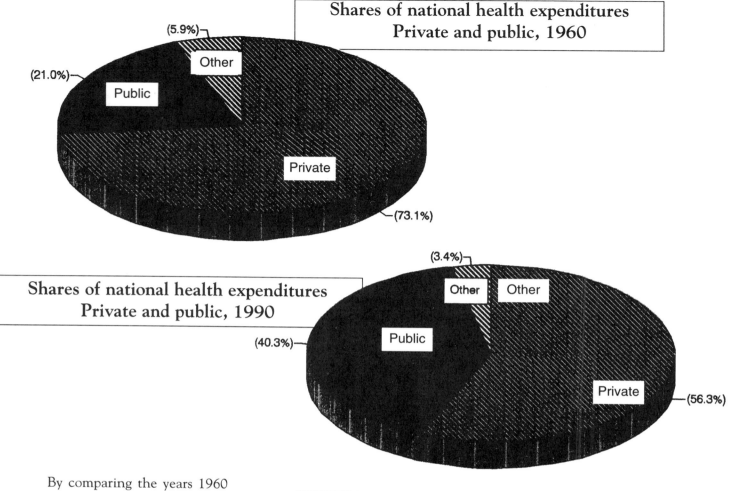

**Shares of national health expenditures
Private and public, 1960**

(5.9%) Other

(21.0%) Public

(73.1%) Private

**Shares of national health expenditures
Private and public, 1990**

(3.4%) Other

(40.3%) Public

Other

(56.3%) Private

By comparing the years 1960 and 1990, Cal Beisner graphically illustrates for us the shift of the burden of health care expenditures from private payment sources to public sources. There has been a corresponding shift in the proportion of out-of-pocket expenses. (This reduction in proportion should not be confused with a reduction in the actual out-of-pocket expenses, since the total expenditures in the same interval have increased. Individuals pay *more* from our pockets than we did in 1960, despite insurance.) From these graphs we may note that the private and out-of-pocket expenditures become less prominent in the total cost, these two loci of governance of cost and quality are rendered economically less potent.

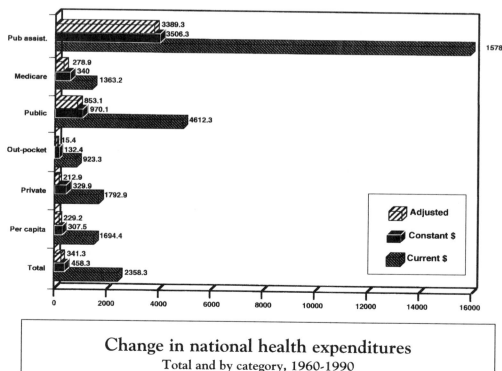

Pub assist. 3389.3 / 3506.3 / 15780

Medicare 278.9 / 340 / 1363.2

Public 853.1 / 970.1 / 4612.3

Out-pocket 15.4 / 132.4 / 923.3

Private 212.9 / 329.9 / 1792.9

Per capita 229.2 / 307.5 / 1694.4

Total 341.3 / 458.3 / 2358.3

Legend:
Adjusted
Constant $
Current $

Change in national health expenditures
Total and by category, 1960-1990

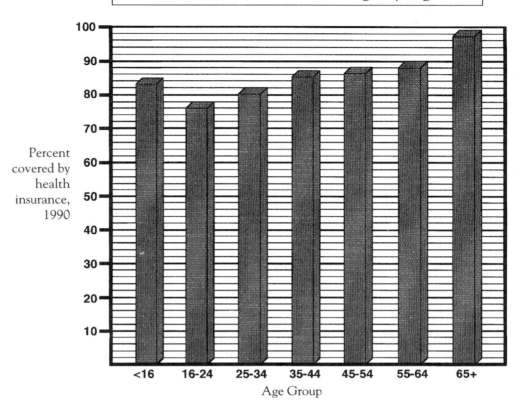

Medical Insurance Coverage by Age

Percent covered by health insurance, 1990

Age Group

In this bar graph taken from data gathered by Cal Beisner we see illustrated the fact that "health insurance coverage, by age group, closely reflects the needs for health care by age group. In the oldest group, at highest health risk, insurance coverage is nearly universal — 99.7% in 1990. Among those 25 - 64 years old and under 16 years, coverage is all over 80%. Only for those 16 - 24 years old does it drop below 80% — to 78%."

Cal Beisner notes that there is good reason to doubt the overall efficacy of much of the increased spending on health care. "The most fundamental work of health care is to extend human life. In the thirty years from 1960 to 1990, while total annual health expenditures, in constant dollars, have risen 458%, from $91.4 billion to $510.3 billion, and annual expenditures per capita have risen 308%, from $482 to $1,966, life expectancy at birth has risen only 8 per cent, from 69.7 years to 75.4 years.

"Additionally, only a small part of the increase in life expectancy appears attributable to health care consumption. Much of it stems from generally healthier living by Americans, whose diets are improving; who reduced their accidental injury rates by 15 per cent from 1970-1989; whose cigarette smoking rate fell by anywhere from 26 to 57 percent, depending on age group, from 1974 to 1991; whose rate of alcohol use fell by anywhere from 4 to 40 percent over the same period; who have become increasingly involved in sports and other forms of healthy physical exercise; and who reduced their accidental death rate by 44 percent from 1970 to 1990.

" ... We must not be too hasty to condemn health care providers for this as if it were a sign of their failure. The blame may instead be on health care consumers, who have unrealistic expectations about the degree of benefits to be expected from additional spending on health care. We may be pressing against the margin of additional life expectancy, and the marginal returns on additional investment may be small to vanishing. We may need to consider whether continued increases in such spending are wise stewardship."

" ... If there is a crisis in American health care, it is more likely that we consume too much, spending money on it wastefully, than that we consume too little. There are exceptions — those who need care that they cannot afford and who are not covered by insurance. But these are few and far between, and private philanthropic resources appear more than adequate to meet their expenses.

" ... Particularly as Christians, we need to recover appreciation for the sovereignty and providence of God. The almost feverish quest for health care, and insurance to pay for it, often betrays a failure to trust in God's faithfulness to keep His promise to work all things together for good toward those who love Him and are called according to His purpose (Romans 8:28), and our anxiety when we don't have insurance indicates our failure to learn, as the Apostle Paul learned, to be content regardless of our circumstances (Philippians 4:12)."

Dr. Beisner gives a personal illustration of an outworking of his views on health insurance. "Our family lived entirely without health insurance from late 1985 through mid-1992, during which four new children were born to us, one child broke an arm, and Debby and I suffered various mild illnesses. We tried early to buy health insurance, but found it unaffordable on our less-than-poverty-level income — and we believed it was wrong to seek or accept government payments for our health care. We never lacked what we needed, even when, during one pregnancy, complications led to the need for a large number of ultrasounds, at a price that we believe would have come to over $2000; we never learned the cost, because the Christian doctor who performed them for us, having learned that I was a self-employed Christian involved in ministry and without insurance, refused to charge us, saying simply that it was his birthday and he could do that for us if he wanted to."

(With national health care in the offing, one wonders if Christians with Dr. Beisner's convictions will be legally permitted to act on our belief that it is wrong to accept government payments for health care. For the plans being proposed now in Washington the proscriptions will not be upon the seeker of self-payed care, but upon the providers, forbidding us from rendering services outside the system. Such systems are slave systems.)

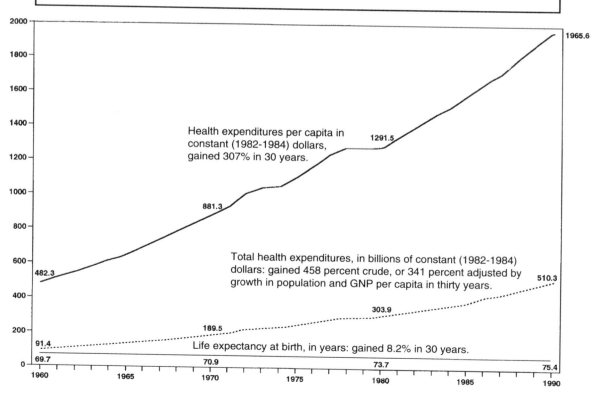

**Life Expectancy and health expenditures
United States, 1960 - 1990**

Health expenditures per capita in constant (1982-1984) dollars, gained 307% in 30 years.

1965.6

1291.5

881.3

482.3

Total health expenditures, in billions of constant (1982-1984) dollars: gained 458 percent crude, or 341 percent adjusted by growth in population and GNP per capita in thirty years.

510.3

303.9

189.5

91.4

Life expectancy at birth, in years: gained 8.2% in 30 years.

69.7   70.9   73.7   75.4

1960   1965   1970   1975   1980   1985   1990

To Care in a Christian Context

Gregory W. Rutecki, M.D. and Gregory E. Nettle

Gregory Rutecki is Associate Professor of Medicine at Northeastern Ohio Universities College of Medicine Affiliated Hospitals at Canton, Ohio. Mr. Nettle is Senior Minister at Jackson Christian Church in Massillon, Ohio.

"In other words, we are likely to be stingy of whatever is most valuable to us: perhaps money, but often time and smiles. The priest and the levite who passed by the beaten traveler in Chapter 10 of Luke's gospel probably tithed but they were stingy — only the Good Samaritan was not." Marvin Olasky[1]

"Words carry a political charge; words shape our ideas and understanding." Marvin Olasky[2]

Contemporary discourse employs a vocabulary detached from the values of traditional etymology. Alterations in word significance — and more importantly in the translation of words into behavior — are not limited to so called politically correct vocabulary. Juxtaposition of 19th century and contemporary definitions of the word compassion may serve as an example of modern language drawn through "the looking glass."[3] In 1834, the first edition of Webster's dictionary defined compassion as "a suffering with another or painful sympathy." However, the second edition redefined compassion as "the feeling or emotion when a person is moved by the suffering or distress of another and by the desire to relieve it." Most recently, the third edition describes compassion as a "deep feeling for and understanding of misery or suffering and the concomitant desire to promote its alleviation." During a period of one hundred and sixty years, the connotation of compassion has been stripped of suffering with and replaced by only feeling or desire — a shell of the original definition. Likewise, our predecessors defined "stingy" as "not sharing that which is most valuable." The word "stingy" is still pejorative, but its meaning is now limited to a feeling for money. Contemporary misuse of the essence and actions of what these and other words originally intended has indeed reshaped our ideas and understanding of the world.

Germane to our discussion, words utilized to describe the *telos* of medicine seem to have suffered a similar fate. One such word, "care" — almost synonymous with medicine itself — appears to have undergone an evolution detached from both traditional and biblical etymology. As a result, medical care has undergone a "connotative transition"[4] in a society expecting care to be represented solely by diagnostic scanners and therapeutic gadgetry aimed at cure.

Recently, I became even more conscious of the connotative transition of care in considering the aphorism that "a picture is worth a thousand words." A recent photographic anthology of medicine 1840 - 1940[5] published a photograph entitled, "Comfort in the Absence of Cure." The disparity in physician attitudes concerning death circa 1840 vis a vis today reveal a striking contrast. The picture shows a physician practicing a nineteenth century definition of medical care as he leans over a dying patient using soothing touch as his medium. The accompanying caption reads, "Physician Johnathan Letterman soothes a dying patient. When this picture was taken, there was often little else a doctor could do for the very ill." Indeed, as I reflected on the meaning of the picture for contemporary medicine, I felt uneasy about a disturbing difference. One hundred and fifty years later, I still have very little of substance to offer regarding cure of the very ill. Does comfort comprise a significant portion of my care?

This paper is a search for the quintessential meaning of the word "care," especially as care describes the good of medicine. Our search will require a contextualization and Biblical study of care; an identification of needs that urge a response of care; resolution of the contemporary confusion between care and cure through a review of the current cosmology and anthropomorphism driving science; and, finally, prescriptions for Biblical change in a prevalent world view dominated by self sufficiency and autonomy.

INTRODUCTION: THE CONTEXT OF MEDICAL CARE

"Care is context dependent. ... it is a notion that is incomplete because its significance depends on further specification in relation to particular roles, principals, expectations and institutions." Stanley Hauerwas[6]

An enterprise to accurately define care must begin with the realization that care is a single word utilized in multiple contexts. Misidentification of the context in which care is rendered may create unnecessary ambiguity. Use of any word in multiple contexts often reveals a final definition greater than the sum of each part. The English word "love" is similar to care in this regard and may serve as an example. In Greek, the language of the New Testament, love is empowered with four separate components applicable to context — agape, philos, eros, and storge. For example, love consummated as eros is only appropriate in the context of marriage. Agape, however, may represent the ultimate of Christian love in any context.

In order to similarly define and evaluate care, we must begin by appreciating that care, like love, should be studied in both context and essential components. For Christians, care in the context of medicine must involve components not normally addressed in contemporary culture.

Care, either individual or corporate, necessitates an intimacy between medical caregiver and Christian community.[7] Medicine needs to be both surrounded and influenced by the church so that medicine may be true to its commitment. Only the church is empowered to make the necessary connections required among illness, suffering, death, and sin — essential to place medical care in appropriate context.[8] This intimate relationship should be inhabited by a theology of medicine recognizing suffering and death as a reality in a fallen world. Final cure of disease is achieved only at the resurrection of the body upon Christ's return. The connection of church and medicine is further intensified in the "central paradox of the New Testament — strength comes only through weakness."[9] as care and community are taken to their biblical conclusion. Thus, the most fundamental and important question of all for medicine and care may be answered: "What kind of community is necessary to sustain the longterm care of the ill according to biblical standards" — since medicine as cure must ultimately fail?[10] Essential to the development of a community-medicine relationship is that the church and the Christian practice of medicine remain distinctive from the culture which they inhabit. Vigilance is necessary, in order to combat contemporary Zeitgeist and resultant misconception of suffering as something always to be overcome. A Biblical goal for medicine is not the eradication of suffering but rather relief of suffering through the formation of a community willing to be with people during illness. Quite simply, medicine and the Christian community must approach care together as they pledge to be at the very least a human presence in the face of suffering.[11] Within this context for care, church and health care workers become inseparable.

A BIBLICAL CONSTRUCT FOR CARE: THE ESSENTIALS

"But God, who comforts the downcast, comforted us by the coming of Titus." (2 Cor. 7:6; 2 Cor. 1:3ff; Mt. 25:31-46)

Hanson realizes that Paul's lesson in this verse "is that the sufferer is not forgotten, because God cares and often expresses His caring through the comfort given by other people."[12] He states further that, "Paul sees an ordinary series of events in theological perspective. The arrival of his friend with good news encourages Paul who is afflicted with anxieties and conflicts in his work; but it is ultimately God who comforted Paul through Titus. Thus for Paul, the aid that one human being gives to the other is a human transaction grounded in and manifesting the character of God, 2 Cor. 1:3."[13] Care manifesting the character of God is expressed by people in medical settings without resort to technology or cure which are best evaluated separate from care. Once we experience care and comfort, God calls us to comfort others as He has comforted or cared for us. We become "stingy" of care whenever we "care" for others or demonstrate compassion in indirect or impersonal ways. Biblical care involves the acts of people who touch, interact, and quietly listen to those who suffer. A fleshing out of care as evidenced in the early Church may be pertinent. A paradigm for "care" involved a witness against abortion and may serve as a worthwhile application of care to daily life. Such care is contained in the early church's adoption and nurture of unwanted children. For a moment allow me to reframe the abortion debate as not only an issue of intrinsic right or wrong but even more so of an issue of comunity response in care. The Reverend Terry

Hamilton considers Mt. 25:31-46 a living model applied by the early church in a working out of care.[14] Care, then, especially as it confronted the immoral practice of abortion and infanticide, was comprised of the idea of 2 Cor. 7:6, 2 Cor. 1:3ff, and Mt. 25:31-46. The Reverend Hamilton's and Hauerwas' impression is that one aspect of such care was intimate and personal as it entailed a constant readiness to receive unwanted children, an explicit sanctification of the family, an appreciation that the new life of children was an enrichment of the Christian community and a celebration of the hospitality of life as a gift. All of these responses spoke out as living testimony against abortion through the positive example of adoption and child rearing. The quintessence of this community response to care resides in a consideration of the word "care" as a verb and not a noun. A contemporary commercial says, "*Care* enough to send the very best," then fails to do so. When a Christian cares enough, the very best is a personal, prayerful presence, not stingy or material substitutes.[15] Contemporary connotation of the verb "care" leads to an impersonal United Way contribution or dependence on entitlement systems both fraught with a number of unacceptable results.[16] Bona fide Christian care humbles rhetoric and check writing and lends credence to the proverb that actions speak louder than words or money. Compassion as an essential component of care requires suffering with as the primary component. An attitude of care disallows stinginess of time and demands presence, commitment, and smiles which manifest the character of God Himself.

THE CHALLENGES OF CONTEMPORARY CARE

"It is precisely because all genuine suffering includes psychological and social dimensions as well as the physical, that comfort from others is so terribly important. The sufferer longs to be assured that others care, and that others are striving to relieve the suffering. To feel abandoned, alone in one's suffering, would crush the sufferer with an unbearable burden." Hanson[17]

"They are tempted to shun the suffering because they stand as a sign of the brokenness of the world. Without a truthful acknowledgement of the brokenness of the world, care givers are tempted to remove all traces of the pain and suffering, even if that finally requires removal of the sufferers." Lammers and Verhey[18]

In order to frame descriptive and prescriptive aspects of contemporary care gone wrong, the spirit of our age, which has redefined care must be discussed. But first, recipients of care — the suffering, dying, and community which they inhabit — will be studied for identifying characteristics. Further scrutiny then will determine where contemporary society stands in relation to scripture and earlier church practice. Since to be human is to both suffer and die, characteristics of suffering and death may at first seem obvious. However, discussion of the characteristics of suffering and dying is essential at this point in order to identify the specific needs residing in recipients of care. Only then may contemporary evaluation be pursued. In order to approach this daunting task, I will list several characteristics of the sufferer that may or may not be apparent.

First, those who suffer are alienated. Scripture describes alienation as an existential reality and as such, alienation may be studied by reading any of the Psalms of disorientation.[19] Care responsive to the disorientation of pain and loss was demonstrated by Job's friends during his trial. His friends sought to apprise him that though he was alienated, he was not alone. Care in Job's context required only being with but remaining silent. In fact, later verbalization of faulty theodicies interfered with the ministry of comfort and care. Less intimate contact as an aspect of care is available to hospital, nursing home, or home bound sufferer in the late 20th century. The material substitute of IVAC's and monitor alarms are grossly inadequate.

The existence of suffering and death also reminds each of us of the reality of brokenness. As a consequence of the fall of man and a post-enlightenment hubris born of scientism, our contemporaries tend to ignore brokenness by ignoring the ones who need care the most — the suffering and dying. Abandonment is often the contemporary response to brokenness — a response totally foreign to a Biblical definition of care. Apropos of our prior discussion of community, only the Christian community understands brokenness in the context of suffering and dying. Only the church has the appropriate world view perspective to respond. Ignorance of brokenness and its relationship to sin leads to the isolation of those who suffer and die at a time when they desire human contact.

A third characteristic of those who suffer and die is their dependence on others. The dependence of the suffering and dying repels the depraved part of our nature which seeks a contemporary mindset of independence and self-sufficiency. This part of our fallen nature relies on government programs and nursing homes for care, rather than families. Dependency will not push away the sufferer if Christians realize that the very content of revelation teaches us precisely that we are *all* a dependent people.[20] We will likewise need to depend on others at some time and must remain cognizant of our total dependence on Christ.

Mutual dependency should also remind the sufferer, in the context of Matthew 25, that he/she is rewarding the one who ministers. This is the second side of care in that the one ministered to actually represents Christ to the minister. Thus the sufferer is simultaneously blessing the one who ministers, as he/she is blessed, in the midst of suffering and death. Hauerwas reminds us that "the very willingness of those who suffer from illness to be in the presence of the well is a form of service." Suffering and pain make us vulnerable, and we try to protect ourselves through "self-sufficiency." "A willingness to be present, as well as to accept the assistance of others when help is needed, is a gift we give one another."[21]

I have reached the point of readiness for contemporary social commentary by digression; a point that will propose a world view metaphor for our age relating to medical care. This commentary will attempt explanation of the mindset that led to connotative transitions in the word "care." Prevalent world view perspectives of our day are divorced from both scripture and tradition. Immersion in the spirit of the age and recognition of its eventual effects on definitions, behavior, and care are instructive to our final prescriptions.

MEDICINE AS RELIGION: A HINDRANCE TO CARE OR "WHY ANTHROPODICY" HAS REPLACED THEODICY[22]

"In the machine age he [Darwin] established a mechanical conception of organic life. He paralleled the human struggle with a natural struggle. In an acquisitive hereditary society he stated acquisition and inheritance as the primary means of survival." Geoffrey West[23]

"Our concepts of nature are supremely anthropomorphic, reflecting our desire to make everything conform to our current image of ourselves. Rank believes that our concepts of nature tell us more about ourselves at any given moment in time than they do about nature itself." Jeremy Rifkin on Otto Rank[24]

The scientific training of health care workers may obscure an essential fact of life: cultural influences substantially affect scientific assumptions. In fact, the realization that science and technology are not pristine empiric observations or free from cultural influence, is essential to rescue Christians from the ultimate of intellectual deceptions (1 Cor. 1:19-20)

In the following section, I will develop two interrelated thoughts. First, through a presentation of Jeremy Rifkin on Charles Darwin, I hope to demonstrate that the "science" of evolution is an example of an anthropomorphic bias masquerading as scientific dogma. The direction of scientific experiments, as well as the interpretation and application of results, are contingent on a desire to make everything conform to our current images of ourselves. I will then extrapolate Rifkin's model of science as anthropomorhism and

apply it to contemporary definitions and expectations of medical care representing a technological and anthropomorphic syncretism that is removed from original intent. Such anthropomorphism drives the *telos* of medicine and is most responsible for changes in a definition of care. It will be apparent to the Christian that today's syncretism represents a medical care system in need of Biblical healing.[25]

Jeremy Rifkin develops a paradigm for a preceding age of science through the example of Charles Darwin and his cosmology.[26] Rifkin makes it clear that one cannot divorce either Darwin or his discoveries from the social context in which they developed. To develop this idea, events concurrent with Darwin's scientific thought will be presented. Darwin inhabited an English colonialism represented by a variety of "natural selection" and "survival of the fittest." The concomitant invention of the telegraph and railroad, as well as the development of technology and industry exceeding the accomplishments of previous cultures, suggested an acquisitiveness and progress in mankind. Finally, a staggering advance in artificial breeding engendered further thought about selection and survival. English culture was at its intellectually "evolved" apex. Rifkin trenchantly observes that, in his scientific writings, Darwin dressed up nature with an English personality, ascribed English motivations and drive, and even provided nature with an English marketplace and an English form of government.[27] The "pure" science of evolution was conformed to Darwin's image of himself and his culture. "Darwin strayed from what could be proven by observation and the naked eye to what had to be imagined and conjectured by a fertile mind."[28] Tom Bethell further suggested that, "what Darwin really discovered was really no more than a Victorian propensity to believe in progress."[29] Darwin could not and did not remove his contemporary English cosmology from his conceptualization of nature in his particular science. More than one hundred years later, the continued holes in the fabric of evolutionary science are not surprising in such a context.

If one accepts Rifkin's example of Darwin's science as telling us more about Darwin and his culture than about nature itself, allow me to look at a more contemporary cosmology to evaluate anthropodicy and prevalent beliefs concerning medicine. In fact, Rifkin took this further step himself as he appreciated that genetic engineering was one attempt of contemporary medicine to perfect the shortcomings of Darwin's cosmology for a new generation; a generation which ahs come to expect more of medicine and science than ever before.

We begin our contemporary study of cosmology by describing the current *telos* of medicine. Medicine strives to eradicate or eliminate suffering and death by a complete elimination of the causes of suffering and death. Society is convinced that such a goal is both reasonable and achievable. A modern technology with the capability to alter genes or their products, to transplant failed single organs, or to open closed arteries demands a desperate faith in its suffering followers. What medicine thinks about, strives and pays for is a barometer of our ethos imprinted on science, not an accurate description of science, per se. Though religion has been closely allied with medicine and its goals throughout the centuries, the unreasonable expectation of medicine to end disease and suffering makes physicians in contempo-

rary society the priests of a new religion. The hubris inherent in continued post-enlightenment scientific discovery and the systematic elimination of God and religion from our marketplace are symptoms and signs of a contemporary cosmology gone wrong. Medicine's expensive science tells us a lot more about our society's expectations and as such is driven by the anthropomorphism of autonomy and absolute faith in science.

Medicine's counterfeit promise of immortality reflects itself most in the contemporary anthropodicy of death. Death is one aspect of the human condition to be avoided at all costs! The suffering that may surround death leads to either despair or a collective silence rather than care.[30]

Allow me to proceed one step further in a contemporary secular anthropodicy — to the question of the elimination of the sufferer. Medicine and society's posit of an unattainable goal — namely the elimination of suffering — is an unacceptable chink in the armor of our new religion. If suffering has no place in this cosmology — might we see the next logical step as removal of the sufferer? Since no agreed upon *telos* is available for aging, suffering or death, what better way to eliminate the visible failures of medicine than by eliminating the source of failure — the sufferers themselves. If suffering is not allowed or explained in this cosmology, euthanasia may readily become an accepted solution.

So how would care be defined in contemporary cosmolgy and then used in idiom and action? Care could only be associated with attempts to cure utilizing the most up-to-date scientific discoveries. For the believer, such discoveries reaffirm a hope in the physical extension of life at all costs. Isn't this why medical care

immediately connotes or becomes the equivalent of cure-related interventions and up-to-date technology? When death is imminent in such a system, care cannot be extricated from cure since death reminds medicine of its failure to attain what is unattainable. We are led then to the inescapable fact that care must be defined most carefully for the Christian in the shadow and inevitability of death. So we proceed. Only then is care distilled to a pure definition unencumbered by technology and science.

HOW SHOULD WE THEN LIVE? THE TASK OF OUR CHRISTIAN COMMUNITY TO CARE FOR THE SUFFERING AND DYING

"The only thing Christians should say about suffering is that God suffers with us. That is the meaning of the cross. If so, medicine may be more important as a gesture of care in the midst of suffering than as a promise of a technological triumph over suffering." Lammers and Verhey[31]

"The problem of the relation between caring and curing is perhaps most clearly but by no means exclusively, illustrated in relation to how we deal with the dying." Stanley Hauerwas[32]

An essential context and component of medical care is its intimate reliance on death for its complete definition. Hauerwas places medicine as theodicy smack in the center of the question of care and the discussion of death. Like Dostoevsky before him, he confronts the most difficult of theodicies and care — that of children dying. To accomplish this, he develops and discusses a play by Bluebond-Langner which studies children dying of leukemia.[33] Jeffrey, a child-leukemic close to death, asks Bluebond-Langner to read to him from *Charlotte's Web*, specifically from the chapter when Charlotte dies. This children's story confronts death and hope; Hauerwas quotes from the book "nobody, of the hundreds of people that had visited the fair, knew that a gray spider had played the most important part of all. No one was with Charlotte when she died."

Hauerwas' following commentary serves as an incisive prescription for medicine and the church relating to care. "But a child's death should not imitate a spider's. It may be that spiders are meant to live a little while and die, but we who are created for friendship with one another and with God cannot believe that this is "all there is." It may be that spiders are destined to die alone, but as those who believe that we are destined to enjoy one another and God, we cannot allow ourselves and our loved ones so to die. We have no theodicy that can soften the pain of our death and the death of our children, but we believe that we share a common story which makes it possible for us to be with one another especially as we die. There can be no way to remove the loneliness of the death of leukemic children unless they see witnessed in the lives of those who care for them a confidence rooted in friendship with God and with one another. That, finally, is the only response we have to "the problem" of the death of our children.[34] Consistent with a definition of care which confronts death, Christian health care workers don't need to discuss theodicy — they need intimate relationships with God and with people. (2 Cor. 1:3ff)

Even though a semblance or component of care may shine through many aspects of medicine, suspension of attempts to cure as death approaches really defines medicine *qua* care. As care is stripped of any pretext of cure, it entails many essential attributes. It is always personal care and never indirect. It is care and medicine connected to the supportive environment of church community. It is a care that understands the existential reality of alienation, disorientation, dependence, brokenness, suffering, and death. As such, it realizes that care may relieve some of these but not prevent any. It does not place faith in technology but rather in the old definitions of love, compassion, and stinginess, all nurtured within a theology of medicine. Care in essence is an attitude of the heart which listens, hugs, and places the cross as the only theodicy in the economy of suffering and death. Only when we are most weak do we rely most on God's strength. Nowhere is this more clear than at the time of death. A Biblical example of care at the time of death will serve as a final description of care.

It is 66 A.D. Nero is emperor of Rome and the Apostle Paul is in prison. The political climate is volatile — especially so if you are a Christian. Nero has just burned the city, not only fiddling while it burned, but to raise public outcry, also spreading rumors that the followers of Christ were to blame.

Paul's final Roman imprisonment is not to be confused with his "house arrest" recorded in the latter chapters of the Book of Acts. It is a widely accepted view that Paul was released after his first imprisonment in Rome and continued his missionary ministry, even perhaps traveling to Spain.[35]

But now, Paul sits in his prison cell at a rough table. And, in the dim light he puts pen to parchment and writes what was to be his final letter.

Paul, an apostle of Christ Jesus by the will of God, according to the promise of life that is in Christ Jesus. To Timothy, my dear son. ... I thank God, whom I serve, as my forefathers did, with a clear conscience, as night and day I constantly remember you in my prayers. Recalling your tears, I long to see you, so that I may be filled with joy.

I am already being poured out like a drink offering, and the time has come for my departure. I have fought the good fight, I have finished the race, I have kept the faith. Now there is in store for me the crown of righteousness, which the Lord, the righteous Judge, will award to me on that day — and not only to me, but also to all who have longed for his appearing.

Do your best to come to me quickly, for Demas, because he loved this world, has deserted me ... Crescens has gone to Galatia, and Titus to Dalmatia. Only Luke is with me. Get Mark and bring him with you, because he is helpful to me in my ministry.

When you come, bring the cloak that I left with Carpus at Troas, and my scrolls, especially the parchments.

Timothy, at my first defense, no one came to my support, but everyone deserted me. May it not be held against them.

My dear son, do your best to get here before winter. ..."

The Lord be with your spirit. Grace be with you. Love, Paul.[36]

Paul the Apostle, the "Great Lion of God." Exposed to death again and again, five times receiving the forty lashes, three times beaten with rods, once stoned, spending a night and a day in the open sea, knowing both hunger and thirst — often going without food, cold and naked he learned to be content no matter the circumstances.[37]

Paul, who stood before kings and preached the Gospel. Who sat with philosophers and challenged their thinking, who traveled over the known world proclaiming the good news that Jesus Christ is Lord — cries out to Timothy: **Do your best to come to me quickly.**

CARE: PAUL'S PHYSICAL NEEDS:

In II Timothy 4:13, Paul writes to Timothy asking him to **bring the cloak I left with Carpus, at Troas, and my scrolls, especially the parchments.** In a cold, dank prison cell, coming to the close of his earthly life, Paul acknowledges that the warmth of his simple cloak would bring him comfort.

As Christians who are called to meet the needs of our neighbor,[38] it is imperative that we care by recognizing not only the physical needs of the poor but also of the diseased and aging. Shel Silverstein captures this need in his simple children's poem.

The Little Boy and the Old Man

Said the little boy, "Sometimes I drop my spoon."
Said the little old man, "I do that, too."
The little boy whispered, "I wet my pants."
"I do that, too," laughed the little old man.

Said the little boy, "I often cry."
The old man nodded, "So do I."
"But worst of all," said the boy, "it seems
Grown-ups don't pay attention to me."
And he felt the warmth of a wrinkled old hand.
"I know what you mean," said the little old man.[39]

When any person — poor, diseased, or aging — is in the winter of life, it behooves us as Christians to *personally* meet physical needs.

CARE: PAUL'S NEED FOR FRIENDSHIP

In II Timothy 4:10,11,16,21 Paul speaks to Timothy of those "friends" who had deserted him. He encourages Timothy to **bring Mark because he is helpful** and Paul concludes with the heart-rending words: **Do your best to get here before winter.**

There is a wonderful scene in the Disney film Huck Finn where Huck, at ropes end, cries out "You're my best friend, Jim!" And Jim in return responds, "You're my only friend, Huck." The two together had been through the thick and the thin. They had discovered the value of friendship as an important means to the end of care.

Unfortunately, in our modern society, more and more people are moving into an isolationist mentality. In *The Popcorn Report*, Faith Popcorn writes that in the coming decade **we'll entrench ourselves in the privacy of the fortress — Every home in America. The purpose of the fortress? To make us feel safe.**[40]

Paul, of course, knew that real safety in life comes through close relationships. And, once again,

aware that he is coming to the close of his earthly life, Paul expresses another need — the need for friendship.

What excitement must have gripped Timothy when the courier delivered this treasured scroll from Rome. Timothy, who for more than fifteen years had been Paul's traveling companion. Who had labored with Paul throughout Greece and Asia. Who had been sent by Paul on special assignments. Who had journeyed with Paul to Jerusalem. Who was with Paul during his first Roman imprisonment.

Timothy opens the letter and perhaps for the first time hears his dear friend express a need. **And Timothy, do your best to get here before winter.**

Many scholars believe that Paul was beheaded only a few days after writing this final pastoral letter.[41] Did Paul die without his cloak? Did Paul leave this world without his friends to comfort him? The real question however persists for us — when those around us are in the winter of their lives who will meet their specific needs for care?

POSTSCRIPT TO MY OWN COMMUNITY

"Because Christians never let anyone die alone!" A leader in the then Soviet Union when asked why active persecution could not repress Christianity.[42]

"Death is not only a crisis of the flesh. It is ... a crisis of community. Death will also reveal starkly and unmistakably something about the communities in which a dying person lives." William May[43]

A spectre hangs across Europe as Holland defines euthanasia as an aspect of terminal "care." A significant number of Americans sympathize with Dr. Kevorkian and his definition of "care" related to the dying. The response of the Christian community cannot be rhetoric and as such "stingy" of time, true care, smiles, and love. The Christian health care professional has to be ready to differ from secular contemporaries who spend less and less time with terminal patients.[44] The predictable failure of cure leaves a vacuum crying out for care. Scrooge was born again only when compassion as true suffering-with prompted his responsibility to Tiny Tim. His personal care shifted responsibility from entitlement programs and enriched multiple lives. A generation of Christian baby boomers who were weaned on entitlement programs, United Way, and contemporary definitions of compassion and care may not be able to meet the challenge.[45] The cross tells us everything we need to know about God's response to sin as the cause of suffering and death. Let us not be stingy! Since the stakes are higher than they've ever been for medicine, care enough to send the very best.

Endnotes

1. Olasky, M. **The Tragedy of American Compassion**. Regnery Gateway, Washington, D.C., 1992, p. 198.
2. *ibid.*, p. 197.
3. *ibid.*, p. 197. See also Ed Payne's book, **Biblical Healing for Modern Medicine**, Covenant Books, Augusta, GA, 1993. On page 17, Dr. Payne illustrates how contemporary definitions distort life expectancy. Also, Dr. Olasky notes that redefinition and connotation began with American abortion practices circa 1870 as the word abortion became "getting rid" and being "helped out of trouble." **Abortion Rites. A Social History of Abortion in America**. Crossway Books, Wheaton, IL, 1992, p. 121.
4. *ibid.*, Olasky, M., 1992, **Abortion Rites**, p. 96.
5. Healing hands in *Hippocrates*, November/December, 1993, p. 33.
6. Hauerwas, S., Care in **Encyclopedia of Bioethics**, Warren T. Reich (Ed.), Vol. 1, 1978, pp. 145-150.
7. Hauerwas, S., *Salvation and Health: Why Medicine Needs the Church* in **Suffering Presence**. University of Notre Dame Press, 1986, pp. 63-83. Dr. Payne also addresses this issue in great detail in **Biblical Healing for Modern Medicine**. On page 30, in the context of James 5:14, John Wesley is quoted concerning the necessity of ministerial involvement in medicine. The same church-health care worker involvement is repeated again for emphasis on pages 41 and 42.
8. *Ibid.*, Payne, F.E., **Biblical Healing**, 1993, p. 91.
9. Amundsen, D., and Ferngren, G., Medicine and Religion: Pre-Christian Antiquity. **In Health/Medicine and the Faith Traditions**, M. Marty and K. Vaux (Ed.), 1982, Fortress Press, Philadelphia, p. 96.
10. *Ibid.*, Hauerwas, S., 1986, p. 75.
11. *Ibid.*, Hauerwas, S., 1986, p. 80.
12. Hanson, B., School of Suffering, *Dialog* 20 (Winter 1981): 39-45.
13. *Ibid.*, Hanson, B., 1981.
14. Hauerwas, S., **Abortion Theologically Understood**. Task Force of the United Methodist Church on Abortion and Sexuality; Ephrata, PA, pp. 1-20. I was curious as to whether the active witness of the early church against abortion was ever repeated. In Olasky, M. (1992), a certain John McDowall led a group in America circa 1838 to "care" for prostitutes — a group frequenting abortion clinics. Mr. McDowall praises a physician who helped a woman when he "had compassion on her and took her into his own family, where she resided two months." (p. 135) I discussed this idea previously in a shorter format (*Biblical Reflections on Modern Medicine*, 1992, Vol. 3, No. 4). When we say that we care about abortion practice in our country, how is this care biblically translated into action? Placard carrying or monetary contributions may be perceived as stingy responses vis a vis compassion, adoption, or personal sacrifice and involvement.
15. As my minister, Greg reminded me that of all things, people may be most stingy of money. My observations are not meant to minimize sacrificial financial giving, but rather to guard against contemporary "giving" in connotative transition. Ron Sider and Marvin Olasky both decry the yearly financial catharsis of Christmas turkeys, handouts, and United Way check writing. Though a "cheerful financial" giver may care, financial contributions are an essential aspect but not all there is to Biblical caring.
16. *Ibid.*, Olasky, M., 1992. This is a must-read book! The evolution of compassion and its effect on the Christian in giving or caring is ele-

gantly described.

17. *Ibid.*, Hanson, B., 1981.

18. Lammers, S.E., and Verhey, A., Care of Patients and Their Suffering in **On Moral Medicine**, 1987, Eerdmans, Grand Rapids, MI, p. 247.

19. Brueggeman, W., **The Message of the Psalms**, 1984, Augsburg, Minnesota, pp. 51 - 121. Stanley Hauerwas gave me this idea and then discussed Job and his friends in **Naming the Silences**, 1990, Eerdmans, Grand Rapids, MI.

20. Hauerwas, S., **Naming the Silences**, 1990, Eerdmans, Grand Rapids, MI, p. 89.

21. *Ibid.*, Hauerwas, S., 1990, p. 89.

22. *Ibid.*, Hauerwas, S., 1990, p. 59.

23. Rifkin, J., **Algeny**, 1984, p. 32.

24. *Ibid.*, Rifkin, J., 1984, p. 32.

25. *Ibid.*, Payne, F.E., 1993.

26. *Ibid.*, Rifkin, J., 1984, pp. 1, 29.

27. *Ibid.*, Rifkin, J., 1984, p. 72.

28. *Ibid.*, Rifkin, J., 1984, pp. 77-78.

29. *Ibid.*, Rifkin, J., 1984, p. 83.

30. *Ibid.*, Hauerwas, S., 1990, pp. 59-64 summarize anthropodicy. Much of the book discusses the wrong ends of contemporary medicine. Chapter III (p. 97) focuses on the topic of death in a pluralistic society and greatly contributed to my summary.

31. *Ibid.*, Lammers and Verhey, 1987, p. 248.

32. *Ibid.*, Hauerwas, S., both 1978 and 1986.

33. Bluebond-Langner, M., **The Private Worlds of Dying Children**, 1978, Princeton University Press, quoted in Hauerwas, S., 1990, p. 147.

34. *Ibid.*, Hauerwas, S., 1990, p. 148.

35. Ogilvie, L.J., and Demarest, G.W., **The Communicator's Commentary: 1,2 Timothy**, Word Books, Waco, Texas, 1984, p. 231.

36. Selected readings from II Timothy, New International Version, Zondervan, Grand Rapids, MI, 1973.

37. II Corinthians 11:23-27 and Philippians 4:11.

38. Luke 10:25-37.

39. Silverstein, S., **A Light in the Attic**, Harper and Row, New York, 1981, p. 95.

40. Popcorn, F., **The Popcorn Report**, Harper Collins, New York, 1991, p. 4.

41. Ogilvie, *op cit.*, p. 285.

42. Personal communication, Harold O.J. Brown, Professor of Theology and Ethics, Trinity Evangelical Divinity Seminary, Deerfield, IL.

43. May, W.F., in **Theological Voices in Medical Ethics**, 1993, Verhey and Lammers (Ed.), Eerdmans, Grand Rapids, MI, p. 254.

44. A specific incrimination of physicians in the abandonment of the dying is contained in Stephen L. Carter's **The Culture of Disbelief** (Basic Books, New York, 1993). Contrast this contemporary scene with the 1840 photograph described in the second paragrah of this paper. On page 247 of Carter's book, Arthur W. Frank describes the euthanasia of Joseph Sauder by a nurse. Per family and physician decisions, Mr. Sauder was disconnected from life support and his physician(s) were not even present. "Whatever relationship Sauder's physicians had with their patient, they defined their task as completed when the patient's death was imminent. NO more medical decisions remained to be made, and their expertise was undoubtedly required elsewhere (medical care equated only with cure)... Just dying isn't much of a medical event, as urban hospital practice goes." To relieve Mr. Sauder's post extubation choking, the nurse administered IV potassium. It apparently was not the doctors' job to "suffer with" when the medical "care" as cure was finished!

45. Sidney, K.H., Boomer Boom and Bust in *Christianity Today*, August 16, 1993, pp. 14-15. Sidney describes the "vibrant" church of the U.S. baby boomer. Average congregants attend church only twice a month. He or she gives little and serves even less and yet expects a high level of service and support from the church. Sidney then juxtaposes boomer "care" with Jesus' care. "I'll pick what meets my needs and stay with it only as long as it does," versus "Take up your cross and follow me." And "The boomer looks out for himself," versus "Love your neighbor as yourself." I also could not pass up justification of my repeated aspersions cast on United Way giving. In our local county in 1993, $106,000 was given to Planned Parenthood; $3,000 to Right to Life. I practice at a Catholic Hospital that wholeheartedly supports United Way. Is this contribution not viewed as complicity? Olasky is extraordinarily accurate when he describes American compassion as a tragedy.

A Time to Live, A Time to Die: Advance Directives and Living Wills

C. Ben Mitchell and Michael K. Whitehead

This article is reprinted by permission of the authors. It first appeared in Ethics & Medicine, Vol. 9, Spring, 1993. Mr. Mitchell and Mr. Whitehead represent the Christian Life Commission of the Southern Baptist Convention in Nashville, Tennessee. Reprints of the article in booklet form are available from this Commission at 401 Commerce St., #550, Nashville, TN 37208-3696.

What is a Living Will?

A "living will" is a type of health care document known as an "Advance Medical Directive." An advance directive is a generic term for a form or document which expresses your preferences in the event you are physically and mentally unable to make medical care decisions for yourself. That is, an Advance Medical Directive is a method of letting others know your wishes about treatment if you are unable to communicate those wishes at the time. There are several varieties of medical directives, including living wills, durable powers of attorney for health care, values inventories, etc.

A "living will" is a specific kind of directive which is "restricted to rejecting life-sustaining medical interventions, usually, although not exclusively, when a person is termi-nally ill."[1] Living wills have been in existence for over 20 years. Nursing homes and senior citizens' centers have been supervising living will signings for several years. Developing medical technologies, publicity about euthanasia, and doctor-assisted suicide, and recent legislation have focused greater attention on living wills.

On December 1, 1991, the Patient Self-Determination Act became federal law. This law requires personnel at all hospitals, nursing homes, and hospices receiving Medicare and Medicaid reimbursement to advise patients upon admission of their right to accept or refuse medical treatments and to execute an Advance Medical Directive. These medical personnel must (1) document whether patients have directives, (2) implement medical directive policies and (3) educate their staffs and communities about medical directives.[2]

Between 4% and 17.5% of adults have completed an advance directive. In a 1988 public opinion survey conducted by the American Medical Association, 56% of adults reported that they had discussed their treatment preferences with family members. Only 15%, however, had completed a living will. ... In one study of nursing home residents, 90% had heard of a living will, but only 18% had signed one; 30% had heard of a durable power of attorney, but only 15% had appointed a decision maker.[3]

While a living will may sound harmless and even desirable, there is the very real potential for future abuses. Before filling out a living will, be certain that you fully understand how much power and responsibility you are giving an attending physician.

Why Might I Want a Living Will?

A living will is, in fact, a "dying declaration," stating the circumstances under which a person wishes to be permitted to die without certain medical treatments.[4] There are several common reasons individuals give for desiring a living will. Most persons find it reassuring to know they will have some control of their treatment, through a living will, even when they become incompetent. Some persons fear too much medical treatment will be forced upon them when they are near death. They don't want to have their dying prolonged by machines and fear leaving their families with exorbitant medical bills. Some individuals find that specific planning eases their anxiety about death. Finally, some want to spare their loved ones from these difficult decisions.

What Biblical Principles Apply to Living Wills?

No matter what the issue or technology, the Christian must always ask the question, "What does the Lord say? Are there precepts, principles, or examples in the Bible which help us understand our Heavenly Father's will on the matter?" While it is true that living wills are not mentioned in the Bible, it is not therefore true that the Bible has nothing to say about them. The Bible has much to say about life and death.

First, the Scripture says that human beings are made in the image of God, and he has invested our lives with sacred value (Gen. 1:26-27). Scholars disagree over the precise ingredients that make up the image of God in humanity, but at least one thing is clear: human beings have a value and a unique place above all other forms of life on earth. "To sanctify" means to "set apart" as special. Since God has set human life apart above all other life, we refer to the sanctity of life. The psalmist declares that we are "made a little lower than the angels" and are "crowned ... with glory and honor" (Ps. 8:5). The sanctity or sacredness of human life is a biblical doctrine that must be considered in any application of the Bible to medicine or science.

Second, the Bible teaches that God himself is the giver and taker of human life. He is sovereign over human life. As Paul puts it in Romans 14:7-8: "For none of us liveth to himself, and no man dieth to himself. For whether we live, we live unto the Lord; and whether we die, we die unto the Lord: whether we live therefore, or die, we are the Lord's." The Lord himself is the giver of life and the one who takes life (Job 1:21). Whatever we decide about end-of-life issues, we must understand that we do not possess ultimate authority over life and death.

Third, the Bible everywhere condemns unjust killing. In fact, God clearly declares capital punishment for anyone, who with premeditation, unjustly kills another person (Gen. 9:6).[5] There is no warrant in Scripture for active euthanasia or the intentional killing of another person because his or her condition appears terminal.

Fourth, Christians have the assurance of eternal life and the promise of the resurrection and must not be enslaved by the fear of death (Heb. 2:14-15). We have been set free from the fear of death through Christ, who conquered death for us. One of the most threatening things about death is that we have so little personal experience of it. But we do have the testimony of Scripture. Paul says, "to be absent from the body is to be present with the Lord." (2 Cor. 5:8), and Jesus tells us that, for the Christian, the life to come is blessed, glorious, and will consummate with a resurrection body (John 14:1-4. See also Paul's powerful description of the resurrection in 1 Cor. 15:12-58).

Fifth, while suicide is not "the unpardonable sin," the Bible nowhere condones or speaks approvingly of suicide (1 Chr. 10:4,13; Matt. 27:3-5; 2 Sam. 17:23; 1 Kings 16:18-19). Whatever you decide about end-of-life issues, suicide or active self-killing is not a biblical option.

As we continue to consider medical directives, it is crucial that we keep these biblical principles in mind. They will be our guide in making decisions about the end of life.

As we have already seen, there are several reasons people support the use of living wills. Doctors, other care givers and family members want to know the wishes of their patient and loved one when the time of death is near. But make no mistake about it, some persons are advocating living wills as one step on the way to active euthanasia or doctor-assited suicide.

What Are Some of the Problems with Living Wills?

1. The standard living will documents refer only to the termination of treatment.

Most living wills only allow you to designate that you want certain medical treatments withheld or withdrawn, and "that [you] be permitted to die naturally with only the administration of medication or the performance of any medical procedure deemed necessary to provide [you] with comfortable care or to allieviate pain."[6] Some standard forms only allow you to say whether or not you want nutrition and fluids and whether or not you wish to donate your organs for transplantation.

The desire to donate your organs at death is a very personal decision and one that you should make freely and without coercion. And, the decision to discontinue food and water is a very complex and critical issue in medicine. First, the provision of food and water is the most basic of care and cannot be characterized as an "extraordinary measure." Second, to cause a person to starve to death intentionally is unjust active killing, which is prohibited in the Bible.[7] Third, euthanasia contradicts the role of the physician as healer.[8] The Christian Medical and Dental Society has declared,

" ... we believe that physicians, other health professionals, and health care facilities should initiate and continue nutritional support and hydration when their patients cannot feed themselves. We are concerned that demented, severely retarded, and comatose individuals are increasingly viewed as 'useless mouths' (we reject this dehumanizing phrase). Rather than encouraging physicians to withhold or withdraw such patients' food and water, we encourage physicians to respond to God's call for improved physical, social, financial, and spiritual support of all vulnerable human beings."[10]

Furthermore, the Christian Life Commission has gone on record as officially opposing "any designation of food and/or water as 'extraordinary' medical care for some patients."[11] An appropriate Advance Medical Directive should at least allow you both to specify the medical treatments you want maintained and the ones you might want discontinued. This leads to the second difficulty with the standard living will document.

2. Living wills may not be specific enough.

Even the best of the approved living wills do not allow for sufficient options or details regarding treatment. For instance, the standard living will document does not allow you to state under what circumstances you do or do not want antibiotic therapy.

"[A patient] might desire penicillin for a painful skin infection but not a relatively toxic antibiotic such as amphotericin B for a probably fatal systemic fungal infection. Or, the patient may not want an antibiotic for a virulent pneumonia that will lead to rapid death but would prefer an antibiotic for an indolent pneumonia that is not expected to result in death but is causing an uncomfortable cough and chest pain."[12]

Living wills do not allow the kind of specificity that most patient's care will demand even in the terminal stage of their illness.

3. Living wills are vague.

Phrases like "life-sustaining procedures," "treatments that prolong the process of dying," and "there is no reasonable expectation of recovery from extreme physical or mental inability" are very common in living will forms. Other phrases and words like "imminent death" and "artificially prolong the dying process" are highly problematic and impossible to define with precision. Their meaning and application will differ from case to case and will probably differ even over the course of one patient's illness.

Note that the person(s) who will interpret these terms and make decisions for the patient is the physician (or two physicians in some states) and not necessarily the patient's family.

Because so much power — the power of life and death — is given to physicians through living will documents, and because it is impossible precisely to define some terms contained in living wills, alternative medical directives may be preferable.

4. A physician and patient are in a covenant relationship which demands consultation and negotiation. The physician promises to provide certain treatments under certain conditions, and the patient promises to comply under certain conditions. During the course of a "normal" illness, the covenant is revised as the patient's condition changes. For instance, a responsible person does not say, "Okay, doc, do whatever you want to do." Rather, the doctor may say, "Here are the treatment options. I think this is the best and recommend it. Are you willing to comply with the therapy?" The patient then may either comply, negotiate or refuse treatment.

Living wills make a nominal effort at honoring such a covenant, but are often too rigid. Living wills usually do not allow for negotiation and revision of treatment decisions. That is not to say that living wills cannot be revised. But they can be revised only as long as you are conscious and competent. If you become unconscious or are in a persistent vegetative state, negotiation becomes impossible. Living wills are not the most flexible means of carrying out your wishes and respecting Christian values in the event that you become incompetent or unconscious.

What Are the Alternatives to a Living Will?

1. Talk with your family about your values and wishes. Though the law is being tested at this point, it is still the case that most physicians will consult with and seek to honor the wishes of a patient's next of kin regarding medical treatment. At least one other person in your family (preferably several) should know what you think about life and death and what you want done or not done if you are near death.

2. Execute a Durable Power of Attorney for Health Care.[13] This medical directive enables you to name a trusted relative or friend to make your medical decisions when you cannot do so for yourself. This includes your right to refuse treat-

ment you would not want. The Durable Power of Attorney for Health Care allows you to designate someone as your "attorney in fact," and empowers him or her to make health care decisions for you. Your "attorney in fact" does not have to be an attorney or doctor. He or she may be a spouse, relative, friend, neighbor, or fellow church member. You should choose someone (1) who knows you well and shares your Christian values, (2) with whom you have discussed your wishes and (3) who is willing and able to serve as a decision-maker in what could be a very stressful time. Unless you otherwise specify, the document may also give your attorney in fact the power after you die to: (1) authorize an autopsy, (2) donate your body or body parts for transplant or scientific purposes and (3) authorize disposition of your body for burial (which may involve cremation, unless you specify otherwise).[14]

Your local hospital administrator or attorney should be able to secure a Durable Power of Attorney for Health Care for you to review and explain it to you. If there is anything you don't understand in the document, you should ask for the assistance of a competent attorney.

3. If you are uncomfortable placing life-and-death decision-making on the shoulders of a loved one, or if you have no one who may serve as your attorney in fact, you may wish to sign a "Will to Live." The Will to Live differs from standard living wills in its strong presumption in favor of life. That is, the Will to Live instructs your physician(s) to do what is necessary to preserve your life "without discrimination based on (your) age or physical or mental disability or the "quality" of (your) life" and rejects "any action or omission that is intended to cause or hasten death."[15]

Very simply, the Will to Live is a pro-life anti-euthanasia alternative to a living will.

The Will to Live designates food and water as basic necessities and allows you to specify treatments you would want withheld or withdrawn under certain circumstances. The document also defines "imminent death" as when "a reasonably prudent physician, knowledgeable about the case and the treatment possibilities with respect to the medical conditions involved, would judge that I will live only a week or less even if lifesaving treatment or care is provided to me ..."

4. Talk to your physician and have the Durable Power of Attorney for Health Care or Will to Live added to your medical records. The document is useless unless your family and physician(s) know it exists, and unless the doctors possess a legal copy of it. You might also talk to your pastor and give him a copy of your Durable Power of Attorney for Health Care or Will to Live.

5. Take a legal copy of your Durable Power of Attorney for Health Care or Will to Live with you should you have to enter the hospital. The hospital personnel are required by law to ask you if you have a medical directive, and it would be wise to provide them with yours at that time, rather than completing whatever standard form they may offer. You are not required to have an advance directive.

6. Remember, like the living will, the Durable Power of Attorney for Health Care does not become effective unless you become unable to make decisions for yourself. The Durable Power of Attorney for Health Care says, "To ensure that decisions about my medical care are

made consistent with these wishes and my personal vlaues, I appoint the following person my attorney in fact to make health care decisions for me whenever I am unable to do so."[16] Likewise, the Will to Live becomes effective only when you are incompetent and your death is imminent.

Endnotes

1. Ezekiel J. Emanuel and Linda L. Emanuel, "Living Wills: Past, Present, and Future," *Journal of Clinical Ethics* 1 (Spring, 1990), p. 9.
2. John LaPuma, David Orentlicher, and Robert J. Moss, "Advance Directives on Admission: Clinical Implications and Analysis of the Patient Self-Determination Act of 1990," *Journal of the American Medical Association*, 266 (July 17, 1991), p. 402.
3. *Ibid.*
4. Michael K. Whitehead, "Whitehead: Living wills mean danger ahead," Light (January-March, 1991), p. 9. See also, Nigel M. De S. Cameron, "Living Wills and the Will to Live," *Christianity Today* (April 6, 1992), pp. 22-24, and Sharon S. Mahone, "Living Wills: Down the Slippery Slope?" *Journal of Christian Nursing*, pp. 4-9.
5. *Capital Punishment*, Nashville: The Christian Life Commission. See also Wayne House and John Howard Yoder, The Death Penalty Debate (Dallas: Word), 1991.
6. Tennessee Living Will, 1991.
7. For a more complete treatment of euthasia and the withholding and withdrawal of treatment, see Franklin E. Payne, Jr., **Biblical/Medical Ethics: The Christian and the Practice of Medicine** (Milford, Mich: Mott Media, 1985); John Jefferson Davis, **Evangelical Ethics: Issues Facing the Church Today** (Phillipsburg, N.J.: Presbyterian and Reformed Publishing Company, 1985); and

Norman L. Geisler, **Christian Ethics, Options and Issues**, (Grand Rapids: Baker Book House, 1989).

8. See the excellent treatment of this theme in Nigel M. de S. Cameron, **The New Medicine: Life and Death After Hippocrates** (Wheaton, Ill.: Crossway Books, 1991).

9. Duncan Vere, *Voluntary Euthanasia — Is There an Alternative?* (London: Christian Medical Fellowship Publications, 1971), p. 50.

10. Christian Medical and Dental Society, Medical Ethics Commission Statement, "The Withholding or Withdrawing of Nutrition and Hydration," approved by the House of Delegates, May 3, 1990, Parentheses theirs.

11. Christian Life Commission of the Southern Baptist Convention, Annual Minutes, September 14, 1988, p. 44.

12. Allan S. Brett, MD, "Limitations of Listing Specific Medical Interventions in Advance Directives," *Journal of the American Medical Association*, 266 (August 14, 1991), p. 826.

13. It is important to distinguish the Durable Power of Attorney for Health Care from other durable powers of attorney. The DPAHC has nothing to do with your finances or estate. It is limited to power over your medical care alone. A durable power of attorney may be drawn up to cover both financial and medical matters in some states.

14. *Durable Power of Attorney for Health Care*, Legal Services of Middle Tennessee, 6/91, p. 1.

15. The Will to Live, may be obtained by sending a self-addressed, stamped envelope to: Will to Live Project, Suite 500, 419 Seventh St., NW, Washington, DC 20004.

16. *Durable Power of Attorney for Health Care*, p. 1.

Ethics & Medicine *is published three* times yearly by Paternoster Periodicals, P.O. Box 300, Carlisle, Cumbria, United Kingdom , CA3 0QS. *The pupose of the publication is to develop a Christian mind on the complex and fundamental challenges posed to society by technological advance in medical science. We commend the publication highly to our readers.*

Pastor's Column

Aging Part II

The Reverend Byron Snapp

Rev. Snapp holds a B.A. from King College and an M. Div. from Reformed Theological Seminary. He is assistant pastor of Covenant Presbyterian Church and principal of Covenant Christian School in Cedar Bluff, Virginia.

Years ago Benjamin Franklin stated that death and taxes are sure things. We are reminded of taxes every time we get our paycheck, make a retail purchase subject to sales tax, and on April 15th. We are not reminded of death quite so often.

In a recent article I surveyed several reasons why death is not a part of our regular thinking. As the medical staff is often on the front line when patients are confronted with debilitating illness, I looked at the most important preparation that needs to be made in the face of a fatal illness. At these times there can be no greater issue than whether or not one is ready to meet God. Is the individual trusting in Jesus Christ alone for salvation? Not only are ill individuals more willing to face the fact of their terminal life, family members often are also. Thus, the spiritual ministry of medical personnel can extend beyond the terminally ill to family members.

Secondly, a properly prepared will is of utmost importance. The death of a loved one is sufficiently traumatic without grieving loved ones being confronted with the legal realities that exist when no will has been prepared. A will should be prepared prior to the advance of old age or the announcement of a fatal illness. No one has the promise of tomorrow nor that one's death will be a slow one. If you are currently unprepared, find out what is required in your state for a legal will and take the steps quickly to have one drawn up. Proper preparation may well keep your property from being unnecessarily tied up, prevent the intervention of the state in determining how your possessions are to be divided, and inform your family how you wish to dispose of what you own. Wills need to be regularly updated.

Thirdly, your covenant children need to be raised in the knowledge of their responsibility to take care of their aged parents, if and when the occasion arises. Joseph in Egypt desired to have his aged father near him (Gen. 45,46). Jacob and Easau apparently took care of their father Isaac in his last days (Gen. 35:27-29). Necessary parental care is one application of the Fifth Commandment. This lesson can be instilled in our children in a number of ways. First, faithful Scriptural teaching of parental and children's covenantal responbilities is foundational. This is to be followed by faithful application. If our parents are still alive are we, to the best of our abilities, looking out for their needs? Has thought been given to any type of homecare should the need arise? When building or purchasing a new home is any thought given to the possible room needed to house an aging and/or terminally ill parent in the future? Are our living parents prayed for often during family devotions? Children can learn much about their role in our care as they note our concern for our own parents.

I believe there will be greater need for the care of the aged by family members as the government continues its advance into the health care field. Health services for the ill that our generation has taken for granted may not be as readily available in future years. If euthanasia for the terminally ill gains wider acceptance in the next generation homecare will become increasingly important. Our children must be prepared now for such apossibility.

Churches also have an important role in terminal illness. Sermons can be preached on preparing for death. A Sunday School series on ministering to the terminally ill could be very valuable when presented to an adult class. Within this class medical personnel can play a vital role as they can present excellent instruction on the stages of two or three terminal illnesses once a theological foundation has been laid. We must remember that for those widows who have no one else, it is the church's duty to care for them spiritually and physically. Churches can also help by having at least a wheelchair, crutches, a walker and a hospital bed on hand for those in need. Deacons can be prepared to build a ramp into a home where that is needed for wheelchair occupants.

Visits to the terminally ill are important. These can allow family members time to get out of the house. In addition, the visitor can become somewhat acquainted with the slow effects of a debilitating disease.

Long before the possible onset of a terminal illness the individual and next of kin should sit down and discuss what measures should and should not be taken in case of terminal illness. This conversation is not a pleasant one but it is important. However, few families really take time for this due to the difficulty of the topic and the unwillingness to think about the possibility of long-term illness. However, modern medical technology makes this conversation a needed one. Do you want to be placed on a respirator? Do you want tests and medical procedures performed on you that are needless for one in your condition? Do you have a doctor that you can trust to deal truthfully with you regarding illness, its prognosis, and the cost of treatment? Do you want hospital care or home care? You can (and should) lengthen this list of sample questions.

Money should be set aside for use in case of a debilitating disease, as one is able to do so. Have you made any preparation for the support of family members in case a chronic illness comes during your years of employment, forcing you to quit work?

The importance of a biblical lifestyle cannot be overly stressed. Our life should be one of restoring broken relationships as much as possible, as soon as possible. When needed, forgiveness needs to be sought by us. When it is asked from us we need to prayerfully and readily give it. Do you need to flee from youthful lusts (II Tim. 2:22)? Often the consequences of youthful sin go with us throughout our lives. Seeking, by God's grace, to live a godly life will prevent many regrets that can fill a weary mind in the midst of chronic illness.

The suffering Job could look back on his life without regret. His hope was in his living Redeemer (Job 19:25). Thus, his suffering was not filled with "if only" or a variety of regrets. He had a habit of seeking forgiveness for his sin and a knowledge that his loving God had faithfully forgiven that sin. One can only speculate as to leprous Uzziah's thinking in the latter part of his life (II Chr. 26:16ff).

We need to gird up our minds to consider that painful and debilitating diseases have a purpose when they come our way. It is very difficult to adjust from an active lifestyle to one of inactivity. Yet, we must remember that as long as God leaves us on earth He has work for us to do. Our illness may restrain our labors. Rather than ministering to others we must learn to humbly accept the ministry of others. Although we cannot visit others, we may well find ourselves ministering to those who visit us. Illness often allows us greater time for prayer. We often forget that one of the best ministries toward others is that of prayer. When called to do so, we must show others how to suffer for God's glory. By this, I mean without an embittered spirit. We should often meditate on God and His character as well as His promises to His people. Cassette tapes of Bible readings, sermons, and religious music can pass the time and enrich our beings.

We should not dwell too much on possible future illnesses. These are in God's sovereign, perfect hands. God deals with Christians in a great variety of ways. (Note John and Peter, two of Christ's closest disciples in John 21.) Our duty in sickness and health is to follow Christ — to glorify and enjoy God.

Quackery
Hilton Terrell, M.D., Ph.D.

Dr. Terrell is Assistant Professor of Family Medicine at McLeod Regional Medical Center in Florece, S.C..

With enactment of medical licensure laws in the latter half of the nineteenth century medical practitioners began an attempt to define and enforce upon the American public our notion of what ought to be orthodox and permissible in healing. The various states granted exclusive privileges to diagnose and treat diseases to certain groups of practitioners who held themselves to be more scientific, more valid, and more effective than others. The century-old maneuver has failed.

Reporting in the January 28, 1993, *New England Journal of Medicine*, Dr. David Eisenberg and others describe a representative survey of a signficant portion of the United States population regarding its use of unconventional therapies. Their findings are amazing: (1) One-third of the English-speaking, adult population used unconventional therapies in 1990, (2) Only one in four of those who used unconventional therapies told their doctor about it, (3) Those who used unconventional therapies spent about $10 billion in the process, comparable to the amount spent out-of-pocket for hospital care, (4) the number of visits to providers of unconventional therapy (425 million) exceeded those to primary care physicians and the average charge per visit was $27.60.

It would appear that the attempt by mainstream medical practitioners for years to control the healing arts has failed both by means of the legal coercion of medical licensure statutes and by persuasion of the public of the sufficiency of "standard" medicine. Although conventional medicine does dominate the mainstream, the nearly half-billion annual visits to practitioners of other more or less outcast providers can't be thrust aside as insignificant or a quirk of the poor and ignorant. Use of unconventional therapies is significantly more common among those with some college education than without, and among those with higher incomes.

Practitioners of orthodox medicine, on the whole, deserve to have failed in our attempt to abolish alternative practices by means of law. Similarly, our failure to persuade the public more thoroughly of the superiority of our methods has earned the leakage to other types of practices. Medical licensure laws render to Caesar authority God has deposited elsewhere. God places the physical health of individuals into the hands of the individual, the family, and the church (see 1 Cor. 6:15-20). Whether such laws "worked" or not is secondary to their biblical propriety. The civil state figures in only for contagious diseases in which coercive isolation measures are called for. The civil ruler's power is coercive. Except for contagious diseases where coerced measures may be beneficial to the whole community, medical care is a business contract or a ministry of compassion and mercy — hardly fit tasks for the hand that bears a sword.

Conventional medicine's inability to thoroughly persuade the public of its superiority has less to do with its public relations perhaps than with its science.[1] Most orthodox medical practices stand on rather little proof, majoring rather in rationale (proposed mechanisms) and groupthink acculturation. Even the positive outcome data we have tends to be narrowly conceived and tested. The fluoride that might have hardened our tooth enamel against decay may also have weakened our cortical bone. Focus on a decrease in dental caries will miss the increase in hip fractures later in life.

Medical training is as much an acculturation process by which initiates are inculcated in "our" way of thinking about health and illness. The give-and-take argumentation over definitions, theories, logic, and philosophy that more often marks other higher education is less prominent in medical education, where the engulfing of masses of pre-digested "facts" occupies our time.

What makes unconventional therapies thrive?

1. The incurability of many ailments. Dr. Eisenberg and his co-workers found that it was the chronic or recurrent diseases which collected more devotees of alternative medicine — back pain, allergies, arthritis, insomnia, headache, etc. The natural history of these kinds of problems is commonly one of exacerbations and remissions. Human tendency toward *post hoc ergo propter hoc* "reasoning" will provide many "proofs" of effectiveness that were only coincidental remissions, even for unconventional therapies of no intrinsic value. Jesus addressed the illogic of *post hoc* reasoning when He taught the error of imputing a specific sin as the reason for the tragedy of a building collapse (Luke 13:1-5). Some would have believed that since the dead men were sinners, and the tower had fallen on them, that the tower fell *because* of their particular sin. Not so, He said.

2. Inordinate desire. Americans, in particular, don't take "no" for an answer to their dilemmas. Sarai's desire for children was inordinate, prompting her to offer Hagar to her husband (Gen. 16:1-5). Any therapy, orthodox or unorthodox, should be sought within a biblical set of priorities. We are not free to go to *any* extent to be rid of a physical ailment. Paul sought three times that his illness be removed (2 Cor. 12:7-10). He could have let his life orbit whatever that thorn in the flesh was. Instead, he boasted in his infirmities and determined to take pleasure in them.

3. Unsatisfying experience with conventional therapies. Orthodox practitioners should be intrigued by the question of why, if our therapies are superior, and theirs are inferior, people continue to pursue the latter.

What *do* they receive elsewhere that they do not receive from us? Could it be, sometimes, that our mechanistic approach omits healing of the spirit? Omits love? Even at our therapeutic best, where we understand mysteries, do we lack love? (1 Cor. 13:2)

4. Proper locus of control. The success of orthodox therapies has been greatest where patient participation has been least. Great things are accomplished in surgery, where a patient's responsibility is, basically, to sign an op permit and hold still for the anesthetic. Great things are accomplished in pharmacology where the patient has but to take a pill, inhale a puff, or stick on a patch. While many, too many, patients prefer that approach, there are others who wish to retain a sense of control. Unorthodox therapies, accurately or not, may offer this sense, which is one to be encouraged since God did place this responsibility first with the individual (1 Cor. 3:16,17; 7:12,19,20, 2 Cor. 7:1).

5. Simple (simplistic?) rationales.[2] The rationales of orthodox medicine are exceedingly well-developed, beyond the ordinary practitioner's ability or interest to impart to many patients. Unconventional therapies may more often have rationales that are easier to grasp.

6. A conspiracy view of orthodox medicine. Insofar as medical care has become a state-granted monopoly, this view is partly justified. The in-group plays footsie with the political powers-that-be to keep others out. Some people respond to being put out by determining to thrive and be happy on the outside. The more licensed practitioners restrict the allowable practices of others the further the unlicensed practitioners are driven from the orthodox center toward a periphery that contains ever more bizarre practices. Massaging the sole of the foot to affect various

organs or analyzing the fibers of the iris for diagnosis is to a physician with standard training intractably irrational. Even if we grant that some orthodox therapies may contain a grain of truth, even if we recall the pigheaded blindness of past orthodox medicine, these practices and rationales just can't be swallowed, and we don't want to be associated with them.

Perhaps, occasionally, our scientific formulations do us a disservice by impounding our imaginations. The medical mainstream also does a disservice to the people by seeking to "guard" them from exercising their God-given responsibility to attend to their own health. Even if all of orthodox medicine's worst opinions about quackery are valid, *the health effects alone of removing that authority from the public will in the long term be worse.* The unorthodox practitioners also have been harmed by the monopoly in that they have been denied legitimate access to the marketplace. There is a way for us to avoid association with them without denying them their desire to sell their services. Title licensure could accomplish that separation, the way that a trademark does. Mainstream physicians can and do acquire legally-enforceable exclusive use of certain titles, such as board-certified obstetrician, to give the public a means to distinguish one school of therapy from another.

Is it hypocritical for the mainstream to characterize unorthodoxy as "quackery?" It is, to the extent that we by law make our treatments the only ones legally available to the public without proof of efficacy. There are very many mainstream therapies which stand on shaky ground. Studies of treatment outcome are not as common as we believe, nor generally that impressive when they do exist. Quackery is often scored for keeping people away from the really effective therapies. No doubt it does at times. So long as it is a choice of the individual to do so, however, the only way to stop it is by using civil police power to prevent it. Such use of the power of the state is not only illegitimate, it is also proving to be impossible according to the revelations of Eisenberg, *et al.* The millions of units of self-governance embodied in the hearts of individuals are often electing to shop in one of these unorthodox markets. Caesar is not sufficiently omnipotent or omnipresent to prevent it.

"Quackery" practices are also warned against by the mainstream as dangerous in themselves. That is an interesting charge. In particular cases it may be so. Overall, however, quack remedies more likely suffer from a *lack* of power to achieve anything at all biomedically, one way or the other. By any rationale it strains credulity to see how sitting under a cardboard tetrahedron, or wearing a quartz crystal around the neck, eating a garlic clove daily, or taking chemicals diluted to the point that not one molecule of the original chemical likely remains in the water, could be harmful in itself. It is rather the orthodox therapies that more often contain biological power, but a power that can cut two ways. Many of our orthodox medicines are dangerously poisonous in larger doses or in patients with certain vulnerabilities such as renal insufficiency. Their beneficial effects are secured by dosing low enough to use the biological change as a treatment. Ergotamine, digoxin, vincristine, and quinidine are examples. For intrinsic danger, what has quackery to compare with cutting open the chest, stopping the heart and lungs, sewing in artificial heart valves and vessels, followed by years

of warfarin therapy?

It would seem that this article should have begun by defining its terms. Surely some listing of what is and what is not quackery is forthcoming! Is chiropractic in our out? What about orthomolecular psychiatry? Colonic irrigation? Chelation therapy?

That no definition of "quackery" has yet been offered is part of the point. The line that would circumscribe quackery would vary according to at least a couple of factors: (1) The rigor of adherence to hard science in understanding mechanism. Considerable areas in *conventional* medicine would be excluded. We (legitimately) use therapies whose mechanisms we don't understand very well. (2) The rigor of adherence to well-conceived therapeutic outcome analyses. Again, much conventional medicine would fall outside the line. We prefer to judge insiders by our intentions and outsiders by their results. When in conventional medicine the mechanisms are unknown, we plead the empirical results. When the empirical results are against us, we plead the cogency of the mechanisms.

The most honest definition of quackery is that it comprises all those diagnostic and therapeutic approaches that are anathematized by a politically-empowered in-group. As the in-group changes in its views, now incorporating a previously denigrated practice, such as acupuncture, or expelling a previously acceptable approach, such as frequent feeding and cream diets for peptic ulcers, the territory of quackery changes inversely to orthodoxy. What quackery *is*, ultimately, is traceable more to what the definer believes about epistemology. How quackery is to be treated is ultimately traceable to what one

believes about economic and political freedom. In empirical medicine we would like to hold that we believe what we see. Actually, in considerable measure, we see what we believe.

Christians, especially, should be circumspect in our treatment of quackery, for we as a group are vulnerable to exclusion on grounds that we hold human beings to be a body/spirit unity, materially affected by spiritual events, and that the Bible is pertinent to medical care. Those positions are already formally anathematized by the larger culture of medical orthodoxy.

Whenever Christians in recent centuries have advanced a belief in the potency and pertinancy of biblical inputs to understanding, we have been subject to recital of a particular piece of history to put us back into our place. In summary, a piece of revisionist history may be offered as warning.

The doctor sits before the august tribunal to which he has been called. He is nervous. His license has been challenged; with it his livelihood is threatened including his ability to pay back his education loans. He has been called a quack in the news media. He has been charged with malpractice. His error is that he maintains that a patient's behavior follows a track around his core beliefs and that the best way to help some patients is to examine these issues at the center of gravity of the person.

The tribunal represents, however, the overwhelmingly dominant belief in the profession that reality is the other way around. The behavior, they say, is the core and the beliefs, if they exist at all, are an electron cloud orbiting the behavior. Each one of those beliefs dutifully exhibits the

Heisenberg uncertainty principle, being ultimately indefinable in precise location or precise velocity. Indeed, the doctor's case is injured by the fact that adherents in his own camp have refused to examine beliefs and behavior with any sort of precision, holding more safely within generalities and platitudes and describing *specific* biblical application to real life issues as "legalism."

Pressure is applied. Dr. Galileo recants his scientific heresy. He will cease to deal with the patients' core beliefs as controlling aspects of therapy. Reality is as they say it must be After all, they are licensed physicians. To be anything else in health is to be a quack. Heaven forbid!

Endnotes

1. Smith, R., Where is the Wisdom...?, *British Medical Journal,* Vol. 303, 1991, pp. 798-799.

2. Gellert, George A., M.D., M.P.H., [letter] *New England Journal of Medicine,* Oct. 14, 1993, pp. 1202-1203.

(continued from right side of page)
denied. That something needs to be done is also true. That the civil authority is usually the appropriate recourse is not necessarily true. The retort that the other authorities of family, church, and workplace "don't work" is *pragmatically* answerable in the observation that the civil authority is even more inept. As example, under the relentless growth of statist approaches, bastardy in the U.S. is 15 times what it was when I was born. Educational levels, which, by the way are clearly positively related to the health of a population, have steadily sunk as the state's hand has become heavier. The retort is answerable *principally* in that God has not left us without an outline of how things should be divided in parceling out authority and responsibility.

Issues abound on the civil state -- family front which involve medicine. Should a physician perform a sterilization procedure on a married person without the knowledge and consent of the partner? Do confidentiality barriers run like a Berlin wall through the halves of a marriage? Is the state justified in requiring mumps vaccine in children over the parents' objection? May a school district require parents to have their children examined by a physician prior to an attendance mandated by law? What saith the Lord?

Editor's Note

The treatment of minors continues to be an inflamed issue in medicine. Indeed, any indication just now that the matter is cooling is likely to be *bad* news, as the momentum is still in the direction of emancipating minors from the governance of their parents. Those who believe minors would then be out from under any governance at all fail to see that this "emancipation" is only a *change* in governance, from family to the civil state. Can a minor elect to undergo abortion without parental consent? Can a minor seek prescription of birth control without parental knowledge and consent? It is interesting that consent for major (or even minor) surgery is not so often the center of controversy -- a clue to the underlying desire for license to do as one pleases without any constrains whatsoever.

All human authority is derivative from God. He has chosen a plurality of repositories for the authority He dispenses to human beings. These are:

* **self-governance** (1 Thess. 4:11,12; Prov. 16:17;19:16; Deut. 5:21; 1 Cor. 11:28; 2 Cor. 13:5).

* **family governance** (Ex. 20:12; Deut. 6:7-9; Eph. 6:1-4, 5:22-33; Col. 3:18-21; 1 Tim. 2:13; 3:4-5; Titus 2:5; 1 Peter 3:1-7).

* **church governance** (2 Thess. 4:11-12; Prov. 16:17; 19:16; 1 Tim. 2:11-15; 3:1-13; 5; Titus 1:5-9; 3:9:11; Ex. 20:12).

* **workplace governance** (Eph. 6:5-9; Col. 3:22-4:1; 1 Tim. 6:1,2; Titus 2:9,10; 1 Peter 2:18,19).

* **civil governance** (Ex. 20:12; Deut. 17:14-20; Luke 20:25; Romans 13:1-7; 1 Peter 2:13-17).

Analagous to the complementary spiritual gifts in the body of Christ, these deposits of authority from God are intended to work together. The tools available to each locus of government, and the extent of authority of each are different. The power of the death penalty belongs to the civil governor. Parents may not execute their children (Deut. 21:18-21). Corporal punishment belongs spiritual authority and discipline (2 Cor. 10:3-6). Confusion reigns when the various repositories raid each other's domain, usurping what is not theirs to have. The tortures, executions, and property seizures of the Inquisition in Europe are a blot against the Name of Christ, seizing civil authority. Through nepotism, family government has illegitimately usurped civil authority.

In our time, however, it appears to be the civil state that is the chief usurper. Family governance, among other loci, is under heavy assault by the civil state. Voices abound which would allow minors to engage in sexual intercourse, even homosexual liaisons, freely, provided of course that they practice birth control or submit to abortion. Children already are tapped to become spies for the civil authorities within the sanctity of the home, on the excuse that because some homes contain evil all homes are thus legitimate targets for surveillance. So also have physicians, teachers, and even baby sitters been statutorily enlisted into the Gestapo watching the family. Laws have made forcible intercourse between a husband and a wife a *criminal* matter. That the marital union is subject to ungodly and unrighteous imposition of the will of the husband upon the wife is certainly true, yet the governance of such matters is for individuals, families, and the church to sort out (1 Cor. 7:2 - 9). The potential criminalization of marital intercourse has to be one of the most fundamentally destructive civil blows against the family in the lengthy list of recent decades.

Christians need to be careful that we are not enlisted into the wrong army on these matters. Pagans typically cast the social problems they wish to see solved in narrow terms and take a pragmatic approach. That horribly abused women and children exist in our nation is not to be
(continued on this page in left column)

The Ethics and Economics of Health Care

John W. Robbins

Mr. Robbins is director of the Trinity Foundation, publisher of The Trinity Review and many excellent books, P.O. Box 1666, Hobbs, New Mexico, 88240. Trinity retains the copyright on this article

Many Americans don't realize that any national health plan is based on *planned scarcity*. Although most Canadians have no trouble getting routine medical care, they tolerate what Americans would regard as unbearable waiting lines for things like bypass surgery, MRI scans, and hip replacements. National systems of health care eventually become bureaucratic, unresponsive to patients, and finally they bring rationing and waiting lines ... The worldwide experience over the last generation seems to show pretty clearly that when government economic controls are applied to health, they prove — in time — to be detrimental. The controls are based on planned scarcity and lead to an erosion of quality, innovation, and creativity.

I think it ironic that at a time when socialist regimes are collapsing all around the world and American disenchantment with politics and government seems at an all-time high, so many Americans clamor for the government to take over the health-care mess.

— C. Everett Koop[2]

TWO STORIES

I would like to begin my talk on the ethics and economics of health care by telling two stories, one of which I'm sure you have already heard.

A certain lawyer stood up and tested him, saying, "Teacher, what shall I do to inherit eternal life?"

He said to him, "What is written in the law? What is your reading of it?"

So he answered and said, "You shall love the Lord your God with all your heart, and with all your soul, and with all your strength, and with all your mind, and your neighbor as yourself."

And he said to him, "You have answered rightly; do this and you will live."

But he, wanting to justify himself, said to Jesus, "And who is my neighbor?"

Then Jesus answered and said, "A certain man went down from Jerusalem to Jericho, and fell among thieves, who stripped him of his clothing, wounded him, and departed, leaving him half dead.

"Now by chance a certain priest came down that road. And when he saw him, he passed by on the other side. Likewise a Levite, when he arrived at the place, came and looked, and passed by on the other side.

"But a certain Samaritan, as he journeyed, came where he was. And when he saw him, he had compassion on him, and went to him and bandaged his wounds, pouring on oil and wine; and he set him on his own animal, brought him to an inn and took care of him.

"On the next day, when he departed, he took out two denarii, and gave them to the innkeeper, and said to him, 'Take care of him; and whatever more you spend, when I come again, I will repay you.'

"So which of these three do you think was neighbor to him who fell among thieves?"

And he said, "He who showed mercy on him."

Then Jesus said to him, "Go and do likewise."

Christ's parable is a gold-mine of instructions about the ethics and economics of health care. Let me unpack a few of its implications.

First, the possession of health and the administration of health care are always individual. There are no such things as "national illness" or "national health care," for nations cannot and do not get sick or injured; nations cannot and do not care; only individuals can and do.

Second, the politico-religious establishment, represented in the parable by the priest and Levite, is uninterested in health care. Perhaps the priest and the Levite were hurrying to a national health care debate

Third, the good Samaritan appears to be on a business trip; He had an animal; he was carrying oil, wine, and money; and he was making a round trip.

Fourth, the Samaritan businessman used his own resources and spent his own time helping the victim.

Fifth, the Samaritan businessman paid the innkeeper for his trouble. He apparently did not think that the innkeeper had an obligation to help him or the crime victim without being paid for his trouble. The good Samaritan was not an altruist who believed that need creates an entitlement to the property of another. He acted out of compassion, not compulsion, and he did not try to compel anyone else to be kind.

Sixth, the Samaritan businessman spent the night in the inn with his victim, making sure he would recover, and after the emergency was past, he continues on his trip, leaving the victim in the care of the innkeeper. The good Samaritan did not organize a lobby to agitate for a National Health Plan, for that has nothing to do with love for one's neighbor. Instead, he continues on about his business. This traveling Samaritan was the good neighbor by sharing both his own goods and his own time with the crime victim, and it is his example, not that of the political and religious leaders, that Christ commands us to imitate.

Now let me turn from the New Testament to American history with a story about Congressman Davy Crockett from his biography, *The Life of Colonel David Crockett*.

Crockett, as a member of the House of Representatives, once voted to give $20,000 to the homeless victims of a fire in Georgetown. One of Crockett's constituents, Horatio Bunce, told Crockett he would not be voting for him in the coming election because of that vote.

Crockett objected, "Certainly nobody will complain that a great and rich country like ours should give the insignificant sum of $20,000 to relieve its suffering women and children, particularly with a full and overflowing treasury.

Mr. Bunce proceeded to explain why the vote was wrong:

"It is not the amount, Colonel, that I complain of; it is the principle. In the first place, the government ought to have in the treasury no more than enough for its legitimate purposes.... The power of collecting and disbursing money at pleasure is the most dangerous power that can be entrusted to man..... While you are voting to relieve one, you are drawing money from thousands... If you had the right to give anything, the amount was simply a matter of discretion with you, and you had as much right to give $20,000,000 as $20,000. If you have the right to give to one, you have the right to give to all; and as the Constitution neither defines charity nor stipulates the amount, you are at liberty to give any and everything which you may believe, or profess to believe, is a charity, to any amount you may think proper. You will very easily perceive what a wide door this would open for fraud and corruption and favoritism, on the one hand, and for robbing the people on the other.

"No, Colonel, Congress has no right to give charity. Individual members may give as much of their own money as they please, but they have no right to touch a dollar of the public money for that purpose....

There are about 240 members of Congress. If they had shown their sympathy for the sufferers by contributing each one week's pay, it would have made over $13,000. There are plenty of wealthy men in and around Washington who could have given $20,000 without depriving themselves of even a luxury of life. The Congressman chose to keep their own money, which, if reports be true, some of them spend not very creditably; and the people about Washington, no doubt, applauded you for relieving them from the necessity of giving what was not yours to give ...

"So, you see, Colonel, you have violated the Constitution in what I consider a vital point. It is a precedent fraught with danger to the country, for when Congress once begins to stretch its power beyond the limits of the Constitution, there is no limit to it, and no security for the people."

MORAL VALUES

In these two stories we see two opposite solutions to health care problems; the Christian solution and the political solution. Dr. C. Everett Koop, who will be our featured speaker this evening, has challenged everyone to debate political health care, and I rise to accept his challenge. Dr. Koop supports the President's Health Security Plan. In his advocacy of politicized medicine, Dr. Koop has written:

Before we can enact the sweeping reform that I think must take place, I think we have to agree on the basic values and ethics upon which our health care system, and our whole society, indeed, is based and from which we draw our moral power. I am convinced that if we could reach an ethical consensus, many of the economic and political problems would fall into place rather easily.[3]

In focusing first on ethics, Dr. Koop has correctly recognized the more important part of the health care debate. Economics is at best secondary, and I shall discuss it in second place. Ethics is of greater importance. Theology is of first importance.

Now what precisely are those basic values and ethics upon which our "whole society is based and from which we draw our moral power?" Certainly the single most important moral value — the moral value that has given the United States whatever moral authority it has had and still has in the world — the moral value which has attracted tens of millions to our shores and created the most humane society of modern times — is individual liberty. Individual liberty logically and historically depends on several other values, among which are the following:

1. **The sovereignty of God**. In political terms this means that God, not the state, society, race, class, *Volk*, or church is the source of security. The modern idolatry of state and politics, for which the eonomist Ludwig Mises coined the word "statolatry," is the cause of the horrific government-caused suffering that has afflicted the modern world, making the twentieth century the bloodiest century in the Christian era. The midieval idolatry of the church, ecclesiolatry, is responsible for most of the suffering and persecution of Christians during the Middle Ages.

2. **Limited Government**. The sovereignty of God entails the limited power and authority of all human institutions. The Constitution of the United States created a government of enumerated and limited powers.

Within that government, there is a separation of powers, so that no man or department exercises all the power of even a limited government. Only God, not men, is to be trusted with power. A nightwatchman state, such as that suggested by the apostle Paul in Romans 13, is a basic moral value of American society.

3. **The primacy of the individual**. The importance of the individual — rooted in the Reformation's recovery of the Bible's doctrines of individual election, individual regeneration, individual justification, individual sanctification, individual responsibility before God at the final judgment, personal immortality in heaven (or hell), justification by belief alone and the priesthood of all believers — is a basic value of American society. From it are derived all the various individual freedoms and protections we enjoy: religion, press, speech, association, privacy, private arms, self-incrimination, trial by jury, double jeopardy, and contract.

4. **Private property**. The mention of freedom of contract calls to mind the idea of private property. No one can seriously deny that private property is one of the basic values of both the Bible and American society. It has been under heavy attack in the twentieth century by atavistic and criminal collectivists who wish either to abolish it or to redistribute it by political means. "Thou shalt not steal" applies to all, both rulers and private citizens. Rulers routinely violate the commandment by taxation, expropriation, and inflation.

5. **The Protestant work ethic**.

What Max Weber called the Protestant work ethic is itself a bundle of economic virtues: Honesty, punctuality, diligence, obedience to the Fourth Commandment — six days you shall labor, obedience to the Eighth Commandment, you shall not steal, and obedience to the Tenth Commandment — you shall not covet. A recognition of the significance of productive work as glorifying God grew out of the Bible and the Reformation.

6. **Individual Responsibility**. The Bible clearly makes each man responsible for himself, both in this world and the world to come. In economics, Paul says that he who does not work shall not eat. Paul recognized no entitlement to the property of another.

7. **Generosity**. Perhaps no people has been as generous to those unable to help themselves as Americans. This is a consequence of two factors: Christianity and capitalism. But compassion, generosity, and capitalism have been under attack throughout the twentieth century by those who wish to substitute envy and compulsion. Compulsory charity is, of course, a contradiction in terms.

8. **The rule of law**. The rule of law, based upon legal principles found in the Bible, includes three major ideas: (1) that settled law, not executive decrees, regulations, or ordinances, is the only proper guide for social conduct; (2) that laws must be both clear and non-absurd, that is, capable of being understood by all and non-contradictory; and (3) that the laws apply equally to all, including rulers.

9. **Federalism**. Modeled on Presbyterian church government, the federal system is a system in which no government has a monopoly of jurisdiction. This division of powers, like the separation of powers, is designed to fragment political power so that it cannot threaten the lives, liberties, and property.

10. **Republicanism**. Republicanism entails not only the idea of limited government, but the notion that monarchies are not proper forms of human government, that they are in fact rejections of divine kingship, and that proper human governments are elected by the people. It was not only the nation of Israel that sinned by asking for a king, but pagan nations around them and throughout history have sinned that way as well.

These are the moral values of America, which have given American whatever moral power and authority it has enjoyed and still enjoys in the world. If we subvert or abandon these values, we will have lost both our moral power and our society. National health care, such as that proposed by the Clintons and Dr. Koop, opposes and subverts every one of these moral values.

DICTATORS AND NATIONAL HEALTH CARE

The fact that national health care is inimical to individual liberty should be obvious, but since some always seem to miss the obvious, let me belabor the point. I shall begin by remarking that every dictator in this century has been an advocate of national health care.

Writing in 1949, the economist Melchior Palyi pointed out that the concept and mechanism of the welfare state —

The systematic dispensing, through political channels and without regard to productivity, of domestic wealth — were at the very core of the Greco-Latin city states, of the midieval city, and of the post-Renaissance absolute monarchy ...

France's Henry IV in the sixteenth century promised a chicken in every pot. Her brilliant Colbert in the seventeenth century and Prussia's enlightened Frederick the Great in the eighteenth, these forerunners of modern dictators, gloried in calling themselves the first servants of the nation. Their police state used the welfare state as its instrument, facade, and justification, as do modern dictatorships. In democracies the welfare state is the beginning and the police state the end...

Bismarck's fundamentally significant role in modern history is rarely understood. His middle-of-the-road socialism was the connecting link between the old autocrats and the coming totalitarians...

The health, or rather sickness, propaganda employed by Bismarck elevated that aspect of social welfare to a prime political issue ... such ruthless men as Bismarck and Hitler [were] ... profoundly interested in the physical well-being of their subjects....

... all modern dictators — Communist, Fascist, or disguised — have at least one thing in common. They all believe in social security, especially in coercing people into governmentalized medicine....4

Adolf Hitler

Hitler, for example, established compulsory health care in occupied Holland in 1941.

The February 1920 Nazi Party Manifesto, the *Twenty-five Points*, included the following statements:

7. We demand that the State shall make it its first duty to promote the industry and livelihood of citizens....

15. We demand extensive development of provision for old age.

21. The State must see to raising the standard of health in the nation.

Vladimir Lenin

The March 1919 declaration of the All-Russian Communist Party, written under the guidance of dictator Vladimir Lenin, includes these paragraphs:

The dictatorship of the proletariat has already made it possible to carry out a series of measures, the realization of which was impossible in bourgeois society: the nationalization of drug stores, of large private medical institutions, of health resorts, compulsory work for all medical men and women, and so on.

In conformity with the above the All-Russian Communist Party sets as its immediate task:

(1) To carry out in the interests of the workers, sanitary measures on a large scale, such as

(1) Sanitation of centers of population (guarding of soil, water and air); ...

(c) The organization of measures preventing the development and spreading of infectious diseases;

(2) The struggle with social diseases (consumption, venereal diseases, alcoholism, etc.)

(3) Free trained medical assistance and medical supplies accessible to all.

It seems that universal access to health care is not a new idea.

Joseph Stalin

Article 120 of the 1936 Constitution of the U.S.S.R., written under the guidance of dictator Joseph Stalin, established a right to social security and health security:

Citizens of the USSR have the right to maintenance in old age and also in cases of sickness and disability. The right is ensured by the extensive development of social insurance of factory and office workers at state expense, free medical service for the working people, and the provision of a wide network of health resorts for the use of the working people.

Fidel Castro

Ten years ago the dictator of Cuba wrote:

Health is an essential right of all men and a responsibility of society as a whole ... It is absolutely necessary to promote mother and child welfare care programs, the control of communicable diseases, environmental protection, distribution of foodstuffs for children ... extend health care services, train the required technical personnel and guaran-

tee the essential basic medicines which such conditions demand.

As long as health fails to be considered a fundamental right of man and a duty of the community; as long as the responsibility of the State and of society in regards to health-care fails to be recognized; as long as inequalities in the distribution of health resources, both internationally and domestically, fail to disappear; as long as poverty, hunger, ignorance and squalor fail to be directly fought against, little will be achieved in improving human health in the underdeveloped world.[5]

Someone might object that despite the unanimous enthusiasm of twentieth century dictators for national health care, it is not necessarily subversive of individual liberty and limited government. Certainly democrats as well as dictators have advocated national health care. C. Everett Koop is no Nazi. The question, then, is who is consistent, the democrats or the dictators? The answer is clearly the dictators. There is something in the idea of national health care itself that is incompatible with individual liberty and all its constituent moral values.

GOVERNMENT PLANNING

The book summarizing President Clinton's Health Security Act is entitled *The President's Security Plan*. Government planning is incompatible with individual liberty, human well-being, and a civilized society

The Nobel Prize winning economist Friedrich Hayek, writing in his 1944 book *The Road to Serfdom*, noted that "The first of modern planners, Saint-Simon, ... predicted that those who did not obey his proposed planning boards would be 'treated as cat-

tle.'"[6] Saint-Simon recognized that planning is incompatible with individual liberty.

In the 1930's the British Labour Party theoretician Harold Laski raised the question whether "in a period of transition to Socialism a Labour Government can risk the overthrow of its measures as a result of the next general election."[7] Laski recognized that planning is incompatible with democracy.

Hayek concluded: "Once you admit that the individual is merely a means to serve the ends of the higher entity called society or the nation, most of those features of totalitarian regimes which horrify us follow of necessity."[8] In other words, there is a necessary connnection between altruism and totalitarianism. It is no accident that the dictators have been enthusiastic advocates of national health care. What is difficult to explain is how democrats can fail to see that connection.

It is obvious that if its plan is to work, the State cannot tolerate any deviation from it. Laski suggested that that entails the end of democracy. In logic it does, and in history it has. Certainly the Clinton health care plan, which "guarantees" coverage that can "never be taken away" implies that no one, Congress or the people, can be permitted to repeal national health care. Government planning is necessarily incompatible with individual freedom and democracy. Paraphrasing national health care advocate Vladimir Lenin, "The whole of society will become a single [doctor's] office and a single hospital with equality of care." And all will be guaranteed care for life.

Leon Trotsky, who understood quite clearly what government monopolies entail, might be paraphrased: "In a country where the sole physician is the State, opposition means death by health care rationing. The old principle, who does not work shall not eat, has been replaced by a new one: Who does not cooperate shall not recover."

The use of the welfare state to enforce the policies of the police state should be too well-known to be questioned at this late date in history. Physicians in the Soviet Union and Nazi Germany acted as employees of the government when they imprisoned dissenters in psychiatric prisons, euphemistically called hospitals; physicians in Nazi Germany, paid by the government, performed experiments on people without their consent; and physicians and scientists in the United States, paid by the government, have conducted radiation, chemical, and drug experiments for the Central Intelligence Agency, the Veterans Administration, the Department of Health, Education, and Welfare, and the Pentagon.

Lest you think the dangers of medical killing in America are remote, let me remind you that there are Nazi doctors and scientists among us in 1994 who think nothing of killing unborn children as a form of preventive medicine; who think nothing of experimenting on fetuses, harvesting their ova and brains for medical and scientific purposes; who think nothing of infanticide and euthanasia; who think nothing of killing rather than healing; and who long for the day when their views will be enforced by the guns of government. National health care will give them the sanction they want.

Those who advocate national health care advocate an immoral system. Their much praised concern for others is ersatz: They do not wish to spend their own time and money, but to force others to spend their time and money. They confuse compulsion with compassion. It is this mentality that has caused the bloodiest century of the Christian era. At least a hundred million people have died by the hands of this century's rulers, all of whom have justified their killing by saying they were doing it for the good of others. The Nazi regime in particular carried out its killings for public health reasons.

THE NAZI DOCTORS

In *The Nazi Doctors*, Robert Jay Lifton describes how the national health care system in Germany killed children in the 1930's:

> The structure served to diffuse individual responsibility. In the entire sequence — from the reporting of cases by midwives or doctors, to the supervision of such reporting by institutional heads, to expert opinions rendered central consultants, to co-ordination of the marked forms by Health Ministry officials, to the appearance of the child at the Reich Committee institutions for killing — there was at no point a sense of personal responsibility for, even involvement in, the murder of another human being. Each participant could feel like no more than a small cog in a vast, officially sanctioned, medical machine.[9]

Dr. Marc Micozzi, director of the National Museum of Health and Medicine in Washington, D.C., has argued that the Nazi medical experiments and holocaust were made possible only because Germany had been developing a political-medical complex for 50 years before the Nazis came to power:

> The German social insurance and health care system began in the 1880's under Bismarck. Ironically, it was part of Bismarck's "anti-socialist" legislation, adopted under the theory that a little socialism would prevent the rise of a more virulent socialism

The increasing involvement of the German government in medical care and funding medical research established government-medical complex that the National Socialists later used to execute their extermination policies.

By the time of [the] Weimar [Republic], German doctors had become accustomed to cooperating with the government in the provision of medical care. The reforms of the Weimar Republic following the medical crises of World War I included government policies to provide health care services to all citizens. Socially minded physicians placed great hope in a new health care system, calling for a single state agency to overcome fragmentation and the lack of influence of individual practitioners and local services. The focus of medicine shifted from private practice to public health and from treating disease to preventive health care ...

Medical concerns which had largely been in the private domain in the nineteenth century increasingly became the concern of the state. The physician began to be transformed into a functionary of the state-initiated laws and policies. Doctors slowly began to see themselves as more responsible for the public health of the nation than the individual health of the patient....

Where traditional individual ethics and Christian charity had once stood, the reformers posited a collective ethic of the benefit of the general population.

Private charity and welfare were nationalized ...

Politicized medicine is not a sufficient cause of the mass extermination of human beings, but it seems to be a necessary cause. The Nazi holocaust did not happen for some inexplicable German reason; it is not an event that we can afford to ignore because we are not German or not Nazis. The history of Germany from 1914 to 1945 is a telescoping of modernity — from monarchy, war, and collapse to democracy and the welfare state, and finally to dictatorship, war, and death.[10]

THE END OF CHARITY

But the loss of freedom for all — freedom for patients, freedom for physicians, freedom for taxpayers — is not the only consequence of national health care. The attempt to impose politicized charity subverts genuine charity. Even Dr. Koop has admitted that

When I first entered medicine and for many years thereafter, I and most physicians did not expect to be paid for everything we did. Donating care to some people who couldn't afford it was something expected of the profession. All that vanished with the coming of entitlement programs like Medicare.[11]

Historically, Americans have been a generous people. In the early nineteenth century, Tocqueville contrasted the spontaneous generosity of Americans and their "free institutions" with the welfare states of Europe where the "state almost exclusively undertakes to supply bread to the hungry, assistance and shelter to the sick, work to the idle, and to act as the sole reliever of all kinds of mis-

ery."

Another nineteenth century observer declared, "New York is, I firmly believe, the most charitable city in the world. Nowhere is there so eager a readiness to help, when it is known that help is worthily wanted; nowhere are there such armies of devoted workers."[12] After decades of the welfare state, New York City has quite a different reputation.

In 1938 an editor of *The New York Times* wrote an essay in *The Atlantic Monthly* entitled "The Collapse of Conscience." He lamented the fact that

personal conscience in the United States has fallen to a new low in our history as a nation. It has been largely lost to our sight in all the din and dither that have been raised about that other moral concept, the social conscience, which we are constantly reminded, has a nobler and more widely embracing function. And, the more we hear of the one, the less we hear of the other. The personal conscience has been steadily submerged; the very foundation upon which any broader conception of individual responsibility toward society must rest is being washed away..

There is a distinct flavor or cant about much of the talk concerning social conscience. The phrase slips readily from the tongue; it offers a large and easy generalization, and substitutes a vague beneficence for definite individual responsibility.[13]

An important part of the process of replacing personal charity with so-called justice involved changing the meaning of charity. Before the twentieth century, altruism, the notion that the poor were somehow entitled to the property of others, had no

place in America. This was as it should be, for the Bible itself teaches no unconditional duty to help others simply because they need help.

For example, there is Paul's command, already alluded to, that he who does not work, neither shall he eat. Paul makes no mention of adverse economic conditions as an excuse for joblessness. As a good economist, Paul knew that there is always plenty of work to be done. Paul says that there is no duty to support anyone who can work and does not. The Bible knows nothing of either legal or moral entitlements to the property of another, simply because the other needs help.

Paul's command, if obeyed, would mean the immediate end of the welfare state. It is not the Bible but the nineteenth century socialist Edward Bellamy, in his very influential novel *Looking Backward, 2000-1887*, who advocated the notion that "The basis of his claim [to the property of others] is the fact that he is a man." The epigrammatic Karl Marx said, "To each according to his need, from each according to his ability." The Bible says, "You shall not steal."

Second, there are Paul's rather detailed instructions about how churches are to dispense charity.

Do not let a widow under sixty years old be taken into the number, and not unless she has been the wife of one man, well reported for good works; if she has brought up children, if she has lodged strangers, if she has washed the saints' feet, if she has relieved the afflicted, if she has diligently followed every good work. But refuse the younger widows...

Here Paul quite clearly says, do not even support widows unless they meet certain qualifications, foremost of which is a lifestyle test. All charity is to be governed by the moral lifestyle of the recipient. Paul not only imposes a means test, he imposes an age test and a morals test that must govern charitable giving. Anyone who advocates legal or moral entitlements, anyone who advocates promiscuous political or private giving, anyone who asserts that some people deserve help simply because they are human beings is disobeying God. Paul says: "Do not feed ..." "Do not let a widow ..." "Refuse younger widows ..."

If one is reluctant to obey Paul's commands — though a Christian should not be — perhaps pondering Christ's healing ministry will help. When Jesus Christ walked on Earth 2,000 years ago, he had the power to end all types of sickness and illness. Yet he did not do so, because he was unwilling to do so, not because he was not all-powerful. He restricted his healing ministry to those in Israel.

There are three conclusions to be drawn from this practice of Christ: First, since Christ never sinned, it was not a sin for him to fail to heal everyone, even when he had the power to do so. Second, Christ had one condition for healing: belief. If a person lacked belief, he did not heal him. His miracles mirrored his salvation: health, justification, and sanctification come through belief of the truth alone. Third, Christ did not want any disciples who were interested only in his ability to feed and heal them. He obviously considered belief of the truth to be more important than physical well-being.

The modern ethic that all must be saved physically — anything less is socially unjust, we are told — reflects the modern theology that requires that all be saved eternally. Theological universalism and ethical universalism are twins. Neither one is

Christian; neither one is true.

Our Calvinist fathers understood Paul and Christ quite well, but their children have been so overcome by a vicious and sentimental universalism and altruism that they find Paul's commands to withhold charity, to refuse help to some people, as shocking as the notion that some people are going to hell. But in 1686 the Scots Charitable Society declared that "no profane or dissolute person, or openly scandalous shall have any part or portion herein."

Sixty years later (1752) in America minister Charles Chauncey told the Society for Encouraging Industry and Employing the Poor that the Society was

restrained as to the distribution of charity; not being allowed to dispense it promiscuously, but obliged to take due care to find out suitable objects; distinguishing properly between those needy people who are able, and those who are unable to employ themselves in labor..

In 1821 New Hampshirites Woodbury and Whipple reflected the thinking of their time and of the Bible by saying that "the poverty which proceeds from improvidence and vice ought to feel the consequences and penalties which God has annexed."

In nineteenth century America "charity organization societies considered 'worthy of relief' only those who were poor through no fault of their own and unable to change their situation quickly."[14] Our fathers distinguished, just as Paul did, between the deserving and the undeserving poor.

FROM LIMITED TO UNLIMITED GOVERNMENT

Since charity is a private responsibility, government has no role in providing it. President Grover Cleveland, at the end of the nineteenth century, vetoed a bill to give disaster relief to farmers in Texas and sent the following veto message to Congress:

I return without my approval House bill No. 10203, entitled, "An Act to enable the Commissioner of Agriculture to make a special distribution of seeds in the drought-stricken counties of Texas, and making an appropriation [of $10,000] therefor."

It is represented that a long-continued and extensive drought has existed in certain portions of the State of Texas, resulting in a failure of crops and consequent distress and destitution.

Though there has been some difference in statements concerning the extent of the people's needs in the localities thus affected, there seems to be no doubt that there has existed a condition calling for relief; and I am willing to believe that, notwithstanding the aid already furnished, a donation of seed grain to the farmers located in this region, to enable them to put in new crops, would serve to avert a continuance or return of an unfortunate blight.

And yet I feel obliged to withhold my approval of the plan as proposed by this bill to indulge a benevolent and charitable sentiment through the appropriation of public funds for that purpose.

I can find no warrant for such an appropriation in the Constitution, and I do not believe that the power and duty of the General Government ought to be extended to the relief of individual suffering, which is in no manner properly related to the public service or benefit. A prevalent tendency to disregard the limited mission of this power and duty should, I think, be steadily resisted, to the end that the lesson should be constantly enforced that though the people support the Government, the Government should not support the people.

The friendliness and charity of our countrymen can always be relied upon to relieve their fellow-citizens in misfortune. This has been repeatedly and quite lately demonstrated. Federal aid in such cases encourages the expectation of paternal care on the part of the Government and weakens the sturdiness of our national character, while it prevents the indulgence among our people of that kindly sentiment and conduct which strengthens the bonds of a common brotherhood.

Government's role in society is well-defined by the Bible: Its purpose is to punish evildoers. Since by its nature government involves the use of force, government is restricted to activities where the use of force is appropriate: the punishment of criminals. This nightwatchman state has no role in the economy, even less in charity. The welfare state, and national health care, are immoral.

GOVERNMENT IS FORCE

This brings us to the central recognition that government is force. Two centuries ago George Washington warned that government is not reason nor eloquence, but force. Like fire, government is a dangerous servant and a fearful master. The United States is operating under the delusion that government is benevolent by nature and that public officials act only in the public interest.

Here are some of the ways force will be applied to the American people under the Clinton Health Security Plan:

1. If it becomes law, you will be forbidden from purchasing basic health insurance of your choice, even if you pay the premium for a government plan first

2. You will be forbidden from receiving any treatment that the government considers unnecessary or inappropriate, even though you and your doctor might disagree.[15]

3. Unless you get Medicare, military or veterans benefits, or work for a company with 5,000 or more employees (which alliances are already government organizations), you must join a government monopoly called a health alliance. If you do not, you will be assigned to one.

4. You will be denied medical care unless you are a member of an alliance. You will be required to carry a health passport which electronically encodes your medical history.

5. You will be forbidden to pay the doctor yourself; he can be paid only by a government approved health care plan.

6. Your doctor will be compelled to provide all your medical information to a national data bank which will keep files on all Americans.[16]

7. State governments and insurers must make "automatic, mandatory, nondiscretionary reductions in payments" to doctors, nurses, and hospitals to "assure that expenditures will not exceed budget." Health care will be rationed.

8. Approved health care plans will be forbidden to deny enrollment to anyone.

9. Doctors and patients will be compelled to accept government set fees for services.

10. Offering a doctor an extra payment is a "bribe" punishable as a crime, including denial of health care. He who does not cooperate shall not receive health care.[17]

11. If a state government fails to cooperate with the National Health Board, which is the Supreme Health Soviet, it will lose all federal health appropriations and new federal taxes will be imposed on all employers in that state.

12. The government approved health plans are forbidden to discriminate among applicants on the basis of individual characteristics, health status, anticipated need for health care, occupation, or affiliation with any person or entity.[18]

13. Medical school applicants will be accepted or rejected by government boards and assigned to a specialty of the government's choosing.[19]

14. Heavy new taxes will be imposed to fund the plan.[20]

The results of this sort of totalitarian medicine were described 30 years ago by the liberal political scientist:

Medicine in the Soviet Union is socialized; complete medical care is available to all citizens free of charge. ...

Soviet doctors, on the whole, are rather poorly paid. Some augment their salaries, semi-legally, by engaging in private practice. Since this pattern seems sufficiently widespread, we can say that people who have wealth or positions of authority receive better medical care than the majority, because they can engage physicians for private service.

.... he [the doctor] is the only person in the social system who has authority to excuse people from work to which they have been assigned. In a society where heavy duties are imposed on all, sickness is one of the few legitimate escapes from obligations ... This ... encourages the citizen, at times, to simulate illness, exaggerate his troubles, or, in real desperation, deliberately induce disease or injury. In turn, the physician's task is complicated by the need to weed out malingerers ... He is, after all, not only the healer of the sick, but also an officer on the staff of the government which is interested in getting socially desirable work done ... Medical care, in short, is a means to promote economic growth.[21]

THE PROMISES OF NATIONAL HEALTH CARE

Meyer's description of the Soviet health care system suggests that the realities of totalitarian medicine are quite different from its promises.

National health care plans promise universal access,[22] but they invariably deny access to some, frequently for non-cooperation with the authorities.

National health care plans guar-antee equality of care,[23] but those with political clout always get more and better care.

National health care plans promise adequate care, but what they always deliver is rationing.[24]

National health care plans promise high quality care, but what they invariably deliver is cookbook medicine, with treatments approved by government officials, not by patients and their doctors.

National health care plans promise cost savings, but they invariably break the budget.[25]

The Health Security Act claims to increase competition, but it actually creates monopolies.[26]

As for the state of competition among American durg companies, the top five drug companies supply 30 per cent of the market. The top five beer companies supply 90 percent of the beer market. The top five car companies supply 80 percent of the automobile market.

The whole apologetic for national health care is based on deception. That deception extends even to the deliberate misuse of certain words by proponents of national health care.

THE MISUSE OF LANGUAGE

In his essay "Politics and the English Language," George Orwell explains how politics corrupts language. That corruption can be clearly seen in the deliberate misuse of words by advocates of national health care.

The first instance of the misuse of language is the word "crisis." Whenever some twentieth century political faction in America has wanted to push its program through or get elected, it has attempted to scare the American people with talk of a crisis.

Candidate John Kennedy did it in 1960 with his warnings about a "missile gap." Socialist Michael Harrington and President Lyndon Johnson did it in the mid-1960s with their warnings about a poverty crisis. In the 1970s and '80s it was the energy crisis. In Germany in the 1930s, it was the Reichstag fire.

The past behavior of socialist politicians should make everyone skeptical of any new crisis politicians might announce. Rather than jumping on command, we should try to discover how the latest alleged crisis will be used to increase political power.

There is no health care crisis. Eighty percent of the American people report that they are "very" or "somewhat" satisfied with their present health care. The uninsured, whose numbers are far less than the 37 million the press reports, receive almost as much health care as the insured. A more accurate number of the chronically uninsured is 5 million. Of the uninsured, more than half are members of families with full-time workers, 40 percent have incomes over $20,000 per year, and 10 percent have incomes over $50,000 per year. They simply choose to spend their money on other things. Thirty-seven percent of the uninsured are under 25; and those with incomes less than $20,000 spend several times as much on alcohol, tobacco, and entertainment as they do on health care. Only one percent of those under 65 are uninsurable, that is, they cannot easily purchase health insurance. There simply is no health care or health insurance crisis.

Here is a second example of the misuse of language: the word *insurance*. What is being discussed is not insurance at all. The notion of insurance includes insurers weighing risks, accepting or rejecting risks, and setting premiums based on risks accepted, but all are specifically forbidden by the Health Security Act. Franklin D. Roosevelt used the same tactic to get Social Security passed in 1935.

Third, the taxes collected to fund this health security plan are not called taxes, but "contributions." Of course, this is not a new misuse of language either; it is at least as old as the Social Security Act. No one pays social security taxes; we all make "contributions." Try to stop making those "contributions," and you will find out exactly what they are.

Fourth, the phrase "universal access" is itself a deception. Today, everyone in the United States has access to health care. Statistics show that the uninsured receive almost as much medical care as the insured. What the phrase "universal access" really means is compulsory participation. The Health Security Act provides that "Implementation involves the enactment of a statute adopting federal program standards, formation of regional health alliances, and imposition of requirements for employers and individuals to obtain coverage." Notice the phrase, "imposition of requirements."

Finally, the biggest deception of all is "equality." We know that all animals are equal, but some are more equal than others. What a politicized health care system means is that anyone with political connections or pull will get better care than those without power. Care will flow to those who wield political power, and the powerless will suffer.

THE AMERICAN HEALTH CARE SYSTEM

One can agree that there are serious problems with the present health care and health insurance systems in the United States. Nothing in this paper should be construed as a defense of the status quo. But those serious problems arose because of government interference in the insurance and care systems.

Costs

In 1993 total spending on health care in the United States was about $940 billion, about 14 percent of our gross national product. In 1950, the amount spent per American on health care was $82; in 1986 it was $1,837; in 1993, over $3,500; and it is projected to be $5,550 in 2000.

Dr. Koop has written: "During the past 30 years ... health care expenditures have risen in the United States from 4 percent to 14 percent [of GNP] ..."[27]

Why have costs risen so fast in the past 30 years? Thirty years ago, the federal government became heavily involved in medicine: It enacted Medicare and Medicaid, creating a higher demand for medical services and driving costs up. At the same time, it took steps to restrict the supply of drugs, personnel, and medical devices.

EMPLOYMENT-RELATED INSURANCE

One of the major criticisms of today's insurance system is that insurance depends on employment. Health insurance is tied to employment only because of government tax policies from 1942 to the present.

Prior to 1930, most Americans paid most of their medical expenses out of their own pockets. (By 1930 the United States had as many or more medical, nursing, and dental schools and hospital beds per capita as it has today.)

Employer-provided health insurance emerged during the 1940s. The price and wage controls illegally imposed during World War II, plus an illegal military conscription, brought about a shortage of civilian labor. Employers were forbidden from increasing salaries to attract workers. In 1942 the War Labor Board decided that fringe benefits up to five percent of wages would be permitted. Employers began to offer health benefits as a way of providing additional compensation and attracting needed workers. Enrollment in group hospital plans grew from less than 7 to about 26 million subscribers from 1942 to 1945.

At the same time, the Internal Revenue Service made two rulings: (1) the purchase of health insurance for workers was a legitimate cost of doing business and could be deducted from taxable business income; and (2) workers did not have to include the value of health insurance benefits in calculating their taxable income. Those tax provisions are still a part of IRS rules.

Labor unions, themselves privileged by federal law, began to demand employer-provided insurance in their contracts. In 1948 the National Labor Relations Board ruled that health insurance was a legitimate subject of collective bargaining, and this encouraged the spread of plans.

STATE RESTRICTION OF INSURANCE

There are almost 1,000 state laws restricting insurance policies that may be offered to customers. In 1970 there were only 30 state-mandated benefit laws nationwide. They are a major reason why many people lack health insurance: state-mandated benefits increase the cost of insurance and price many people out of the insurance market. One study shows that as many as one out of every four uninsured people lack health insurance because state regulations have increased the price. Assuming the figure of 37 million uninsured is correct, this means that as many as 9.3 million people lack health insurance because of state government restriction of the types of policies that may be offered.[28]

DRUG REGULATIONS

In 1962, amendments to the Food, Drug, and Cosmetic Act imposed a requirement that new drugs be shown to be safe and effective before they were marketed. Since then the process by which a new drug receives approval from the FDA has become increasingly complicated, lengthy, and costly. In 1994 the average new drug takes 11 years and $231 million to bring to market. In 1980 the same standards were applied to medical devices. The federal requirements for drug testing, by delaying the introduction of new drugs, have caused the deaths of hundreds of thousands of Americans in the past 30 years. These deaths were the result of a policy of politicized compassion and consumer protection.

INFLATION

Since 1960 the federal budget has been balanced only once, and the official national debt has increased by four trillion dollars. The Federal Reserve has increased the money supply, the last silver has been removed from our coins, silver certificates were removed from circulation, the last gold backing for our paper currency was abolished, and consumer prices have increased about 500 percent. All of these government policies have affected the cost of health care since the 1960s. Creating a new health care bureaucracy and new spending, when the federal government has no

money, must result in higher taxes and more inflation. Both are forms of institutionalized stealing by government.

LICENSING

The American Medical Association, an industry cartel, which, in cooperation with government, controls the licensing of physicians and nurses, has restricted the supply of medical personnel for much of this century. Occupational licensing has no beneficial economic effects; its principal effect is to restrict supply of services and thus raise prices.

The Department of Veterans Affairs

The United States already has one national health care system: The Department of Veterans Affairs. In September 1990 the television show *Primetime Live* filmed conditions at some VA hospitals. They found blood-stained needles lying openly on tables, and old and broken equipment in the Cleveland hospital. Patients told reporters that the nurses hadn't shaved or bathed them for three weeks. Several had been lying in their own feces for hours. One VA hospital employee described the system as "Bad facilities, incompetent doctors, and medications that are ordered but don't get there." Some nurses reported that doctors did not change their gloves and routinely spread dangerous bacterial infections.

Primetime hid a camera in the room of a Vietnam veteran. According to nurses and staff the patient did not receive prompt treatment when he entered the hospital, and as a result, surgery became necessary. His family accused the hospital of failing to treat his spinal abscess in time, and now the patient is quadriplegic. The camera showed that although the food was brought to the patient, no effort

was made to feed him, and he went without food for three days until another patient wandered into his room and fed him.

Patients at the Washington, D.C., VA Medical Center sometimes "walk around with a catheter for three or four months" awaiting prostate surgery, states Chief of Medicine James Finkelstein. "It makes them vulnerable to infection and discomfort," he says. We're doing the same thing they do in Great Britain." A World War II veteran had all his upper teeth pulled by the Denver VA in September 1988, but he didn't receive his dentures until November 1989.

The New York Times reported that six men treated at the VA Medical Center in North Chicago during 1989 and 1990 died due to inadequate care. Two died from undiagnosed aneurysms, one from undiagnosed heart blockage, one from hemorrhage following surgery, one from a misdiagnosed ulcer, and another from an artery nicked during prostate surgery. During one of the emergency surgeries to repair the aneurysm, the small intestine and an artery were torn by a clamp. The torn artery was not discovered until the autopsy. The man who died from heart blockage was given Maalox for indigestion. The fatal hemorrhage following vocal cord surgery was observed by a doctor, who did nothing to stop the bleeding.

Even Dr. Koop admits that "the federal track record in the health care business is dismal."

CONCLUSION

Our consideration of the ethics and economics of health care leads us to several conclusions

1. The proposed Health Security Plan, and indeed any political

health care plan, is subversive of the fundamental moral values that have given the United States whatever moral authority it has in the world. Government planning is incompatible with freedom of choice in health care, freedom of contract, private planning, limited government, federalism, the rule of law, individual responsibility, the work ethic, and Christian charity.

2. The proposed Health Security Plan is inimical to the Biblical ideas of sovereignty of God; the primacy of the individual; the proper function of the state; the sinfulness of theft, idleness, and envy; and the exercise of Christian charity.

3. The proposed Health Security Plan is no different in principle from the various plans advocated by all of the dictators of the twentieth century.

4. The creation of a political-medical complex as proposed by the Health Security Plan is a necessary condition of a totalitarian state, as illustrated by the history of Germany.

5. The Health Security Plan is antithetical to the Christian idea of charity and is based on the Marxist credo: "From each according to his ability, to each according to his need."

6. The Health Security Plan involves the immoral use of force against patients, doctors, hospitals, insurance companies, drug companies, and taxpayers.

7. The promises of the plan — universal access, equality of treatment, high quality of care, low cost, adequacy of care, and so forth — are false. Both economics and history demonstrate the necessary failure of politicized medicine.

8. The language used by proponents of the health security plan, as well as some of the statements they make, are deliberately deceptive and false.

9. The origins of most if not all the problems perceived in our present health care system — rising costs, lack of insurance coverage, shortages of personnel — are the previous actions of both state and federal governments.

We must conclude that the proposed Health Care Plan — and every Plan that involves government in medicine — is both immoral and impractical. That implies, of course, that our present system, which already suffers from severe government interference, does need to be reformed. But the reforms needed have not been suggested by either President Clinton or the Republican Party. They include the following:

1. The abolition of all government health care programs, including Medicare, Medicaid, and the VA.

2. The repeal of all taxes used to support such health care.

3. The repeal of all regulations on drug testing and licensing.

4. The repeal of laws requiring certain drugs to be prescribed only by a physician.

5. The repeal of all occupational and insitutional licensing laws.

6. The repeal of all state restrictions on insurance plans.

7. The modification of income tax rules to allow full deductions to individuals for insurance and medical care. Better yet, the repeal of all local, state, and federal income tax laws.

The present health care system needs reform, but improvement will come only with less government interference, not more. These seven measures will make the government more compatible with Christianity and America's fundamental moral values.

Thank you.

This paper was delivered at the regional meeting of the Evangelical Theological Society at Westminster, Philadelphia, Pennsylvania, March 4, 1994.

REFERENCES

2. C. Everett Koop "is one of the most thoughtful, courageous, and independent health care leaders in the nation.... For many years, Dr. Koop has campaigned to reform the health care system. He has been a passionate advocate of primary and preventive care, of universal coverage and cost containment." — Hillary Rodham Clinton, The White House, September 20, 1993. The Koop quotation is from **Let's Talk**, pages 102-104.

3. C. Everett Koop, "Will the Crisis in Healthcare Deprive Us of Its Opportunities?" *Transactions and Studies of the College of Physicians of Philadelphia*, Ser. 5, Vol. 15 (1993), 58.

4. **Compulsory Medical Care and the Welfare State**. Chicago: National Institute of Professional Services, 1949.

5. Fidel Castro, **The World Economic and Social Crisis**. Havana: Publishing Office of the Council of State, 1983, pp. 215, 188.

6. University of Chicago Press, 24.

7. As quoted in **The Road to Serfdom**, 63.

8. **The Road to Serfdom**, 149.

9. New York: Basic Books, 1986, 55.

10. "National Health Care: Medicine in Germany, 1918-1945," *The Freeman*, November 1993, 416-420.

11. C. Everett Koop and Timothy Johnson, **Let's Talk**, 133. Oddly, Dr. Koop thinks Medicare is one of the "most noble" things the U.S. government has done.

12. As quoted in Marvin Olasky, **The Tragedy of American Compassion**. Washington: Regnery Gateway, 1992, 100-101.

13. J. Donald Adams, "The Collapse of Conscience," *The Atlantic Monthly*, January, 1938, 56.

14. **The Tragedy of American Compassion**, 104. The previous quotations are taken from Olasky as well.

15. Dr. Koop says: " ... treatments for individual patients should not be based in 'society values' but on 'patient values,' which often differ from society values and even from physicians values." **Let's Talk**, 121. But of course the Plan Dr. Koop supports eliminates "patient values" from consideration.

16. Dr. Koop says: "Nothing is more important to me than doing what I can to restore a trusting doctor-patient relationship." Who will be able to trust his doctor knowing that everything must be reported to the government?

17. Dr. Koop says: "the federal government should follow the lead of states that prohibit any physician from owning a facility to which a patient could be referred with financial profit going back to the referring physician." **Let's Talk**, 91.

18. Dr. Koop says: "Pre-existing health conditions should not exclude people from insurance coverage." **Let's Talk**, 111.

19. Dr. Koop says: "We need a rational plan for the training and allocation of physicians ..." **Let's Talk**, 92. Also: "We can no longer be the only industrialized nation that does not subsidize or completely pay for the education of its physicians."

20. Dr. Koop says Congress should "slap a hefty tax on cigarettes" and impose new taxes on alcoholic beverages, handguns, and ammunition. He goes on to advocate the politics of avarice: "Instead of blindly opposing the $2 cigarette tax, tobacco-state members of Congress should be fighting for their share of the pie to help move their states into the economy of the 21st century." *The Washington Post*, September 21, 1993.

21. Alfred Meyer, **The Soviet Political System**, New York: Random House, 1965, 366-368.

22. Dr. Koop Says: "All Americans must have access to basic health insurance for primary and preventive care, and catastrophic health insurance." "Will the Crisis in Healthcare Deprive Us of Its Opportunities?" *Transactions and Studies of the College of Physicians of Philadelphia*, ser. 5, vol. 15, 1993.

23. Dr. Koop says: "Some things — like universal access — are not negotiable, and that's exactly the way it should be ... When I read the first draft of the [Clinton] plan, ... I was supportive of the plan, even if there were specific issues with which I disagreed." The White House, September 20, 1993.

24. Dr. Koop says: "The real problem is that far too many Americans have too much health care." He favors politically restricting the health care available to Americans.

25. Alain C. Enthoven, Professor of Economics at Stanford University and a leading proponent of

managed competition, has criticized the Clinton plan as a "wolf in sheep's clothing" deceptively hiding behind the language of market competition while creating a "complete federal takeover in health care." The National Health Board is "a huge power grab" and the financing plan "puts the federal budget at risk."

26. The German Marxist Rudolf Hilferding explained the role of prices in a socialist economy almost a century ago: "What a government economy does is precisely to abolish the autonomy of economic laws; it is not a market economy, but an economy for use. What is produced, and how it is produced, is no longer determined by the price but by the state planning commission [in this case, the National Health Board], which fixes the character and extent of production. To outward appearances, prices and wages still exist, but their function has completely changed. They no longer determine the course of production. That is directed by the central government ... Prices and wages are now only instruments of distribution determining the share that each individual shall receive out of the sum total which the central government allots to the whole population. Prices have now become the technical means of distribution, a means simpler than would be a direct order stipulating the amount of the various products (which have ceased to be 'commodities') to be received by each individual. Prices have become symbols of distribution, but they are no longer the regulators of the nation's economy. While the form has been maintained, the function has been completely changed."

27. "Reducing Health Care Costs by Replacing the Need and Demand for Medical Services," *New England Journal of Medicine*, July 29, 1993.

28. Dr. Koop says: "State legislature should eliminate state-mandated insurance benefits ... People should be able to pick a plan that best suits their individual and family circumstances." **Let's Talk**, 111. But of course the Health Security Act, which Koop supports, prevents people from picking a plan that suits them best.

Politicization of Medical Training: Coercing Abortion Training

Byron Calhoun, M.D.

Dr. Calhoun is Assistant Clinical Professor at the University of South Alabama at Mobile, and Vice Chairman of the Department of OB/GYN at Keesler Medical Center in Biloxi, Mississippi.

Over one and a half million babies have perished yearly since Roe v. Wade in 1973. This sum is not enough for the abortionist. Recently, Grimes, *et al.* publishing in *Obstetrics and Gynecology*, 1993, bemoaned the fact that "abortionists" were a vanishing breed. They blamed this decline, of course, on the pro-life movement in general. They also castigated the obstetrician/gynecologists in this country for not "supporting" women in providing safe abortions. The same tired statistics were trotted out which showed how "terrible" things were in 1973 before legal abortions and how "safe" they are now. This comparison is utter nonsense. Abortion complications are just no longer reportable to the Center for Disease Control or state agencies. I venture to estimate that I see at least one abortion-related complication a week. I suspect any obstetrician in a university or indigent practice sees the same. There are numerous abortionists of the indigent who do the procedures and then leave town. Any complications are seen by the local obstetricians in the emergency rooms.

In October, 1993, the American Council on Graduate Medical Education (ACGME) and the Residency Review Council (RRC) released a new salvo in the abortion battle. They want to *require* that abortion training be offered by all

> *Righteousness exalts a nation but sin is a disgrace to any people.*
> Proverbs 14:34

training programs. The new RRC wording is as follows:

> **The program must provide a structured didactic and clinical training experience in the full range of family planning techniques including contraception, sterilization, and abortion. This must include experience in management of complications as well as training in the performance of these procedures. Experience with induced abortion must be a part of residency training, except for residents with moral or religious objections. This education can be provided on or off campus.**

This statement contains a classical logical *non-sequitur*. The statement attempts to imply that abortion training must be required and then goes on to maintain that a resident may opt out on "*moral or religious objections.*" This makes no sense. How can training be "required" if one may opt out of it? This exception implies that the RRC may not *require* a resident or program to participate in abortion if they morally object. If training is considered optional then it may not be used to determine a resident's board eligibility or a program's fitness

under RRC review.

The requirement for an abortion rotation in every residency program does not allow Catholic, Protestant, or military residencies to decline as a matter of conscience to participate in abortion and still maintain their residency status. The statement implies that a religious or military residency may be required to finance a resident's off-site rotation to an abortion clinic even though they are morally opposed to or legally forbidden to participate in abortion. Residents are (for the time being) allowed to have consciences, but their teachers and supporting institutions are not. By this does the RRC demonstrate that it believes professional maturity means moral eunuchism?

Surely, this heavy-handed treatment of community residencies smacks of rank politicization of the educational process. There is even a hint here that the pro-abortionists, having been unable to convince the hearts of the majority of practitioners, are willing to try coercion. Mere coercion is a last resort of a side which is losing the moral battle in the hearts of people.

The ACGME/RRC obviously intends to reverse the declining trend of abortion providers in this country through a well-orchestrated campaign. The "seizing of the robes" is essential to gain control of the abortion industry. Since virtually 90% of the practicing Ob/Gyns in this country do not perform abortions (ACOG survey, 1980) and only 1 - 2% do more than a handful in any one year, the abortion ranks are dying out. The abortionists intend to grab the training programs after radicalizing the RRC. The abortionists know they must plan a step-by-step campaign to legitimize the practice of baby-murder. The best place to do this is in training. To gain control, they must eliminate any and all rivals. This strategy is entirely consistent with the humanist doctrine. There must be no king but Caesar. If they are able to corrupt or close the Catholic, Protestant, and military residencies and force them into compliance, all institutional resistance to abortion in training programs is lost. There will be no legal Godly alternatives. The conscience clause will be increasingly difficult for residents to make use of in secular residencies and abortion will gain another step in legitimacy.

Therefore, we suggest that physicians who participate in female care write, call, and protest this onerous rule in residency. The American Association of Pro-life Obstetrician/Gynecologists (AAPLOG) supports that this new guideline be stricken. We suggest that programs and program directors be allowed, for conscience sake, *not* to develop abortion rotations as part of their curriculum. Exodus 20:13 says, "You shall not murder."

It is not enough to identify the problem in residency training and attack abortion as murder of the infant. We must provide alternatives to the practice. All Christian physicians ought to be involved in adoption placement and referral. Christian physicians also should not be making referrals for abortion for any reason, but rather should help young women to make correct decisions for their babies' lives. Our command from the Lord is "love one another" and " ... look after orphans and widows in their distress..." (James 1:27) Let us be part of the solution to this problem and not part of the problem.

Editor's note: *The address of Paul O'Conner, Ph.D., of the ACGME is 515 N. State St., Suite 2000, Chicago, IL 60610.*

Clean Arteries, Clean Heart
Randall W. Crenshaw, M.D., M.B.S.

After fifteen years in emergency medicine, Dr. Crenshaw has been for four years medical director of an HMO headquartered in Birmingham, Alabama. He earned his M.D. degree from the University of Tennessee and Master of Biblical Studies from Birmingham Theological Seminary. He, his wife, and two daughters attend Mountain Brook Community Church.

President Clinton's Task Force on Health Care Reform has released its recommendations to an anxiously awaiting American audience. The reform package must now run the gauntlet between Congress and hundreds of special interest groups from the American Medical Association to Xerox Corporation. The potential economic shifts will make this the hottest debate since the abolition of slavery and breaking away from England.

Health care reform rose to the surface of President Clinton's agenda because economists had predicted that, by the year 2000, America would spend 20% of its Gross Domestic Product on medical services. Expenses totaled about nine hundred billion dollars, or 13% of GDP, in 1992. Failure to control the increases will make it difficult, if not impossible, to balance the Federal budget and to make American businesses more competitive in a global marketplace. The task force chose "managed competition" as the cornerstone of its cost reducing strategy. Simply put, managed competition is the notion that doctors and hospitals will band together to compete for large blocks of patients on the basis of cost and quality measures. If the Physician-Hospital Organizations can render all the services their patients need with a fixed budget, they will profit. If not, they will presumably go broke.

HOW WILL THE REFORM PLAN DIFFER?

Those who now have limited access to medical services will like the plan. Those currently enjoying unlimited access will probably find it too restrictive. The successful managed care plans upon which the reform package was modeled have several features in common that serve to keep costs low while maintaining high quality.

They emphasize prevention of disease by regular screening and immunizations to improve productivity during the working years and extend those years. They educate their members about disease processes, empowering them to take more responsibility for their health instead of abdicating it to professionals.

They render more services through primary care physicians, nurse practitioners, and physician's assistants. Specialists are consulted only after the generalist has evaluated the problem and treated it to the best of his or her ability.

They rely on drug therapy and less on surgery. For example, they tend to have lower rates of such operations as coronary artery bypass, hysterectomy, and tube placement in children's ears.

Regardless of its chances of passage through a Congress which is rapidly losing confidence in the Chief Executive, the Health Care Reform Act will not achieve its goal of making Americans healthier. It will fail because it does not recognize what leads to health or even what "health" is.

Studies have shown that higher levels of education and income are associated with better health. Better nutrition and sanitation are, too. Medical research and treatment, however, have little impact on the health of entire populations.

Empirical evidence from the United States confirms these findings. We have the most advanced medical technology of any nation on earth. Magnetic images projected onto a large screen will soon allow physicians to "walk" from chamber to chamber through the human heart. Tiny, balloon-tipped catheters remove fatty deposits from the arteries that feed the muscular pump. When all else fails, for $200,000 we can transplant a dead man's heart into the body of the barely alive.

The social policies of the federal government have extended these technological treasures to most of our citizens. If personal medical services (the diagnosis and treatment of individuals) make people healthy, how can we explain the fact that we rank nineteenth in the world in infant mortality? Or, how do we account for the fact that our life expectancy is only seven years longer than our ancestors who were born at the turn of the century? (In 1900, if a child survived fatal infections like diphtheria, hemophilus meningitis, and polio, he could expect to live to age 65. Vaccines have drastically reduced those childhood killers. Yet, a baby born today will live, on the average, only to age 72.)

We have, I believe, greatly overestimated the benefits of modern medical technology

I also said that health reform would not make us healthier because it does not know what health is. It does not recognize that emotional and spiritual well-being are as essential to "health" as freedom from physical disorders.

The World Health Organization acknowledges as much in its definition of health. The Hebrews of Biblical times understood it as well. A word commonly used in the Old Testament for health is *salom*, and it carries the sense of inner peace, safety, prosperity, and satisfaction. Consider the following "report card" on the emotional and spiritual well-being of the American people.

Former Secretary of Education, William J. Bennett, has assembled eight cultural indicators that he says quantify America's decline. During the thirty year period 1960-1990 he found that, "there has been a 560% increase in violent crime; a 419% increase in illegitimate births; a qua-

drupling of divorce rates; a tripling of the percentage of children living in single parent homes; more than a 200% increase in teenage suicide rate; and a drop of almost 80 points in SAT scores."

Bill Bennett concludes that "although the Great Society and its many social programs have had some good effects, there is a vast body of evidence suggesting that these 'remedies' have reached the limits of their success."

President Clinton's social blueprint, like President Lyndon Johnson's, will not make Americans healthier. It will, however, cost a lot

For those of you wo prefer charts to narratives, consider these figures from New York City.

	1943	1993
Population	7,472,564	7,322,564
Welfare recipients	73,000	1,200,000
Homicides	44	1,497
Illegitimacy rate	3%	45%

more. When Medicare was enacted the U.S. was spending $41.6 billion a year on medical services - 5% of GDP. No one knows what President Clinton's reform package will cost. At a minimum, it will cost a trillion dollars, or roughly 15% of GDP. As stewards of the resources entrusted to us, we should ask if this is a wise use of those resources.

The results suggest that, as a nation, we are looking in the wrong places for health, peace, and satisfaction. Someone has said that the hospital is modern America's temple and physicians her high priests. An astounding number of us abuse alco-

hol or take drugs like Prozac and Xanax to make ourselves feel good. Many others have operations, like coronary bypass, that give only temporary relief of pain and do not prolong life in the vast majority of cases.

SCRIPTURAL VIEW OF HEALTH AND HEALING

Psalm 90 says that man has seventy to eighty years on earth. There is a biological limit to life in this world. The Bible also uses the words healing and salvation synonymously. The Holy Spirit, through Isaiah the prophet declares that we are healed by Christ's punishment for our sin. (Isaiah 53:5) In other words, an intimate relationship with the Lord Jesus Christ, based on repentance and faith, is the only sure route to health.

The peace in knowing that God forgives us for leading such self-centered lives releases us from the ever-present fear and frustration of life in a fallen world. His love is a balm for the wounds of our accumulated hurts and humiliations. We have hope because we know that one day He will come and bring things to a righteous and joyous conclusion.

This peace, this love, this hope — this is real health. And, it comes not from clean arteries but a clean heart.

God alone can provide this change the Bible calls a new heart. "I will cleanse you from all your impurities ... I will give you a new heart and put a new spirit in you; I will remove from you your heart of stone and give you a heart of flesh. And I will put my Spirit in you and move you to follow my decrees and be careful to keep my laws ... I will save you from all your uncleanness." (Ezekiel 36:25-27,29

NIV)

Incidentally, scientific studies have recently shown that blockages in coronary arteries disappear with such changes in attitude, without drugs or surgery. Ph, the price? It's free for the asking.

Editor's Note

This *Journal* and others have published several papers[1,2] which have warned of the dangers of professional licensing by the government. Licensing laws lack Biblical, economic, and research support for their stated purpose of "protecting the public." What was only a hint of using licensing to enforce social policy a few years ago has now become an accepted reality in some states.

A recent national newspaper article described the loss of driving licenses by eight "deadbeat dads" in Maine.[3] These fathers had not paid child support despite several warnings. The Maine legislature passed the Family Financial Responsibility Act in 1993 which empowered the Human Services Commissioner to suspend both driving and professional licenses. Mr. Peter Fore, a spokesman for Human Services, declared, "If someone has a driver's and professional license, we'll go after both of them." In addition, President Clinton's $9.3 billion welfare reform proposal recently sent to Congress would *require* that *all states* be able to suspend the driving and professional licenses of delinquent parents.

The Bible exhorts us to support our families; those who do not are "worse than an unbeliever" (I Timothy 5:8b). However, any civil government penalty should be clearly related to the crime. State licensing laws were not passed as a means of promoting social policy. The changing use of licensing laws allows for increasing power of government to demand obedience to other government policies related to socialized medicine, humanistic education, etc. As a society, we have failed thus far to heed God's warning in Proverbs 13:15 that "Good understanding wins favor, but the way of the unfaithful is hard."

In His Name,

Joseph K. Neumann, Ph.D.

References

1. Neumann, J.K., Licensing of Health Care Professionals From a Biblical Perspective. *Journal of Biblical Ethics in Medicine,* Vol. 2, No. 2, pp. 21-26, 1988.

2. Holzer, H.M., The Physician's License: An Achilles Heel? *The Journal of Legal Medicine,* Vol. 12, pp. 201-220, 1991.

3. Adams, G., "Deadbeat dads" lose license in Main. AP story in *Johnson City Press,* Vol. 74, No. 324, pp. 1,6, 1994 (June 28.)

Physician-Assisted Death Should Remain Illegal: A Debate

Douglas C. Heimburger, M.D.

Dr. Heimburger is Associate Professor and Director of the Division of Clinical Nutrition in the Departments of Nutrition Sciences and Medicine at the University of Alabama at Birmingham.

The following article is the text of arguments delivered in a public debate at the University of Alabama at Birmingham on the topic: "Physician-Assisted Death: Should It Remain Illegal?"

OPENING STATEMENT

The issue of optimal medical care and the most appropriate ways of dealing with pain and suffering, while maintaining human dignity as debilitating diseases bring us toward the ends of our lives, is extremely important, and one that warrants much more public discussion than it has received. It is an issue that strikes at the core of what it means to be a physician, and what it means to treat and heal persons. I will argue that there has never been a time in human history in which the means to take one's life were unavailable — they have always been at hand — and yet only in the last several years has there been a public call for legalization of physician-assisted death (PAD). It is ironic, in fact, that this call comes at a time when we have better means than ever for treating pain. For this reason and others, I will argue that the call for PAD is not being made now primarily out of fear of a prolonged, painful dying process or of a loss of dignity and control in the face of

advancing technology. Although each of those plays a part, the call for PAD arises from a shift in society's view of what determines the value of life and a growing mistrust of the commitment of physicians and family members to provide attentive care when one reaches a state of debilitation and decline. I will attempt to communicate a vision for life in which value is based on objective truth, transcends the boundaries of birth and death, and is therefore independent of ability; and a vision for caring and compassion that will virtually obviate the need to consider assisted death. I will also argue that because the call for PAD arises from the concept of a life not worth living (not just from pain), the legalization of PAD will lead subtly but definitely to the concept of a life not worthy to be lived. This concept will seriously jeopardize the rights of many persons in society whom some consider to be unproductive and burdensome.

DEFINITIONS

The term physician-assisted death is not specific. I will take it to refer to two things: *physician-assisted suicide*, in which a physician provides the means, or access to the means, by which a patient can end

his life, and *voluntary active euthanasia* (a term used by the American Geriatrics Society), in which the physician or some other agent, but not the patient, administers the means of death. As I use the term physician-assisted death, I will be referring to both of its forms. The position I will argue tonight is that both forms of PAD are killing, and should remain illegal.

Let me be equally clear about what I do not oppose. I will argue that terminally ill persons should be allowed to die, and that treatments that a terminally ill patient deems useless or excessively burdensome should be withdrawn or withheld in order to avoid unnecessary prolongation of the dying process. When extending life has become impossible, the appropriate course of action is not blindly to attempt to postpone death by using every last technological tool available to us, to squeeze in every possible moment of biological life. There are many in this room who will attest that I have promoted this view over the last decade. For example, I would not argue that the state should have required that William Bartling, a patient with severe end-stage lung disease, must continue being treated with a mechanical ventilator when he had requested that it be discontinued. Although I am not entirely comfortable with all aspects of the decisions made in the well known cases of Karen Ann Quinlan and Nancy Beth Cruzan, the patients in persistent vegetative states whose families petitioned to have their mechanical ventilator and enteral tube feeding discontinued, respectively, I would argue that after providing sufficient safeguards, the state should not prevent these treatments from being discontinued when the wishes of the patient or of a properly designated proxy are clearly known to favor discontinuation. These cases involve allowing to die rather than killing, and should be allowed. I will apply the terms *withdrawing or withholding therapy* to these situations, in order to distinguish them from PAD. In these cases, the decision is about the benefits and burdens of *therapies* and not about the benefits and burdens of *lives*, a distinction that will be crucial to my arguments.

Nor will I be arguing that one should be overly cautious in providing pain relief out of the fear that it may hasten death. When pain medications are given to a patient with terminal cancer or another painful condition in order to alleviate suffering, even when the doses required may risk shortening the patient's life, they are permitted because the *intention* is to alleviate suffering rather than to kill. Caring for a dying person means assisting her through the sometimes painful and frightening process of dying, but caring does not permit killing. Allowing to die is courageous and admirable, and should be taught and modeled for and by physicians; killing is not and should not.

FOUNDATIONS OF THE CALL FOR PHYSICIAN-ASSISTED DEATH

Of the three major aspects of ethical issues, the normative, the situational, and the existential (motivational), most persons probably assume that the current pressure to legalize PAD arises from the situational. Many people are greatly concerned that as their health declines and medical technologies are applied to them, they will lose control over what is done to them. They are also concerned that if they experience pain, it will not be adequately treated, and they will be abandoned to die an undignified death, in excruciating pain. Indeed, a Dutch government-sponsored survey on the practice of euthanasia in the Netherlands, where it is officially tolerated, indicated that the principal reasons patients there request euthanasia are loss of dignity [in the face of modern technology] (57% of cases), pain (46%), unworthy dying (46%), being dependent on others (33%), and tiredness of life (23%).[1]

However, I would submit that this is only as it appears on the surface. The fact that a call is being made now for PAD is only partially related to pain itself, for though we have always had very effective means for ending life when we chose to do so, never before have we had methods at our disposal for the treatment of pain that are as good as those we have now. Hospice practitioners, who are experienced in and committed to the use of adequate pain control and other palliative measures for dying patients, insist that no one needs to die in extreme discomfort or indignity. One of these, Dr. Joanne Lynn, "has cared for over 1000 hospice patients, and only two of these patients seriously and repeatedly requested physician

assistance in active euthanasia. Even these two patients did not seek another health care provider when it was explained that their requests could not be honored."[2] It has been asserted that in England, where palliative care is emphasized, requests for euthanasia are rare. In Holland, on the other hand, where euthanasia is easy to obtain, palliative care is said to receive lower priority.

Rather, the fact that PAD is being called for now is evidence of a normative choice that western society made long ago, to reject the concept of objective universal truth. Having done this, men and women themselves have become the arbiters of what is true and right, and accountability to anyone other than oneself has been rejected. We have decided that we are not stewards of our lives, as western culture believed for centuries, but that we have *dominion* over it. It is not a *gift* that we have been given in *trust*, but is something we possess as our own, and over which we have absolute autonomy. This principle of human autonomy leads to patient autonomy, and forms the essential foundation for the call for PAD. Richard McCormick has noted that this *absolutization of autonomy* tends to eclipse moral reasoning, because "the sheer fact that a choice is the patient's tends to be viewed as the sole right-making characteristic of the choice."[3] He points out that this total accomodation to the patient's values and wishes ignores, or rejects, the fact that there are good choices and bad choices, and that particular features make them so. When one engages, therefore, in PAD, one is not just taking a small step further in relieving pain and anguish, but is acknowledging that a subtle but giant leap has already been taken in which the creature has supplanted the creator.

PAD is little more than a logical consequence of the presupposition that the meaning of our lives and our deaths is determined by ourselves and by no one else, including God.

This being the case, the important and practical problem that arises, and the point from which I will now argue against PAD, is that if God does not exist, everything is permitted (this was Sartre's point); nothing is finally impermissible on these grounds. As I now describe what could be the untoward consequences of the acceptance of PAD by our culture, keep in mind that they are consequences of the foundational presuppositions. In my mind the only certain way to avoid the consequences, to reverse the trend, is to abandon the presuppositions and embrace objective truth. PAD should represent an "ethical stop sign" warning us of a cliff ahead. If we ignore it and fail to stop, we may find ourselves over a precipice. A slight turn of the wheel or a small change in velocity will be no substitute for coming to a full stop.

CONSEQUENCES OF LEGALIZED PHYSICIAN-ASSISTED DEATH

A cardinal feature of the call for assisted suicide is the assertion that the value of a person's life is diminished if the person's ability to be active or productive is impaired, or if suffering becomes substantial. Such a life, it is asserted, may not be worth living. To accept this notion will have profound implications beyond PAD, for the culture that, in its ethical autonomy, has sown the

conceptual seed of a "life not worth living" will reap the harvest of a cheapened view of life in general.

Consider this: many requests for assisted suicide represent a cry for love, for touching, and for caring, out of a fear that when one reaches a point of disability and dependence on others, they may begin to consider one's existence a net burden to them. Many ethicists have pointed out that in this context, ready acceptance of a request for assisted death could be disastrous if interpreted by the patient as confirmation of her worthlessness. Over time, after legalization of PAD, this dynamic would progress to an anticipation by persons with advancing

> *Physician-assisted death is ... a logical consequence of the presupposition that the meaning of our lives ... is determined by ourselves and by no one else, including God.*

disease that they will be considered by others to be worthless, and perhaps to have lives unworthy to be lived. This could result in preemptive suicides and involuntary euthanasia.

I remember well a young resident physician for whom I had the opportunity to care a number of years ago here at UAB. He was diagnosed with cancer of the colon during his internship, and by the end of his residency it had progressed to the point where his intestines were obstructed by entanglement in a matted mass of tumor in his pelvis. But he was otherwise still quite strong, and able to be active in the hospital, mainly teaching medical students. So we began treating him with total parenteral nutrition in order to maintain his nutrition and hydration. After about two months of the

therapy, when he was still rather active, Alex suggested that perhaps there was no point in continuing with it further. Sensing that he was really asking whether his wife and physicians and others still cared for him, and whether we still considered his life to have value — crying out for love and caring — I encouraged him that there was every reason to continue on, that there was no reason to consider his life of less value, and that we would all be by his side until the end. He continued the therapy for another eight months, during which time he was able to support his wife as she dealt not only with his illness but with a serious illness in her father as well. The way he valiantly responded to his progressive suffering — discontinuing the therapy shortly before his death because it was obviously no longer prolonging his life, but not asking for assisted death — deeply touched all of those who cared for him. We will never be the same again. But, if we had acquiesced to his suggestion eight months earlier that there was no point in continuing further, he would likely have died feeling abandoned, and those who survived him would have missed a great blessing.

More specifically, various ethicists enunciate the following serious adverse consequences of legalized PAD.

1. Distortion of the healing relationship

The knowledge that PAD is a possible course of action, even if its use is unlikely in a given case, will seriously distort the relationship between a physician and her patient. The first aspect of this is that PAD will represent a fundamental change in the calling of physicians, and alter the "internal morality" of medicine, or the moral obligations that have always been inherent in medical care.[4] The purpose of medicine, which has always been to restore health when it is possible, and to enable the patient to cope with disability and death when it is not, will be undermined. The second aspect of it is that the doctor-patient relationship is "ineradicably grounded in trust." It is fundamentally important for the patient to trust that the physician will always act in an attempt to heal, and not to consider even the possibility of removing the need to heal by killing him. In Dr. Edmund Pellegrino's words," How can patients trust that the doctor will pursue every effective and beneficent measure when she can relieve herself of a difficult challenge by influencing the patient to choose death?"[4] The availability of PAD will only magnify the uncertainty, mistrust, and even suspicion that are already too prevalent today in the healing relationship. Consider the scenario of a person who may or may not have a terminal condition (prognostication is an extremely difficult art), and may not feel as though she is receiving a great deal of communication from her physician (an all-too-common and unfortunate occurrence). If PAD is known by both physician and patient to be a legal option, the patient will inevitably begin to wonder whether her physician is still giving her care due consideration. Even changing nothing, in the *current* medical climate, she may justifiably wonder whether the physician really has her best interests in mind. She may wonder whether he is frustrated over her case, emotionally spent, or (looking toward the future) pressured by a government health care alliance to

lower the costs he incurs in caring for his patients.

Without question, in many situations physicians will be tempted to accept assisted death as an easier course of care, and this will undercut the incentives to provide attentive care to suffering persons. Medical training and experience already have the effect of desensitizing physicians to witnessing the loss of life; will not legal PAD only inure them to it further, and make it an all-too-welcome alternative? Again, Pellegrino: "If [assisted suicide] is known to be a viable option at the outset, it cannot fail to influence the patient, the physician, and everyone else involved in the patient's care. If it is not known at the outset, the patient is deprived of the clues needed to interpret her physician's actions."[5]

I have treated many patients in my years as a physician or medical student. Although I trust that those I have cared for, and those whom I have worked with in doing so, would consider me a compassionate and caring physician, I know my own heart well enough to know that I fully have the capability to be tempted, when feeling frustrated and helpless, to make a therapeutic decision that suits my own selfish desires before the needs of my patients. In a recent conversation Dr. Pence [a philosophy professor who moderated the debate] described physicians to me as being "incredibly self-serving." While he cited this fact as a reason used by *physicians* to opposed legalized PAD (perhaps because they don't have the courage to deal with it or don't want their incomes reduced by decreasing their patient populations), I believe any self-serving tendency physicians may have, as all persons have, provides a compelling reason why

you and he should insist that PAD remain illegal. You see, while the observation that physicians can be self-serving only qualifies them as ordinary human beings (it could equally be applied to philosophy professors!), I think it is true. Ladies and gentlemen, I do not ask you to opposed PAD because you need to be protected from someone else. I ask you to oppose it because you need to be protected from *me*. Do not entrust me with a prerogative that I may very well use to your detriment. Do not ask for your relationship with me to be altered in such a way that I could decide, and even convince you, that the best I can do for you is to provide you with the means of a certain death, at your hands or mine: for I will be tempted to do just that, even if it is not the best I can do.

2. Abuses against persons, and abrogation of rights

Once we have crossed the line that has prevented us until now from practicing PAD, we will have abandoned the historic tradition of "state's interest" in human life.[4] We will have embraced the concept that there are lives that should be ended, and open our society to grave moral and social consequences. Abuses of vulnerable members of society will increase; we will witness the abrogation of the rights of "unproductive" persons who are thought to represent a "burden" on society — impoverished persons, mentally handicapped persons, very old and especially demented persons, others with disabilities that keep them below some acceptable level of functional ability, and persons in persistent vegetative states.

I had a close friend who died last

year after being confined to a bed and wheelchair for many years because of a spinal cord injury. He felt powerless and chronically vulnerable, and was terrified over trends he saw in society that have the potential to disenfranchise disabled persons.

Increasing concerns over the costs of medical care, and progressive involvement of impersonal health care networks serving as surrogates of the federal government, will amplify this risk. This is especially true with regard to the elderly, as the distribution of our population shifts toward an inverted pyramid, with a smaller number of persons in the workforce supporting a growing elderly population. While some have expressed fear that the federal government might forcibly prolong our dying process, surely the opposite is far more likely as the temperature of cost-consciousness and health care rationing increases in our climate. On a smaller scale, abuses by families and other caregivers will likely increase as well, toward persons who they think should request PAD but do not.

If you doubt the validity of this argument, let me ask you to consider two things. First, I would ask, once we have removed from one segment of our community the time-honored protection to which all (adult) life heretofore has been entitled in the U.S., by what standard will you argue that it should not be removed from others? For instance, there are more than a few persons in society who argue in favor of labelling mentally handicapped individuals as non-persons. It is asserted that this label is used as a justification for the use of involuntary euthanasia with individuals who have severe and even moderate

intellectual disabilities.[6] If voluntary euthanasia were legalized, the practice of euthanasia on retarded persons could easily receive further justification. The line of reasoning may go something like, "if persons who are competent to request euthanasia or assisted suicide can now do so legally, why should persons who are incapable to express their wishes be deprived of the opportunity?" Following this reasoning, the late novelist and physician Walker Percy asserted that "once the line is crossed, once the principle is accepted — juricially, medically, socially — innocent human life can be destroyed for whatever reason."[7] If God is dead, everything is permitted.

Second, I would ask you to consider that in Holland, the best example of a country that has officially tolerated (though not legalized) euthanasia, the practice has progressed to include nonvoluntary euthanasia. Cases of "life termination by [a physician] administering lethal drugs without an explicit and persistent request from the patient" were estimated by the 1991 Dutch government survey to represent up to a third of all cases of euthanasia there.[1] In interviewing the families and physicians of Dutch patients who had been euthanized, Dr. Carlos Gomez came across the case of a 56 year old man who was given a lethal injection of potassium chloride in an emergency room after suffering massive trauma.[8] Not only was the patient unconscious and unable to express his wishes, but the

physician did not even wait for the family to arrive in order to interview them, much less to give them the opportunity to see him before the end came. They never knew their loved one had been euthanized. In this instance the physician acted in what I can only interpret as a paternalistic way, a practice that PAD is intended to minimize by maximizing patient autonomy. Nevertheless, the physician who performed euthanasia felt totally justified in what he did, and defended his decision vigorously. He did not admit that he had ventured outside the Dutch guidelines, which require repeated documented requests for euthanasia from the patient before it can be performed.

Other aspects of Gomez's research make a strong case as well for the notion that euthanasia is unregulatable. From his extensive interviews of persons who are involved in euthanasia in the Netherlands, he documents the extremely intricate and often ambiguous nature of informed consent for assisted death. Questions such as who first suggested it as an option (was it really the patient who requested it, or did the physician first suggest it? if the latter, how much was the request truly the patient's?) and who will blow the whistle if anyone abuses the practice (dead persons cannot testify, prosecutors are unlikely to be present, and physicians [being self-serving!] virtually never inform on each other) will be almost impossible to answer. Perhaps most telling is the report that elderly persons generally oppose euthanasia in Holland because they fear being involuntarily euthanized.[8] Elderly Dutch physicians reportedly fear being admitted to the very hospitals where they have practiced, for the same reason.[4] There is obviously great

> *In allowing to die, one is making judgments about treatments, in physician-assisted death one is making judgments about lives.*

concern in their minds that physicians will not only not always act in their best interests, but that physicians in fact may not always follow their wishes. What began as an expansion of patient autonomy has in their minds become a dangerous expansion of physicians' power.

Dr. Pellegrino sums it up, "The Dutch experience shows that even when euthanasia is not legal but is tolerated, expansion of its boundaries — from voluntary to involuntary, from adults to children, from terminally ill to chronically ill, from intolerable suffering to dissatisfaction with the quality of life, from consent to contrived consent — is inevitable."[4]

But as I have alluded, physicians are not the only ones who will use the issues surrounding PAD to serve their own interests. One of the most ardent and well-known proponents of euthanasia, Mr. Derek Humphry, the author of *Final Exit* and founder of the Hemlock Society (an organization whose mission is to help persons who wish to end their lives to do so), was accused by his wife and co-laborer in the cause of forcing his agenda on her, to her detriment and ultimate demise. The suicide note of his wife, Ann Wickett Humphry, accused him of abandoning her, harassing her, and trying to hasten her death when she refused euthanasia after she was diagnosed with cancer.[9] She also accused him of having suffocated his first wife, Jean, whose celebrated "suicide" energized the right-to-die movement. Regardless of the accuracy of her claims, it is clear that assisted suicide can create serious interpersonal tensions even among its most ardent proponents, and does not always eventuate in "death with dignity." Rather, the call for PAD arises from and will result in a general devaluation of life that will prove correct Albert Schweitzer's assertion that if a man loses reverence for any part of life, he will lose reverence for all of life.

3. Intolerance of dependence on others

A third side effect of legalized PAD that McCormick attributes to the absolutization of autonomy is a progressive intolerance of dependence on others. Autonomy limits the definition of "death with dignity" to death in *my way*, at *my time*, and by *my hand*. Yet, interdependence has always been one of the most noble features of human relationships, as has the sharing of pain and suffering in order to alleviate it. McCormick quotes the Anglican Study Group:

There is a movement of giving and receiving. At the beginning and at the end of life receiving predominates over and even excludes giving. But the value of human life does not depend only on its capacity to give. Love, *agape*, is the equal and unalterable regard for the value of other human beings independent of their particular characteristics. It extends to the helpless and hopeless, to those who have no value in their own eyes and seemingly none for society. Such neighbor-love is costly and sacrificial. It is easily destroyed. In the giver it demands unlimited caring, in the recipient absolute trust. The question must be asked whether the practice of voluntary euthanasia is consistent with the fostering of such care and trust.[10]

As such, McCormick insists that "assisted suicide is a flight from compassion, not an expression of it. It should be suspect not because it is too hard, but because it is too easy."[3] If we reject interdependence with others and embrace PAD, we will fail to see assisted death for what it so often is: an act of isolation and abandonment.

Robert Spitzer descries this as "the total decline of culture. It is the epitome of a culture that no longer recognizes love or goodness to be the value of life. It is a culture that values only one thing: convenience, function, some kind of production beyond consumption. That is a crass utilitarian culture. And that is the culture we are trying to prevent."[11]

POLICY ISSUES

Although they represent a minor plank in my argument, I think PAD could be ably opposed on policy issues. I am not convinced, for instance, that PAD needs to be legalized in order for it to occur in the way that its proponents wish. Indeed, to this date the Dutch have said as much, since they have not legalized euthanasia. Many physicians write many prescriptions for enough narcotics that, if taken all at once, would result in the patient's death. Undoubtedly some prescriptions — who knows how many? — are written expressly for this purpose. In light of this potentiality, the main change that may occur with legalized PAD, as I have argued earlier, is the explicit acceptance of the concept of a life not worth living, and the removal of the most important obstacle preventing the declaration of a class of persons whose lives are not worthy to be lived. This will result in a net *reduction* of patient autonomy at the expense of self-serving physicians or cost-cutting health care alliances and government operatives. It will threaten the very goals the proponents of PAD are attempting to reach.

Secondly, even if PAD is accepted by society, in light of the deleterious effects I have insisted will occur in doctor-patient relationships, why should doctors necessarily be the ones to perform it? Although I opposed any legalization of assisted death on the principles outlined earlier, it would seem to be strategically important for its proponents to suggest that someone other than physicians be designated to carry it out, thus protecting patients from ambiguity and suspicion in their relationships with their physicians.

KILLING VS. ALLOWING TO DIE

At the root of my case against physician-assisted suicide and voluntary active euthanasia is a subtle but monumentally important distinction between killing and allowing to die. It is based on two very important differences.

First, in killing and in PAD, it is the instrument one administers that effects the demise of the patient, whereas in allowing to die, one removes a therapy that is ineffective at restoring health, and the disease kills the patient.

In the first instance it is a person's action that kills, and in the second the person acts in order to allow the disease to kill. Second, in killing and in PAD, the death of the patient is the intended result of one's actions, whereas in allowing to die, the intended result is that ineffective or excessively burdensome impediments to the patient's death should be removed.

In allowing to die, one is making judgments about treatments, in PAD one is making judgments about lives. I maintain that because it is a gift and a trust. Life — even one's own — is a thing about which we are not at liberty to make value judgments. On the other hand, therapeutic technologies invented by our ingenuity have benefits and burdens, and we can and do legitimately make judgements about the balance of those. As the Ramsey Colloquium put it, "Our decisions, whether for or against a specific treatment, are to be always in the service of life. We can and should allow the dying to die; we must never intend the death of the living. We may reject a treatment; we must never reject a life."[12]

CONCLUSION

Physician-assisted death is not an appropriate means of avoiding the prolongation of dying (to do so is to play God), of alleviating suffering (other means are sufficient for this), or of relinquishing life when it is no longer possible to maintain a grasp on it (allowing to die accomplishes this). To embrace PAD as a means of maintaining dignity and control over one's fate will result in a further cheapening of life and will establish dangerous precedents. Once we have decided that life is a thing that can be taken away voluntarily, on demand, it will be a very small step to take it involuntarily, on command. One who grants requests for PAD thinks that he does so in love, but he does not.

Rather, if we recapture the belief that life is a gift and a trust whose value extends beyond the time the heart stops beating — that meaning transcends biology — and if we reaffirm that the sort of caring for a person that is truly noble includes touching, holding, enduring, maintaining vigil, and medicating, then the call to end one's anguish by ending one's life will become unnecessary. We must reaffirm out commitment "always to care, never to kill."[12] Requests for PAD that are met in this way are truly met by love.

REFERENCES

1. van der Maas, P.J., van Delden, J.J.M., Pijnenborg, L., Looman, C.W.N., Euthanasia and other medical decisions concerning the end of life, *Lancet*, Vol. 338, 1991, pp. 669-674.

2. Teno, J., Lynn, J., Voluntary active euthanasia: The individual case and public policy, *Jour. Amer. Geriatr Soc*, Vol. 39, 1991, pp. 827-130.

3. McCormick, R.A,. Physician-assisted suicide: Flight from compassion, *The Christian Century*, Dec. 4, 1991, pp. 1132-1134.

4. Pellegrino, E.D., Doctors must not kill, *J. Clin. Ethics*, Vol. 3, 1992, pp. 95-102.

5. Pellegrino, E.D., Compassion needs reason too, *JAMA*, Vol. 270, 1993, pp. 874-875.

6. Lusthaus, E.W., Involuntary euthanasia and current attempts to define persons with mental retardation as less than human, *Mental Retardation*, Vol. 23, 1985, pp.

148-154.

7. Percy, W., An unpublished letter to the *Times*. In: Samway, P., ed., **Signposts in a strange land**, Farrar, Strauss, & Giroux, 1991.

8. Gomez, C.F., **Regulating death: Euthanasia and the case of the Netherlands**. New York: Free Press, 1991.

9. McCrystal, C., Ann Humphry's final exit, *Vanity Fair*, Vol. 55, 1992, pp. 80*ff*.

10. Anglican Study Group, On dying well, 1975, Quoted in McCormick, R.A., Physician-assisted suicide: Flight from compassion, *The Christian Century*, Dec. 4, 1991, pp. 1132-1134.

11. Cited in Oakes, J.S., ed., Killing as caring: The false charity of euthanasia, *Critical Issues I*: pp. 1-8.

12. Ramsey Colloquium. Always to care, never to kill: A declaration on euthanasia. *First Things*, Feb., 1992, pp. 45-47.

An Evangelical Critique of Advance Directives

Gregory W. Rutecki, M.D.

Dr. Rutecki is Associate Professor of Internal Medicine at Northeastern Ohio Universities College of Medicine in Canton, Ohio.

HISTORY AND SIGNIFICANCE OF ADVANCE DIRECTIVES

The well publicized legal imbroglios that surrounded Karen Quinlan and Nancy Cruzan's terminal care have led to a brave new era of patient self-determination. That era began on April 14, 1975, when twenty-one year old Karen Quinlan sustained an enigmatic brain injury described as a "chronic vegetative state" which resulted in ventilator dependence. Her family filed a plea in New Jersey's Superior Court to gain legal permission to disconnect Karen from the Ventilator. Karen's mother, sister, and friend testified that Karen often spoke about her desire not to be kept alive by machines.[1] After being weaned from the ventilator, Karen — now spontaneously breathing — was transferred to an extended care facility on June 9, 1976. Nine years later, Karen Quinlan died. She brought the disturbing and very painful questions surrounding end-of-life care, autonomy and persistent vegetative state to national prominence.

Then on January 11, 1983, twenty-five year old Nancy Cruzan suffered irreversible brain injury in a car accident. Again, Nancy's family and friends testified that she

would not want to be kept alive in her condition, "just as a vegetable."[2] The Cruzan family petitioned the courts in order to discontinue Nancy's tube feeding during her persistent vegetative state. The discontinuation of nutrition and hydration eventuated in Nancy Cruzan's death on December 26, 1990. The Supreme Court molded Nancy Cruzan's terminal care into a far-reaching paradigm for end-of-life decision-making. In so doing, the Justices acknowledged the right of incompetent patients to refuse unnecessarily burdensome treatment but at the same time emphasized the necessity for written evidence documenting patient wishes which empowered surrogates to make end-of-life decisions.[3] For the first time, America's terminal care vocabulary would include, "clear and convincing evidence," and a "right to die."[4]

The Cruzan family's agonizing choices vis-a-vis the Justices' interpretation of the Constitution eventually culminated in the federal Patient Self-Determination Act (PSDA) (12/1/91) requiring: 1. the provision of written information to patients regarding the right to refuse treatment and the formulation of advance directives under state law; 2. inquiry as to whether a

patient has an advance directive and documentation of the presence or absence thereof in the medical record; 3. the provision of education to hospital staff concerning advance directives; 4. compliance with state law concerning advance directives (all fifty states have enacted living will legislation); and 5. maintenance of written institutional policies concerning all of the above.[5]

Advance directives may be defined as instruments which are intended to conclusively establish an individual's preference in writing with respect to the degree of medical care and treatment he or she desires to receive. Advance directives may also be designed to document how an individual would like to be treated or who should make treatment decisions if the individual should become incapacitated and lose the ability to make or communicate medical decisions. Advance directives include written instruments such as living wills, durable powers of attorney for health care, and health care proxies, as recognized by state law.[6]

Response to the PSDA by both patients and health care workers may be characterized as lukewarm at best with approximately 15% of hospitalized patients availing themselves of such documents.[7] Certain groups, however, have become targeted for more aggressive advance directive implementation and study. One such group, in whom advance directives are already presumed to lead to "good deaths," is comprised of patients with end stage renal disease (ESRD).[8] The rationale for heightened advance directive utilization in this specific group includes the following: ESRD patients sustain a yearly mortality approximating 20%; already dialysis dependent, these patients are familiar with life support; discontinuation of dialysis followed by death may be the second leading cause of mortality in this population; and 50% of ESRD patients who discontinue dialysis and die are deemed incompetent at the time of important end-of-life decisions.[9]

Even though advance directives are generally purported to have multiplied benefits,[10] they concomitantly raise a disconcerting specter. Recently, my thought as an evangelical was crystallized concerning the potential negative fallout of advance directives. My colleagues and I in nephrology completed a questionnaire investigation of ESRD patients and advance directives which resulted in some disturbing observations.[11] In the study, ESRD patients themselves desired a review of personal advance directives as frequently as four times per year. How valid and binding could such end-of-life documents be if they were no more temporally substantial? Prior studies in the same population have shown that over 40% of ESRD patients would allow significant leeway with potential surrogate override of their written advance directive decision.[12] In a document whose raison d'etre is autonomy, nearly one-half of patients would still have "significant others" making decisions potentially quite different from their own. With previous, substantial empiric evidence documenting the inaccuracy of proxy decision-making, there is no guarantee that the surrogate's choice would be in the patient's best interest.[13] In spite of these and other perceived shortcomings of advance directives, the National Kidney Foundation (NKF) has suggested more vigorous implementation policies throughout the U.S. dialysis facilities.[14] With further government involvement in medicine assured in a short-term future, ESRD patients may become an experiment leading to further enforcement of the PSDA in seriously ill populations.

In response to the concerns raised by empiric study, as well as to the pressure brought to bear by the NKF, I propose to develop a Biblical foundation from which to evaluate the pros and cons of advance directives as they confront a multiplicity of end-of-life treatments. I would like then to proceed and contrast the Biblical foundation with the primary secular force driving implementation of advance directives, i.e., autonomy. Finally, I will engage the future implications of advance directives in a mileu of a post-Hippocratic ethos in medicine.

ADVANCE DIRECTIVES: A BIBLICAL-THEOLOGICAL PERSPECTIVE OR A GOD-CENTERED, REALITY-BOUNDED AND LOVE-IMPELLED VIEW OF TERMINAL CARE[15]

The engagement of advance directives within a Biblical world view perspective will discuss the sanctity of human life, a respect for patient freedom, suffering in the economy of existence, and the utilization of advance directive instruments in deciding for or against treatments at the end of life. Each of these four areas will be considered individually throughout the following sections.

"The first guide we will examine is life, not because it is necessarily more important than the others but because it is foundational to the entire enterprise of medicine." John Kilner[16]

Advance directives may represent the ultimate reduction of agonizing patient and family choice necessarily leading to either life or death. For the Christian, these terminal choices must valuate life as singularly unique since human life is created in the image of God (Gen. 9:5-6; Ps. 8:3-5; 100:3; 139:3ff; Acts 17:25). Other "important mandates (e.g., personal freedom, an end to suffering) must yield when they stand in the way of the sustenance of life."[17]

Christians must place advance directives first and foremost in the context of Biblical injunctions against killing (e.g., specifically applied to euthanasia or assisted suicide) (Gen. 9:6; Mt. 5:21; Ex. 20:13; Mt. 6:52; John 8:10; Deut. 4:19). All created life shares the *imago dei* regardless of whether it is still fallen or even belongs to our enemy (Mt. 5:43-45; Rom. 12:20).

"The grave is also the fruit of sin, an obscene irruption into human experience, severing plans and relationships asunder. Death is the last enemy indeed." Nigel Cameron[18]

Even though physical death is inevitable in our fallen world, the

Biblical view of death — in direct contradistinction to that of life — describes death as "the king of terrors" (Job 18:14). This observation is further developed in Ps. 23:4; Isa. 25:7-8; Mt. 10:5-8. To intend or facilitate death is contrary to the Bible which clearly teaches that God alone controls death (Job 1:21; Rom. 5:12; Rom. 14:7-8; 1 Cor. 15:20-26; Rev. 21:3-4) and that death is our final enemy. Any intention which actively facilitates death is antithetical to a God-centered, reality-bounded and love-impelled Biblical ethic which mandates the preservation of life. We are only set free from death through Christ's victory and only by His control of death. (2 Cor. 5:8).

As a result, Biblical study makes it abundantly clear that advance directives may never be utilized by Christians as instruments of active euthanasia or as means to a premature or contrived death in any person.

"A God-centered approach also emphasizes the importance of seeking God's purposes for the world and living in accordance with them. In the context of treatment decisions, this includes recognizing that disobedience may lie in doing too much as well as doing too little. There is no virtue in over-treating 'just to be sure.' One can become so zealous in trying to sustain biological life that one ceases to attend to the God who created it." John Kilner[19]

The utilization of advance directives when deciding against treatment, in some instances however, uncovers the tension between the protection (vide supra) and the inevitability of death. Advance directives have the potential to protect loving surrogates from agonizing decisions and an unnecessary prolongation of the dying process in their loved one.

In this context, advance directive decisions which are made to limit or discontinue terminal care must be fenced in by a Biblical ethic founded on the sanctity of life and then should proceed to consider the following: terminal care decisions must be free of any intention to cause death; they must never be driven solely to end suffering; they must never be used to eliminate suffering by eliminating the sufferer; they must address the moral issue of who is entrusted with treatment decisions for another; they cannot rely on quality of life determinations alone and must remain as clear as possible in the differentiation between terminal and imminent. Such a distinction is essential so as not to lead to an early abandonment of medical interventions and should leave the door open later to the ministry of terminal care appropriate when attempts at cure are exhausted.[20] Vaguely stated advance directives (i.e., no heroic care) must never be permitted to lead to either benign neglect or the absence of compassion.

"Some people are even reinterpreting the moral mandate to love to include ending life to end great suffering ... Such 'love' is not shaped and guided by God's created reality ... to reject the ending of life imparied by illness is not to accord erroneously high value to that life; it is to place it outside the realm of valuing." John Kilner[21]

"It is not medicine's place to lift from us the burden of that suffering which turns on the meaning we assign to the decay of the body and its eventual death. It is not medicine's place to determine when lives are not worth living or when the burden of life is too great to be borne. Doctors have no conceivable way of evaluating such claims on the part of patients, and they should have no right to act in response to them. Medicine should try to relieve human suffering, but only that suffering which is brought on by illness and dying as biological phenomena, not that suffering which comes from anguish or despair at the human condition." D. Callahan[22]

By necessity, end-of-life decision making must confront contemporary attitudes towards suffering and place them in Biblical context. Even though we, like Job, cannot completely understand suffering nor are we able to formulate a perfect theodicy, we nonetheless are able to appreciate that suffering "provides us with an occasion to trust and praise God."[23] Commitment to God is required during suffering and is precedent over any attempt to hasten death actively in order to end suffering. Scripture makes it clear (Jas. 1:2-8; Heb. 5:7-9; Phil. 4:11-12; Rom. 8:35-37; 2 Cor. 12:7-10; 1 Pet. 1:5-7; Heb. 12:11) that God is also sovereign over suffering as He is over death and expects care as our Christian response (2 Cor. 1:3-4; Mt. 10:8; Lk. 9:6; Jas. 5:14-16)[24] which precludes both removal and abandoment of the sufferer.

In summary, even though Biblical study does not exclude advance directives per se, any documents addressing care at the end-of-life must make the sanctity of human life an absolute criterion and appreciate that suffering may be relieved but never by any means which hastens death. Furthermore, when decisions are made to abandon curative medicine, medicine as care and ministry must continue and this consideration is often lacking in advance directives.

CONTEMPORARY SOCIETY ATTITUDES AND ADVANCE DIRECTIVES: CONFLICTS WITH THE BIBLICAL FOUNDATION

The PSDA grew out of an effort to increase patient autonomy in end-of-life decision making. Unfortunately, though this prima facie seems to be good, our zeitgeist has confused the concept of freedom as God intended vis-a-vis the contemporary concept of autonomy.[25] Biblical freedom is a means to an end in that Biblical freedom represents being freed for something not from something. Thus, it is a freedom fulfilled in the love of God and neighbor or best described as being free to accomplish righteousness. Autonomy, unlike freedom, represents self-law, and contemporary interpretations of freedom as removal from any spiritual or moral restrictions affects the implementation of advance directives. In contemporary society, autonomy has become an end in itself, a summum bonum and a consistent trump card in a hierarchy of pluralistic values.

Autonomy, as distinct from freedom in the context of advance directives, may be seen in the results of a recent study. Caralis and associates[26] polled 139 patients concerning their perception of autonomy during end-of-life decision making. Nearly half agreed that doctors

should assist patients to die; 36% would desire such assistance for themselves. One-fifth would desire euthanasia for suffering, even if the suffering occurred in a proven non-terminal situation! Our empiric study of advance directives in ESRD showed that 40% of patients would allow another to discontinue their dialysis if they had reversible depression.[27] Advance directives motivated by such autonomy would be incompatible with a Biblical exposition of terminal care. Christian health care wokers should not only counsel against autonomy as the summum bonum guiding advance directives, but should foster covenant-modeled interaction with their patients as a witness against this most unsettling abuse of terminal care.

THE DANGER OF ADVANCE DIRECTIVES IN A POST-HIPPOCRATIC MEDICAL SOCIETY[28]

Medicine used to be suffused with Christian values and remained a moral enterprise for thousands of years by a marriage of Christianity with Hippocratism. Medical ethics was grounded in two horizontal relationships (doctor-doctor; doctor-patient) and one essential vertical relationship (doctor-God) through a fear of God and a common oath. The loss of the hold the Hippocratic oath had on the practice of medicine in the U.S.A. was first detected with the onset of liberal abortion. It is clear today however that abortion is only a symptom of a worse disease — one that gnaws at the heart of what it really means to be human. Advance directives represent one aspect of a disturbing evolution of values in that covenantal medical relation-

ships are now contractual; patients pick from a wide variety and blend of values (vide supra) and the only moral ground for medical decision-making is patient or surrogate consent. The moral dimension in medicine is now reduced to individual preference rather than traditional consensus grounded through a vertical dimension.

A review of advance directives in this context of a post-Hippocratic ethos raises some very perplexing issues. Emanuel[29] followed nursing home patients for two years after the completion of an advance directive. After medical record review and physician interview, the authors concluded that in many cases the patient's choices were overridden because their physician disagreed with the wisdom of their choice. On occasion, the override represented the withholding of treatment because the physician decided it would not benefit the patient. End-of-life choices through vaguely worded advance directives may be primarily relegated to physicians who lack a consensus about what it means to be human.[30] When physicians were polled[31] and asked criteria for the selection of patient treatment in the face of limited resources, decision-making criteria would include age (88%), social value (56%) and ability to pay (43.1%). A continued deterioration in medical ethics would make contemporary physicians very poor guarantors of a sanctity of life ethic at a time of terminal decision-making. In reality, the negative aspect of autonomy cuts both ways in that physician autonomy in the era of "The New Medicine" may become as morally unreliable as that of patient autonomy in the Caralis study.[32] A review of the Remmelink report addressing the practice of euthanasia in the Netherlands empirically documents a corrosive effect of assisted death which leads to physician involvement in the "black side" of medicine.[33] With increasing governmental and third party intrusion into the contemporary contract model of medical care, will advance directives become a coercive tool that rations end-of-life care by offering euthanasia as a cheaper alternative to life?

AN EVANGELICAL CLINICIAN'S CONCLUSIONARY OBSERVATIONS

"Do we want the best medical skills in the world when we secretly fear they may be used to draw out the dying process, holding us on a rack of suffering when we should be left alone to die and experience all God has in store for us after this life? We feel we need protection from that kind of medicine." N. Cameron[34]

Since most Christian health care workers are involved with advance directives in some capacity, I'd like to posit selected, practical suggestions. These suggestions are "fenced-in" by the Biblical injunctions reviewed earlier as well as tempered by my concern with our contemporary zeitgeist and post-Hippocratic ethos.

When advance directives are utilized, they must be discussed thoroughly with patients and their families and reviewed openly and frequently. Otherwise, advance directives may represent a version of the "moral cop-out."[35] Physicians who practice medicine as technique only without an ethical "vertical dimension" may use living wills as a legalistic substitute for frank ethical discourse. Such documents then may lead either to abrogation of valid

physician moral authority or relegate patients to vague end-of-life euphemisms without substance. Advance directives cannot function in a world of "I want everything done" and "nothing heroic." Contractual models of the patient-doctor relationship will make it easier for secular physicians to under-treat patients for economic reasons or to prescribe euthanasia if such terminal "care" is legalized. Covenantal relationshps, however, will allow the physician more freedom in discussing the Biblical "pros and cons" of advance directives.[36] The addition of a "values-history" to the directive will force more discussion, reflection, valuation and true freedom in decision making[37] and is essential to rescue advance directives from being a haphazard checklist.

The final and most difficult aspect of advance directives will involve a hefty dose of Christian discernment. When elderly Christian patients seek to avoid a prolongation of the dying process, when should aggressive attempts at cure be abandoned and Christian care substituted? In the past, I felt that "futility" would become apparent in the course of terminal care.[38] Though many Christians disagree with medicine's ability to define futility, the attempt at a definition grew out of my concern that the elderly were being mistreated by technology with little to no chance of meaningful cure. When the average duration of hospital time from a DNR order to death is only one day on a surgical service; when the average hospital bill is $60,000 more for patients who die with an in-hospital DNR order versus a pre-hospital DNR order,[39] American medicine must be made culpable for relying on science as a panacea in lieu of a recognition of death's inevitability.

Until we can substitute a workable and ethical concept for "futility," Christian health care workers will have to pray for the discernment to recognize the time when they commend the spirit of those entrusted to them to a peaceful end. This is the terrible "gray" area of advance directives that will at least for now remain an agonizing unknown.

REFERENCES

1. Munson, R., **Intervention and Reflection: Basic Issues in Medical Ethics**, 4th ed., Wadsworth, Inc., 1992, pp. 145-147.

2. *bid.*, Munson, R., 1992, pp. 142-145.

3. "Few individuals provide explicit oral or written instructions regarding their intent to refuse medical treatment should they become incompetent. States which decline to consider any evidence other than such instructions may frequently fail to honor a patient's intent. Such failures might be avoided if the State considered an equally probative source of evidence: the patient's appointment of a proxy to make health care decisions on her behalf. ... These procedures for surrogate decision making, which appear to be rapidly gaining an acceptance, may be a valuable additional safeguard of the patient's interest in directing his medical care." Sandra Day O'Connor's concurring opinion in Cruzan v. Director, Missouri, Dept. of Health, 110 S. Ct. 2841 (1990).

4. *op. cit.*, Munson, R., 1992, p. 145.

5. Caralis, P.V., Davis, B., Wright, K., Marcial, E., The influence

of ethnicity and race on attitudes towards advance directives, life-prolonging treatment and euthanasia. *The Journal of Clinical Ethics*, Vol. 4, 1993, p. 155.

6. **Implementing Advance Directives: Suggested Guidelines for Dialysis Facilities**, National Kidney Foundation, December, 1993, p. 1.

7. Singer, P.A., The end-stage renal disease network of New England. Nephrologists' experience with and attitudes toward decisions to forego dialysis, *J. Am. Soc. Nephrol*, Vol. 2, 1992, p. 1235.

8. Swartz, R.D., 7 Perry, E., Advance directives are associated with "good deaths" in chronic dialysis patients, *J. Am. Soc. Nephrol.*, Vol. 3, 1993, pp. 1623-1630.

9. Rutecki, G.W., Rodriguez, L., Cugino, A., Jarjoura, D., Hastings, F., Whittier, F.C., End-of-life issues in ESRD: a study of three decision variables which affect patient attitudes. In press. *ASAIO Journal*, 1994.

10. Presumed benefits include: a reaffirmation of patient authority recognizing everyone's particular way of living and dying; physicians to abide by the clearly expressed wishes of their patients; a decrease in legal liability for hospitals; advance directives save families the agony of decision making for relatives; stop physicians from preempting patient choice; stimulate patient's reflection on death; help resolve fear of patient-technology entrapment. From E.H. Loewy "Advance Directives: Panacea

for safeguarding patient autonomy or a convenient way of avoiding responsibility? in **Health Care Ethics: Critical Issues**. (Ed.) J.K. Monagle, D.L. Thomasma, Aspen Pub., 1994, p. 116.

11. *op. cit.*, Rutecki, G.W., *et al.*, 1994.

12. Sehgal, A., Galbraith, A., Chesney, M., Schoenfeld, P., Charles, G., Lo, B., How strictly do dialysis patients want their advance directives followed? *JAMA*, Vol. 267, 1992, pp. 59-63.

13. Emanuel, E.J., Emanuel, L.L., Proxy decision making for incompetent patients, *JAMA*, Vol. 267, 1992, pp. 2067-2071, and Uhlmann, R.F., Pearlman, R.A., Cain, K.C., Physicians and spouses predictions of elderly patients resuscitation preferences, *J. of Gerontology*, Vol. 43, 1988, M-115-121.

14. *op. cit.*, National Kidney Foundation, 1993.

15. Kilner, J.F., **Life on the LIne: Ethics, Aging, Ending Patients Lives, and Allocating Vital Resources**, Eerdmans, 1992, pp. 13-72. I am indebted to Dr. Kilner for his exposition of a model which allows the Biblical scrutiny of end-of-life decisions. In addition, Mitchell, C.B., Whitehead, M.K., A time to live, a time to die: advance directives and living wills. *Ethics and Medicine*, Vol. 9, 1993, pp. 2-5 was utilized, specifically p. 2 *ff*; answering the question: which Biblical principles apply to living wills?

16. *ibid.*, Kilner, J.F., 1992, p. 54.

17. *ibid.*, Kilner, J.F., 1992, p. 67.

18. Cameron, N. M. deS., Living wills and the will to live,

Christianity Today, April 6, 1992, p. 23.

19. *op. cit.*, Kilner, J.F., 1992, p. 126.

20. Rutecki, G.W., Nettle, G.E., To Care in a Christian Context, In press, *Jour. of Biblical Ethics in Medicine*, 1994.

21. *op. cit.*, Kilner, J.F., 1992, p. 115.

22. Callahan, D., When self-determination runs amok, *Hastings Center Report*, 22(2):52-55, 1992, p. 55.

23. *op. cit.*, Kilner, J.F., 1992, 105.

24. Living wills - the issues examined. A briefing paper from CARE, London. *Ethics and Medicine*, 0.1, 1993, p. 7, assisted me in the Scriptural valuation of suffering.

25. *op. cit.*, Kilner, J.F., 1992, pp. 57-59; 83-94. I am indebted to Dr. Kilner for his contrast of Biblical freedom and contemporary autonomy.

26. *op. cit.*, Caralis, P.V., *et al.*, 1993, p. 155-165.

27. *op. cit.*, Rutecki, G.W., *et al.*, 1994, in press *ASAIO*.

28. Cameron, N.D., de S., "State of the question" at the Christian Stake in Bioethics May 19-21, 1994. Sponsored by Trinity Evangelical Divinity Seminary and the Christian Medical and Dental Society. See also: **The New Medicine**, N. M. de S. Cameron. Crossway Books, 1991.

29. *op. cit.*, Emanuel, E.J., et al., 1988.

30. Under ideal circumstances, it appears that both clinical and ethical decision making are "atomised" in contemporary medicine. See McIntyre, K.M., Failure of "Predictors" of cardiopulmonary resuscitation

outcomes to predict cardiopulmonary resuscitation outcomes, *Arch. Intern. Med.*, Vol. 153, 1993, pp. 1293-1996. Dr. McIntyre demonstrated that none of the "futile" markers for CPR were reliable. Used as "Predictors" for the marginalized, they could be lethal.

31. Kilner, J.F., Selecting patients when resources are limited: a study of U.S. Medical Directors of kidney dialysis and transplantation facilities, *AJPH*, Vol. 78, 1988, pp. 144-147.

32. *op. cit.*, Caralis, P.V., 1993.

33. Fenigsen, R., The report of the Dutch governmental committee on euthanasia. *Issues in Law and Medicine*, Vol. 7, 1991, pp. 339-344. See also: Van Delden, J.M., Pijenborg, L., Van der Maas, P.J., The Remmelink study two years later, *Hastings Center Report*, Vol. 23(6), 1993, pp. 24-27. As disturbing as the practice of euthanasia is in the Netherlands (1990-2300 cases of euthanasia, 400 assisted suicides), the fact 1000 persons were euthanized without explicit consent should sober even the most committed proponent of physician-assisted death.

34. *op. cit.*, Cameron, N.M. deS., 1992, p. 23.

35. Loewy, E.H., Advance directives and surrogate laws: Ethical instruments or moral copouts? *Arch. Intern. Med.*, Vol. 152, 1992, pp. 1973-1976. See also: Wolf, J.M., et al., Sources of conern about the patient self-determination act, *NEJM*, Vol. 325, 1991, pp. 1666-1671.

36. May, W.F., Code, covenant, contract or philanthropy. *Hastings Center Report*, Vol. 5, 1975, pp. 29-38. The key for many is that medicine as covenant involves an ontologic change in both the doctor and patient.

37. The major shortcoming of advance directives is that they present the complexity of end-of-life interventions in a vague and incomplete manner. The "values-history" should include an explicit identification of both physician and patient/family values and inclusion of both sets of values in the directive. For further reading see, Doukas, D.J., McCullough, L.B., The values history: the evaluation of the patient's values and advance directives, *J. Fam. Prac*, Vol. 32, 1991, pp. 145-153; and Doukas, D.S., Gorenflow, D.W., Analyzing the values history: An evaluation of patient medical values and advance directives, *J. of Clin Ethics*, Vol. 4, 1993, pp. 41-45. Please note that I feel strongly that both patients' and physicians' values should be explicitly stated. The Christian physician could then make it clear to the patient at the outset, that any intention to lead to early death is not part of the covenantal relationship. This will also assist Christian patients in identifying physicians with world view perspectives consistent with Biblical teaching.

38. Rutecki, G.W., Rationing Medical Care to the Elderly Revisited: Futility as a Just Criterion, *J. Biblical Ethics in Medicine*, Vol. 7, 1993, pp. 67-74. Some have hinted that the term futility is only an excuse to stop care. If, however, the tension is not maintained between treating when there is still hope and stopping when diminishing returns occur, we run the risk of making technology an idol and thinking just like our post-enlightenment secular contemporaries.

39. Maksoud, A., Jahnigen, D.W., Skibinski, C.I., Do not resuscitate orders and the cost of death, *Arch. Intern. Med.*, Vol. 153, 1993, pp. 1249-1953.

Book Review

Daniel E. Deaton, L.Cdr., Chaplain Corps, US Navy

How We Die, Sherwin B. Nuland, Alfred A. Knopf, 1994, 278 pp., $24.00

All patients eventually die. The denial of that unpleasant fact is the source of much bitter disappointment and many unfulfilled expectations in modern medicine. In the introduction to his book, Sherwin Nuland, surgeon and professor at Yale University, observes: "We have erected the method of modern dying. Modern dying takes place in the modern hospital, where it can be hidden, cleansed of its organic blight, and finally packaged for modern burial. We can now deny the power not only of death, but of nature itself. We hide our faces from its face, but still we spread our fingers just a bit, because there is something in us that cannot resist a peek."

In the pages that follow, readers get far more than a peek. The ugly reality of death, graphically depicted in descriptions of the six major avenues by which the end of this life will come for eighty-five percent of us, is held harrowingly before our eyes. Nuland's aim is to "demythologize the process of dying" so that we can be prepared for it and "rid ourselves of the fear of the terra incognita of death that leads to self-deception and disillusions."

Those who affirm the truth of Scripture will realize immediately that this is an unattainable aim. The fear of death comes not from our lack of knowledge about the physiological and biological details of terminal disease processes, but from the cause of death, sin (Romans 6:23), and the effect, judgment (Hebrews 9:27), when we are called to give an account of our lives to God. Therefore, only Christians are delivered from the fear of death since Christ shared in our human nature "so that by his death he might destroy him who holds the power of death — that is, the devil — and free those who all their lives were held in slavery by their fear of death." (Hebrews 2:14-15).

While Nuland does not succeed in ridding us of the fear of death, *How We Die* powerfully confronts our death-denying culture with the repulsive and inexorable necessity of death. Along the way, Nuland chides and challenges his colleagues in medicine who "are trained to think only about life and the diseases that threaten it." (p. 61) and therefore ignore the fact that "there is plenty of evidence that life does have its natural, inherent limits. When these limits are reached, the taper of life, even in the absence of any specific disease or accident, simply sputters out" (p. 70). Heresy though it may be to the modern mind, we die of old age because "we have been worn and torn and programmed to cave in. The very old do not succumb to disease — they implode their way into eternity" (p. 83).

The value of this book lies in its plea for an understanding of the limitations, as well as the potentials of modern medicine. The implications from the standpoint of bioethics are profound and practical. Wise physicians and patients will heed Nuland's exhortations and place every decision about treatment options in the context of the aging process. Too often in my own care of critically ill patients, I have observed the propensity of some physicians to recommend highly invasive and burdensome interventions which yield exceedingly small benefits (or have no realistic expectation of success) and merely serve to imprison elderly patients in intensive care beds for the last days of their lives. To Nuland, this symbolizes "the purest form of our society's denial of the naturalness, and even the necessity of death." (p. 254). These patients are deprived of any final comfort, of sharing life's last moments with loved ones, of opportunities to affirm their faith and often of an awareness that they are dying.

Nuland also takes aim at physicians (he calls them "biomedical problem-solvers") who unwittingly abandon their patients by emotionally, if not physically, disappearing when it becomes obvious that the biomedical problems refuse to yield to their best efforts. Without a problem to solve, and with death drawing near, the physician loses interest: "To stay and oversee the triumph of unrestrained nature is to acquiesce to his own impotence," writes Nuland. "Every time a patient dies, his doctor is reminded that his own and mankind's control over natural forces is limited and will always remain so" (p. 259).

Nuland's Jewish faith shines only dimly in his work. He quotes from the Old Testament a few times (pp. 73, 84-85, 167) and affirms that we are God's creatures (p. 56) but in the end strikes an agnostic pose: "If there is a God, He is present as much in the creation of each of us as He was at the creation of the earth." (p. 263).

The candid criticisms of the medical profession by one of its own and the critique of our death-denying culture make this book worth reading. It is most valuable as an "unspoken plea for the resurrection of the family doctor" (p. 266) and as a poignant cry for compassion to be married to competence, so that physicians will be more than highly skilled technocrats.

"For as in Adam all die" wrote the inspired Apsotle Paul, "so in Christ all will be made alive" (I Corinthians 15:22). *How We Die* gets it half right. By hammering readers relentlessly with the certainty of the last enemy's grip on the human race, Nuland inadvertently, but convincingly, demonstrates the first half of that verse.

Dander

U.S. Congressional Representative from New York Edolphus towns was recently in the news criticizing a decision of the National Cancer Institute to change its recommendation on mammography to exclude many women who are in their forties. Members of Congress, who held a subcommittee hearing on the Institute guidelines, accused the National Cancer Institute of being "sexist, racist, and political . . ." because of the decision.

Let's see, now . . . politicians, holding a political hearing on the decision of a scientific consensus group, accuse the group of being "political," Just who is it that is politicizing medicine? When Paul wrote to Timothy he included health maintenance advice which was to be directed to the individuals, not to Caesar.

The *Intercessors for America Newsletter* of March, 1994, describes proposed regulatory guidelines by the Equal Employment Opportunity Guidelines. These Guidelines would purportedly "protect" employees from religious harassment by prohibiting verbal conduct that has the *effect* of creating an offensive work environment.

Do you ever talk about Jesus in the course of your work-

day? Did it ever occur to you that such talk might have the "effect" of religious "harassment" to someone who does not share your beliefs? Aside from the fact that Christians certainly can be needlessly offensive with the gospel message, the gospel *itself* contains offense. As to that intrinsic offense, we need to respond to Caesar as did Peter and John in Acts 5:29.

Sherwin Nuland in his book, *Doctors: The Biography of Medicine*, recounts the excellent character of Joseph Lister, the clinician who finally established antiseptic surgery. After reminding his students of Ambroise Pare's aphorism: "I dressed him, God healed him," he told them what two great requisites there are for a healer. "First, a warm, loving heart; and secondly, truth in an earnest spirit."

Where in medical teaching today do students have access to this sort of wisdom? "Why is there in the hand of a fool the purchase price of wisdom, since he has no heart for it?" [Prov. 17:16] Are some of medicine's current problems related to the omission of character, wisdom, and compassion from the selection

process in preference to competitiveness, knowledge, and aloofness? Indeed, would Dr. Lister today be cited by the EEO for religious harassment?

In 1989 the Society of Teachers of Family Medicine [STFM] delivered itself of a set of guidelines for teaching family practice residents about substance abuse. These guidelines are still rattling around and contain the following assertions: "Substance abuse is a preventable, diagnosable, and treatable, chronic, relapsing, and remitting, individual and family disease . . . Expressions of denial, dishonesty, anger, and irrationality, and other potentially offensive behaviors are often inherent symptoms of substance abuse to be expected, understood, *accepted,* and managed by family physicians." [emphasis added]

This is not only a theological/philosophical assertion rather than one based on science, it is a wrong assertion, for among other errors it labels lying, anger, and who knows what other malbehaviors as *disease.* Far from "accepting" lying and drunkenness, God says we should depart from these behaviors because they are *sinful.* "And

do not be drunk with wine, in which is dissipation; but be filled with the Spirit." [Eph. 5:18]. How far would a physician be tolerated who rephrased the STFM as follows: "Expressions of disagreement with and disbelief in the disease model of alcoholism are often inherent symptoms of biblical Christianity and are to be expected, understood, and accepted within the STFM?"

Dr. Cecil Jacobsen entered a federal prison in February for a five year sentence, according to the *American Medical News*. Dr. Jacobson was convicted of fraud for using his own sperm while artificially inseminating women in his fertility practice. He had told the women he was using sperm from anonymous donors.

Perhaps if Dr. Jacobson had been an *alcoholic* his misbehavior could have been *accepted,* rather than dealt with so punitively.

We received notice of "The First National Conference on Abortion Malpractice Litigation" held in Dallas for personal injury attorneys interested in "today's most prolific litigation opportunity." Information was available on litigating for emotional injury without accompanying physical injury, the minimum standard of medical care in abortion clinics, "counseling systems for clients with no cause of action," etc.

Those of us who are opposed to abortion need to fit our opposition methodology into a biblical framework just as we do our ends and our motives. Is the end of abortion so needful that any means at all may be used justly? If we agree to all means to stop abortion, do we have any complaint against the pro-aborts as to the recent use of the RICO law against us? Are pro-lifers really prepared to honestly testify as the *right way* to do an abortion? Do we really want to open further the "emotional injury" can of worms? Will there not be plaintiffs who allege, perhaps, "emotional injury" from carrying a pregnancy of term after anti-abortion counsel? Will there not be "emotional injury" alleged by families whose members converted to Christianity through the witness of a health care worker?

Shock waves are emanating from the recent Federal investigations that a Canadian physician falsified data in a large breast cancer study. Though not as well-known, the same federal "Office of Research Integrity" has recently also called for recantation by Herbert Needleman, who published a "ground-breaking" study on lead and children's IQ in the New England Journal of Medicine in 1979.

One wonders where moral outrage comes from in a scientific community which has transmogrified immoralities such as lying into diseases. Why not just launch a dispassionate scientific study of fraud? Then a dispassionate study of the fraud in the fraud studies? Ad infinitum.

A "child advocate" recently appeared before the South Carolina Joint Legislative Committee on Children and Families to inform that body that physical punishment" . . . leads to bullying, domestic violence, and violent crime." Peter Newell, who is the head of End Physical Punishment of Children Worldwide {EPOCH] condemns "violence which involves a large person hitting often a very small person."

The rhythm of blows against biblically-sanctioned corporal punishment of children thus continues, led by a tyranny of experts, while large segments of Christ's church give assent by silence. God is, however, not silent on the matter, being unimpressed with retrospective or short-term studies which are careful to focus upon some outcome measures and avoid others. "Do not withhold correction from a child, for if you beat him with a rod, he will not die. You shall beat him with a rod, and deliver his soul from Hell."

Editor's Note

For years I have seen a trickle of parents who have a concern about the safety and effectiveness of childhood immunizations. Many of the concerned parents are Christian, and many of the Christians are at odds with their culture because they believe in biblical corporal punishment, a young earth, home schooling, large families or something else which the larger culture ridicules or squelches. Some use unorthodox medical remedies. Already somewhat involuntarily alienated, they are accustomed to questioning the accuracy and the authority of academia and the civil state. Questions include: "Is it wise to load an infant's immune system? What else is in the vaccine besides the intended material? another virus perhaps? Does the shot cause seizures or brain damage? Aren't the natural infections more effective in producing immunity? How likely is my child to contract one of these illnesses anyway?

State officials rely on calculations based on reasonable (though not certain) assumptions that the benefits from the injections are far greater than the risks. The state's view is that of a herdsman overseeing the welfare of an entire heard; the family's view is that of the welfare of a few individuals in the herd.

Without going into the details of each of the many immunizations "offered" (read "required") today, there are some general principles which may help in the decision. (1) Keep your priorities straight. If refusal to accept immunizations is going to get you into trouble with state officials, especially if you are already potentially on a list as a dangerous "fundamentalist" right-wing Christian, recognize that the health values of biblical discipline and education in general greatly exceed the dangers of immunizations. If refusal of immunizations may endanger your other contracultural activities, choose to win the greater battle. The more important battle will almost never be the one over immunizations. (2) If immunities are not life-long, then boosters are going to become the norm lest we have an epidemic of childhood illnesses in adults or the elderly where their danger is greater. Realize, however, that the opportunity for your children to catch the "wild type" or natural infections during childhood is small, due to the large numbers of immunized children. While it seems likely to me that at least some of the immunizations now used are not going to produce lifelong immunity, you don't really have a choice to see your child catch measles or mumps or the like. The changes that an immunization will last for a lifetime is better than the near certainty that your child will enter adult life without any immunity at all to those diseases. (3) The dangers of vaccines, while undeniable, including such disasters as large-scale vaccine-caused polio several decades ago and small-scale transmission today, apparently are quite small. The dangers fall into a background static that requires huge numbers of people and careful statistical study to sort out. Single case studies or testimonials are bootless to answer the question. Anyone against anything can dig up or adapt scary stories. The risk your child takes riding a bicycle for a total of a few hours may well exceed the risk you are trying to calculate. (4) Just as the proponents of immunizations have their agendas, so also do those who oppose them. Be as discerning about these agendas as about those of the statists who want to control the herd. A fascinating look at how the virologist insiders behave can be had in the book, "Why We Will Never Win the War On AIDS," by Peter Duisberg and Bryan J. Ellison, 1994, Inside Story Communications. (5) Do not confuse the matter of the right of the civil authorities to require immunizations with the efficacy issue. Both are legitimate issues and should be dealt with separately. The right, for example, of the state to require a healthy infant to have an alien substance injected into his body because he *might,* someday, be a risk to an unborn baby whose mother has *not* protected herself with the vaccine, needs to be questioned even if the vaccines are completely effective and safe.

Having glossed over some general principles, it must be remembered that the devil is in the details. Each vaccine is different. Some have a long history of use, such as tetanus. Some are recently developed, such as haemophilus influenzae. Some are live virus, some are killed. Some induce antibodies in the blood, some in the bowel. If you wish to make your decision based on the basic research, you have your work cut out for you. It won't do just to read the package insert for that is, as one correspondent recently stated it, propaganda. You will need to read and comprehend reams of technical data on each vaccine. It would be a work of months for someone conversant with the vocabulary and methodology. Maybe some Christian with these qualifications and the time will undertake to provide this service.

Journal of Biblical Ethics in Medicine

Index of Scripture: Volumes 5 - 8

1991-1994

Bold listings refer to substantive discussions of a particular text. Normal print refers to any citation of a text.

Scripture references are arranged by year of publication and page number. Pages are numbered sequentially for each year so that there are no duplicate page numbers in any one year. The first number given is the year of publication and the second is the page number. For example, 91:58 is found in 1991, page 58. Years of reference are separated by a semi-colon. Page numbers for references in the same year are separated by commas.

An "n" following a page number indicates that the reference is in the footnotes on that page, e.g., 13n. A "t" following a page number indicates that the Bible text appears in a table on that page, e.g., 13t.

28:39; 91:25
32:4; 91:65
32:39; 91:19; 92:74

Joshua

18:1; 91:25
24:14; 91:65

Judges

1:1-9; 91:30
5:13; 91:25

I Samuel

1:20; 92:78n
12:24; 91:66
17; 91:30

II Samuel

7:14; 92:65
12:15;
16:7; 93:27
17:23; 94:11
19:28; 93:48

I Kings

2:4; 91:65
3:14; 91:19
16:18-19; 94:11
19:3-4; 91:35
19:5-9; 91:35

II Kings

20; 92:56

I Chronicles

10:4, 13; 94:11
10:13-14; 93:43

II Chronicles

16:12; 91:49
26:16ff; 94:15
26:20; 92:83

Nehemiah

7:2; 91:65

Esther

2:20; 91:74

Job

1; 91:59

1:21; 94:11, 51
2; 91:59
2:7; 91:35
3:26; 91:35
5:18; 92:83
10:10-12; 91:15
18:14; 94:51
19:25-27; 91:21; 94:15
38:2; 91:15

Psalms

8:3-4; 92:79; 94:50
8:5-6; 91:24, 25, 26; 94:11
9:4; 93:48
15:2; 91:65
23:4; 94:51
31:15; 92:78
37:7; 92:80
40:11; 91:66
41:1-3; 93:43
43:3-4; 91:66
46:10; 92:80
49:7-8; 92:97
51:5; 91:48; 92:25, 55, 78
55:21; 91:75
68:5; 92:22
82:3; 93:3
86:11; 91:65
90:1-2; 93:70
90:1-6; 92:98; 93:70
90:3; 92:98
90:10-12; 91:11; 92:54, **95-102**; **93:67**, 94:39
90:16-17; 92:98
91:4; 91:65
91:9-10; 93:43
100:3; 92:98; 94:50
103:3; 92:83
104:10; 91:16
104:15: 91:16
107:17; 92:83; 93:43
111; 91:66
119:71; 93:43
119:142; 91:65
119:151; 91:65
119:160; 91:65
127:3-5; 92:27, 55
139:3ff; 94:50
139:13-16; 91:48; 92:25, 55
139:15; 91:15; 93:1
139:16; 91:48
140:12; 93:48

Proverbs

3:1-2; 93:43
4:20-22; 93:43
5:7-13; 93:43
5:18-19; 91:48; 92:92
6-7; 91:6
6:1; 93:80A
8:7; 91:66
8:36; 93:19
9:10-11; 93:43
11:13; 91:74; 93:18
12:5; 93:48
12:22; 91:65
13:15; 94:40
13:22; 91:6
13:24; 92:65

14:30; 93:44
15:27; 91:60
16:6; 91:66
16:8; 93:48
16:17; 94:20
16:27-28; 91:75
16:31; 93:44
17:16; 94:58
17:18; 93:80A
18:17; 91:18
19:16; 94:20
19:17; 93:19
20:1; 93:98
22:15; 92:65
22:26; 93:80A
23:13-14; 93:33; 94:59
23:23; 91:66
23:29-35; 93:98
24:11-12; 91:75

Ecclesiastes

1:9; 92:73
3:2; 91:11; 92:54
3:7; 91:73-74
3:7; 92:44
3:10-11; 91:35; 93:13
3:21; 91:24
10:14; 93:18
11:10-12:7; 92:96
12:1-8; 92:99, 104; 93:70
12:7; 91:34
12:10; 93:70

The Song of Solomon

1-8; 91:48
4:5; 92:92

Isaiah

5:8-25; 93:44
10:2; 93:48
10:18; 91:34
25:7-8; 94:51
38:3; 91:65
48:5; 91:48
53:5; 94:39
55:8; 93:65
59:1-3; 93:19

Jeremiah

1:5; 91:48; 92:25, 55
3:1; 91:31
3:2; 91:31
3:6; 91:31
3:8; 91:31
7:28; 91:66
31:33; 92:66
32:7-8; 93:48
36; 91:74
38; 91:75

Ezekiel

18:20; 91:21
36:25-29; 94:39

36:26; 93:61

Daniel

3:35; 93:48
8; 91:77

Amos

3:3; 93:80A

Zephaniah

3:5; 91:77

Zechariah

8:16; 91:65

Matthew

1:20; 92:55
4:4; 91:16; 93:44
5:8; 93:18
5:16; 92:76
5:17-20; 91:76
5:21; 94:50
5:38-42; 93:3
5:43-45; 94:50
5:45; 92:79
6:3; 93:50
6:52; 94:50
10:5-8; 94:51
10:8; 94:51
10:19-20; 93:15
10:28; 91:33, 34; 93:6, 60
10:30; 54
10:34; 92:82
11:27; 93:16
12:24-37; 91:75
13:10-17; 93:47
13:58; 92:85
15:18; 93:27
15:30; 92:79
16:16; 93:47
16:17; 91:66
17:9; 91:74
18:15; 91:77; 92:44
18:16; 91:74
18:21-35; 92:97
19:15; 91:48
20:1-6; 92:97; 93:50
20:3; 93:80A
21:33-41; 92:97
22:37; 93:27
22:44; 93:50
23:4; 92:66
24:3; 91:74
25:14-15; 92:97
25:31-46; 91:16; 92:100; 94:2, 3
25:33; 93:50
25:40; 92:80
26:9; 93:80A
27:3-5; 94:11
27:42; 92:78

Mark

2:27; 91:8
4:10-12; 93:47
5:15; 93:50
5:34; 92:85
7:13; 91:41
7:21-23; 93:35
8:34-38; 92:98
9:28; 91:74
12:30; 91:37
12:42-43; 92:79
13:3; 91:74

Luke

1:41-48; 91:48; 92:74, 78
3:37; 92:22
6:31; 92:68
6:37-45; 91:13
7:25; 93:19
8:9-10; 93:47
8:35; 93:50
8:43ff; 92:91
9:6; 94:51
10:22; 93:16
10:23; 91:74
10:25-37; 92:100; 93:19; 94:9; **94:21-22**
10:28; 93:50
11:27-28; 91:75
12:57; 93:50
13:1-5; 94:18
16:19-31; 93:61
17; 92:84
17:23; 92:91
20:25; 94:20
24:39; 93:27
24:44; 91:74

John

1:3; 91:23
1:10; 91:23
1:12-13; 91:66; 93:49-50
1:14; 91:65
1:17;; 91:65
4:24; 93:27
5:1-30; 91:74
5:31-47; 91:74
6:44; 93:47
8:10; 94:50
8:31-32; 91:66
8:40-45; 91:75
9:3; 91:59, 80, 83
10:1; 91:55
10:9; 91:55
12:27; 93:44
12:38; 93:16
13:8; 91:69
14:1-4; 94:11
14:6; 91:55, 65
16:7-11; 93:16
16:13; 91:66
16:13-15; 93:16
16:20; 92:80
16:33; 92:84
17:17; 91:65
18:37; 91:66
20:31-32; 92:85
21; 94:15

The Acts

2:27; 93:60
2:35; 93:50
2:39; 92:55
2:45; 93:19
4; 91:77
4:12; 92:104
4:20; 92:79
5:4; 93:80A
5:29; 93:18; 94:58
5:38; 92:78
7:56; 92:84
10:34; 92:79
14:22; 92:79
17:15-34; 93:16
17:25; 92:85; 94:50
17:26; 92:54
20:28; 93:55

Romans

1; 93:16
1:18; 91:63
1:18-32; 91:41; 93:13; 93:16
1:21ff; 91:24, 92:52
1:25; 91:63
1:26-27; 91:48, 69; 92:48
1:28; 93:51
2:1-16; 91:73
2:8; 91:66
3:4; 93:50
3:23; 92:79
5:3; 92:80
5:12; 92:80; 94:51
5:20; 93:62
6:13; 93:25
6:23; 92:83; 93:47; 94:56
6-8; 93:22-24
7:19; 92:78
7:23-25; 93:26
8:1-4; 91:76
8:11; 93:22
8:18-39; 92:96; 93:24
8:24-25; 93:16
8:28-30; 91:45, 48, 60; 92:86, 97; 93:70, 79, 103
8:29; 91:25; 92:22
8:35-37; 94:51
9:6-22; 91:6; 93:47
9:11; 93:47
9:12; 93:50
9:16; 93:47
9:18; 93:47
9:21; 93:50
10:8-11; 93:27
10:17; 92:79
11:33; 93:47
12:1-2; 93:22
12:6-8; 92:79
12:9-21; 93:24
12:17; 93:50
12:20; 94:50
13:1-6; 93:19; 94:20
13:8-10; 91:76
13:10; 91:75
14; 91:25
14:7-8; 94:11, 51
14:22; 91:75

I Corinthians

1; 93:47
1:20-21; 93:15; 94:4
1:25-31; 92:106, 108
2; 93:58
2:10-11; 93:65
2:14; 93:58
3:10-15; 91:25; 92:104
3:16-17; 94:18
4:1-5; 91:25
5:1; 91:31
5:5; 91:77
6:9-10; 91:63, 67; 93:98
6:13-20; 91:48; 92:55; 93:44; 94:17
6:19-20; 92:96, 98; 93:22
7:2; 91:63
7:3-4; 91:48
7:5; 92:55
7:12-20;
8; 91:25
9; 93:50
9:4; 93:50
10; 91:25
10:13; 91:75
10:23; 91:34
10:31; 91:48; 92:84
11:28; 94:20
11:30; 93:63
11:30-32; 91:19; 92:83; 93:44
13:2; 94:18
14:14-15; 93:28
14:26; 93:18
14:32; 93:28
15; 91:25
15:12-58; 94:11
15:22; 94:57
15:20-26; 94:51
15:26; 93:78
15:45-49; 92:96; 92:97; 93:70

II Corinthians

1:3ff; 94:2, 3, 51
1:18-25; 91:66
2:5-11; 91:77
3:3; 92:66
3:18; 91:25; 92:97; 93:70
3:18-4:6; 92:96
4:4; 92:97; 93:58, 70
4:16; 91:34, 59; 93:65
5:1-10; 93:57
5:8; 93:60; 94:11, 51
5:10; 91:25
5:18; 91:67
5:21; 92:79
6:19-20; 92:97
7:1; 94:18
7:2-9; 94:20
7:6; 94:2, 3
8; 93:19
8:21; 93:50
9:7; 92:66
10:3-6; 94:20
11:5-9; 91:48
11:22-23; 91:30
11:23-27; 94:9
12:1-4; **93:64**
12:3; 92:79
12:7-10; 94:18, 51
12:9; 92:80
12:14; 91:6

12:20; 91:75
13:1; 91:74
13:5; 94:20

Galatians

1:11-12; 93:16
2:10; 93:19
3:26-29; 92:96
4:28; 91:72
5; 93:16
5:13-14; 91:76
5:19-21; 91:67
6:1; 92:44

Ephesians

1:10; 92:97
1:11; 92:54
1:17-18; 92:97
1:20-23; 91:23
2:1; 93:47
2:6; 92:101
2:8; 93:47
2:12; 93:47
3:10; 92:97
4:11; 92:79
4:15; 92:79
4:24; 92:22, 23
4:24-29; 91:76
4:25; 93:18
4:28; 93:19, 36
4:29; 93:18
5:18; 93:98; 94:59
5:20; 93:55
5:22-23; 94:20
5:31; 91:48
6:1-3; 93:44, 50; 94:20
6:5-9; 94:20
6:10-18; 92:82
6:12; 92:82

Philippians

1:20-26; 93:19
1:22; 93:30
1:23-25; 92:80; 93:60
2:3; 92:80
2:8-11; 91:23
3:19; 91:6
3:20-21; 91:58; 93:24
3:21; 91:21
4:8; 93:50
4:11-12; 93:98; 94:9, 51

Colossians

1:3; 92:21
1:15; 91:23
1:15-20; 92:21
1:17; 91:60
2:16; 91:26
3:10; 92:22, 23
3:18-21; 94:20
3:22-4:1; 94:20
4:26; 91:75

I Thessalonians

4:11-12; 94:20
4:13-14; 92:77, 80
5:23; 91:33, 37n

II Thessalonians

2:12-13; 91:66
3:7-12; 91:71
3:13; 93:50

I Timothy

2:4; 91:66
2:11-15; 94:20
2:13; 94:20
3:1-13; 94:20
3:2; 91:48
3:4-5; 94:20
3:15; 91:66
4:2; 93:42
4:3; 91:26
4:8; 93:6, 44
5; 94:20
5:1-2; 92:100
5:3-16; 92:100; **94:27**
5:8; 94:40
5:16; 92:100
5:19; 91:74
6:1-2; 94:20
6:5; 91:66

II Timothy

2:8-10; 92:79; 94:20
2:25; 91:66
3:7; 91:66
3:16-17; 92:106, 108; 93:16
4:1-5; 92:78
4:4; 91:66
4:10-21; 94:7
4:13; 94:7

Titus

1:1; 91:66
1:5-9; 94:20
2:5; 94:20
3:9-11; 94:20

Hebrews

1:3; 91:23; 92:22
1:5; 92:22
2:14-15; 94:11, 56
4:12; 91:33, 37n; 93:65
5:7-9; 94:51
8:10; 92:66
9:27; 92:79; 94:56
10:26; 91:66
11; 91:24
12:1; **93:96-99**
12:11; 94:51
12:23; 93:61
13:10; 93:50

James

1:2-8; 94:51
1:4; 91:19; 92:84
1:5-6; 93:16
1:8; 91:65
1:17; 92:22
1:27; 94:37
2:1; 92:79
2:8; 91:75; 93:50
2:17; 92:79
2:26; 91:33, 34; 93:25, 64
2:27; 92:22
3; 91:75
3:2; 91:75
4:17; 91:25
5:14-16; 91:19; 92:56, 83, 84, 104;
   63f; 94:8, 51

I Peter

1:5-7; 91:48; 94:51
1:15; 91:24
1:18-19; 92:79, 97; 93:61, 70; 94:20
1:22; 91:75
1:24-25; 91:65
2:9; 93:1
2:12; 92:79
2:13-17; 94:20
2:19; 92:80
3:1-7; 94:20
3:14; 93:50
3:15; 92:77
3:22; 91:23
4:4; 93:98

II Peter

1:3-4; 91:66
1:5-7; 91:75

I John

1:5; 92:99
1:9; 92:50
2:1-2; 92:50, 79
2:21; 91:66
2:29; 93:50
3:1-3; 92:97
4:7-8; 92:99
5:6-12; 91:74
5:7; 91:65

II John

4; 91:66

III John

3-4; 91:66

Jude

7; 91:31

The Revelation

1:10; 93:64
2:27; 93:50
3:21; 93:50, 51
4:1-2; 93:64
4:11; 91:26
9:20-21; 92:51, 52
19-22; 91:23
21:1; 91:21
21:3-4; 92:85; 94:51
22:14; 93:50

Journal of Biblical Ethics in Medicine

Index of Subjects and Proper Names: Volumes 5 - 8

1991 - 1994

This is a **comprehensive index**. Every effort was made to reference any and all topics with any significant discussion in the text. Also, many topics are referenced under two or more subject headings to assist researchers in a comprehensive search. A few **persons** other than authors of articles in these issues of the *Journal* are listed when mention of their names includes discussion of a substantive issue. **All authors** who have had articles in these issues of the *Journal* are cited in this index.

Bold listings refer to substantive discussions of a particular subject. Normal print refers to any significant mention of a subject.

References are arranged by year of publication and page number. Pages are numbered sequentially for each year so that there are no duplicate page numbers in any one year. The first number given is the year of publication and the second is the page number. For example, 91:58 is found in 1991, page 58. Page numbers in the same year are separated with commas and years by semi-colons.

Book reviews are listed under the category "Book Reviews." Neither book titles nor their authors are otherwise referenced here.